Introduction to Ordinary
Differential Equations

Introduction to Ordinary Differential Equations

ALBERT L. RABENSTEIN
MACALESTER COLLEGE
ST. PAUL, MINNESOTA

ACADEMIC PRESS   New York and London

ACADEMIC PRESS INC.
111 Fifth Avenue, New York, New York 10003

United Kingdom Edition published by
ACADEMIC PRESS INC. (LONDON) LTD.
Berkeley Square House, London W.1

LIBRARY OF CONGRESS CATALOG CARD NUMBER: 66-16443

First Printing, April 1966
Second Printing, August 1966
Third Printing, December 1966

PRINTED IN THE UNITED STATES OF AMERICA

PREFACE

This book is intended primarily for undergraduate students of engineering and the sciences who are interested in applications of differential equations. It contains a fairly conventional, but careful, description of the more useful elementary methods of finding solutions. It also contains a number of topics that are of particular interest in applications. These include Laplace transforms, eigenvalue problems, special functions, Fourier series, and boundary-value problems of mathematical physics. The emphasis is on the mathematical techniques, although a number of applications from elementary mechanics and electric circuit theory are presented for purposes of motivation. Finally, some topics that are not directly concerned with finding solutions, and that should be of interest to the mathematics major, are considered. Theorems about the existence and uniqueness of solutions are carefully stated. The final chapter includes a discussion of the stability of critical points of plane autonomous systems (the approach is via Liapunov's direct method), and results about the existence of periodic solutions of nonlinear equations.

The level is such that the material is accessible to the student whose background includes elementary but not advanced calculus. Because of the minimum prerequisites, a number of basic theorems have been stated but not proved. One example of this is the basic existence and uniqueness theorem for initial value problems. However, the method of successive approximations, which can be used to prove this theorem and which is important in itself, is presented and illustrated in the examples and exercises. Elementary properties of determinants and theorems about the consistency of systems of linear algebraic equations are used fairly often. The notion of a matrix is used on two occasions. The needed results from linear algebra are presented in a brief appendix, which contains its own set of exercises. There is sufficient material and flexibility in the book that it can be used either for an introductory course or for a second course in differential equations. In a second course, some of the material on elementary methods of solution might be omitted, or else used for review purposes. Sample course outlines are given below. There is just about the right amount of material in the entire book for two semesters' work.

A brief description of the various chapters and some of their special features is as follows. Much of the material in Chapters 1, 9, and 12 is fundamental. These chapters deal with the basic theory of single linear equations and nonlinear equations, respectively. Chapter 2 concerns itself with topics in linear equations which, although important, are not of such immediate use in applications as those of Chapter 1. Chapter 3 serves primarily to review the subject of power series, but from the standpoint of complex variables.

Chapters 5, 6, 7, 10, and 12 are independent of one another, so a fair amount of flexibility is available in choosing topics. Chapter 11 depends on Chapter 8, which in turn depends on both Chapters 6 and 7. Chapter 2 can be omitted entirely with little loss of continuity. With students well versed in the subject of real power series, Chapter 3 can also be omitted. Only Section 9 of Chapter 4 requires a knowledge of series with complex terms. Possible outlines for a one-semester introductory course (Course I) and for a second course (Course II) are given below.

Course I	*Course II*
Ch. 1	Ch. 1, 1.1–1.10
Ch. 2, 2.1	Ch. 4, 4.1–4.8, 4.10
Ch. 3	Ch. 5
Ch. 4, 4.1–4.6	Ch. 6, 6.1–6.8, 6.10
Ch. 5, 5.1–5.2	Ch. 7
Ch. 9	Ch. 8
Ch. 10	
Ch. 12, 12.1–12.5	

An effort has been made to provide exercises of varying levels of difficulty. Some of the more challenging ones extend the theory presented in the text, and can be used as bases for classroom presentations if desired by the instructor. Answers to about half the exercises have been placed at the end of the book.

The author wishes to express here his appreciation to Professor George Sell of the University of Minnesota, who reviewed the manuscript and made many helpful suggestions for its improvement.

St. Paul, Minnesota   A.L.R.

CONTENTS

8. Fourier Series

9. Systems of Differential Equations

10. Laplace Transforms

11. Partial Differential Equations and Boundary-Value Problems

12. Nonlinear Differential Equations

Appendix   407

Answers to Miscellaneous Exercises   413

Introduction to Ordinary
Differential Equations

CHAPTER 1

LINEAR DIFFERENTIAL EQUATIONS

1.1 Introduction

An ordinary differential equation is simply an equation that involves a single unknown function, of a single variable, and some finite number of its derivatives. Examples of differential equations for an unknown function $y(x)$ are

$$\text{(a)} \quad \frac{dy}{dx} + xy^2 = 2x,$$

$$\text{(b)} \quad \frac{d^2y}{dx^2} + e^x \frac{dy}{dx} - y = 0.$$

The *order* of a differential equation is the order of the highest order derivative of the unknown function that appears in the equation. The orders of the equations in the above examples are one and two, respectively.

The adjective "ordinary" is used to distinguish a differential equation from one that involves an unknown function of several variables, along with the partial derivatives of the function. Equations of this latter type are called *partial* differential equations. An example of a partial differential equation for a function $u(x,t)$ of two variables is

$$\frac{\partial^2 u}{\partial t^2} = \frac{\partial^2 u}{\partial x^2} + 2 \frac{\partial u}{\partial x} + u.$$

Except for Chapter 11, this book concerns itself mainly with ordinary differential equations.

A *linear* ordinary differential equation is an equation of the special form

$$a_0(x) \frac{d^n y}{dx^n} + a_1(x) \frac{d^{n-1}y}{dx^{n-1}} + \cdots + a_{n-1}(x) \frac{dy}{dx} + a_n(x)y = f(x), \qquad (1.1)$$

3

where the functions $a_i(x)$ and $f(x)$ are given functions. The functions $a_i(x)$ are called the *coefficients* of the equation. When $f(x) \equiv 0$, the equation is said to be homogeneous; otherwise it is said to be *nonhomogeneous*. It is with equations of the form (1.1) that we shall be mainly concerned in this chapter.

It will be convenient for us to introduce the operator L by means of the definition

$$L = a_0(x)\frac{d^n}{dx^n} + a_1(x)\frac{d^{n-1}}{dx^{n-1}} + \cdots + a_{n-1}(x)\frac{d}{dx} + a_n(x). \tag{1.2}$$

If $u(x)$ is any function that possesses n derivatives, the result of operating on $u(x)$ with the operator L is the function $Lu(x)$, where

$$Lu(x) = a_0(x)\frac{d^n u(x)}{dx^n} + a_1(x)\frac{d^{n-1}u(x)}{dx^{n-1}} + \cdots + a_n(x)u(x).$$

The differential equation (1.1) can now be written more briefly as

$$Ly = f.$$

If $u_1(x)$ and $u_2(x)$ are any two functions that are n times differentiable, and if C_1 and C_2 are any two constants, then

$$\frac{d^m}{dx^m}[C_1u_1(x) + C_2u_2(x)] = C_1\frac{d^m u_1(x)}{dx^m} + C^2\frac{d^m u_2(x)}{dx^m}, \qquad 1 \le m \le n.$$

As a consequence, the operator L has the property that

$$L[C_1u_1(x) + C_2u_2(x)] = C_1Lu_1(x) + C_2Lu_2(x). \tag{1.3}$$

This property is described by saying that L is a *linear operator*. If $u_1(x)$, $u_2(x), \ldots, u_m(x)$ are functions that possess n derivatives, and if $C_1, C_2, \ldots, C_m$ are constants, it can be shown by mathematical induction that

$$L(C_1u_1 + C_2u_2 + \cdots + C_mu_m) = C_1Lu_1 + C_2Lu_2 + \cdots + C_mLu_m. \tag{1.4}$$

By an *interval* I is meant a set of real numbers of one of the following types:

$$a < x < b, \qquad a \le x < b, \qquad a < x \le b,$$

$$a \le x \le b, \qquad a \le x < +\infty, \qquad a < x < +\infty,$$

$$-\infty < x \le b, \qquad -\infty < x < b, \qquad -\infty < x < +\infty,$$

where a and b are constants, with $a < b$. We shall also use the following corresponding notations for the nine types of intervals:

$$(a, b) \qquad [a, b) \qquad (a, b]$$

$$[a, b] \qquad [a, +\infty) \qquad (a, +\infty)$$

$$(-\infty, b] \qquad (-\infty, b) \qquad (-\infty, +\infty).$$

A real *solution* of a differential equation is a function that, on some interval, possesses the requisite number of derivatives and satisfies the equation. Thus a function $u(x)$ is a solution of the linear equation (1.1) on an interval I if it is n times differentiable on I and is such that

$$Lu(x) \equiv f(x)$$

on I. For example, the function x^2 is a solution of the equation

$$Ly \equiv y'' + 3xy' - y = 2 + 5x^2$$

on the interval $(-\infty, +\infty)$ because

$$L(x^2) \equiv (x^2)'' + 3x(x^2)' - x^2 = 2 + 6x^2 - x^2 = 2 + 5x^2$$

for all x.

By a *complex function* of the real variable x, we mean an expression of the form $u(x) + iv(x)$, where $u(x)$ and $v(x)$ are real functions and i is the imaginary unit. Arithmetic laws for complex functions are defined in accordance with the usual laws for complex numbers. The derivative of a complex function is defined as

$$\frac{d}{dx}[u(x) + iv(x)] = \frac{du(x)}{dx} + i\frac{dv(x)}{dx}.$$

Thus the derivative of a complex function is also a complex function.

From now on it will be assumed that the coefficients $a_i(x)$ in the operator L are *real* functions. Then the result of operating on a complex function $u + iv$ with L is

$$L(u + iv) = Lu + iLv,$$

which is also a complex function. If $w_1(x) = u_1(x) + iv_1(x)$ and $w_2(x) = u_2(x) + iv_2(x)$ are complex functions, and if $C_1 = a_1 + ib_1$ and $C_2 = a_2 + ib_2$ are complex constants, it is easily verified that

$$L(C_1 w_1 + C_2 w_2) = C_1 L w_1 + C_2 L w_2. \tag{1.5}$$

In fact, for a set of m complex functions $w_1, w_2, \ldots, w_m$, and a set of complex constants $C_1, C_2, \ldots, C_m$, we have

$$L(C_1 w_1 + C_2 w_2 + \cdots + C_m w_m) = C_1 L w_1 + C_2 L w_2 + \cdots + C_m L w_m. \tag{1.6}$$

A complex function $u(x) + iv(x)$ is a (complex) solution of the differential equation (1.1) on an interval I if

$$L[u(x) + iv(x)] = f(x)$$

on I. Evidently a complex function $w = u + iv$ is a solution of the *homogeneous* equation $Ly = 0$ if, and only if, its real and imaginary parts are real solutions—that is, if, and only if, $Lu = 0$ and $Lv = 0$. If each of the functions $w_1, w_2, \ldots, w_m$ is a solution, real or complex, of the homogeneous equation $Ly = 0$ on an interval I, and if $C_1, C_2, \ldots, C_m$ are any constants, real or complex, then the function

$$C_1 w_1 + C_2 w_2 + \cdots + C_m w_m$$

is also a solution of the equation on the interval I. This result follows from the property (1.6) of the linear operator L. It is known as the *superposition principle* for real linear homogeneous differential equations.

One particular complex function is of special importance in the study of certain classes of linear differential equations. This is the complex exponential function, which we shall define presently. First, however, we define the complex number e^{p+iq}, where p and q are any real numbers, as

$$e^{p+iq} = e^p \cos q + i e^p \sin q. \tag{1.7}$$

The number e here is the base of natural logarithms. It should be noted that when $q = 0$, the number (1.7) is simply the real number e^p. As other special cases, we have

$$e^{iq} = \cos q + i \sin q, \qquad e^{-iq} = \cos q - i \sin q. \tag{1.8}$$

Consequently, upon solving for $\cos q$ and $\sin q$, we have

$$\cos q = \frac{e^{iq} + e^{-iq}}{2}, \qquad \sin q = \frac{e^{iq} - e^{-iq}}{2i}. \tag{1.9}$$

From the relations (1.7) and (1.8) it follows that

$$e^{p+iq} = e^p \cdot e^{iq}.$$

The general laws of exponents,

$$e^{z_1+z_2} = e^{z_1} \cdot e^{z_2}, \qquad \frac{e^{z_1}}{e^{z_2}} = e^{z_1-z_2}, \tag{1.10}$$

where z_1 and z_2 are any two complex numbers, follow from the definition (1.7) and well-known trigonometric identities. Their verification is left as an exercise.

Let $c = a + ib$ be an arbitrary complex constant. A complex function of the form

$$e^{cx} = e^{ax} \cos bx + i e^{ax} \sin bx \tag{1.11}$$

is called a complex exponential function. A little calculation shows that the derivative of such a function is given by the familiar formula

$$\frac{d}{dx} e^{cx} = c e^{cx}.$$

If α is a positive real number and c is any complex number, we define

$$\alpha^c = e^{c \log \alpha}. \tag{1.12}$$

The laws of exponents,

$$\alpha^{z_1+z_2} = \alpha^{z_1} \cdot \alpha^{z_2}, \qquad \frac{\alpha^{z_1}}{\alpha^{z_2}} = \alpha^{z_1-z_2}$$

follow from the laws (1.10). The complex function x^c, where $c = a + ib$, is defined for $x > 0$ by means of the formula

$$x^c = e^{c \log x}. \tag{1.13}$$

The differentiation formula

$$\frac{d}{dx} x^c = cx^{c-1}$$

follows from the differentiation formula for exponential functions.

1.1 EXERCISES

1. Let the operator L be defined by means of the relationship

$$Ly = y'' - 2xy' + 3(x - 1)y.$$

Let $u_1(x) = 4x^2$, $u_2(x) = e^x$, and $w(x) = x^3 + ix^2$.

(a) Compute Lu_1 and Lu_2.
(b) Show that $L(u_1 + u_2) = Lu_1 + Lu_2$.
(c) Compute Lw, and show that $Lw = Lx^3 + iLx^2$.

2. Given the linear differential equation $y'' + 4y = 0$, verify that the given functions are solutions on the interval $(-\infty, +\infty)$:

(a) $\cos 2x$ and $\sin 2x$ (b) $4\cos 2x - 3\sin 2x$ (c) e^{2ix} and e^{-2ix}

3. Given the linear equation $x^2y'' - 2xy' + 2y = 0$, verify that the given functions are solutions on the interval $(0, +\infty)$:

(a) x and x^2 (b) $3x^2 + (1 - 2i)x$

4. Show that each of the functions $y_1(x) = 1$ and $y_2(x) = 2/x$ is a solution of the nonlinear differential equation $y'' + yy' = 0$ on the interval $(0, +\infty)$. Show that the function $y_1(x) + y_2(x)$ is *not* a solution.

5. (a) Let $w_1(x)$ and $w_2(x)$ be complex solutions of the real differential equation $Ly = 0$ on an interval I. If C_1 and C_2 are complex constants, show that the function $C_1w_1 + C_2w_2$ is a solution.
(b) Let $w_1, w_2, \ldots, w_m$ be complex solutions of the real equation $Ly = 0$ on an interval. Prove, by induction, that $C_1w_1 + C_2w_2 + \cdots + C_mw_m$ is a solution, where the quantities C_i are complex constants.

6. (a) Let $w(x) = u(x) + iv(x)$ be a solution of the equation $Ly = F(x)$, where L has real coefficients and $F(x) = f(x) + ig(x)$. Show that $u(x)$ and $v(x)$ are real solutions of the equations $Ly = f(x)$ and $Ly = g(x)$, respectively.

(b) Given that the function $-(1 + 2i)e^{2ix}$ is a solution of the equation $Ly \equiv y'' + 2y' + 2y = 10e^{2ix}$, find real solutions of the equations $Ly = 10 \cos 2x$ and $Ly = 10 \sin 2x$.

7. (a) A solution of the equation

$$y^{(n)} + a_1(x)y^{(n-1)} + \cdots + a_n(x)y = 0$$

on an interval I possesses at least n derivatives on I. If the coefficients $a_i(x)$ possess m derivatives on I, show that every solution possesses at least $n + m$ derivatives on I.

(b) Show that every solution of an equation of the form

$$y^{(n)} + a_1 y^{(n-1)} + \cdots + a_n y = 0,$$

where $a_1, a_2, \ldots, a_n$ are constants, possesses derivatives of all orders.

8. Verify the laws of exponents (1.10) and the formula $(e^{cx})' = ce^{cx}$.

9. A first-order differential equation of the form

$$\frac{dy}{dx} = \frac{f(x)}{g(y)}$$

is said to be *separable*. Suppose that there exist functions $F(x)$ and $G(y)$ such that $F'(x) = f(x)$ and $G'(y) = g(y)$ on the domains of f and g. If the equation possesses a solution $y = \phi(x)$ on an interval I, show that the solution satisfies a relation of the form

$$G(y) = F(x) + C,$$

where C is a constant. Conversely, show that any differentiable function that satisfies a relation of this form is a solution of the differential equation.

10. By using the result of Problem 9, find all solutions of the given equation:

(a) $\dfrac{dy}{dx} = x^2$ (c) $\dfrac{dy}{dx} = \dfrac{y}{x}$

(b) $\dfrac{dy}{dx} = \dfrac{x}{y}$ (d) $\dfrac{dy}{dx} = \dfrac{y^2 + 1}{x^2 + 1}$

1.2 The Fundamental Theorem

In many applications involving differential equations, it is desired to find a specific solution of a differential equation that satisfies certain *initial conditions* at a point $x = x_0$. For a differential equation of order n, these conditions are of the form

$$y(x_0) = k_0, \ y'(x_0) = k_1, \ldots, \ y^{(n-1)}(x_0) = k_{n-1}, \tag{1.14}$$

where $k_0, k_1, \ldots, k_{n-1}$ are specific constants. Thus the values of the unknown function $y(x)$ and its first $n - 1$ derivatives are specified at the point x_0. A differential equation of order n, together with the initial conditions (1.14), constitute an *initial value problem*. We shall assume without proof the following basic theorem for initial value problems associated with *linear* differential equations.

Theorem 1. On an interval I let the functions $a_0(x), a_1(x), \ldots, a_n(x)$, and $f(x)$ be real and continuous, with $a_0(x) \neq 0$.† Let x_0 be any point of I, and let $k_0, k_1, \ldots, k_{n-1}$ be any n real constants. Then there exists one, and only one, solution of the differential equation $Ly = f(x)$ on the interval I that satisfies the initial conditions (1.14).

Theorem 1 is an *existence theorem* because it says that the initial value problem does have a solution. It is also a *uniqueness theorem*, because it says that there is only one solution. The proof that a solution exists involves concepts not usually treated in a beginning calculus course. We shall therefore omit the proof here. Given that a solution exists, however, it is not so hard to prove that the solution is unique. A proof of the uniqueness of solutions is outlined in the exercises. We shall make use of Theorem 1 to prove other theorems about linear differential equations in this and other chapters.

As an example of the use of Theorem 1, let us consider the initial value problem

$$y'' - 3y' + 2y = 0, \qquad y(0) = 2, \qquad y'(0) = -1,$$

on the interval $(-\infty, +\infty)$. The coefficients in the differential equation are $a_0(x) = 1$, $a_1(x) = -3$, $a_2(x) = 2$, and $f(x) = 0$. These functions are constants, and therefore are continuous for all x. It is easy to verify that each of the functions e^x and e^{2x} is a solution of the equation on the given interval. Since the equation is homogeneous, the expression

$$y = C_1 e^x + C_2 e^{2x}$$

is also a solution of the equation for every choice of the constants C_1 and C_2. In order to satisfy the initial conditions of our problem, we try to choose these constants so that

$$y(0) = C_1 + C_2 = 2 \qquad y'(0) = C_1 + 2C_2 = -1.$$

Evidently these two equations for C_1 and C_2 are satisfied if $C_1 = 5$ and $C_2 = -3$. Therefore the function

$$y = 5e^x - 3e^{2x}$$

is a solution of our initial value problem. According to Theorem 1, it is the only solution.

† By $a_0(x) \neq 0$, we mean that $a_0(x)$ is *never* zero on I.

We can regard an initial value problem as *defining* a function over an interval. For instance, the initial value problem

$$y'' + e^x y' + (x^2 - \sin x)y = 0$$

$$y(3) = 2, \qquad y'(3) = -7$$

defines a unique, twice differentiable function on the interval $(-\infty, +\infty)$. However, it may be impossible to express the function that is defined by an initial value problem in a simple way in terms of elementary functions. It may be quite difficult even to discover some of the chief characteristics of the function. In some instances, the function defined by an initial value problem may be of sufficient importance (for physical or other reasons) to merit the effort. Nonelementary functions that arise as solutions of differential equations are included in a category of functions called *special functions*. Some of them have been tabulated numerically. Examples of such functions are the Bessel functions, which are discussed in Chapter 5.

Initial value problems arise in the analysis of many physical problems. Consider, for example, the dynamical problem of a body whose center of mass moves along a straight line. Let y denote the directed distance of the center of mass from a fixed point on the line and let t denote time. Then, according to Newton's second law of motion,

$$m \frac{d^2 y}{dt^2} = F \tag{1.15}$$

where m is the mass of the body and F represents the force exerted on it. The initial conditions

$$y(t_0) = y_0, \qquad y'(t_0) = v_0 \tag{1.16}$$

correspond to a knowledge of the position and the velocity of the center of mass at time $t = t_0$.

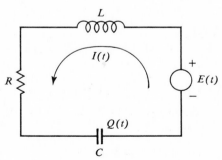

FIGURE 1.1

As a second example, let us consider an electric circuit that involves a resistance, a capacitance, and an inductance connected in series with a voltage source (Figure 1.1). The values of the resistance, inductance, and capacitance are denoted by the constants R, L, and C, respectively. The applied voltage is described by the function $E(t)$, where t denotes time. The charge $Q(t)$ on the capacitance and the current $I(t)$ in the loop are related by the equation

$$I = \frac{dQ}{dt}.$$

According to one of Kirchhoff's laws, the sum of the voltage drops around the loop must be equal to the applied voltage. Expressed analytically, this equality becomes

$$L\frac{dI}{dt} + RI + \frac{1}{C}Q = E(t),$$

or

$$L\frac{d^2Q}{dt^2} + R\frac{dQ}{dt} + \frac{1}{C}Q = E(t). \tag{1.17}$$

Hence the charge $Q(t)$ is a solution of a second-order linear differential equation. The initial conditions

$$Q(t_0) = Q_0, \qquad Q'(t_0) = I_0 \tag{1.18}$$

correspond to a knowledge of the charge and current at time $t = t_0$.

Applications of linear differential equations are considered in more detail in Section 1.14. More complicated mechanical and electrical systems are considered in Chapter 9.

1.2 EXERCISES

1. (a) Verify that each of the functions $\cos 3x$, $\sin 3x$ is a solution of the differential equation $y'' + 9y = 0$ on the interval $(-\infty, +\infty)$.
(b) Find a solution of the equation for which $y(0) = 1$ and $y'(0) = -2$. Is this the only such solution?

2. (a) Verify that each of the functions $\cos x$, $\sin x$, e^{2x} is a solution of the equation $y''' - 2y'' + y' - 2y = 0$ on the interval $(-\infty, +\infty)$.
(b) Find a solution of the equation for which $y(0) = -5$, $y'(0) = 0$, and $y''(0) = 10$. Is this the only such solution?

3. (a) Verify that each of the functions x, x^{-2} is a solution of the equation $x^2y'' + 2xy' - 2y = 0$ on the interval $(0, +\infty)$.
(b) Find a solution for which $y(1) = -3$ and $y'(1) = -6$. Is this the only such solution?

4. Consider the complex initial value problem

$$Ly = F, \qquad y^{(j)}(x_0) = K_j, \qquad 1 \le j \le n - 1,$$

where the coefficients $a^i(x)$ in L are real and continuous, with $a_0(x) \ne 0$

on an interval I, and $F(x) = f(x) + ig(x)$, where $f(x)$ and $g(x)$ are real and continuous on I. The constants K_j may be complex. Use Theorem 1 to prove that this complex initial value problem possesses a unique (complex) solution on I.

5. Consider the real first-order initial value problem

$$y' + a(x)y = f(x), \qquad y(x_0) = k.$$

(a) Let $A(x) = \int_{x_0}^{x} a(t)\, dt$. By multiplying through in the differential equation by $A(x)$, show that it can be written in the form

$$[yA(x)]' = f(x)A(x).$$

(b) Show that if the initial value problem has a solution, it must be the function

$$y = \frac{k}{A(x)} \int_{x_0}^{x} f(s)A(s)\, ds.$$

(c) Prove that the function defined in part (b) is a solution of the initial value problem.

(d) Explain why the above analysis proves that the initial value problem has a unique solution.

6. On an interval I, which contains the point x_0, let the function $w(x)$ be defined and continuous, and satisfy an inequality of the form

$$|w(x)| \leq M \left| \int_{x_0}^{x} |w(t)|\, dt \right|, \tag{1}$$

where M is a positive constant. Prove that $w(x)$ is identically zero on I. Suggestion: for $x \geq x_0$, let

$$W(x) = \int_{x_0}^{x} |w(t)|\, dt.$$

Then $W(x_0) = 0$ and $W'(x) - MW(x) \leq 0$ for $x \geq x_0$. If both sides of the inequality are multiplied by the quantity $e^{-M(x-x_0)}$, it becomes

$$\frac{d}{dx}\left[W(x)e^{-M(x-x_0)} \right] \leq 0.$$

An integration from x_0 to x yields the inequality

$$W(x) \leq W(x_0)e^{M(x-x_0)}.$$

Hence $W(x) = 0$, and from the original inequality (1) we have $w(x) = 0$. In order to treat the case where $x \leq x_0$, let

$$W(x) = -\int_{x_0}^{x} |w(t)|\, dt,$$

and proceed as before.

7. This problem uses the result of Problem 6 to establish the uniqueness of solutions of the first-order initial value problem

$$y' + a(x)y = f(x), \qquad y(x_0) = k_0.$$

Suppose that $y_1(x)$ and $y_2(x)$ are both solutions on an interval I. Let $w(x) = y_1(x) - y_2(x)$. Then $w'(x) + a(x)w(x) = 0$ and $w(x_0) = 0$, so

$$w(x) = -\int_{x_0}^{x} a(t)w(t)\, dt.$$

Let J be a finite closed interval contained in I and containing x_0. (Every point in I belongs to some such interval.) Then there is a positive constant M such that $|a(x)| \le M$ for x in J, and

$$|w(x)| \le M \left| \int_{x_0}^{x} |w(t)|\, dt \right|$$

for x in J. Now use the result of Problem 6.

8. The problem is to show that a solution of the second-order problem

$$y'' + a_1(x)y' + a_2(x)y = f(x), \qquad y(x_0) = k_0, \qquad y'(x_0) = k_1$$

is unique. Suppose that $y_1(x)$ and $y_2(x)$ are both solutions. Let $w_1(x) = y_1(x) - y_2(x)$ and $w_2(x) = w_1'(x)$. Then $w_1(x_0) = w_2(x_0) = 0$ and $w_2'(x) = -a_1(x)w_2(x) - a_2(x)w_1(x)$. Hence,

$$w_1(x) = \int_{x_0}^{x} w_2(t)\, dt, \qquad w_2(x) = -\int_{x_0}^{x} [a_1(t)w_2(t) + a_2(t)w_1(t)]\, dt.$$

Let J be a finite closed interval containing x_0. There is a positive constant M such that $|a_1(x)| \le M$, $|a_2(x)| \le M$ for x in J. Then

$$|w_1(x)| \le \left| \int_{x_0}^{x} |w_2(t)|\, dt \right|, \qquad |w_2(x)| \le M \left| \int_{x_0}^{x} [|w_1(t)| + |w_2(t)|]\, dt \right|,$$

so

$$|w_1(x)| + |w_2(x)| \le (M+1) \left| \int_{x_0}^{x} [|w_1(t)| + |w_2(t)|]\, dt \right|.$$

Now use the result of Problem 1.6.

9. Prove that a solution of the nth-order initial value problem

$$Ly = f(x), \qquad y^{(j)}(x_0) = k_j, \qquad 0 \le j \le n-1,$$

is unique by generalizing the procedure used in Problem 8.

1.3 First-Order Linear Equations

A first-order linear differential equation is an equation of the form

$$a_0(x)\frac{dy}{dx} + a_1(x)y = f(x). \tag{1.19}$$

Such an equation can be treated by simple methods that do not apply to higher-order equations, in general. It is for this reason that we give a separate discussion of the first-order case. The structure of the solutions of higher-order linear differential equations will be investigated in the ensuing sections of this chapter.

Let us consider the equation (1.19) on an interval I where $a_0(x)$ is never zero. Dividing through by $a_0(x)$, we can write the equation in the form

$$\frac{dy}{dx} + a(x)y = b(x), \tag{1.20}$$

where $a(x) = a_1(x)/a_0(x)$ and $b(x) = f(x)/a_0(x)$. Suppose that the function $y(x)$ is a solution of equation (1.20) on I. Then

$$y'(x) + a(x)y(x) = b(x), \qquad x \text{ in } I. \tag{1.21}$$

Let $A(x)$ be any function such that $A'(x) = a(x)$. If we multiply both sides of equation (1.21) by $e^{A(x)}$, we find that

$$e^{A(x)}y'(x) + a(x)e^{A(x)}y(x) = b(x)e^{A(x)}$$

or

$$[e^{A(x)}y(x)]' = b(x)e^{A(x)}. \tag{1.22}$$

Taking antiderivatives, we have

$$e^{A(x)}y(x) = \int b(x)e^{A(x)}\,dx + C \tag{1.23}$$

or

$$y(x) = Ce^{-A(x)} + e^{-A(x)}\int b(x)e^{A(x)}\,dx, \tag{1.24}$$

where C is a constant. Thus every solution of equation (1.20) is of the form (1.24). On the other hand, it can be verified by retracing steps that every function of the form (1.24) is a solution of equation (1.20).

The set of all solutions of a differential equation is called the *general solution* of the equation. An expression of the form (1.24), where C is regarded as an *arbitrary* constant, is said to represent the general solution of equation (1.20), since every solution is of this form. Actually it is the custom to call the expression (1.24) itself the general solution, and we shall follow this practice henceforth. To *solve* a differential equation means to find its general solution.

As an example, let us consider the equation

$$\frac{dy}{dx} - \frac{2}{x}y = x^2 \sin x \tag{1.25}$$

on the interval $0 < x < +\infty$. As a first step in solving this equation, we must find a function $A(x)$ such that $A'(x) = -2/x$. Evidently such a function is

$$A(x) = -2\log x = \log x^{-2}.$$

Then

$$e^{A(x)} = e^{\log x^{-2}} = \frac{1}{x^2}.$$

From formula (1.23), we have

$$\frac{1}{x^2} y = C + \int \frac{1}{x^2} x^2 \sin x \, dx.$$

Hence the general solution of equation (1.25) is

$$y = Cx^2 - x^2 \cos x. \tag{1.26}$$

Suppose we desire the specific solution that satisfies the initial condition

$$y(\pi) = 1. \tag{1.27}$$

If we substitute the values $x = \pi$, $y = 1$ into equation (1.26), we find that

$$1 = C\pi^2 + \pi^2.$$

Consequently, the constant C must have the value

$$C = \frac{1 - \pi^2}{\pi^2}$$

and the desired solution is

$$y = \frac{1 - \pi^2}{\pi^2} x^2 - x^2 \cos x. \tag{1.28}$$

The homogeneous equation

$$\frac{dy}{dx} + a(x)y = 0 \tag{1.29}$$

is, of course, a special case of the general equation (1.20), and can be treated by the method described above. However, the following alternative procedure is sometimes advantageous. Suppose that the function $y(x)$ is a solution of equation (1.29). Then we have

$$\frac{dy(x)}{y(x)} = -a(x) \, dx.$$

Integrating, we have

$$\int \frac{dy}{y} = - \int a(x) \, dx.$$

If $A(x)$ is any function such that $A'(x) = a(x)$, then

$$\log |y| = -A(x) + k$$

or

$$y = \pm e^k e^{-A(x)},$$

where k is a constant. Thus every solution of equation (1.29) is of the form

$$y = Ce^{-A(x)} \tag{1.30}$$

where C is a constant. Conversely, it is easy to verify that every function of the form (1.30) is a solution of the equation (1.29). If we choose $A(x) = \int_{x_0}^{x} a(t)\, dt$, then $A(x_0) = 0$ and $e^{A(x_0)} = 1$. Therefore the solution of equation (1.29) that satisfies the initial condition $y(x_0) = y_0$ is

$$y = y_0 \exp\left(-\int_{x_0}^{x} a(t)\, dt\right). \tag{1.31}$$

As an example of a physical situation that gives rise to a first-order linear equation, let us consider the decay of a radioactive substance. Such a substance decays at a rate that is proportional to the mass of material present. Thus, if $y(t)$ denotes the mass of radioactive material present at time t, we have

$$\frac{dy}{dt} = -ky, \tag{1.32}$$

where k is a constant. If y_0 is the mass of material present at time t_0, the initial condition is

$$y(t_0) = y_0. \tag{1.33}$$

The solution of equation (1.32) that satisfies the initial condition is

$$y(t) = y_0 e^{-k(t-t_0)}. \tag{1.34}$$

If the material is known to have a half-life of duration T, then $y(t_0 + T) = \frac{1}{2}y_0$, or

$$\tfrac{1}{2}y_0 = y_0 e^{-kT}.$$

According to this relation, the constant k must have the value

$$k = \frac{\log 2}{T}.$$

Then, from formula (1.34), we have

$$y(t) = y_0 \exp\left(-\frac{t - t_0}{T} \log 2\right) \tag{1.35}$$

or

$$y(t) = y_0 2^{-(t-t_0)/T}. \tag{1.36}$$

1.3 EXERCISES

1. Find the general solution of the given equation. If an initial condition is given, also find the solution that satisfies that condition.

(a) $xy' + (x + 2)y = 0,$ $y(1) = 2$ (c) $(x + 1)y' + y = 0,$ $y(0) = 3$
(b) $x^2y' - y = 0$ (d) $y' - 2y = 0$

2. Show that the differential equation of Problem 1(a) has no solution that satisfies the condition $y(0) = 1$. Is this a contradiction of Theorem 1?

3. Find the general solution of the given equation. If an initial condition is given, also find the solution that satisfies that condition.

(a) $xy' + (x + 2)y = x^2e^{-x}$ (d) $y' - 2y = x,$ $y(0) = 3/4$

(b) $y' - \dfrac{1}{x + 1} y = x^2 - 1$ (e) $y' - \dfrac{1}{x} y = \log x,$ $y(1) = 2$

(c) $x^2y' - y = 1$

4. Let $A(x) = \displaystyle\int_{x_0}^{x} a(t)\, dt$. Derive the formula

$$y = y_0 e^{-A(x)} + \int_{x_0}^{x} e^{-[A(x) - A(t)]} b(t)\, dt$$

for the solution of the initial value problem

$$y' + a(x)y = b(x),   y(x_0) = y_0.$$

5. Let $y = \phi(x, \alpha)$ denote the solution of the initial value problem

$$y' + a(x)y = b(x),   y(x_0) = \alpha$$

on the interval $x_0 \le x < +\infty$. Let $A(x) = \displaystyle\int_{x_0}^{x} a(t)\, dt$.

(a) Show that

$$|\phi(x, \alpha_1) - \phi(x, \alpha_2)| = |\alpha_1 - \alpha_2|\, e^{-A(x)}.$$

(b) Show that

$$\lim_{x \to +\infty} |\phi(x, \alpha_1) - \phi(x, \alpha_2)| = 0$$

if, and only if,

$$\int_{x_0}^{+\infty} a(t)\, dt = +\infty.$$

6. Let $y = \phi(x, \alpha)$ denote the solution of the initial value problem

$$y' + a(x)y = b(x),   y(x_0) = \alpha$$

on the interval $x_0 \le x < +\infty$. Show that to each fixed $x > x_0$ and to each positive number ε, there corresponds a positive number δ such that $|\phi(x, \alpha + \Delta\alpha) - \phi(x, \alpha)| < \varepsilon$ whenever $|\Delta\alpha| < \delta$. In other words, show that $\phi(x, \alpha)$ is continuous with respect to the parameter α. This property is important in applications where the initial values must be obtained by physical measurement. We do not want a small error in the measurement of y at $x = x_0$ to give rise to a large error in the calculation of y for $x > x_0$.

7. A radioactive substance has a half-life of 12 years. If 50 grams of the material is present after 4 years, how much material was present to begin with?

8. After one year, 25 grams, of an original 30 grams, of a radioactive substance remain. How much of the material is left after 2 years?

9. A tank is filled with 100 gallons of brine containing 25 pounds of dissolved salt. Water is then passed into the tank at the rate of 2 gallons per minute, and the mixture is drained off at the same rate. The mixture in the tank is kept uniform by constant stirring. How much salt remains in the tank after 1 hour?

10. A tank initially contains 60 gallons of brine containing 40 pounds of dissolved salt. A salt solution containing 1 pound of salt per gallon is passed into the tank at the rate of 2 gallons per minute, and the solution in the tank is drained off at the rate of 3 gallons per minute. How much salt is in the tank after 30 minutes?

1.4   Linear Dependence

A set of m functions $u_1(x)$, $u_2(x)$, ..., $u_m(x)$ is said to be *linearly dependent* (we also say that the functions $u_i(x)$ are linearly dependent) on an interval I if there exist constants C_1, C_2, ..., C_m, not all zero, such that

$$C_1 u_1(x) + C_2 u_2(x) + \cdots + C_m u_m(x) = 0 \qquad (1.37)$$

on I. If $C_1 \neq 0$, for instance, this means that

$$u_1(x) = -\frac{C_2}{C_1} u_2(x) - \frac{C_3}{C_1} u_3(x) - \cdots - \frac{C_m}{C_1} u_m(x) \qquad (1.38)$$

for x in I. Thus if a set of functions is linearly dependent, at least one of the functions can be expressed as a linear combination of the others. On the other hand, if one of the functions of the set, say $u_1(x)$, is a linear combination of the others, so that

$$u_1(x) = A_2 u_2(x) + A_3 u_3(x) + \cdots + A_m u_m(x), \qquad (1.39)$$

then the set is linearly dependent. For the relation (1.39) may be written

$$u_1(x) - A_2 u_2(x) - \cdots - A_m u_m(x) = 0, \qquad (1.40)$$

and obviously the coefficient of $u_1(x)$ in this equation is not zero. Thus a linearly dependent set of functions might also be defined to be a set of functions, at least one of which can be expressed as a linear combination of the others.

As an example, let us consider the set of three functions

$$u_1(x) = 3e^x, \qquad u_2(x) = x^2, \qquad u_3(x) = -7e^x$$

on the interval $(-\infty, +\infty)$. We see immediately that the set is linearly dependent, because $u_1(x) = -\frac{3}{7}u_3(x)$, and hence

$$u_1(x) = 0 \cdot u_2(x) - \tfrac{3}{7}u_3(x).$$

The function $u_1(x)$ is a linear combination of $u_2(x)$ and $u_3(x)$. We can also deduce that the functions are linearly dependent by using the original definition of linear dependence and observing that

$$7u_1(x) + 0 \cdot u_2(x) + 3u_3(x) = 0.$$

A set of functions that is not linearly dependent on an interval I is said to be *linearly independent* on I. As an example, let us consider the set of two functions $u_1(x) = e^x$, $u_2(x) = e^{2x}$ on the interval $0 \le x < 5$. Suppose that C_1 and C_2 are constants such that

$$C_1 e^x + C_2 e^{2x} = 0. \tag{1.41}$$

Then we may divide through by e^x, which is never zero, to obtain the relation

$$C_1 + C_2 e^x = 0.$$

If the function on the left is identically zero, its derivative is also, and hence $C_2 e^x = 0$. Then C_2 must be zero. But then equation (1.41) becomes $C_1 e^x = 0$, so C_1 must be zero too. Thus if a relationship of the form (1.41) holds, the constants C_1 and C_2 must both be zero, so the functions are not linearly dependent on the given interval. We conclude that they are linearly independent.

The linear independence of the functions in the above example can be established in another way. If equation (1.41) is to hold for $0 \le x < 5$, it must hold for any two points in this interval. Taking $x = 0$ and $x = 1$, we have

$$C_1 + C_2 = 0$$
$$C_1 e + C_2 e^2 = 0.$$

The only solution of this system of equations is $C_1 = C_2 = 0$. Hence the functions are linearly independent.

It should be noted that it is possible to talk about linear dependence and independence either with respect to the set of real numbers or with respect to the set of complex numbers, depending on whether we restrict the constants in the equation (1.37) to be real or allow them to be complex. In what follows, we shall deal mainly with real functions, and shall assume that the constants are restricted to be real unless otherwise indicated. It should be noted, however, that if a set of functions is linearly independent with respect to the set of complex numbers, it is automatically linearly independent with respect to the set of real numbers.

It should be noted that in the definitions of linear dependence and independence, an *interval* is involved. Indeed, a given set of functions may be linearly dependent on one interval and linearly independent on another interval. The following example illustrates this fact.

Let $u_1(x) = x$ and $u_2(x) = |x|$ for all x. On the interval $[0, +\infty)$, $u_1(x) = u_2(x)$, so the functions are linearly dependent on this interval. Next let us consider the interval $(-2, 2)$. Suppose that the constants C_1 and C_2 are such that

$$C_1 x + C_2 |x| = 0$$

on this interval. In particular, then, this relationship must hold for $x = 1$ and $x = -1$, so

$$C_1 + C_2 = 0$$
$$C_1 - C_2 = 0.$$

But then $C_1 = C_2 = 0$, so the functions are linearly independent on the interval $(-2, 2)$.

In the next section we shall investigate a certain criterion for the linear independence of a set of functions. We shall be especially concerned with the case where the functions are solutions of a linear homogeneous differential equation.

1.4   EXERCISES

1. Show that each of the given sets of functions is linearly dependent on the interval $(-\infty, +\infty)$:

(a) $x^2, \quad -4x^2$ 　　　　　　 (c) $\cos x, \quad \sin x, \quad \cos\left(x + \dfrac{\pi}{6}\right)$

(b) $x, \quad e^x, \quad 2x - 3e^x$

2. Show that each of the given sets of functions is linearly dependent with respect to the set of complex numbers on the interval $(-\infty, +\infty)$:

(a) $\cos 2x, \quad \sin 2x, \quad e^{2ix}$
(b) $x - 2ix^2, \quad (1 + i)x, \quad 3x^2$

3. Show that each of the given sets of functions is linearly independent on the interval $(-\infty, +\infty)$:

(a) $e^{-2x}, \quad e^{3x}$ 　　　　　 (c) $1 - x, \quad 3x, \quad x^2$
(b) $1, \quad x^2, \quad e^x$

4. Let the functions $u_1(x)$ and $u_2(x)$ be linearly independent on an interval I, and let $v_1(x) = Au_1(x) + Bu_2(x)$, $v_2(x) = Cu_1(x) + Du_2(x)$. Prove that the functions $v_1(x)$ and $v_2(x)$ are linearly independent on I if, and only if, $AD - BC \neq 0$.

5. Let the functions $u_1(x)$, $u_2(x)$, ..., $u_m(x)$ be linearly independent on an interval I. If a function $f(x)$ is such that

$$f(x) = \sum_{i=1}^{m} a_i u_i(x) \qquad \text{and} \qquad f(x) = \sum_{i=1}^{m} b_i u_i(x)$$

for x in I, where a_i and b_i are constants, show that $a_i = b_i$, $1 \le i \le m$.

6. Let the functions $u_i(x)$, $1 \le i \le m$, be linearly dependent on an interval I. If a function $f(x)$ can be expressed as a linear combination of these functions on I, that is,

$$f(x) = \sum_{i=1}^{m} C_i u_i(x),$$

show that $f(x)$ can be expressed as a linear combination of $m - 1$ of these functions.

7. (a) Prove that if a set of functions is linearly independent on an interval I, then any subset of these functions is also linearly independent on I.
(b) If a set of functions is linearly dependent on an interval I, is it necessarily true that any subset of these functions is linearly dependent on I? Give an example.

8. Two functions $f(x)$ and $g(x)$ are said to be *orthogonal* on the interval $[a, b]$ if

$$\int_a^b f(x) \, g(x) \, dx = 0.$$

Prove that if $f(x)$ and $g(x)$ are orthogonal on $[a, b]$, they are linearly independent on $[a, b]$. Prove that if the functions $f_i(x)$, $1 \le i \le m$, are pairwise orthogonal on $[a, b]$, they are linearly independent on $[a, b]$.

1.5 The Wronskian

Let the m functions $u_1(x)$, $u_2(x)$, ..., $u_m(x)$ each possess at least $m - 1$ derivatives. The determinant

$$\begin{vmatrix} u_1(x) & u_2(x) & \cdots & u_m(x) \\ u_1'(x) & u_2'(x) & \cdots & u_m'(x) \\ \cdots\cdots\cdots\cdots\cdots\cdots\cdots\cdots\cdots\cdots\cdots\cdots\cdots \\ u_1^{(m-1)}(x) & u_2^{(m-1)}(x) & \cdots & u_m^{(m-1)}(x) \end{vmatrix} \qquad (1.42)$$

is called the *Wronskian* of the set of functions. We shall denote it by the symbol $W(x; u_1, u_2, \ldots, u_m)$, or sometimes simply by $W(x)$. This determinant is closely related to the question of whether or not the set of functions is linearly independent.

Theorem 2.   Let $\{u_i(x)\}$, $i = 1, 2, \ldots, m$ be a linearly dependent set of functions on an interval I, and let each function be $(m - 1)$ times differentiable on I. Then the Wronskian of the set of functions is identically zero.

Proof.   Since, by hypothesis, the functions are linearly dependent on I, there exist constants C_i, $i = 1, 2, \ldots, m$, not all zero, such that

$$C_1 u_1(x) + C_2 u_2(x) + \cdots + C_m u_m(x) \equiv 0$$

on I. Since the quantity on the left is identically zero, its derivatives must also vanish identically, and hence we have the m relations.

$$C_1 u_1(x) + C_2 u_2(x) + \cdots + C_m u_m(x) \equiv 0$$

$$C_1 u_1'(x) + C_2 u_2'(x) + \cdots + C_m u_m'(x) \equiv 0 \qquad (1.43)$$

$$\cdots\cdots\cdots\cdots\cdots\cdots\cdots\cdots\cdots\cdots\cdots\cdots\cdots\cdots\cdots$$

$$C_1 u_1^{(m-1)}(x) + C_2 u_2^{(m-1)}(x) + \cdots + C_m u_m^{(m-1)}(x) \equiv 0.$$

If we let x have any specific value in the interval I, say $x = x_0$, the set of relation (1.43) becomes an algebraic system of m equations that must be satisfied by $C_1, C_2, \ldots, C_m$. These constants are not all zero, so the system of equations has a nontrivial solution. But this can occur only if the determinant of the system vanishes. The determinant in this case is the Wronskian of the set $\{u_i(x)\}$, $i = 1, 2, \ldots, m$, evaluated at $x = x_0$. But x_0 can be any point of the interval I, so $W(x) \equiv 0$ on I.

In view of this theorem, the following corollary is true.

Corollary.   If the Wronskian of a set of functions is not zero, even at one point of an interval I, then the functions are linearly independent on I.

Proof.   If the functions were linearly dependent on I, their Wronskian would have to be identically zero, by Theorem 1. Since the Wronskian is not identically zero, the functions must be linearly independent.

As an example, let us consider the set of three functions $u_1(x) = x$, $u_2(x) = x^2$, $u_3(x) = \sin x$ on the interval $-\infty < x < +\infty$. The Wronskian of the set is

$$W(x) = \begin{vmatrix} x & x^2 & \sin x \\ 1 & 2x & \cos x \\ 0 & 2 & -\sin x \end{vmatrix} = (2 - x^2) \sin x - 2x \cos x.$$

At $x = \pi$, W has the value 2π. Since $W(x) \not\equiv 0$, the functions are linearly independent.

A reasonable question to ask at this point is whether the converse of Theorem 2 is true. That is, does the identical vanishing of the Wronskian imply the linear dependence of the functions? That the answer is "no" can be seen from the following example. On the interval $-\infty < x < +\infty$, let

$$u_1(x) = x^2, \qquad u_2(x) = x|x| = \begin{cases} x^2, & x \geq 0 \\ -x^2, & x < 0. \end{cases}$$

It should be noted that $u_2{}'(0)$ does exist and is equal to zero. When $x \geq 0$ we have

$$W(x) = \begin{vmatrix} x^2 & x^2 \\ 2x & 2x \end{vmatrix} = 0$$

and when $x < 0$, we have

$$W(x) = \begin{vmatrix} x^2 & -x^2 \\ 2x & -2x \end{vmatrix} = 0.$$

Thus the Wronskian vanishes identically for $-\infty < x < +\infty$. Yet the functions are linearly independent on this interval, as we shall now show. Suppose that C_1 and C_2 are constants such that

$$C_1 u_1(x) + C_2 u_2(x) \equiv 0$$

for all x. In particular this equality must hold at $x = 1$ and $x = -1$. Therefore

$$C_1 + C_2 = 0$$
$$C_1 - C_2 = 0$$

and we must have $C_1 = C_2 = 0$. Thus the functions u_1 and u_2 are linearly independent even though their Wronskian vanishes identically.

For an arbitrary set of functions, then, the vanishing of the Wronskian does not necessarily imply linear dependence. The situation is different, however, when the functions are solutions of the same linear homogeneous differential equation.

Theorem 3.   Let the n functions $y_i(x)$, $i = 1, 2, \ldots, n$, be solutions of a linear homogeneous differential equation $Ly = 0$ of order n on an interval I. (It is assumed that the coefficients $a_i(x)$, $i = 1, 2, \ldots, n$, in the differential equation are continuous and that $a_0(x) \neq 0$ on I.) If the Wronskian $W(x; y_1, y_2, \ldots, y_n)$ vanishes at even one point of I, the functions are linearly dependent on I.

Proof.   We first note that the number of functions, n, is the same as the order of the differential equation, according to the hypotheses of the theorem. Let x_0 be a point of I at which the Wronskian vanishes, and let us consider the system of algebraic equations

$$C_1 y_1(x_0) + C_2 y_2(x_0) + \cdots + C_n y_n(x_0) = 0$$
$$C_1 y_1{}'(x_0) + C_2 y_2{}'(x_0) + \cdots + C_n y_n{}'(x_0) = 0$$
$$\cdots\cdots\cdots\cdots\cdots\cdots\cdots\cdots\cdots\cdots\cdots\cdots\cdots\cdots\cdots$$
$$C_1 y_1^{(n-1)}(x_0) + C_2 y_2^{(n-1)}(x_0) + \cdots + C_n y_n^{(n-1)}(x_0) = 0$$

for the quantities $C_1, C_2, \ldots, C_n$. Since the determinant of the system is zero, it is possible to find values for $C_1, C_2, \ldots, C_n$ *which are not all zero* and which satisfy the system. Let us choose such a set of values and define a function $u(x)$ by means of the formula

$$u(x) = C_1 y_1(x) + C_2 y_2(x) + \cdots + C_n y_n(x).$$

This function is a solution of the nth-order equation $Ly = 0$. Furthermore,

$$u(x_0) = u'(x_0) = \cdots = u^{(n-1)}(x_0) = 0.$$

But the identically zero function is also a solution of the differential equation, and its initial values at the point $x = x_0$ are all zero. By Theorem 1, we must conclude that $u(x) \equiv 0$; that is, that

$$C_1 y_1(x) + C_2 y_2(x) + \cdots + C_n y_n(x) \equiv 0$$

on the interval I. Since the constants C_i are not all zero, it follows that the functions $y_i(x)$, $i = 1, 2, \ldots, n$, are linearly dependent on I.

Theorem 4.   Let the functions $y_i(x)$, $i = 1, 2, \ldots, n$, be solutions of an nth-order linear homogeneous differential equation on an interval I. Then either the Wronskian of these functions is identically zero on I (in which case the functions are linearly dependent) or it does not vanish at any point of I (in which case the functions are linearly independent).

Proof.   The functions are either linearly dependent or linearly independent on I. If they are dependent, their Wronskian vanishes identically on I, by Theorem 2. If the functions are independent, their Wronskian cannot vanish at any point of I. For if it did, the functions would be linearly dependent according to Theorem 3.

1.6   Abel's Formula

As remarked after Theorem 1, a linear differential equation $Ly = 0$, together with a set of initial values at a point, completely specifies a function, this function being the unique solution of the initial value problem. It could also be said that the function is determined by the coefficient functions $a_i(x)$, $i = 1, 2, \ldots, n$, in the operator L, together with the initial values. It turns out that the Wronskian of a set of n solutions of an nth-order homogeneous equation can be expressed in a particularly simple way in terms of the *two* coefficient functions $a_0(x)$ and $a_1(x)$, and the initial values of the solutions at a point.

To begin with, let us consider a second-order equation

$$a_0(x)y'' + a_1(x)y' + a_2(x)y = 0, \tag{1.44}$$

for which the functions $y_1(x)$ and $y_2(x)$ are solutions. The Wronskian of y_1 and y_2 is

$$W(x) = y_1 y_2' - y_2 y_1' \tag{1.45}$$

so

$$\frac{dW}{dx} = y_1 y_2'' + y_1' y_2' - y_2 y_1'' - y_2' y_1' = y_1 y_1'' - y_2 y_1''. \tag{1.46}$$

Since y_1 and y_2 are solutions of equation (1.44),

$$y_i'' = -\frac{a_1}{a_0} y_i' - \frac{a_2}{a_0} y_i, \qquad i = 1, 2. \tag{1.47}$$

Upon substituting the expressions for y_1'' and y_2'' into equation (1.46), we find that

$$\frac{dW}{dx} = -\frac{a_1}{a_0} (y_1 y_2' - y_2 y_1')$$

or

$$\frac{dW}{dx} + \frac{a_1}{a_0} W = 0. \tag{1.48}$$

Thus the Wronskian satisfies a first-order linear homogeneous differential equation. By the methods of Section 3 we have

$$W(x) = C \exp\left[-\int \frac{a_1(x)}{a_0(x)} dx\right], \tag{1.49}$$

where C is a constant and the integral is any indefinite integral of a_1/a_0. If x_0 is any fixed point, we have

$$W(x) = W(x_0) \exp\left[-\int_{x_0}^{x} \frac{a_1(t)}{a_0(t)} dt\right]. \tag{1.50}$$

Formula (1.49) and formula (1.50) are each known as *Abel's formula* for the second-order equation (1.44).

The derivation of the corresponding formulas for the general nth-order equation

$$a_0(x)y^{(n)} + a_1(x)y^{(n-1)} + \cdots + a_n(x)y = 0 \tag{1.51}$$

requires a knowledge of the formula for the derivative of an nth-order determinant. It may be recalled that an nth-order determinant

$$M = \begin{vmatrix} b_{11} & b_{12} & \cdots & b_{1n} \\ b_{21} & b_{22} & \cdots & b_{2n} \\ \cdots\cdots\cdots\cdots\cdots\cdots\cdots \\ b_{n1} & b_{n2} & \cdots & b_{nn} \end{vmatrix} \tag{1.52}$$

is the sum of $n!$ products, each product containing n factors. In fact,

$$M = \sum \pm (b_{i_1 1} b_{i_2 2} \cdots b_{i_n n}) \tag{1.53}$$

where the plus or minus sign is to be chosen according to whether the ordered n-tuple $(i_1, i_2, \ldots, i_n)$ is an even or odd permutation of the n-tuple $(1, 2, \ldots, n)$. Assuming that the elements b_{ij} of the determinant M are differentiable functions of a variable x, we have

$$\frac{dM}{dx} = \sum \pm (b'_{i1} b_{i2} \cdots b_{in}) + \sum \pm (b_{i1} b'_{i2} \cdots b_{in})$$
$$+ \cdots + \sum \pm (b_{i1} b_{i2} \cdots b'_{in}), \quad (1.54)$$

or

$$\frac{dM}{dx} = \begin{vmatrix} b'_{11} & b'_{12} & \cdots & b'_{1n} \\ b_{21} & b_{22} & \cdots & b_{2n} \\ \cdots\cdots\cdots\cdots\cdots\cdots\cdots \\ b_{n1} & b_{n2} & \cdots & b_{nn} \end{vmatrix} + \begin{vmatrix} b_{11} & b_{12} & \cdots & b_{1n} \\ b'_{21} & b'_{22} & \cdots & b'_{2n} \\ \cdots\cdots\cdots\cdots\cdots\cdots\cdots \\ b_{n1} & b_{n2} & \cdots & b_{nn} \end{vmatrix}$$
$$+ \cdots + \begin{vmatrix} b_{11} & b_{12} & \cdots & b_{1n} \\ b_{21} & b_{22} & \cdots & b_{2n} \\ \cdots\cdots\cdots\cdots\cdots\cdots\cdots \\ b'_{n1} & b'_{n2} & \cdots & b'_{nn} \end{vmatrix}. \quad (1.55)$$

Thus the derivative of an nth-order determinant is equal to the sum of n determinants, which are obtained by successively differentiating the rows[†] of the original determinant.

Now let $y_1, y_2, \ldots, y_n$ be solutions of the nth-order equation (1.51). In calculating the derivative of the Wronskian of these functions by the use of formula (1.55), we find that in all but the last of the n determinants in the sum, two rows are identical. Therefore

$$\frac{dW}{dx} = \begin{vmatrix} y_1 & y_2 & \cdots & y_n \\ y_1' & y_2' & \cdots & y_n' \\ \cdots\cdots\cdots\cdots\cdots\cdots\cdots\cdots\cdots \\ y_1^{(n-2)} & y_2^{(n-2)} & \cdots & y_n^{(n-2)} \\ y_1^{(n)} & y_2^{(n)} & \cdots & y_n^{(n)} \end{vmatrix}. \quad (1.56)$$

Since the functions $y_i(x)$ are solutions of equation (1.51), we have

$$y_i^{(n)} = -\frac{a_1}{a_0} y_i^{(n-1)} - \frac{a_2}{a_0} y_i^{(n-2)} - \cdots - \frac{a_n}{a_0} y_i \quad (i = 1, 2, \ldots, n) \quad (1.57)$$

Upon substituting these expressions for the elements in the last row of the

---

† One can also obtain the derivative of a determinant by successively differentiating its columns instead of its rows.

determinant of formula (1.56), and using elementary properties of determinants, we find that

$$\frac{dW}{dx} = -\frac{a_1}{a_0} \begin{vmatrix} y_1' & y_2 & \cdots & y_n \\ y_1' & y_2' & \cdots & y_n' \\ \cdots\cdots\cdots\cdots\cdots\cdots\cdots\cdots \\ y_1^{(n-1)} & y_2^{(n-1)} & \cdots & y_n^{(n-1)} \end{vmatrix} \tag{1.58}$$

or

$$\frac{dW}{dx} = -\frac{a_1}{a_0} W. \tag{1.59}$$

Proceeding with this equation as we did in the second-order case, we find that

$$W(x) = C \exp\left[-\int \frac{a_1(x)}{a_0(x)} \, dx \right] \tag{1.60}$$

or

$$W(x) = W(x_0) \exp\left[-\int_{x_0}^{x} \frac{a_1(t)}{a_0(t)} \, dt \right]. \tag{1.61}$$

In order to apply Abel's formula in a specific case, let us consider the differential equation

$$y'' + 2xy' + e^x \sin xy = 0.$$

Let $y_1(x)$ and $y_2(x)$ be the solutions of this equation for which

$$y_1(0) = 2 \qquad y_2(0) = -3$$

$$y_1'(0) = 1 \qquad y_2'(0) = 2.$$

Here $a_0(x) = 1$, $a_1(x) = 2x$, and $W(0) = 7$. According to formula (1.61),

$$W(x) = 7 \exp\left(-\int_0^x 2x \, dx \right) = 7e^{-x^2}.$$

Thus we have found an explicit formula for the Wronskian of the solutions y_1 and y_2, although nothing is known about these functions themselves other than their initial values at the point $x = 0$. It should be noted that these functions are linearly independent on every interval, since their Wronskian is nowhere zero.

Abel's formula (1.61) gives an alternative proof of the fact that the Wronskian of a set of n solutions of an nth-order differential equation is either identically zero or else is never zero, on an interval where $a_0(x) \neq 0$. For the exponential term in (1.61) is never zero, and so the Wronskian either vanishes identically or not at all, according to whether $W(x_0)$ is, or is not, zero.

1.6 EXERCISES

1. Find the Wronskian of each of the following sets of functions, and determine whether or not the set is linearly independent on the interval $-\infty < x < +\infty$.

(a) $1, \quad x, \quad x^2$ (c) $\sin ax, \quad \cos ax$ (e) $e^x, \quad e^{2x}, \quad e^{-x}$
(b) $1, \quad x, \quad 2 - x$ (d) $e^x, \quad e^{2x}$ (f) $x^3, \quad |x|x^2$

2. Let $y_1(x)$ and $y_2(x)$ be the solutions of the differential equation

$$y'' - \frac{3}{x} y' + (\sin 2x)y = 0$$

on the interval $x > 0$ for which

$$y_1(1) = 0, \qquad y_1'(1) = 3, \qquad y_2(1) = 2, \qquad y_2'(1) = 1.$$

Find the Wronskian of the functions.

3. Let $y_1(x)$ and $y_2(x)$ be the solutions of the differential equation

$$(1 - x^2)y'' - 2xy' + 12y = 0$$

on the interval $|x| < 1$, for which

$$y_1(0) = 1, \qquad y_1'(0) = 1, \qquad y_2(0) = -1, \qquad y_2'(0) = -2.$$

Find the Wronskian of these solutions.

4. For a differential equation of the form

$$a_0(x)y^{(n)} + a_2(x)y^{(n-2)} + \cdots + a_n(x)y = 0,$$

in which there is no derivative term of order $n - 1$, show that the Wronskian of a set of n solutions is a constant.

5. If the functions $y_1, y_2, \ldots, y_n$ are solutions of the nth-order equation $Ly = 0$ on the interval $a < x < b$, and are linearly independent on the interval $c < x < d$, where $a < c < d < b$, show that they are linearly independent on the interval $a < x < b$.

6. Let $u_1(x) = e^{r_1 x}, u_2(x) = e^{r_2 x}, \ldots, u_n(x) = e^{r_n x}$.

(a) Show that

$$W(x; u_1, u_2, \ldots, u_n) = \Delta_n e^{(r_1 + r_2 + \cdots + r_n)x},$$

where

$$\Delta_n = \begin{vmatrix} 1 & 1 & \cdots & 1 \\ r_1 & r_2 & \cdots & r_n \\ \cdots\cdots\cdots\cdots\cdots\cdots\cdots\cdots \\ r_1^{n-1} & r_2^{n-1} & \cdots & r_n^{n-1} \end{vmatrix}$$

(b) Prove, by induction, that

$$\Delta_n = (r_2 - r_1)[(r_3 - r_1)(r_3 - r_2)][(r_4 - r_1)(r_4 - r_2)(r_4 - r_3)] \cdots$$

$$[(r_n - r_1) \cdots (r_n - r_{n-1})].$$

Suggestion: let $P(r)$ be the polynomial

$$P(r) = \begin{vmatrix} 1 & 1 & \cdots & 1 & 1 \\ r_1 & r_2 & \cdots & r_k & r \\ \cdots & \cdots & \cdots & \cdots & \cdots \\ r_1^{k-1} & r_2^{k-1} & \cdots & r_k^{k-1} & r^{k-1} \\ r_1^{k} & r_2^{k} & \cdots & r_k^{k} & r^{k} \end{vmatrix}.$$

Then

$$P(r_1) = P(r_2) = \cdots = P(r_k) = 0,$$

so

$$P(r) = \Delta_k(r - r_1)(r - r_2) \cdots (r - r_k).$$

But

$$P(r_{k+1}) = \Delta_{k+1}.$$

7. Let $u(x)$ and $v(x)$ be functions that possess two continuous derivatives on an interval I and which are such that $W(x; u, v) \neq 0$ for x in I. Show that the equation

$$\begin{vmatrix} y & y' & y'' \\ u(x) & u'(x) & u''(x) \\ v(x) & v'(x) & v''(x) \end{vmatrix} = 0$$

is a linear homogeneous second-order differential equation for which $u(x)$ and $v(x)$ are solutions on I.

8. By using the result of Problem 7, construct a linear homogeneous second-order differential equation that has the given functions as solutions on the given intervals.

(a) $u(x) = x$, $v(x) = e^x$, $-\infty < x < 1$, $1 < x < +\infty$

(b) $u(x) = \dfrac{1}{x}$, $v(x) = e^{-x}$, $-\infty < x < 0$, $1 < x < +\infty$

(c) $u(x) = e^x$, $v(x) = e^{1/x}$, $-\infty < x < -1$ $1 < x < +\infty$

1.7   Fundamental Sets of Solutions

A set of n linearly independent solutions of an nth-order linear homogeneous differential equation is called a *fundamental set* of solutions for the equation. We can easily show that a fundamental set always exists. For instance, let $y_i(x)$, $1 \le i \le n$, be the solutions of the equation that satisfy the initial conditions

$$y_1(x_0) = 1, \qquad y_2(x_0) = 0, \ldots, \qquad y_n(x_0) = 0$$
$$y_1'(x_0) = 0, \qquad y_2'(x_0) = 1, \ldots, \qquad y_n'(x_0) = 0$$

$$\cdots\cdots\cdots\cdots\cdots\cdots\cdots\cdots\cdots\cdots\cdots\cdots\cdots\cdots\cdots\cdots\cdots$$

$$y_1^{(n-1)}(x_0) = 0, \qquad y_2^{(n-1)} = 0, \ldots, \qquad y_n^{(n-1)}(x_0) = 1.$$

The existence of such solutions is guaranteed by Theorem 1. Evidently

$$W(x_0) = \begin{vmatrix} 1 & 0 & 0 & \cdots & 0 \\ 0 & 1 & 0 & \cdots & 0 \\ 0 & 0 & 1 & \cdots & 0 \\ & & \cdots\cdots\cdots & & \\ 0 & 0 & 0 & \cdots & 1 \end{vmatrix} = 1 \neq 0,$$

so these solutions are linearly independent.

The importance of being able to find a fundamental set of solutions for a differential equation is shown by the following theorem.

Theorem 5.   Let the solutions $y_i(x)$, $1 \le i \le n$, constitute a fundamental set for the nth-order homogeneous equation $Ly = 0$. Then every solution of the equation is of the form

$$C_1 y_1(x) + C_2 y_2(x) + \cdots + C_n y_n(x), \tag{1.62}$$

where the quantities C_i are constants.

Proof.   Let $u(x)$ be any solution of the differential equation, and at a point x_0 let

$$u(x_0) = k_0, \qquad u'(x_0) = k_1, \ldots, u^{(n-1)}(x_0) = k_{n-1}.$$

If $u(x)$ can be written in the form (1.62), then the constants C_i must be such that

$$C_1 y_1(x_0) + C_2 y_2(x_0) + \cdots + C_n y_n(x_0) = k_0$$
$$C_1 y_1'(x_0) + C_2 y_2'(x_0) + \cdots + C_n y_n'(x_0) = k_1$$

$$\cdots\cdots\cdots\cdots\cdots\cdots\cdots\cdots\cdots\cdots\cdots\cdots\cdots\cdots\cdots\cdots$$

$$C_1 y_1^{(n-1)}(x_0) + C_2 y_2^{(n-1)}(x_0) + \cdots + C_n y_n^{(n-1)}(x_0) = k_{n-1}.$$

This system of equations for the constants C_i has a unique solution, since its determinant is the Wronskian $W(x_0)$, which is not zero. Let us choose the constants C_i to have the values that satisfy this system. Then the corresponding function

$$C_1y_1(x) + C_2y_2(x) + \cdots + C_ny_n(x)$$

is a solution of the differential equation and has the same initial values at $x = x_0$ as does the solution $u(x)$. By Theorem 1, this function must be identically equal to $u(x)$.

The set of all functions that are solutions of a differential equation is called the *general solution* of the equation. Let $y_i(x)$, $1 \le i \le n$, constitute a fundamental set for the linear homogeneous equation $Ly = 0$. An expression of the form

$$C_1y_1(x) + C_2y_2(x) + \cdots + C_ny_n(x), \tag{1.63}$$

where the quantities C_i are *arbitrary* constants, represents the general solution of the equation. Any particular solution can be obtained from it by a correct specification of the arbitrary constants. Following custom, we shall call the expression (1.63) itself the general solution.

As an illustration of the principles we have been discussing, let us consider the differential equation

$$y''' - 3y'' + 2y' = 0$$

on the interval $(-\infty, +\infty)$. It can be verified that each of the functions $y_1(x) = 1$, $y_2(x) = e^x$, $y_3(x) = e^{2x}$ is a solution of the equation. The Wronskian of these functions,

$$W(x) = \begin{vmatrix} 1 & e^x & e^{2x} \\ 0 & e^x & 2e^{2x} \\ 0 & e^x & 4e^{2x} \end{vmatrix} = 2e^{3x},$$

does not vanish on the given interval. Therefore the functions form a fundamental set for the differential equation, and the general solution is

$$y = C_1 + C_2e^x + C_3e^{2x}.$$

In the case of a first-order linear homogeneous equation

$$\frac{dy}{dx} + a(x)y = 0,$$

any single nontrivial solution constitutes a fundamental set. The general solution can be written as

$$y = Ce^{-A(x)},$$

where $A(x)$ is any function such that $A'(x) = a(x)$.

1.7   EXERCISES

1. Show that the given functions form a fundamental set for the given differential equation on the indicated interval, and write down the general solution.

(a) $y'' - 4y = 0$, $\quad (-\infty, +\infty)$, $\quad y_1 = e^{2x}$, $\quad y_2 = e^{-2x}$
(b) $2x^2 y'' + 3xy' - y = 0$, $\quad (0, +\infty)$, $\quad y_1 = x^{1/2}$, $\quad y_2 = x^{-1}$
(c) $y''' - y' = 0$, $\quad (-\infty, +\infty)$, $\quad y_1 = 1$, $\quad y_2 = e^x$, $\quad y_3 = e^{-x}$

2. Show that a linear homogeneous differential equation of order n cannot possess a set of more than n linearly independent solutions.

3. Let x_0 be a point of a finite closed interval I. Let $y_1(x)$ and $y_2(x)$ be the solutions of the equation $y'' + a(x)y' + b(x)y = 0$ on I for which $y_1(x_0) = \alpha_1, y_1'(x_0) = \beta_1, y_2(x_0) = \alpha_2, y_2'(x_0) = \beta_2$. Let $\alpha = \alpha_1 - \alpha_2$ and $\beta = \beta_1 - \beta_2$. On I, let $|a(x)| \leq M$ and $|b(x)| \leq M$. Prove that

$$|y_1(x) - y_2(x)| \leq |\alpha| + \frac{|\alpha| + |\beta|}{M + 1} [e^{(M+1)|x - x_0|} - 1]$$

and

$$|y_1'(x) - y_2'(x)| \leq |\beta| + \frac{M}{M + 1} (|\alpha| + |\beta|)[e^{(M+1)|x - x_0|} - 1].$$

Show that, for each fixed x in I, $y_2(x) \to y_1(x)$ and $y_2'(x) \to y_1'(x)$ as $\alpha_2 \to \alpha_1$ and $\beta_2 \to \beta_1$. (Suggestion: modify the procedure of Exercise 8, Section 1.2.)

1.8 Polynomial Operators

Let us introduce the symbol D for the derivative operator d/dx. We say that the result of operating on a function $u(x)$ with the operator D is du/dx, and we write

$$Du = \frac{du}{dx}. \tag{1.64}$$

If m is a positive integer, we define the operator D^m by means of the relation

$$D^m u = \frac{d^m u}{dx^m}. \tag{1.65}$$

We also define

$$D^0 u = 1 \cdot u = u. \tag{1.66}$$

Let a_i, $i = 1, 2, \ldots, n$, be constants, real or complex. We define a *polynomial operator* of order n,

$$P(D) = a_0 D^n + a_1 D^{n-1} + \cdots + a_{n-1} D + a_n, \tag{1.67}$$

by means of the relation

$$P(D)u = a_0 u^{(n)} + a_1 u^{(n-1)} + \cdots + a_{n-1} u' + a_n u. \tag{1.68}$$

Two polynomial operators $P(D)$ and $Q(D)$ are said to be *equal*, written $P(D) = Q(D)$, if, and only if, they are of the same order and their corresponding coefficients are equal.† The operators $P(D) + Q(D)$ and $P(D)Q(D)$ are defined to be those polynomial operators obtained by applying the laws for addition and multiplication for ordinary polynomials to the polynomial operators $P(D)$ and $Q(D)$. It follows that the commutative, associative, and distributive laws for ordinary polynomials also apply to polynomial operators. In particular, it follows that

$$(D^m D^n)u = D^{m+n}u.$$

For two polynomial operators $P(D)$ and $Q(D)$ it is easy to verify that

$$[P(D) + Q(D)]u = P(D)u + Q(D)u. \tag{1.69}$$

We shall now show that

$$Q(D)[P(D)u] = [Q(D)P(D)]u. \tag{1.70}$$

We first consider the case when $Q(D) = bD^k$, that is, when $Q(D)$ is a monomial operator. We have

$$Q(D)[P(D)u] = bD^k[a_0 u^{(n)} + a_1 u^{(n-1)} + \cdots + a_n u]$$

$$= ba_0 u^{(n+k)} + ba_1 u^{(n+k-1)} + \cdots + ba_n u^{(k)}$$

$$= [ba_0 D^{n+k} + ba_1 D^{n+k-1} + \cdots + ba_n D^k]u$$

$$= [Q(D)P(D)]u,$$

so the relationship (1.70) holds when $Q(D)$ is such an operator. In the general case, when $Q(D) = b_0 D^m + b_1 D^{m-1} + \cdots + b_m$, we therefore have

$$Q(D)[P(D)u] = b_0 D^m[P(D)u] + b_1 D^{m-1}[P(D)u] + \cdots + b_m[P(D)u]$$

$$= [b_0 D^m P(D)]u + [b_1 D^{m-1}P(D)]u + \cdots + [b_m P(D)]u$$

$$= [(b_0 D^m + b_1 D^{m-1} + \cdots + b_m)P(D)]u$$

$$= [Q(D)P(D)]u.$$

Thus if we operate on a function $u(x)$ first with $P(D)$ and then operate on the result with $Q(D)$, the final result is the same as that which we obtain by operating on $u(x)$ with the operator $Q(D)P(D)$. Since polynomial operators commute, that is, $Q(D)P(D) = P(D)Q(D)$, the same result is also obtained by operating on $u(x)$ first with $Q(D)$ and then operating on the result with $P(D)$. In the case of a finite number of operators $P_1, P_2, \ldots, P_n$, it can be shown by induction that

$$P_1(P_2 \cdots (P_{n-1}(P_n u)) \cdots) = (P_1 P_2 \cdots P_n)u. \tag{1.71}$$

Associated with the polynomial operator

$$P(D) = a_0 D^n + a_1 D^{n-1} + \cdots + a_0 \tag{1.72}$$

† See also Exercise 5.

is the ordinary polynomial

$$P(r) = a_0 r^n + a_1 r^{n-1} + \cdots + a_n. \tag{1.73}$$

If the polynomial $P(r)$ has zeros $r_1, r_2, \ldots, r_n$, so that

$$P(r) = a_0(r - r_1)(r - r_2) \cdots (r - r_n), \tag{1.74}$$

then the differential operator $P(D)$ can be written in the factored form

$$P(D) = a_0(D - r_1)(D - r_2) \cdots (D - r_n). \tag{1.75}$$

The order and manner of grouping of the factors $(D - r_i)$ is immaterial. If the polynomial P has *real coefficients*, its complex zeros occur in pairs. Thus if $r_1 = a + ib$ is a zero, the number $r_2 = a - ib$ is also a zero. Now the second-order operator

$$(D - r_1)(D - r_2) = [D - (a + ib)][D - (a - ib)] = (D - a)^2 + b^2$$

has real coefficients. Therefore any polynomial operator $P(D)$ with real coefficients can be written as the product of first and second order polynomial operators with real coefficients.

1.8 EXERCISES

1. Write the given differential equation in factored form, in terms of real factors of first and second order.

(a) $(D^2 + D - 6)y = 0$ (c) $(D^3 - 3D^2 + 4)y = 0$
(b) $(3D^2 + 5D - 2)y = 0$ (d) $(D^4 + 5D^2 + 6)y = 0$

2. Write the given differential equation in the form $P(D)y = 0$.

(a) $y'' - 4y' + 5y = 0$ (c) $y''' - 5y'' - y' - 15y = 0$
(b) $y''' - y'' + 4y' - 4y = 0$

3. Find a linear homogeneous differential equation, with real constant coefficients, whose auxiliary polynomial equation has the given numbers among its roots.

(a) $r_1 = 3, \quad r_2 = -2$ (d) $r_1 = 0, \quad r_2 = 0, \quad r_3 = 3$
(b) $r_1 = 3, \quad r_2 = 3, \quad r_3 = -1$ (e) $r_1 = 3 + 2i, \quad r_2 = -1$
(c) $r_1 = 1 + i$

4. Let $P(D)$ be a polynomial operator and let $u(x) = e^{rx}$, where r is any constant, real or complex. Show that $P(D)u(x) = P(r)e^{rx}$. Show that if the number r_1 is a root of the polynomial equation $P(r) = 0$, then the function $e^{r_1 x}$ is a solution of the differential equation $P(D)y = 0$.

5. Let $P(D)$ and $Q(D)$ be two polynomial operators of degree n. Show that $P(D) = Q(D)$ if, and only if, $P(D)u(x) = Q(D)u(x)$ for every function $u(x)$ which possesses at least n derivatives on the interval $(-\infty, +\infty)$.

1.9 Equations with Constant Coefficients

We consider, on the interval $(-\infty, +\infty)$, a differential equation of the form

$$a_0 y^{(n)} + a_1 y^{(n-1)} + \cdots + a_{n-1} y' + a_n y = 0, \tag{1.76}$$

where the coefficients a_i are *real constants*, and $a_0 \neq 0$. By using the operator notation of the previous section, we can write this equation more briefly as

$$P(D)y = 0, \tag{1.77}$$

where $P(D)$ is the polynomial operator.

$$P(D) = a_0 D^n + a_1 D^{n-1} + \cdots + a_n.$$

A solution of equation (1.77) is a function such that a certain linear combination of it and its first n derivatives vanishes. Of all the elementary functions, the only ones whose derivatives are multiples of the original function are the exponential functions. In fact, if r is any constant, real or complex, we have

$$D^m e^{rx} = r^m e^{rx}, \qquad m = 0, 1, 2, \ldots . \tag{1.78}$$

It is therefore somewhat natural to expect that at least some of the solutions of equation (1.77) will be of the form

$$y = e^{rx}.$$

Upon substituting an expression of this form into the differential equation (1.77), we find, in view of the formula (1.78), that

$$P(D)e^{rx} = P(r)e^{rx},$$

where the polynomial

$$P(r) = a_0 r^n + a_1 r^{n-1} + \cdots + a_n \tag{1.79}$$

is called the *auxiliary polynomial* associated with the differential equation (1.77). Denoting the zeros of this polynomial by $r_1, r_2, \ldots, r_n$, we have

$$P(D)e^{rx} = a_0(r - r_1)(r - r_2) \cdots (r - r_n)e^{rx}.$$

Evidently each of the functions $e^{r_i x}$ is a solution of the differential equation. The zeros r_i may not all be distinct, however, in which case our procedure does not yield n linearly independent solutions.

In order to treat the case of a multiple zero of $P(r)$, we need the following result.

Lemma. Let r_1 be a complex constant and let $u(x)$ be any function that possesses derivatives of all orders. Then

$$(D - r_1)^n [e^{r_1 x} u(x)] = e^{r_1 x} D^n u(x) \tag{1.80}$$

for every positive integer n.

Proof.   The proof is by induction. For $n = 1$ we have

$$(D - r_1)(e^{r_1 x}u) = r_1 e^{r_1 x}u + e^{r_1 x}u' - r_1 e^{r_1 x}u = e^{r_1 x}Du,$$

so proposition (1.80) holds for $n = 1$. Suppose now that it holds for an arbitrary positive integer k, that is, that

$$(D - r_1)^k(e^{r_1 x}u) = e^{r_1 x}D^k u.$$

Then

$$(D - r_1)^{k+1}(e^{r_1 x}u) = (D - r_1)(D - r_1)^k(e^{r_1 x}u)$$

$$= (D - r_1)(e^{r_1 x}D^k u)$$

$$= r_1 e^{r_1 x}D^k u + e^{r_1 x}D^{k+1}u - r_1 e^{r_1 x}D^k u$$

$$= e^{r_1 x}D^{k+1}u.$$

Thus if the proposition holds for $n = k$, it also holds for $n = k + 1$. Since it holds for $n = 1$, it must hold for every positive integer n.

Suppose that r_1 is a zero of $P(r)$ of multiplicity k. We shall show that each of the k functions

$$x^j e^{r_1 x}, \qquad 0 \le j \le k - 1, \tag{1.81}$$

is a solution of the differential equation (1.77). Let

$$P(D) = Q(D)(D - r_1)^k,$$

where $Q(D)$ is a polynomial operator of degree $n - k$. Then

$$P(D)(x^j e^{r_1 x}) = Q(D)[(D - r_1)^k(x^j e^{r_1 x})]$$

$$= Q(D)[e^{r_1 x}D^k(x^j)]$$

$$= Q(D)(0)$$

$$= 0,$$

since $D^k(x^j) = 0$ when $0 \le j \le k - 1$. Thus, even when $P(r)$ has multiple zeros, it is still possible to find n solutions of the differential equation which we may hope are linearly independent.

Some of the zeros of $P(r)$ may, of course, be complex. Since $P(D)$ has real coefficients, it follows that if $r = a + ib$ is a zero of multiplicity k, then $\bar{r} = a - ib$ is also a zero of multiplicity k. In this case, the $2k$ functions

$$x^j e^{(a+ib)x} = x^j e^{ax}(\cos bx + i \sin bx)$$

$$x^j e^{(a-ib)x} = x^j e^{ax}(\cos bx - i \sin bx), \qquad 0 \le j \le k - 1,$$

are complex solutions of the equation. Consequently, the $2k$ functions

$$x^j e^{ax} \cos bx, \qquad x^j e^{ax} \sin bx. \qquad 0 \le j \le k - 1, \tag{1.82}$$

are real solutions. Thus it is always possible to find n real solutions. We summarize the results obtained thus far in the following theorem.

Theorem 6. Let the nth-order differential equation $P(D)y = 0$ have real coefficients. If r_1 is a real root, of multiplicity k, of the auxiliary polynomial equation $P(r) = 0$, then each of the k functions $x^j e^{r_1 x}$, $0 \leq j \leq k - 1$, is a solution of the differential equation. If $r_2 = a + ib$ is a complex root of multiplicity k (in which case $\bar{r}_2 = a - ib$ is also a root of multiplicity k), then each of the $2k$ functions $x^j e^{r_2 x}$, $x^j e^{\bar{r}_2 x}$, $0 \leq j \leq k - 1$, is a complex solution of the equation, and each of the $2k$ functions

$$x^j e^{ax} \cos bx, \qquad x^j e^{ax} \sin bx, \qquad 0 \leq j \leq k - 1,$$

is a real solution.

We shall now show that the n real solutions we have obtained are linearly independent. Let r_1, r_2, ..., r_s be the *distinct* zeros of $P(r)$. Some of these numbers may be complex. Let m_i be the multiplicity of r_i. If the n solutions are linearly dependent, then there exist constants A_1, A_2, ..., A_{m_i}, B_1, B_2, ..., B_{m_2}, ..., not all zero, such that

$$(A_1 + A_2 x + \cdots + A_{m_1} x^{m_1 - 1}) e^{r_1 x} + (B_1 + B_2 x + \cdots + B_{m_2} x^{m_2 - 1}) e^{r_2 x} + \cdots \equiv 0.$$

That is, there must hold a relationship of the form

$$\sum_{i=1}^{s} p_i(x) e^{r_i x} \equiv 0, \tag{1.83}$$

where $p_i(x)$ is a polynomial of degree $< m_i$, and not all these polynomials are identically zero. We can assume, without loss of generality, that $p_s(x) \not\equiv 0$. Let M_i be the degree of $p_i(x)$. Multiplying through in equation (1.83) by $e^{-r_1 x}$, differentiating $M_1 + 1$ times, and then multiplying through by $e^{r_1 x}$, we obtain a relationship of the form

$$\sum_{i=2}^{s} q_i(x) e^{r_i x} \equiv 0, \tag{1.84}$$

where $q_i(x)$ is a polynomial of the same degree as $p_i(x)$. (If $p_1(x) \equiv 0$, we omit this step.) Next, we multiply through in equation (1.85) by $e^{-r_2 x}$, differentiate $M_2 + 1$ times, and then multiply through by $e^{r_2 x}$. This step yields a relationship of the form

$$\sum_{i=3}^{s} g_i(x) e^{r_i x} \equiv 0, \tag{1.85}$$

where $g_i(x)$ is a polynomial of the same degree as $q_i(x)$ and $p_i(x)$, $i = 3$, 4, ..., s. (If $q_2(x) \equiv 0$, we can omit this step.) Continuing in this way, we finally obtain a relationship of the form

$$f_s(x) e^{r_s x} \equiv 0, \tag{1.86}$$

where $f_s(x)$ is a polynomial of the same degree as $p_s(x)$, namely, M_s. Multiplying through in equation (1.86) by $e^{-r_s x}$ and differentiating M_s

times, we find that

$$\frac{d^{M_s}}{dx^{M_s}} f_s(x) \equiv 0.$$

But this is impossible, since $f_s(x)$ is of degree M_s. Hence our assumption that the n solutions were linearly dependent is false; they must be linearly independent.

If we replace each pair of complex solutions

$$x^j e^{(a+ib)x}, \qquad x^j e^{(a-ib)x} \tag{1.87}$$

by the corresponding pair of real solutions

$$x^j e^{ax} \cos bx, \qquad x^j e^{ax} \sin bx, \tag{1.88}$$

the resulting set of n real solutions is still linearly independent. For suppose that a relationship of the form

$$A x^j e^{ax} \cos bx + B x^j e^{ax} \sin bx + \cdots = 0 \tag{1.89}$$

holds. Then, since

$$x^j e^{ax} \cos bx = \frac{1}{2} x^j [e^{(a+ib)x} + e^{(a-ib)x}]$$

$$x^j e^{ax} \sin bx = \frac{1}{2i} x^j [e^{(a+ib)x} - e^{(a-ib)x}]$$

a relationship of the form

$$A' x^j e^{(a+ib)x} + B' x^j e^{(a-ib)x} + \cdots \equiv 0 \tag{1.90}$$

must hold, where

$$A = A' + B', \qquad B = i(A' - B').$$

But A' and B' must be zero, so A and B must be zero also. The set of n real solutions is therefore linearly independent.

As a first example, we consider the equation

$$y''' - 3y'' + 4y = 0.$$

If e^{rx} is to be a solution of this equation, r must be a root of the polynomial equation

$$r^3 - 3r^2 + 4 = 0.$$

The roots are found to be $r_1 = 2, r_2 = 2, r_3 = -1$. Then each of the functions e^{-x}, e^{2x}, xe^{2x} is a solution of the differential equation and the general solution is

$$y = C_1 e^{-x} + (C_2 + C_3 x)e^{2x}.$$

As a second example, we consider the equation

$$y'' + 4y' + 5y = 0.$$

In this case, the auxiliary polynomial equation is

$$r^2 + 4r + 5 = 0.$$

The roots are $r_1 = -2 + i$ and $r_2 = -2 - i$. The functions $e^{(-2+i)x}$ and $e^{-(2+i)x}$ are therefore complex solutions of the differential equation. The corresponding real solutions are $e^{-2x} \cos x$ and $e^{-2x} \sin x$. The general solution is

$$y = e^{-2x}(C_1 \cos x + C_2 \sin x).$$

1.9 EXERCISES

1. Find a fundamental set of solutions for the given differential equation and write down the general solution.

   (a) $y'' - 5y' + 6y = 0$ (d) $y'' - 6y' + 9y = 0$
   (b) $2y'' + 5y' = 0$ (e) $y'' + 4y = 0$
   (c) $y'' + 4y' + 4y = 0$ (f) $y'' + 2y' + 5y = 0$

2. Find the general solution of the given equation.

   (a) $y''' - 3y'' + 3y' - y = 0$ (d) $y^{(4)} + 9y'' = 0$
   (b) $y^{(4)} - y = 0$ (e) $y^{(4)} + 8y'' + 16y = 0$
   (c) $y''' - 3y'' + 4y = 0$

3. Find the solution of the initial value problem.

   (a) $y'' - 4y' + 3y = 0,$ $y(0) = 6,$ $y'(0) = 3$
   (b) $y'' - 4y' + 4y = 0,$ $y(0) = -1,$ $y'(0) = 2$
   (c) $y'' + y = 0,$ $y(\pi/6) = 0,$ $y'(\pi/6) = 2$
   (d) $y''' - y'' + 4y' - 4y = 0,$ $y(0) = 7,$ $y'(0) = 0,$ $y''(0) = 2$

4. Show that the functions

   $$\cosh ax = \frac{e^{ax} + e^{-ax}}{2}, \qquad \sinh ax = \frac{e^{ax} - e^{-ax}}{2}$$

   form a fundamental set for the equation $y'' - a^2 y = 0$.

5. Show that each of the expressions

   $$y = A \cos (kx + \alpha), \qquad y = B \sin (kx + \beta),$$

   where A, B, α, and β are arbitrary constants, is a representation of the general solution of the differential equation $y'' + k^2 y = 0$.

6. Show that every solution of an equation with constant coefficients approaches zero as x becomes positively infinite if, and only if, all roots of the auxiliary equation have negative real parts.

7. Find a polynomial operator $P(D)$, with real coefficients, such that $P(D)u(x) = 0$, if $u(x)$ is as given.

   (a) $u(x) = xe^{2x}$ (b) $u(x) = e^{-2x} \sin x$ (c) $u(x) = 2e^x + e^{2x}$

1.10 Equations of Cauchy Type

A linear differential equation of the form

$$Ly = a_0 x^n y^{(n)} + a_1 x^{n-1} y^{(n-1)} + \cdots + a_{n-1} xy' + a_n y = 0, \qquad (1.91)$$

where $a_0, a_1, \ldots, a_n$ are constants, is known as an equation of *Cauchy type*.†
Such an equation can be transformed into an equation with constant coefficients by means of the change of independent variable

$$x = e^t, \qquad -\infty < t < +\infty \qquad (1.92)$$

$$t = \log x, \qquad x > 0.$$

For then

$$x \frac{du}{dx} = \frac{dy}{dt} \qquad x^2 \frac{d^2 y}{dx^2} = \frac{d}{dt} \left(\frac{d}{dt} - 1 \right) y$$

and in general

$$x^k \frac{d^k y}{dx^k} = \frac{d}{dt} \left(\frac{d}{dt} - 1 \right) \left(\frac{d}{dt} - 2 \right) \cdots \left(\frac{d}{dt} - k + 1 \right) y \qquad (1.93)$$

for any positive integer k. Formula (1.93) may be verified by mathematical
induction. With the change of variable (1.92), equation (1.91) takes on the
form

$$[a_0 \theta(\theta - 1) \cdots (\theta - n + 1) + a_1 \theta(\theta - 1) \cdots (\theta - n + 2) + \cdots$$

$$+ a_{n-1} \theta + a_n] y = 0, \quad (1.94)$$

where θ is the operator d/dt. Seeking solutions of the form $y = e^{rt}$ for equation
(1.94), we find that the auxiliary equation for r is

$$Q(r) = a_0 r(r - 1) \cdots (r - n + 1) + a_1 r(r - 1) \cdots (r - n + 2) + \cdots$$

$$+ a_{n-1} r + a_n = 0. \quad (1.95)$$

If $r = r_1$ is a real root with multiplicity k of this nth-degree polynomial
equation, then each of the functions

$$t^j e^{r_1 t} \qquad (j = 0, 1, \ldots, k - 1)$$

is a real solution of equation (1.94). The corresponding functions of x,

$$(\log x)^j x^{r_1} \qquad (j = 0, 1, \ldots, k - 1) \qquad (1.96)$$

are then real solutions of equation (1.91) on the interval $x > 0$. In case
$r_1 = a + ib$ and $r_2 = a - ib$ are complex roots of equation (1.95) with multiplicity k, the functions

$$t^j e^{at} \cos bt, \qquad t^j e^{at} \sin bt \qquad (j = 0, 1, \ldots, k - 1)$$

---

† Such an equation is also sometimes referred to in the literature as an *Euler* equation or
as an *equidimensional* equation.

are real solutions of equation (1.94). The corresponding functions of x,

$$x^a(\log x)^j \cos (b \log x), \qquad x^a(\log x)^j \sin (b \log x) \qquad (1.97)$$

are then real solutions of equation (1.91). Because of the theory of Section 1.9 for equations with constant coefficients, this method yields a set of n real linearly independent solutions for equation (1.94) for $-\infty < t < +\infty$. The corresponding solutions of equation (1.91) are therefore linearly independent on the interval $x > 0$, and form a fundamental set on this interval.

Solutions of equation (1.91) can be obtained more directly by attempting to find solutions of the form x^r, without any change of independent variable. Since

$$x^k \frac{d^k}{dx^k} (x^r) = r(r-1)(r-2) \cdots (r-k+1)x^r \qquad (1.98)$$

for every positive integer k, we have

$$L(x^r) = Q(r)x^r, \qquad (1.99)$$

where $Q(r)$ is the same polynomial as in equation (1.95). If r_1 is a zero of $Q(r)$, then the function x^{r_1} is a solution of equation (1.91). If r_1 is a zero of multiplicity k, each of the functions (1.96) is a solution.

We illustrate the procedure for Cauchy-type equations with some examples. Let us consider first the differential equation

$$x^3 y''' + 3x^2 y'' - 2xy' + 2y = 0.$$

We find that if a function of the form x^r is to be a solution, then the constant r must be such that

$$r(r-1)(r-2) + 3r(r-1) - 2r + 2 = 0,$$

or

$$r^3 - 3r + 2 = 0.$$

The roots of this auxiliary equation are found to be $r_1 = 1$, $r_2 = 1$, and $r_3 = -2$. Therefore, the general solution on the interval $x > 0$ is

$$y = C_1 x + C_2 x \log x + C_3 x^{-2}.$$

As a second example, we consider the differential equation

$$x^2 y'' - 3xy' + 5y = 0.$$

The auxiliary equation is found to be

$$r(r-1) - 3r + 5 = 0$$

or

$$r^2 - 4r + 5 = 0.$$

The roots of this equation are $r_1 = 2 + i$ and $r_2 = 2 - i$. Therefore the general solution of the differential equation is

$$y = C_1 x^2 \cos (\log x) + C_2 x^2 \sin (\log x).$$

1.10   EXERCISES

1. Find the general solution if x is restricted to the interval $(0, +\infty)$.

(a) $x^2y'' - 3xy' - 12y = 0$ (f) $x^2y'' + 3xy' + y = 0$
(b) $2x^2y'' + 3xy' - y = 0$ (g) $x^2y'' + 2xy' + 2y = 0$
(c) $x^2y'' - 3xy' + 4y = 0$ (h) $x^3y''' + 2x^2y'' - xy' + y = 0$
(d) $4x^2y'' + y = 0$ (i) $x^3y''' + 4x^2y'' + 6xy' + 4y = 0$
(e) $x^2y'' + xy' + 9y = 0$

2. Find the solutions of the initial value problem on the interval $(0, +\infty)$:

(a) $x^2y'' - 2xy' + 2y = 0,$ $y(2) = 3,$ $y'(2) = 1$
(b) $x^2y'' + 5xy' + 4y = 0,$ $y(1) = 2,$ $y'(1) = -3$
(c) $x^2y'' - 3xy' + 5y = 0,$ $y(1) = 2,$ $y'(1) = 0$

3. Show that if $y = \phi(x)$ is a solution of a Cauchy equation on the interval $(0, +\infty)$, then the function $y = \phi(|x|) = \phi(-x)$ is a solution on the interval $(-\infty, 0)$.

4. By using the result of Problem 3, find the general solution of the given equation on the interval $(-\infty, 0)$:

(a) The equation of Problem 1(a)   (c) The equation of Prolem 1(d)
(b) The equation of Problem 1(c)

5. Show that the change of variable $t = ax + b$ transforms the equation

$$a_0(ax + b)^n y^{(n)} + a_1(ax + b)^{n-1}y^{(n-1)} + \cdots + a_n y = 0$$

into a Cauchy equation.

6. Use the result of Problem 5 to find the general solution of the given equation on the indicated interval:

(a) $(x + 2)^2 y'' + 3(x + 2)y' - 3y = 0,$ $-2 < x < +\infty$
(b) $(2x - 1)^2 y'' + 5(2x - 1)y' + 4y = 0,$ $\frac{1}{2} < x < +\infty$

1.11   The Nonhomogeneous Equation

We now consider nonhomogeneous equations, of the form†

$$Ly = y^{(n)} + a_1(x)y^{(n-1)} + \cdots + a_n(x)y = f(x), \qquad (1.100)$$

where the functions $a_i(x)$ and $f(x)$ are continuous on an interval I. Associated with this equation is the corresponding homogeneous equation

$$Ly = y^{(n)} + a_1(x)y^{(n-1)} + \cdots + a_n(x)y = 0. \qquad (1.101)$$

As we shall see, the theory for the nonhomogeneous equation is closely related to that for the homogeneous equation.

---

† If $a_0(x) \neq 0$ in the equation $a_0 y^{(n)} + a_1 y^{(n-1)} + \cdots + a_n y = f$, we can always divide through by a_0 to write the equation in the form (1.100).

Theorem 7. Let the functions $y_1(x)$, $y_2(x)$, ..., $y_n(x)$ constitute a fundamental set for the homogeneous equation (1.101) and let $y_p(x)$ be any one particular solution of the nonhomogeneous equation (1.100). Then every solution of the nonhomogeneous equation is of the form

$$C_1y_1(x) + C_2y_2(x) + \cdots + C_ny_n(x) + y_p(x), \tag{1.102}$$

where the quantities C_i are constants.

Proof. First of all, we note that an expression of the form (1.102) is a solution of the nonhomogeneous equation for every choice of the constants C_i. For $Ly_i = 0$, $1 \le i \le n$, and $Ly_p = f$, so that

$$L(C_1y_1 + C_2y_2 + \cdots + C_ny_n + y_p) = C_1Ly_1 + \cdots + C_nLy_n + Ly_p = f.$$

Now let $u(x)$ be any solution of the equation (1.100) on the interval I. Then $u(x) - y_p(x)$ is a solution of the homogeneous equation (1.101), because

$$L(u - y_p) = Lu - Ly_p = f - f = 0.$$

Consequently, $u - y_p$ must be of the form

$$u - y_p = C_1y_1 + C_2y_2 + \cdots + C_ny_n$$

and u must be of the form

$$u = C_1y_1 + \cdots + C_ny_n + y_p.$$

An expression of the form

$$C_1y_1(x) + \cdots + C_ny_n(x) + y_p(x), \tag{1.103}$$

where the constants C_i are arbitrary, represents the general solution of the equation (1.100). If we can find a fundamental set of solutions for the homogeneous equation (1.101), and if we can find just one solution of the nonhomogeneous equation (1.100), then we can write down the general solution for the nonhomogeneous equation. In Section 1.12 we shall show that a solution $y_p(x)$ of equation (1.100) can always be expressed in terms of the nonhomogeneous term $f(x)$ and the functions of a fundamental set for the equation (1.101).

1.12 Variation of Parameters

Let the functions $y_i(x)$, $1 \le i \le n$, form a fundamental set of solutions for the homogeneous equation (1.101). We shall show that there exist functions $C_i(x)$, $1 \le i \le n$, such that the function

$$y_p(x) = C_1(x)y_1(x) + C_2(x)y_2(x) + \cdots + C_n(x)y_n(x) \tag{1.104}$$

is a solution of the nonhomogeneous equation (1.100).

Assuming for the moment that a solution of the form (1.104) does exist, let us try to find out how the functions $C_i(x)$ can be determined. If we simply calculate the derivatives y_p', y_p'', ..., $y_p^{(n)}$ and substitute these expressions, along with y_p, into the differential equation (1.100), we shall obtain *one* relationship which the n functions $C_i(x)$ must satisfy. The first derivative is

$$y_p' = (C_1 y_1' + \cdots + C_n y_n') + (C_1' y_1 + \cdots + C_n' y_n). \qquad (1.105)$$

If we arbitrarily require that

$$C_1' y_1 + \cdots + C_n' y_n = 0, \qquad (1.106)$$

we obtain an additional condition for the functions $C_i(x)$ to satisfy. We also simplify the expression for y_p' so that it becomes

$$y_p' = C_1 y_1' + \cdots + C_n y_n'. \qquad (1.107)$$

Taking the second derivative, we have

$$y_p'' = (C_1 y_1'' + \cdots + C_n y_n'') + (C_1' y_1' + \cdots + C_n' y_n'). \qquad (1.108)$$

We shall also require that

$$C_1' y_1' + \cdots + C_n' y_n' = 0. \qquad (1.109)$$

Then the expression for y_p'' simplifies to

$$y_p'' = C_1 y_1'' + \cdots + C_n y_n''. \qquad (1.110)$$

Continuing in this way, we find that the $(n-1)$th derivative will be of the form

$$y_p^{(n-1)} = C_1 y_1^{(n-1)} + \cdots + C_n y_n^{(n-1)} \qquad (1.111)$$

if we require that

$$C_1' y_1^{(n-2)} + \cdots + C_n' y_n^{(n-2)} = 0. \qquad (1.112)$$

So far we have imposed $(n-1)$ conditions of the types (1.106), (1.109), and (1.112) on the n functions $C_i(x)$. If we now require that the function $y_p(x)$ be a solution of the differential equation

$$y^{(n)} + a_1 y^{(n-1)} + \cdots + a_{n-1} y' + a_n y = f, \qquad (1.113)$$

we obtain the additional condition

$$[C_1 y_1^{(n)} + \cdots + C_n y_n^{(n)}] + [C_1' y_1^{(n-1)} + \cdots + C_n' y_n^{(n-1)}]$$
$$+ a_1 [C_1 y_1^{(n-1)} + \cdots + C_n y_n^{(n-1)}] + a_2 [C_1 y_1^{(n-2)} + \cdots + C_n y_n^{(n-2)}]$$
$$+ \cdots + a_n [C_1 y_1 + \cdots + C_n y_n] = f. \qquad (1.114)$$

Upon regrouping terms, this becomes

$$C_1 [y_1^{(n)} + a_1 y_1^{(n-1)} + \cdots + a_n y_1]$$
$$+ C_2 [y_2^{(n)} + a_1 y_2^{(n-1)} + \cdots + a_n y_2]$$
$$+ \cdots + C_n [y_n^{(n)} + a_1 y_n^{(n-1)} + \cdots + a_n y_n]$$
$$+ [C_1' y_1^{(n-1)} + \cdots + C_n' y_n^{(n-1)}] = f. \qquad (1.115)$$

Each group of terms on the left-hand side of this equation, except the last group, vanishes because the functions y_i are solutions of the homogeneous equation. Therefore this equation becomes simply

$$C_1'y_1^{(n-1)} + \cdots + C_n'y_n^{(n-1)} = f(x). \tag{1.116}$$

We have now obtained the following set of n conditions that are to be satisfied by the n functions $C_i(x)$:

$$C_1'y_1 + \cdots + C_n'y_n = 0$$

$$C_1'y_1' + \cdots + C_n'y_n' = 0$$

$$\cdots\cdots\cdots\cdots\cdots\cdots\cdots\cdots\cdots \tag{1.117}$$

$$C_1'y_1^{(n-2)} + \cdots + C_n'y_n^{(n-2)} = 0$$

$$C_1'y_1^{(n-1)} + \cdots + C_n'y_n^{(n-1)} = f(x).$$

This system of equations for the quantities C_i' possesses a unique solution, since the determinant of the system is the Wronskian of the set of independent solutions $y_i(x)$. In fact, by Cramer's rule,

$$C_i'(x) = \frac{\Delta_i(x)}{W(x)} f(x) \qquad (i = 1, 2, \ldots, n) \tag{1.118}$$

where the determinant $\Delta_i(x)$ is the cofactor of the element $y_i^{(n-1)}$ in the Wronskian $W(x)$. Integrating, we obtain the formula

$$C_i(x) = \int \frac{\Delta_i(x)}{W(x)} f(x) \, dx \qquad (i = 1, 2, \ldots, n) \tag{1.119}$$

The derivation of the formula (1.119) was based on the assumption that the equation (1.113) possessed a solution of the form

$$y_p(x) = C_1(x)y_1(x) + \cdots + C_n(x)y_n(x). \tag{1.120}$$

We can now show that this assumption is valid. Let the functions $C_i(x)$ be chosen according to formula (1.119). Then their derivatives, $C_i'(x)$, satisfy the system of equations (1.117). Because of this fact, the derivatives of y_p are given by the formulas

$$y_p^{(j)} = C_1 y_1^{(j)} + \cdots + C_n y_n^{(j)} \qquad (j = 1, 2, \ldots, n-1)$$

$$y_p^{(n)} = C_1 y_1^{(n)} + \cdots + C_n y_n^{(n)} + C_1'y_1^{(n-1)} + \cdots + C_n'y_n^{(n-1)}.$$

Making use of these formulas and the fact that the functions y_p are solutions of the homogeneous equation, we find that

$$Ly_p = C_1'y_1^{(n-1)} + \cdots + C_n'y_n^{(n-1)}.$$

By virtue of the last of equations (1.117), we have $Ly_p = f(x)$. Therefore the function (1.120), where the quantities $C_i(x)$ are chosen according to formula (1.119), is indeed a solution of the nonhomogeneous equation.

We have given a method for the determination of a solution of the non-homogeneous equation in the case when a fundamental set of solutions for the associated homogeneous equation is known. This method is known as the method of *variation of parameters*, or *variation of constants*. As an example of its use, let us consider the differential equation

$$y'' + 2y' + y = \frac{e^{-x}}{x + 1}$$

on an interval that does not include the point $x = -1$. The associated homogeneous equation has constant coefficients, so a fundamental set of solutions can be found by the methods of Section 1.9. Two independent solutions are

$$y_1(x) = e^{-x}, \qquad y_2(x) = xe^{-x}.$$

We therefore seek a particular solution of the nonhomogeneous equation which is of the form

$$y_p(x) = C_1(x)e^{-x} + C_2(x)xe^{-x}.$$

The system of equations (1.117) becomes, in this case,

$$C_1'e^{-x} + C_2'xe^{-x} = 0$$

$$-C_1'e^{-x} + C_2'(1 - x)e^{-x} = \frac{e^{-x}}{x + 1}.$$

Solving for C_1' and C_2', we find that

$$C_1' = -1 + \frac{1}{x + 1}, \qquad C_2' = \frac{1}{x + 1}.$$

We may therefore take

$$C_1 = \log|x + 1| - x, \qquad C_2 = \log|x + 1|.$$

The general solution of the differential equation is

$$y = Ae^{-x} + Bxe^{-x} + e^{-x}\log|x + 1| + xe^{-x}\log|x + 1|,$$

where A and B are arbitrary constants.

1.12   EXERCISES

1. If $y_1(x)$ and $y_2(x)$ are solutions of the equations $Ly = f_1$ and $Ly = f_2$, respectively, show that $y_1(x) + y_2(x)$ is a solution of the equation $Ly = f_1 + f_2$.

2. Find the general solution of the given differential equation:

    (a) $y'' + y = \tan^2 x$ (b) $y'' - 3y' + 2y = \dfrac{e^{2x}}{e^x + 1}$

(c) $y'' - 2y' + y = \dfrac{e^x}{x^2 + 1}$ (d) $y''' - y'' - y' + y = \dfrac{e^x}{x}$

3. Find the solution of the given initial value problem:

(a) $y'' + y = \sec x$, $-\dfrac{\pi}{2} < x < \dfrac{\pi}{2}$, $y(0) = 0$, $y'(0) = 1$

(b) $y'' - 2y' + y = \dfrac{e^x \log x}{x}$, $x > 0$, $y(1) = 0$, $y'(1) = 2e$

4. Find the general solution, given two independent solutions of the associated homogeneous equation:

(a) $x^2 y'' - (x^2 + 2x)y' + (x + 2)y = x^3$, $y_1 = x$, $y_2 = xe^x$

(b) $xy'' + 2(1 - x)y' + (x - 2)y = e^x$, $y_1 = e^x$, $y_2 = \dfrac{1}{x}e^x$

(c) $xy'' + (x + 1)y' + y = 2x^2 e^x$, $y_1 = x + 1$, $y_2 = e^x$

5. Let $f(x) = 0$ when $x < 0$ and $f(x) = 1$ when $x > 0$. Find a function $y(x)$ with the following properties:

(a) $y(x)$ and $y'(x)$ are continuous for all x,

(b) $y(0) = y'(0) = 0$,

(c) $y(x)$ is a solution of the differential equation $y'' - y = f(x)$ on each of the intervals $(-\infty, 0)$ and $(0, +\infty)$.

6. Let $y_1(x)$ and $y_2(x)$ be the solutions of the differential equation

$$y'' + a(x)y' + b(x)y = 0$$

for which $y_1(x_0) = 1$, $y_1'(x_0) = 0$, $y_2(x_0) = 0$, $y_2'(x_0) = 1$. Show that the solution of the initial value problem

$$y'' + a(x)y' + b(x)y = f(x),   y(x_0) = k_0,   y'(x_0) = k_1$$

is given by the formula

$$y = k_0 y_1(x) + k_1 y_2(x) + \int_{x_0}^{x} e^{A(t)}[y_2(x)y_1(t) - y_1(x)y_2(t)]f(t)\, dt,$$

where

$$A(t) = \int_{x_0}^{t} a(s)\, ds$$

7. Derive the formula

$$y_p(x) = \dfrac{1}{k} \int_{x_0}^{x} f(t)\sin k(t - x)\, dt$$

for a particular solution of the differential equation

$$y'' + k^2 y = f(x).$$

1.13   The Method of Undetermined Coefficients

If a fundamental set of solutions for the homogeneous equation $Ly = 0$ is known, a particular solution of the nonhomogeneous equation $Ly = f$ can always be found by the method of variation of parameters. For a certain class of nonhomogeneous equations, an alternative procedure, known as the *method of undetermined coefficients*, can also be used to find a particular solution. When it applies, this latter method is usually simpler.

The method of undetermined coefficients applies to linear differential equations of the form $Ly = f$ when the following two conditions are *both* met:

(a) The operator L has constant coefficients.

(b) The nonhomogeneous term $f(x)$ is a function that is the solution of *some* linear homogeneous differential equation with constant coefficients. The nonhomogeneous term must therefore consist of a linear combination of functions of the types

$$x^j \tag{1.121a}$$

$$x^j e^{ax} \tag{1.121b}$$

$$x^j e^{ax} \cos bx, \qquad x^j e^{ax} \sin bx, \tag{1.121c}$$

where j is a nonnegative integer.

Let us consider a differential equation with constant coefficients of order n,

$$P(D)y = f, \tag{1.122}$$

where $P(D)$ is a polynomial operator of order n, and $f(x)$ is a function of the appropriate type. Then there exists a polynomial operator $Q(D)$ such that

$$Q(D)f(x) = 0. \tag{1.123}$$

We say that the operator $Q(D)$ *annihilates* $f(x)$. Let the order of $Q(D)$ be m. If we operate on both members of equation (1.122) with $Q(D)$, we obtain the homogeneous equation

$$Q(D)P(D)y = 0, \tag{1.124}$$

whose order is $m + n$. A function that is a solution of equation (1.122) is also a solution of equation (1.124).† Also, every solution of the equation

$$P(D)y = 0 \tag{1.125}$$

is a solution of equation (1.124). Let the general solution of equation (1.124) be

$$A_1 u_1(x) + \cdots + A_m u_m(x) + B_1 v_1(x) + \cdots + B_n v_n(x), \tag{1.126}$$

where the functions u_i and v_i are of the types (1.121) and the functions v_i are solutions of equation (1.125). The functions u_i are solutions of equation (1.124) which are *not* solutions of equation (1.125). If the polynomials

---

† Every solution of equation (1.122) possesses derivatives of all orders.

$P(r)$ and $Q(r)$ have no common zeros, then the functions u_i are solutions of the equation

$$Q(D)y = 0. \tag{1.127}$$

However, if r_1 is a zero of $Q(r)$ that is also a zero, of multiplicity k, of $P(r)$, then the corresponding solutions of equation (1.124) are obtained by multiplying the appropriate solutions of (1.127) by x^k. This situation arises when $f(x)$ contains a term that is a solution of the associated homogeneous equation (1.125). For then $Q(D)$ and $P(D)$ contain a common factor.

Every solution of equation (1.122) is expressible in the form (1.126). Therefore, it must be possible to choose the constants in this expression so that

$$P(D)(A_1u_1 + \cdots + A_mu_m + B_1v_1 + \cdots + B_nv_n) = f(x).$$

Since

$$P(D)(B_1v_1 + \cdots + B_nv_n) = 0,$$

it must be possible to choose the constants A_i in the expression

$$A_1u_1 + \cdots + A_mu_m \tag{1.128}$$

so that it is a solution of equation (1.122). An expression of the form (1.128) is called a *trial solution* for the equation (1.122). The values of the constants can be determined by substituting the expression in the differential equation and requiring that the latter be satisfied identically.

Let us now consider the differential equation

$$P(D)y = f, \tag{1.129}$$

where $f(x)$ consists of a single term of one of the types (1.121). If

$$f(x) = Cx^j,$$

the operator of lowest order that annihilates $f(x)$ is $Q(D) = D^{j+1}$. The tentative trial solution is therefore

$$y_p(x) = A_1 + A_2x + \cdots + A_{j+1}x^j. \tag{1.130}$$

But if the operator $P(D)$ contains the factor D^k, that is, if the functions $1, x, x^2, \ldots, x^{k-1}$ are solutions of the associated homogeneous equation, we must multiply the right-hand member of (1.130) by x^k to obtain the trial solution.

If

$$f(x) = Cx^je^{ax},$$

the operator of lowest order that annihilates $f(x)$ is $Q(D) = (D - a)^{j+1}$. The tentative trial solution is then

$$y_p(x) = (A_1 + A_2x + \cdots + A_{j+1}x^j) e^{ax}. \tag{1.131}$$

If $P(D)$ contains the factor $(D - a)^k$, we must multiply the expression on the right in (1.131) by x^k. (In this case, the homogeneous equation has the solutions e^{ax}, xe^{ax}, $\ldots$, $x^{k-1}e^{ax}$.)

If

$$f(x) = Cx^j e^{ax} \cos bx, \qquad \text{or} \qquad f(x) = Cx^j e^{ax} \sin bx,$$

the real operator of lowest order that annihilates $f(x)$ is

$$Q(D) = [D - (a + ib)]^{j+1}[D - (a - ib)]^{j+1} = [(D - a)^2 + b^2]^{j+1}$$

The tentative trial solution is therefore

$$y_p(x) = (A_1 + A_2 x + \cdots + A_{j+1}x^j)e^{ax} \cos bx$$

$$+ (B_1 + B_2 x + \cdots + B_{j+1}x^j)e^{ax} \sin bx. \qquad (1.132)$$

However, if $P(D)$ contains the factor $[(D - a)^2 + b^2]^k$, we must multiply the expression on the right by x^k to obtain the trial solution.

We can summarize the rules for forming a trial solution as follows: If the nonhomogeneous term $f(x)$ consists of a single term, we first write down a tentative trial solution of one of the appropriate types, (1.130), (1.131), or (1.132), whichever is appropriate. Then, if any term in this tentative trial solution is a solution of the homogeneous equation, we multiply the *entire expression* by the lowest integral power of x that alters the expression in such a way that no term in the new expression so formed is a solution of the homogeneous equation. If $f(x)$ consists of a linear combination of terms of the types (1.121), we can form a trial solution for each term separately.

We now illustrate the procedure by means of some examples.

EXAMPLE 1. $y'' - y = 6e^{2x}$.
The general solution of the homogeneous equation is

$$C_1 e^x + C_2 e^{-x}.$$

The tentative trial solution which corresponds to the nonhomogeneous term $6e^{2x}$ is

$$y_p = Ae^{2x}.$$

Since this term is not a solution of the homogeneous equation, it is a satisfactory trial solution as it stands. The derivatives are

$$y_p' = 2Ae^{2x}, \qquad y_p'' = 4Ae^{2x}.$$

Substituting in the differential equation, we find that the constant A must be chosen so that

$$4Ae^{2x} - Ae^{2x} = 6e^{2x},$$

or

$$3Ae^{2x} = 6e^{2x}.$$

Evidently $A = 2$. A particular solution for the differential equation is therefore

$$y_p = 2e^{2x},$$

and the general solution is

$$y = C_1 e^x + C_2 e^{-x} + 2e^{2x}.$$

EXAMPLE 2. $y'' - y = 3xe^x$.
The general solution of the homogeneous equation is again

$$C_1 e^x + C_2 e^{-x}.$$

The tentative trial solution that corresponds to the nonhomogeneous term is

$$y_p = Ae^x + Bxe^x.$$

But one of the terms in this expression is a solution of the homogeneous equation. We must therefore take as a trial solution

$$y_p = Axe^x + Bx^2 e^x.$$

The derivatives are found to be

$$y_p' = A(x + 1)e^x + B(x^2 + 2x)e^x$$
$$y_p'' = A(x + 2)e^x + B(x^2 + 4x + 2)e^x.$$

Substituting in the equation, we require that

$$A(x + 2)e^x + B(x^2 + 4x + 2)e^x - Axe^x - Bx^2 e^x = 3xe^x,$$

or

$$(2A + 2B)e^x + 4Bxe^x = 3xe^x.$$

Since the functions e^x and xe^x are linearly independent, we must have

$$4B = 3, \qquad 2A + 2B = 0,$$

or

$$A = -\tfrac{3}{4}, \qquad B = \tfrac{3}{4}.$$

A particular solution of the differential equation is

$$y_p = \tfrac{3}{4}(x^2 - x)e^x,$$

and the general solution is

$$y = C_1 e^x + C_2 e^{-x} + \tfrac{3}{4}(x^2 - x)e^x.$$

EXAMPLE 3. $y'' - 2y' = -4 \cos x + 2x$.
The general solution of the homogeneous equation is

$$C_1 + C_2 e^{2x}.$$

The tentative trial solution is

$$y_p = A \cos x + B \sin x + Cx + D.$$

One term in the group of terms that corresponds to the function $2x$ is a solution of the homogeneous equation. Therefore we must multiply each term in that group by x. The trial solution now becomes

$$y_p = A \cos x + B \sin x + Cx^2 + Dx.$$

Then

$$y_p' = -A \sin x + B \cos x + 2Cx + D$$

$$y_p'' = -A \cos x - B \sin x + 2C.$$

Substituting in the differential equation and collecting like terms, we obtain the condition

$$(-A - 2B) \cos x + (-B + 2A) \sin x - 4Cx + (2C - 2D) = -4 \cos x + 2x.$$

This leads to the system of equations

$$A + 2B = 4, \qquad -B + 2A = 0, \qquad -4C = 2, \qquad 2C - 2D = 0,$$

whose solution is

$$A = \tfrac{4}{5}, \qquad B = \tfrac{8}{5}, \qquad C = -\tfrac{1}{2}, \qquad D = -\tfrac{1}{2}.$$

The general solution of the original equation is

$$y = C_1 + C_2 e^{2x} + \tfrac{4}{5} \cos x + \tfrac{8}{5} \sin x - \tfrac{1}{2}x^2 - \tfrac{1}{2}x.$$

1.13   EXERCISES

1. Find the general solution for the given differential equation. When initial conditions are given, also find the solution that satisfies those conditions.

(a)$y'' - 2y' + y = 4e^{-3x}$
(b)$y'' + 2y' - 3y = 8e^{2x}, \qquad y(0) = -3, \qquad y'(0) = -1$
(c)$y'' - 3y' = 6e^{3x}, \qquad y(0) = -1, \qquad y'(0) = 8$
(d)$y'' + 4y' + 4y = -6e^{-2x}$
(e)$y'' - y' - 2y = 2e^x - e^{-x}$
(f)$y'' + 4y = 3x^2, \qquad y(0) = \tfrac{1}{8}, \qquad y'(0) = 2$
(g)$y'' + 2y' = -3x$
(h)$y'' + 5y' + 6y = 5 \sin x$
(i)$y'' + y = 6 \cos 2x, \qquad y(\pi/2) = -1, \qquad y'(\pi/2) = 1$
(j)$y'' + 4y = \sin 2x$
(k)$y'' - 2y' + 2y = 3e^x + \cos x$
(l)$y'' - y' - 6y = 3$
(m)$y'' + y = 2x^2 e^x$
(n)$y'' + 3y' + 2y = 4 - \cos 3x$
(o)$y''' - 3y'' + 3y' - y = 4e^x$
(p)$y''' - 3y'' + 2y' = 6 - 2e^{-x}$

2. Find the general solution of the given equation if $0 < x < +\infty$:

(a) $x^2y'' + 4xy' - 10y = 2x$ (c) $x^2y'' - 2y' = x^2$

(b) $x^2y'' - xy' + y = \log^2 x$

3. If the constant a is not a root of the polynomial equation $P(r) = 0$, then the function

$$y = \frac{A}{P(a)}\, e^{ax}$$

is a solution of the differential equation

$$P(D)y = Ae^{ax}.$$

Verify this fact.

4. Use the result of Problem 3 to obtain particular solutions of the equations in Problems 1(a) and 1(b).

5. If the constant a is a root, of multiplicity m, of the polynomial equation $P(r) = 0$, then $P(r) = Q(r)(r - a)^m$, where $Q(a) \neq 0$. Verify that the function

$$y = \frac{A}{m!\, Q(a)}\, x^m e^{ax}$$

is a solution of the differential equation

$$P(D)y = Ae^{ax}.$$

6. Use the result of Problem 5 to find particular solutions of the equations in Problems 1(c) and 1(d).

7. If the function $y_p(x)$ is a solution of the equation

$$P(D)y = Ae^{iax} \qquad (A \text{ is real}),$$

then the real and imaginary parts of $y_p(x)$ are real solutions of the equations

$$P(D)y = A \cos ax, \qquad P(D)y = A \sin ax,$$

respectively. Use this fact to find particular solutions of the equations in Problems 1(i) and 1(j).

1.14 Applications

In this section we shall consider some elementary problems in mechanics and in electric circuit theory that lead to initial value problems for linear differential equations.

First let us consider problems that involve a body whose center of mass moves in a straight line. Let the number x stand for the directed distance of the center of mass of the body from a fixed point on the line of motion at time t. We assume that the motion of the body is described by means of a function

$x = x(t)$. The velocity v and the acceleration a of the center of mass are given by the formulas

$$v = \frac{dx}{dt}, \qquad a = \frac{d^2x}{dt^2}.$$

When $dx/dt > 0$, the body is moving in the positive direction along the line of motion; when $dx/dt < 0$, it is moving in the negative direction.

According to Newton's second law of motion,

$$m \frac{d^2x}{dt^2} = F, \tag{1.133}$$

where m is the mass of the body and F is the force exerted on the body. When the force is exerted in the positive direction, $F > 0$, and when the force is exerted in the negative direction, $F < 0$. If the force F can be described in terms of t, x, and the derivatives of x, then equation (1.133) becomes a differential equation for the function $x(t)$. In order to obtain a description of the motion of the body, we must solve this equation, subject to the initial conditions

$$x(t_0) = x_0, \qquad x'(t_0) = v_0,$$

where the numbers x_0 and v_0 represent the position and velocity, respectively, of the body at the time $t = t_0$.

We now consider two subclasses of problems that involve the linear motion of a body.

(a) Spring Problems

Consider a spring with natural length L. By the natural length, we mean the length of the spring when no external forces are applied (Figure 1.2a). When a

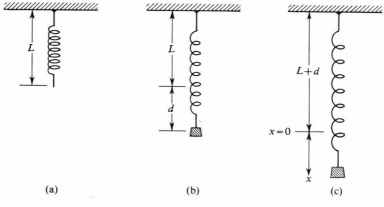

(a) (b) (c)

FIGURE I.2

spring is stretched (or compressed) a distance s by a force F applied at the ends, it is found by experiment that the magnitude of the force is approximately proportional to the distance s. Thus $|F| = ks$, where the positive constant k is known as the spring constant. The numerical value of k depends on the particular spring, as well as on the system of units used to describe F and s. Thus if a force of 40 pounds is required to stretch a spring 2 inches,

$$40 = 2k,$$

or

$$k = 20 \text{ pounds per inch.}$$

When a body of mass m is attached to the spring, the body will remain at rest in a position corresponding to an extension d of the spring from its natural length L (Figure 1.2b). The distance d is determined by the condition

$$mg = kd,$$

which requires that the downward force mg (due to gravity) acting on the body be balanced by the upward restoring force kd exerted on the body by the spring. Let x be the directed distance of the center of mass of the body from the position of rest, or equilibrium. The downward direction we take as positive (Figure 1.2c). The differential equation of motion of the body is

$$m \frac{d^2x}{dt^2} = mg - k(x + d),$$

or

$$m \frac{d^2x}{dt^2} + kx = 0. \tag{1.134}$$

If the body is held in the position $x = x_0$ and released from rest at time $t = 0$, the initial conditions are

$$x(0) = x_0, \qquad x'(0) = 0. \tag{1.135}$$

The solution of the initial value problem is

$$x = x_0 \cos \omega t,$$

where

$$\omega = \sqrt{\frac{k}{m}}.$$

We see that the body oscillates periodically about the equilibrium position, between the points $x = \pm|x_0|$, without ever coming to rest.

Straight-line motion that is described by a function of the form

$$x = x_0 \cos (\omega t + \theta_0), \qquad \text{or} \qquad x = x_0 \sin (\omega t + \theta_0) \tag{1.136}$$

is called *simple harmonic motion*. The number $|x_0|$ is called the *amplitude* of the motion. Note that $|x(t)| \leq |x_0|$ for all t. The *period* P of the motion is given by the formula $P = 2\pi/\omega$. This is the time required for the body to move through one cycle. The frequency f is the number of cycles per unit time. It is given by the formula $f = 1/P = \omega/2\pi$.

Actually, the medium that surrounds the body (air, for instance) tends to oppose its motion. The medium exerts a damping force F_d on the body that is approximately proportional to the velocity of the body. In the case of the body on the spring,

$$F_d = -c \frac{dx}{dt},$$

where c is a positive constant, and where the minus sign indicates that the force opposes the motion. When this force is taken into account, the equation of motion of the body on the spring becomes

$$m \frac{d^2x}{dt^2} = -kx - c \frac{dx}{dt},$$

or

$$m \frac{d^2x}{dt^2} + c \frac{dx}{dt} + kx = 0. \tag{1.137}$$

The general solution of this equation is

$$x = C_1 e^{-\alpha t} \cos \omega t + C_2 e^{-\alpha t} \sin \omega t,$$

where

$$\alpha = \frac{c}{2m}, \qquad \omega = \frac{\sqrt{4mk - c^2}}{2m}.$$

(We assume that $c^2 < 4mk$ for the moment.) We note that every solution of the equation tends to zero as t becomes infinite. The solution that satisfies the initial conditions (1.135) is

$$x = x_0 e^{-\alpha t} \left[\cos \omega t + \frac{\alpha}{\omega} \sin \omega t \right]$$

or

$$x = \sqrt{1 + \left(\frac{\alpha}{\omega}\right)^2} \, x_0 e^{-\alpha t} \cos(\omega t - \theta_0)$$

where

$$\theta_0 = \tan^{-1} \frac{\alpha}{\omega}.$$

In this case, the body still oscillates back and forth across the equilibrium position, but its oscillations are *damped*. It should be noted that although $x \to 0$, the body never actually comes to rest. If this seems contrary to reality, it should be remembered that the formulas used to describe the forces acting on the body are only approximate. We can therefore expect only an approximate description of the physical situation from our mathematical model.

(b) Falling Body Problems

Consider a body of mass m which falls from rest from a height h above the surface of the earth. Let x be the directed distance (positive direction downward) from the point above the earth. The two most important forces acting on the body are the force

$$F_1 = mg$$

due to gravity, and the force

$$F_2 = -c\,\frac{dx}{dt}$$

due to air resistance. The differential equation of motion of the body is

$$m\,\frac{d^2x}{dt^2} = mg - c\,\frac{dx}{dt},$$

or

$$m\,\frac{d^2x}{dt^2} + c\,\frac{dx}{dt} = mg. \tag{1.138}$$

The initial conditions are

$$x(0) = 0, \qquad x'(0) = 0. \tag{1.139}$$

The differential equation is nonhomogeneous, but has constant coefficients. Its general solution is found to be

$$x = C_1 + C_2 e^{-(c/m)t} + \frac{mg}{c}\,t.$$

The solution that satisfies the initial conditions is

$$x = \left(\frac{m}{c}\right)^2 g[e^{-(c/m)t} - 1] + \frac{mg}{c}\,t,$$

The velocity of the body is

$$v = \frac{dx}{dt} = \frac{mg}{c}\,[1 - e^{-(c/m)t}].$$

We note that as $t \to +\infty$, the velocity approaches the limiting value

$$v_L = \frac{mg}{c}\,.$$

Let us next consider some applications of differential equations to electric circuits. Suppose that a resistance, a capacitance, and an inductance are connected in series with a voltage source, as shown in Figure 1.3. When the switch S is closed at time $t = 0$, a current $I(t)$ will flow in the loop. ($I(t)$ may be negative, in which case the flow is opposite to the direction indicated in the figure.) Let voltage be given in *volts*, resistance R in *ohms*, inductance L in *henrys*, current I in *amperes*, and time t in *seconds*. Then the voltage drops across the resistance and inductance are, respectively, RI and $L dI/dt$. Let the capacitance C be given in *farads* and the charge $Q(t)$ on the capacitance in *coulombs*. Then the voltage drop across the capacitance is Q/C. The charge Q and the current I are related by the equations

$$I = \frac{dQ}{dt}, \qquad Q(t) = \int_0^t I(s)\, ds + Q_0,$$

(1.140)

where Q_0 is the charge on the capacitance at time $t = 0$.

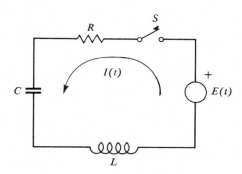

FIGURE I.3

According to one of Kirchhoff's laws, the voltage drop around the loop must be equal to the applied voltage. Consequently, we must have, for $t > 0$,

$$L \frac{dI}{dt} + RI + \frac{1}{C} Q = E(t).$$

(1.141)

Upon differentiating through in this equation with respect to t, we have

$$L \frac{d^2 I}{dt^2} + R \frac{dI}{dt} + \frac{1}{C} I = \frac{dE(t)}{dt}.$$

(1.142)

There remains the determination of the initial conditions. It can be demonstrated that the current through an inductance must be the same immediately before and after a sudden change† in the voltage drop across it. Since $I(t) = 0$ before the switch is closed, we have

$$I(0) = 0.$$

(1.143)

This condition is to be interpreted as meaning that $I(0+) = 0$, where

$$I(0+) = \lim_{t \to 0+} I(t).$$

It can also be shown that the charge on a capacitance is the same immediately before and after a sudden change† in the current through it. Using this fact,

---

† Unless the change is infinite, as happens in some idealized situations.

we can find the initial value of dI/dt from equation (1.141). If the initial charge on the capacitance is zero, then

$$LI'(0) = E(0),$$

or

$$I'(0) = \frac{E(0)}{L}. \qquad (1.144)$$

This condition is to be interpreted as meaning that $I'(0+) = E(0)/L$.

Let us now assume that the applied voltage has the constant value E_0. Then equation (1.142) becomes

$$L\frac{d^2I}{dt^2} + R\frac{dI}{dt} + \frac{1}{C}I = 0. \qquad (1.145)$$

In order to determine the current $I(t)$, we must find the solution of this equation that satisfies the initial conditions

$$I(0) = 0, \qquad I'(0) = \frac{E_0}{L}. \qquad (1.146)$$

Routine calculations show that

$$I(t) = 2\frac{E_0}{\alpha} e^{-Rt/2L} \sinh\frac{\alpha t}{2L}, \qquad (1.147)$$

where

$$\alpha = \sqrt{R^2 - \frac{4L}{C}},$$

provided that $R^2 > 4L/C$. In cases where R^2 is less than, or equal to, $4L/C$ the nature of the solution changes. In any case, however, $I(t) \to 0$ as $t \to \infty$.

In closing, let us note the similarity between the dynamical equation

$$m\frac{d^2x}{dt^2} + c\frac{dx}{dt} + kx = F(t) \qquad (1.148)$$

and the electrical equation

$$L\frac{d^2I}{dt^2} + R\frac{dI}{dt} + \frac{1}{C}I = E'(t). \qquad (1.149)$$

It is because of such similarities that electrical circuits can be used to investigate mechanical systems. It should be noted that the inductance L in equation (1.149) corresponds to the mass m in equation (1.148). The "inertia" of the inductance helps to explain the remark preceding equation (1.143).

1.14 EXERCISES

1. In the centimeter-gram-second system of measurement, mass is measured in grams and force in dynes. For a certain spring, it is found that a force of 64 dynes is necessary to stretch the spring a distance of 4 cm. A body whose mass is 2 grams is attached to the end of the spring. The effect of air resistance is to be neglected.

(a) If the body is pulled down a distance of 5 cm, and then is released from rest, find the position of the body as a function of time. Find the amplitude and period of the motion.

(b) If the body crosses the equilibrium position at time $t = 0$, moving in the upward direction with speed 10 cm/sec, find its position at an arbitrary later time t. Find the amplitude and period of the motion.

2. A force proportional to the velocity of a body and opposing its motion is represented schematically by means of a *dashpot*, as in Figure 1.4. The constant c is the constant of proportionality. The equation of motion of the body on the spring is

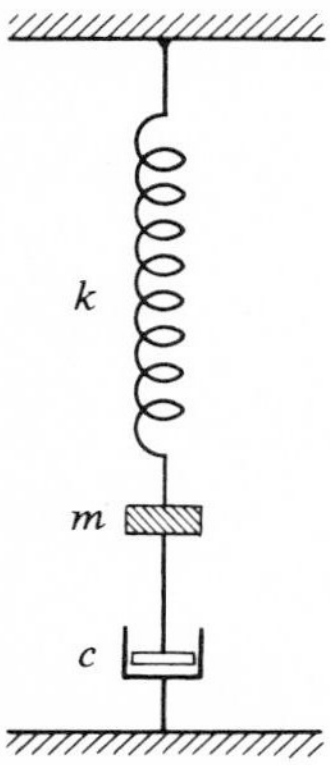

$$m \frac{d^2x}{dt^2} + c \frac{dx}{dt} + kx = 0.$$

The motion of the body is said to be *underdamped, critically damped,* or *overdamped* according as $c^2 < 4mk$, $c^2 = 4mk$, or $c^2 > 4mk$.

(a) Find the solution of the differential equation that satisfies the initial conditions $x(0) = x_0$, $x'(0) = 0$ in each of the three cases. Show that in the critically damped case, the body passes through the equilibrium position exactly once, whereas in the overdamped case it never reaches the equilibrium position.

FIGURE 1.4

(b) Draw a graph showing the a behavior of typical solution in each of the three cases in part (a).

3. In the case when an external force $F(t)$ is applied to the body on the spring, its equation of motion becomes

$$m \frac{d^2x}{dt^2} + c \frac{dx}{dt} + kx = F(t).$$

Consider the case when damping is neglected ($c = 0$) and the body is initially at rest in the equilibrium position. If $F(t)$ is a periodic force, of the form $F(t) = A \cos \gamma t$, show that

(a) $x(t) = \dfrac{A}{m(\omega^2 - \gamma^2)} (\cos \gamma t - \cos \omega t)$

where $\omega = \sqrt{\dfrac{k}{m}}$, if $\gamma \neq \omega$, but that

(b) $x(t) = \dfrac{A}{2m\omega} t \sin \omega t$

if $\gamma = \omega$. Note that in this latter case (resonance) the oscillations of the body become larger with time.

(c) Draw a graph showing the solution in part (b).

4. Consider the situation of Problem 3, but with the effect of damping considered ($c \neq 0$). Assume that $c^2 < 4mk$, and let

$$\alpha = \frac{c}{2m}, \qquad \omega = \frac{\sqrt{4km - c^2}}{2m}.$$

Find the position of the body as a function of time. Is there any significant change in the motion in the case when $\gamma = \omega$?

5. A body falls from rest from a point above the earth. If air resistance is neglected, show that the body falls the distance

$$x = \tfrac{1}{2}gt^2$$

in time t.

6. A body is thrown vertically upward from the surface of the earth with velocity v_0. Neglecting air resistance, find:

(a) The time required for the body to reach its maximum height
(b) The maximum height attained by the body
(c) The time required for the body to return to earth
(d) The velocity with which the returning body strikes the earth
(Suggestion: Let x represent the directed distance (positive direction upward) of the body from the surface of the earth.)

7. A body is thrown vertically upward from the surface of the earth with velocity v_0. Considering the effect of air resistance, find

(a) The time required for the body to reach its maximum height
(b) The maximum height attained by the body.

8. Find the current $I(t)$ in the problem (1.145), (1.146) in the case when

(a) $R^2 = \dfrac{4L}{C}$ (b) $R^2 < \dfrac{4L}{C}$

Show that the charge $Q(t)$ on the capacitance tends to the value $E_0 C$ as t becomes infinite.

9. In the circuit of Figure 1.5, a charge Q_0 is placed on the capacitance. If the switch S is closed at time $t = 0$, find the current $I(t)$, assuming that $R^2 < 4L/C$.

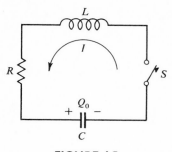

FIGURE I.5   **FIGURE I.6**

10. In the circuit of Figure 1.6, let

$$E(t) = \begin{cases} 0, & t \leq 0 \\ E_0 \sin \alpha t, & t > 0. \end{cases}$$

Show that

$$I(t) = \frac{\alpha E_0}{L(\omega^2 - \alpha^2)}(\cos \alpha t - \cos \omega t),$$

where $\omega^2 = \dfrac{1}{LC}$, provided that $\omega \neq \alpha$.

11. A resistance of 200 ohms and an inductance of 100 henrys are connected, at time $t = 0$, in series with a 5-volt battery. Find the current $I(t)$ and show that $I(t) \to 1/40$ as $t \to \infty$.

REFERENCES

1. Agnew, R. P., *Differential Equations*, 2nd ed. McGraw-Hill, New York, 1960.
2. Birkhoff, G., and Rota, G., *Ordinary Differential Equations*. Ginn, Boston, 1962.
3. Coddington, E. A., and Levinson, N., *Theory of Ordinary Differential Equations*. McGraw-Hill, New York, 1955.
4. Ince, E. L., *Ordinary Differential Equations*, 4th ed. Dover, New York, 1956.
5. Kaplan, W., *Ordinary Differential Equations*. Addison-Wesley, Reading, Mass., 1958.

CHAPTER **2**

FURTHER PROPERTIES OF
LINEAR DIFFERENTIAL EQUATIONS

2.1 Reduction of Order

If m linearly independent solutions of an nth-order linear homogeneous differential equation

$$a_0(x)y^{(n)} + a_1(x)y^{(n-1)} + \cdots + a_n(x)y = 0 \qquad (2.1)$$

are known, the problem of finding the general solution can be reduced to the problem of finding the general solution of a linear differential equation of order $n - m$.

Before we verify this statement, let us pause to look at a useful differentiation formula. From elementary algebra, we have, for any two numbers a and b,

$$(a + b)^1 = a + b,$$

$$(a + b)^2 = a^2 + 2ab + b^2, \qquad (2.2)$$

$$(a + b)^3 = a^3 + 3a^2b + 3ab^2 + b^3.$$

In general, for any positive integer n,

$$\left(a + b\right)^n = a^n + na^{n-1}b + \frac{n(n-1)}{2!}\, a^{n-2}b^2 + \cdots$$

$$+ \frac{n(n-1)\cdots(n-k+1)}{k!}\, a^{n-k}b^k + \cdots + nab^{n-1} + b^n. \qquad (2.3)$$

This formula is known as the binomial theorem.

If $u(x)$ and $v(x)$ are functions that possess a sufficient number of derivatives, it may be verified that

$$\frac{d}{dx}(uv) = u'v + uv',$$

$$\frac{d^2}{dx^2}(uv) = u''v + 2u'v' + uv'', \qquad (2.4)$$

$$\frac{d^3}{dx^3}(uv) = u'''v + 3u''v' + 3u'v'' + uv'''.$$

The analogy with formulas (2.2) should be noted. It can be shown, by induction, that for any positive integer n,

$$\frac{d^n}{dx^n}(uv) = u^{(n)}v + nu^{(n-1)}v' + \frac{n(n-1)}{2!}u^{(n-2)}v'' + \cdots$$

$$+ \frac{n(n-1)\cdots(n-k+1)}{k!}u^{(n-k)}v^{(k)} + \cdots + nu'v^{(n-1)} + uv^{(n)}. \qquad (2.5)$$

This analogue of formula (2.3) is known as *Leibniz' formula* for the derivative of a product.

Returning now to the statement made at the beginning of this section, let us suppose that $y_1(x)$ is a nontrivial solution of equation (2.1). If we introduce a new dependent variable v by means of the transformation

$$y = y_1(x)v,$$

we find, with the aid of Leibniz' formula, that equation (2.1) becomes

$$a_0[v^{(n)}y_1 + nv^{(n-1)}y_1' + \cdots + vy_1^{(n)}]$$

$$+ a_1[v^{(n-1)}y_1 + (n-1)v^{(n-2)}y_1' + \cdots + vy_1^{(n-1)}] + \cdots$$

$$+ a_{n-1}[v'y_1 + vy_1'] + a_n vy_1 = 0.$$

Upon collecting terms that involve derivatives of v of the same order, we have

$$a_0 y_1 v^{(n)} + [na_0 y_1' + a_1 y_1]v^{(n-1)} + \cdots$$

$$+ [a_0 y_1^{(n)} + a_1 y_1^{(n-1)} + \cdots + a_{n-1}y_1' + a_n y_1]v = 0.$$

The coefficient of v vanishes, since y_1 is a solution of equation (2.1). Therefore the differential equation for v has the form†

$$b_0(x)v^{(n)} + b_1(x)v^{(n-1)} + \cdots + b_{n-1}(x)v' = 0. \qquad (2.6)$$

Since this equation has no term involving v itself, it can be regarded as an

---

† At a point where $y_1(x)$ is zero, the coefficient function $b_0(x)$ is also zero. We therefore restrict ourselves to an interval on which $y_1(x) \neq 0$.

equation of order $n - 1$ for the derivative v'. Putting $v' = w$, we obtain the equation

$$b_0(x)w^{(n-1)} + b_1(x)w^{(n-2)} + \cdots + b_{n-1}(x)w = 0. \tag{2.7}$$

If $w(x)$ is a nontrivial solution of this equation, any function $v(x)$ such that $v'(x) = w(x)$ is a solution of equation (2.6). The function $y(x) = y_1(x)v(x)$ is a solution of the original equation (2.1). If $w_2(x)$, $w_3(x)$, $\ldots$, $w_n(x)$ constitute a fundamental set for equation (2.7), this procedure leads to a set of $n - 1$ solutions of equation (2.1). These $n - 1$ solutions, together with $y_1(x)$, form a fundamental set for equation (2.1). (The establishment of the linear independence of these n functions is left as an exercise.)

Now suppose that $y_2(x)$ is a second solution of equation (2.1) which is independent of $y_1(x)$. Then the function $v_1 = y_2/y_1$ is a nonconstant solution of equation (2.6), and the function $w_1 = (y_2/y_1)'$ is a nontrivial solution of equation (2.7). Equation (2.7) can then be reduced to an equation of order $n - 2$ by the same procedure used to reduce the order of equation (2.1). If m independent solutions of equation (2.1) are known, the process can be repeated to reduce the equation to one of order $n - m$.

If one nontrivial solution of a second order equation

$$a_0(x)y'' + a_1(x)y' + a_2(x)y = 0 \tag{2.8}$$

is known, the reduction process yields a first-order linear equation. The nonhomogeneous equation

$$a_0(x)y'' + a_1(x)y' + a_2(x)y = f(x) \tag{2.9}$$

can also be reduced in order when a nontrivial solution of the homogeneous equation is known. If $y_1(x)$ is a solution of equation (2.8), the change of dependent variable $y = y_1(x)v$ in equation (2.9) leads to the equation

$$(a_0y_1)v'' + (2a_0y_1' + a_1y_1)v' = f(x). \tag{2.10}$$

This equation can be regarded as a first-order linear equation for v'.

In order to illustrate the method, let us consider the differential equation

$$xy'' + xy' - y = xe^{-x}. \tag{2.11}$$

It is easily verified that the function $y_1(x) = x$ is a solution of the associated homogeneous equation. Making the substitution $y = vy_1 = vx$ in equation (2.11), we obtain the equation

$$v'' + \left(1 + \frac{2}{x}\right)v' = \frac{e^{-x}}{x} \tag{2.12}$$

for v. Solving first for v', we find that

$$v' = C_2x^{-2}e^{-x} + \tfrac{1}{2}e^{-x},$$

where C_2 is an arbitrary constant. Integrating, we find that

$$v = C_2 \int x^{-2} e^{-x} \, dx - \tfrac{1}{2} e^{-x}.$$

The general solution of equation (2.11) is

$$y = C_1 y_1 + y_1 v = C_1 x + C_2 x \int x^{-2} e^{-x} \, dx - \tfrac{1}{2} x e^{-x}.$$

2.1 EXERCISES

1. Find the general solution, given a solution of the homogeneous equation:

(a) $x^3 y'' + x y' - y = 0$, $y = x$.
(b) $(x^3 + x^2) y'' - 2 x y' + 2 y = 0$, $y = x$
easy (c) $x y'' + (1 - 2x) y' + (x - 1) y = 0$, $y = e^x$
(d) $x y'' + 2(1 - x) y' + (x - 2) y = 1$, $y = e^x$
(e) $x^2 y'' + x(x - 4) y' + 2(3 - x) y = 2x^4 e^x$, $y_1 = x^2$
(f) $2 x y'' + (1 - 4x) y' + (2x - 1) y = e^x$, $y = e^x$

2. Find the general solution, given two independent solutions:

(a) $(x^2 - x) y''' + (3x - 3 - x^2) y'' - x y' + y = 0$, $y_1 = x, y_2 = \dfrac{1}{x}$

(b) $(x - 1)^2 y''' + (1 - x^2) y'' + 2 x y' - 2 y = 0$, $y_1 = e^x, y_2 = x$.

3. Let $w_2(x)$, $w_3(x)$, $\ldots$, $w_n(x)$ be linearly independent solutions of equation (2.7) and let $y_2(x)$, $y_3(x)$, $\ldots$, $y_n(x)$ be the corresponding solutions of equation (2.1). Prove that the solutions y_1, y_2, $\ldots$, y_n of equation (2.1) are linearly independent.

4. Let $y_1(x)$ be a nontrivial solution of the second-order equation

$$y'' + a_1(x) y' + a_2(x) y = 0.$$

Derive the formula

$$y_2(x) = y_1(x) \int \frac{1}{[y_1(x)]^2} \exp\left[-\int a_1(x) \, dx \right] dx$$

for a second independent solution.

2.2 Factorization of Operators

A linear differential operator of order n may be written in the form

$$a_0(x) D^n + a_1(x) D^{n-1} + \cdots + a_{n-1}(x) D + a_n(x) \tag{2.13}$$

where D is the derivative operator d/dx. We assume that $a_0(x) \neq 0$. Two linear operators L and M of the same order n are said to be equal (written $L = M$) if, and only if, $Lw(x) = Mw(x)$ for every function $w(x)$ that possesses

n derivatives. As might be expected, two linear operators are equal if, and only if, their corresponding coefficients are equal.

Theorem 1. The linear differential operators

$$L = a_0(x)D^n + a_1(x)D^{n-1} + \cdots + a_{n-1}(x)D + a_n(x) \qquad (2.14)$$

$$M = b_0(x)D^n + b_1(x)D^{n-1} + \cdots + b_{n-1}(x)D + b_n(x) \qquad (2.15)$$

are equal if, and only if,

$$a_i(x) = b_i(x), \qquad i = 0, 1, 2, \ldots, n. \qquad (2.16)$$

Proof. If the operators are equal, then

$$Lw - Mw = (a_0 - b_0)w^{(n)} + (a_1 - b_1)w^{(n-1)} + \cdots$$

$$+ (a_{n-1} - b_{n-1})w' + (a_n - b_n)w = 0$$

for every function w that possesses n derivatives. Taking $w(x) = 1$, we see that

$$L(1) - M(1) = a_n - b_n = 0,$$

so $a_n = b_n$. Suppose that $a_{n-i} = b_{n-i}$ for $i = 0, 1, 2, \ldots, k - 1$, where $k \le n$. Taking $w(x) = x^k$, we have

$$L(x^k) - M(x^k) = a_{n-k} - b_{n-k} = 0,$$

or

$$a_{n-k} = b_{n-k}.$$

By mathematical induction,

$$a_{n-i} = b_{n-2}, \qquad i = 0, 1, 2, \ldots, n.$$

Thus, if the operators are equal, their corresponding coefficients are equal. Conversely, if the operators have equal corresponding coefficients, it is obvious that $Lw = Mw$ for every function w that is n times differentiable. Then the operators are equal, by definition.

If L_1 and L_2 are linear differential operators, and if y is a function of x, then by the expression L_1L_2y we mean $L_1(L_2y)$. That is, to obtain the function L_1L_2y which corresponds to y, we first operate on y with the operator L_2 and then operate on the result with the operator L_1. The final result is a linear combination of y and its derivatives, so that the expression L_1L_2 may be regarded as a linear differential operator. In general, however, $L_1L_2 \ne L_2L_1$. For example, let

$$L_1 = (x + 2)D + 1, \qquad L_2 = D - 3x.$$

Then

$$L_1L_2y = [(x + 2)D + 1](y' - 3xy)$$

$$= (x + 2)y'' - (3x^2 + 6x - 1)y' - 6(x + 1)y$$

but

$$L_2L_1y = (D - 3x)[(x + 2)y' + y] = (x + 2)y'' - (3x^2 + 6x - 2)y' - 3xy.$$

For several differential operators $L_1, L_2, \ldots, L_m$, we define the product $L_1 L_2 \cdots L_m$ according to the relation

$$L_1 L_2 \cdots L_{m-1} L_m y = (L_1 \cdots (L_{m-1}(L_m y)) \cdots).$$

If a differential operator L can be written in factored form as the product of *first-order* operators, then the differential equation $Ly = f(x)$ can be solved by quadratures. We shall illustrate the procedure for a third-order equation. However, the same method can be applied to a factored equation of arbitrary order.

Suppose that $y(x)$ is a solution of the equation

$$[p_1(x)D + p_2(x)][q_1(x)D + q_2(x)][r_1(x)D + r_2(x)]y = f(x). \tag{2.17}$$

Let

$$u(x) = (q_1 D + q_2)(r_1 D + r_2)y(x). \tag{2.18}$$

This function $u(x)$ must satisfy the first-order equation

$$(p_1 D + p_2)u = f, \tag{2.19}$$

and so must be of the form

$$u = \exp\left(-\int \frac{p_2}{p_1} dx\right)\left[C_1 + \int \frac{f}{p_1} \exp\left(\int \frac{p_2}{p_1} dx\right) dx\right]. \tag{2.20}$$

If we let

$$v(x) = (r_1 D + r_2)y, \tag{2.21}$$

then $v(x)$ satisfies the equation

$$(q_1 D + q_2)v = u; \tag{2.22}$$

it must therefore be of the form

$$v = \exp\left(-\int \frac{q_2}{q_1} dx\right)\left[C_2 + \int \frac{u}{q_1} \exp\left(\int \frac{q_2}{q_1} dx\right) dx\right]. \tag{2.23}$$

Since

$$(r_1 D + r_2)y = v, \tag{2.24}$$

$y(x)$ must be of the form

$$y = \exp\left(-\int \frac{r_2}{r_1} dx\right)\left[C_3 + \int \frac{v}{r_1} \exp\left(\int \frac{r_2}{r_1} dx\right) dx\right]. \tag{2.25}$$

We shall now show that *every* function $y(x)$ of the form (2.25), where $v(x)$ and $u(x)$ are defined by formulas (2.23) and (2.20), respectively, is a solution of equation (2.14). Since every function of the form (2.25) satisfies equation (2.24), we have

$$(r_1 D + r_2)y(x) = v(x).$$

Since $v(x)$ satisfies equation (2.22), we have

$$(q_1 D + q_2)(r_1 D + r_2)y = (q_1 D + q_2)v = u.$$

Since $u(x)$ satisfies equation (2.19), we have

$$(p_1 D + p_2)(q_1 D + q_2)(r_1 D + r_2)y = (p_1 D + p_2)u = f.$$

We now consider a specific example—namely, the differential equation

$$x^2 y'' + (2x^2 + 5x)y' + (6x + 3)y = 0. \tag{2.26}$$

It can be verified that this equation can be written in the factored form

$$[xD + (2x + 1)](xD + 3)y = 0. \tag{2.27}$$

Setting

$$u = (xD + 3)y, \tag{2.28}$$

we have

$$[xD + (2x + 1)]u = 0. \tag{2.29}$$

The general solution of this first-order equation is

$$u = C_1 \frac{1}{x} e^{-2x}.$$

Substituting back into equation (2.28) for u, we have

$$(xD + 3)y = C_1 \frac{1}{x} e^{-2x}. \tag{2.30}$$

Then

$$y = C_1(-\tfrac{1}{2}x^{-2} - \tfrac{1}{4}x^{-3})e^{-2x} + C_2 x^{-3}. \tag{2.31}$$

Although a second-order differential equation

$$P(x)y'' + Q(x)y' + R(x)y = 0 \tag{2.32}$$

can theoretically always be factored, in actual practice it may be quite difficult to carry out the factorization. The coefficients in the linear factors may be extremely complicated functions. In attempting to factor an equation of the form (2.32), a systematic procedure would be to try to choose the functions $a_1(x)$, $a_2(x)$, $b_1(x)$, $b_2(x)$ in the expression

$$(a_1 D + a_2)(b_1 D + b_2)y$$
$$= [a_1 b_1 D^2 + (a_1 b_1' + a_1 b_2 + a_2 b_1)D + (a_1 b_2' + a_2 b_2)]y \tag{2.33}$$

in such a way that

$$a_1 b_1 = P$$
$$a_1 b_1' + a_1 b_2 + a_2 b_1 = Q \tag{2.34}$$
$$a_1 b_2' + a_2 b_2 = R.$$

In general, however, this problem is as difficult as that of solving the original differential equation (2.32).

In attempting to factor a specific differential equation, we may be able to make intelligent guesses about the nature of the factors that will simplify the problem. As an illustration, let us consider the equation

$$Ly = x^2 y'' + (2 - x^3)y' - (2x + x^2)y = 0. \tag{2.35}$$

Here it seems reasonable to expect that the operator L might be factorable in one of the forms

$$[x^2 D + (ax + b)][D + (cx + d)] \tag{2.36a}$$

$$[D + (ax + b)][x^2 D + (cx + d)] \tag{2.36b}$$

$$[xD + (ax + b)][xD + (cx + d)] \tag{2.36c}$$

where a, b, c, d are constants. Taking first the form (2.36a), we have

$$[x^2 D + (ax + b)][D + (cx + d)]y$$
$$= x^2 y'' + (cx^3 + dx^2 + ax + b)y' + [(a + 1)cx^2 + (bc + ad)x + bd]y.$$

If equation (2.35) can be written in this form, we must have

$$c = -1, \qquad d = 0, \qquad a = 0, \qquad b = 2,$$
$$(a + 1)c = -1, \qquad bc + ad = -2, \qquad bd = 0.$$

But if we take

$$a = 0, \qquad b = 2, \qquad c = -1, \qquad d = 0,$$

then

$$(a + 1)c = c = -1$$
$$bc + ad = -2 + 0 = -2$$
$$bd = 0$$

and all the conditions are satisfied. Therefore equation (2.35) can be written in the factored form

$$(x^2 D + 2)(D - x)y = 0.$$

2.2 EXERCISES

1. Verify that the differential equation can be written in the indicated factored form:

   (b) $x(x + 1)y'' + (x - 2)y' - 4y = (xD - 2)[(x + 1)D + 2]y = 0$
   (a) $x(x + 1)y'' + (x - 1)y' - 4y = [(x + 1)D + 2](xD - 2)y = 0$
   (c) $xy'' + (x^2 + 2x - 1)y' - 2y = (xD - 1)[D + (x + 2)]y = 0$

2. Find the general solution of the given equation:

   (a) $(D + 2)(xD + 1)y = 0$
   (b) $(D + 1)[D + (2/x + 1)]y = 0$
   (c) $(xD + 1)[xD + (x + 2)]y = e^{-x}$
   (d) $[xD + (3 - 2x)](xD + 4)y = x^{-2}$

3. Factor the differential equation and find the general solution:

(a) $y'' + 2(x + 1)y' + (x^2 + 2x + 2)y = 0$
(b) $y'' + (2x + 1)y' + (x^2 + x - 1)y = 0$
(c) $xy'' + (2x + 1)y' + (x + 1)y = 1$
(d) $(x + 1)y'' + (2x + 4)y' + 2y = e^{-x}$

4. Show that the operators $L_1 = a_1(x)D + a_2(x)$ and $L_2 = b_1(x)D + b_2(x)$ commute, that is, that $L_1L_2 = L_2L_1$, if, and only if, $b_1(x) = ka_1(x)$ and $b_2(x) = ka_2(x) + K$, where k and K are constant.

5. Show that the operators $L_1 = D + f(x)$ and $L_2 = D + g(x)$ commute if, and only if, $g(x) = f(x) + C$, where C is a constant.

6. Show that the differential operator $D^2 + P(x)D + Q(x)$ can be written in the factored form $[D + f(x)][D + g(x)]$ if, and only if, $g(x)$ is a solution of the first-order nonlinear equation

$$g' + P(x)g - g^2 - Q(x) = 0$$

and

$$f(x) = P(x) - g(x).$$

7. By using the result of the previous problem, derive the formula

$$D^2 + 1 = (D - \tan x)(D + \tan x).$$

2.3   Some Variable Changes

By means of a change of dependent variable, the nth-order equation

$$a_0 y^{(n)} + a_1 y^{(n-1)} + \cdots + a_n y = f(x) \tag{2.37}$$

can be put in a form that is still linear and of degree n, but in which the derivative term of order $n - 1$ is missing. Let us make a change of variable of the form

$$y = uF(x), \tag{2.38}$$

where the function $F(x)$ is to be determined. Equation (2.37) becomes an equation for u,

$$a_0[u^{(n)}F + nu^{(n-1)}F' + \cdots + uF^{(n)}] + a_1[u^{(n-1)}F + (n-1)u^{(n-2)}F' + \cdots$$

$$+ uF^{(n-1)}] + \cdots + a_{n-1}[u'F + uF'] + a_n uF = f.$$

Here we have used Leibniz' formula (Section 2.1) for the derivative of a product. Upon collecting terms involving derivatives of u of the same order, we have

$$a_0 Fu^{(n)} + [na_0 F' + a_1 F]u^{(n-1)} + \cdots + [a_0 F^{(n)} + \cdots + a_n F]u = f. \tag{2.39}$$

We now try to choose the function $F(x)$ so that the coefficient of $u^{(n-1)}$ in this equation vanishes. For this to happen, F must satisfy the first-order equation

$$na_0 F' + a_1 F = 0, \tag{2.40}$$

and therefore F must be of the form

$$F(x) = \exp\left(-\frac{1}{n}\int \frac{a_1}{a_0}\,dx\right). \tag{2.41}$$

With such a choice for F, equation (2.39) takes on the form

$$b_0(x)u^{(n)} + b_2(x)u^{(n-2)} + \cdots + b_n(x)u = f(x). \tag{2.42}$$

The solutions of equation (2.42) and those of equation (2.37) are related by means of the formula

$$y = u \exp\left(-\frac{1}{n}\int \frac{a_1}{a_0}\,dx\right). \tag{2.43}$$

While equation (2.42) will, in general, be no easier to solve than the original equation, the removal of one term of the equation does constitute a simplification for some purposes. For instance, the study of second-order linear homogeneous equations is now seen to be equivalent to the study of equations of the form

$$y'' + g(x)y = 0, \tag{2.44}$$

in which only one arbitrary coefficient function appears.

If we try to choose the function $F(x)$ in the transformation (2.38) so as to remove some other derivative term (other than the one of order $n-1$) in equation (2.37), we find that F must satisfy a differential equation of order higher than one. In this case, no simple formula for F, such as formula (2.41), exists, in general.

As an example, let us consider the equation

$$xy'' + 2y' - xy = 0, \tag{2.45}$$

on the interval $(0, +\infty)$. Here $n = 2$, $a_0 = x$, and $a_1 = 2$, so to remove the first derivative term, we should choose

$$F(x) = \exp\left(-\frac{1}{2}\int \frac{2}{x}\,dx\right) = x^{-1},$$

according to formula (2.41). Setting $y = x^{-1}u$, we find that

$$y' = x^{-1}u' - x^{-2}u, \qquad y'' = x^{-1}u'' - 2x^{-2}u' + 2x^{-3}u.$$

Upon substituting back into equation (2.45), we obtain the equation

$$u'' - u = 0$$

for u.

A linear homogeneous second-order differential equation

$$a_0(x)y'' + a_1(x)y' + a_2(x)y = 0 \tag{2.46}$$

can be transformed into a first-order *nonlinear* differential equation by means of a change of dependent variable

$$y = \exp\left(\int f(x)v\,dx\right),\tag{2.47}$$

where $f(x)$ is any nonvanishing differentiable function. In particular, if we take $f(x) = a_0(x)$, we have

$$y = \exp\left(\int a_0 v\,dx\right), \qquad y' = a_0 v \exp\left(\int a_0 v\,dx\right),$$

$$y'' = (a_0 v' + a_0' v + a_0^2 v^2)\exp\left(\int a_0 v\,dx\right),\tag{2.48}$$

and equation (2.46) becomes

$$\frac{dv}{dx} + a_0 v^2 + \frac{a_0' + a_1}{a_0}v + \frac{a_2}{a_0^2} = 0.\tag{2.49}$$

If $v(x)$ is a solution of equation (2.49), the corresponding function $y(x) = \exp(\left(\int a_0 v\,dx\right)$ is a nontrivial solution of equation (2.46).

Equation (2.49) belongs to the class of differential equations

$$\frac{dv}{dx} + b_0(x)v^2 + b_1(x)v + b_2(x) = 0\tag{2.50}$$

known as *Riccati equations*. Such an equation can, by means of the change of variable

$$v = \frac{-y'}{b_0(x)y}\tag{2.51}$$

be transformed into a linear homogeneous equation of second order,

$$b_0 y'' + (b_0 b_1 - b_0')y' + b_0^2 b_2 y = 0.\tag{2.52}$$

Verification of this fact is left as an exercise. If $y(x)$ is a solution of equation (2.52), formula (2.51) yields a corresponding solution of equation (2.50). Riccati equations are important for reasons other than their relationships with second-order linear equations, and have been studied extensively. Discussions are given in the two references listed at the end of this chapter.

Let us consider as an example the linear equation

$$xy'' - y' + x^3 y = 0.\tag{2.53}$$

The change of variable $y = \exp\left(\int xv\,dx\right)$ leads to the Riccati equation

$$\frac{dv}{dx} + x(v^2 + 1) = 0,\tag{2.54}$$

which is easily solved. [It should be noted that the Riccati equation which is derived from the linear equation (2.46) depends on the choice of the function $f(x)$ in the transformation (2.47). In this particular example, the choice $f(x) = x$ was a fortunate one.] Writing this equation in the form

$$\frac{dv}{v^2 + 1} = -x \, dx,$$

and integrating, we have

$$\tan^{-1} v = -\tfrac{1}{2}x^2 - C,$$

or

$$v = -\tan(\tfrac{1}{2}x^2 + C), \tag{2.55}$$

where C is an arbitrary constant. The values $C = 0$ and $C = \pi/2$ yield the particular solutions

$$v_1 = -\tan(\tfrac{1}{2}x^2), \qquad v_2 = \cot(\tfrac{1}{2}x^2) \tag{2.56}$$

of equation (2.54). The corresponding solutions of equation (2.53) are

$$y_1 = \exp\left[-\int x \tan(\tfrac{1}{2}x^2) \, dx\right] = \cos(\tfrac{1}{2}x^2),$$
$$y_2 = \exp\left[\int x \cot(\tfrac{1}{2}x^2) \, dx\right] = \sin(\tfrac{1}{2}x^2). \tag{2.57}$$

These functions are linearly independent on every interval, since the functions $\cos \theta$ and $\sin \theta$ are linearly independent on every interval. The general solution of equation (2.53) is therefore

$$y = C_1 \cos(\tfrac{1}{2}x^2) + C_2 \sin(\tfrac{1}{2}x^2). \tag{2.58}$$

2.3   EXERCISES

1. Remove the next-to-highest order derivative term in the given differential equation by means of a change of dependent variable:

   (a) $y'' - 2y' + 3y = 0$ (c) $xy''' - 6y'' + 2xy = 0$
   (b) $(1 + x^2)y'' - 2xy' + y = 0$ (d) $x^2y''' + 3xy' + y' + y = 0$

2. Let the function $f(x)$ be a nontrivial solution of the equation $f'' + p(x)f' = 0$ on an interval I.

   (a) Show that the change of variable $t = f(x)$, $x = f^{-1}(t)$ in the differential equation

   $$\frac{d^2y}{dx^2} + p(x)\frac{dy}{dx} + q(x)y = 0$$

   leads to a differential equation of the form

   $$\frac{d^2y}{dt^2} + b(t)y = 0.$$

(b) Show that any function of the form

$$t = f(x) = c \int \exp\left(-\int p \, dx\right) dx, \qquad c \neq 0,$$

satisfies the conditions described above.

3. Using the result of Problem 2, remove the first derivative term in the given differential equation by means of a change of independent variable. Find the corresponding interval for the new variable.

(a) $\quad y'' + \dfrac{2}{x} y' + (x^3 + 1)y = 0, \qquad 0 < x < +\infty$

(b) $\quad xy'' - y' + 2xy = 0, \qquad 0 < x < +\infty$

(c) $\quad xy'' - y' + 2xy = 0, \qquad -\infty < x < 0$

4. Show that a second-order linear homogeneous equation can be transformed into a Riccati equation by means of a change of variable

$$y = \exp\left(\int f(x)v \, dx\right),$$

where $f(x)$ is any nonvanishing differentiable function.

5. Use the transformation $y = \exp\left(\int a_0 v \, dx\right)$ to find a Riccati equation that corresponds to the given linear equation. In parts (a) and (b), find the general solution of the linear equation.

(a) $xy'' + (3x^2 - 1)y' + 2x^3 y = 0$
(b) $y'' + (1 + 2e^x)y' + e^{3x}y = 0$
(c) $x^2 y'' + xy' - y = 0$

6. Verify that the Riccati equation

$$v' + b_0(x)v^2 + b_1(x)v + b_2(x) = 0$$

can be transformed into a second-order linear differential equation by means of the change of variable

$$v = \frac{y'}{b_0(x)y}.$$

7. Transform the Riccati equation into a second-order linear equation:

(a) $v' = v^2 + x^2,$ (b) $v' = x^2 v^2 + xv + 1,$ (c) $x^2 v' = v^2 - 1$

2.4   Zeros of Solutions

In certain applications that involve a differential equation, a knowledge of the existence, number, and location of zeros of solutions of the equation is important. In particular, this knowledge is important in applications that involve eigenvalue problems—the topic of Chapter 7. We shall state and prove two theorems about zeros of solutions of second-order differential equations. Both theorems belong to a class known as *comparison theorems*. In the first theorem, we compare the number of zeros of two solutions of the same differential equation. In the second, we compare the number of zeros of solutions of two different equations.

Theorem 2.   Let $y_1(x)$ and $y_2(x)$ be linearly independent solutions of the second-order differential equation

$$a_0(x)y'' + a_1(x)y' + a_2(x)y = 0 \tag{2.59}$$

on an interval where $a_0(x) \neq 0$. Then between two successive zeros of $y_1(x)$, there is exactly one zero of $y_2(x)$, and vice versa.

Proof.   It should be explained first that the notion of successive zeros of $y_1(x)$ is well defined. If $y_1(x_0) = 0$, there is an interval $(x_0 - \alpha, x_0 + \alpha)$, where $\alpha > 0$, on which $y_1(x)$ has no other zero. For otherwise $y_1'(x_0) = 0$. But then $y_1(x) \equiv 0$, by Theorem 1 of Chapter 1. Next, we observe that y_1 and y_2 cannot vanish at the same point. For if they did, their Wronskian would be zero at that point, and they could not be linearly independent. Now let x_1 and x_2 be successive zeros of y_1. Then $y_2(x_1) \neq 0$ and $y_2(x_2) \neq 0$. Suppose that y_2 does not vanish between x_1 and x_2. Then the function y_1/y_2 is defined and twice differentiable on the interval $x_1 < x < x_2$. It vanishes at x_1 and x_2. By Rolle's theorem, its first derivative must vanish at at least one point of the open interval $x_1 < x < x_2$. But

$$\frac{d}{dx}\left(\frac{y_1}{y_2}\right) = \frac{y_1'y_2 - y_1y_2'}{(y_2)^2} = \frac{W(x; y_1, y_2)}{(y_2)^2} \neq 0.$$

This contradiction insures that y_2 has at least one zero on the interval $x_1 < x < x_2$. If y_2 had two or more zeros between x_1 and x_2, the same sort of argument, with the roles of y_1 and y_2 reversed, would show that y_1 had at least one zero between x_1 and x_2. This is impossible, because of our hypothesis that x_1 and x_2 are *successive* zeros of y_1. Hence y_2 has exactly one zero between x_1 and x_2. Similarly, y_1 has exactly one zero between two successive zeros of y_2.

This theorem says that two nontrivial solutions of the same second-order equation have, roughly speaking, the same number of zeros on a given interval. More precisely, if N_1 and N_2 are the finite numbers of zeros of y_1 and y_2, respectively, on any interval, then N_1 and N_2 differ at most by one.

As illustrations, let us consider the two equations

$$y'' + y = 0 \tag{2.60}$$

$$y'' - y = 0. \tag{2.61}$$

Independent solutions of equation (2.60) are $y_1 = \sin x$ and $y_2 = \cos x$. The first has the zeros $x = n\pi$ and the second has the zeros $x = (n + \frac{1}{2})\pi$, where n is any integer. Independent solutions of equation (2.61) are $y_1 = e^x$ and $y_2 = e^{-x}$. Neither has any zeros. The functions $y_1 = e^x$ and $y_3 = e^x - e^{-x}$ are also independent solutions. The solution y_3 has exactly one zero, at $x = 0$. It cannot have more than one zero, since y_1 has no zeros.

The situation is different for higher-order equations. For instance, the equation

$$y''' - y'' + y' - y = 0 \tag{2.62}$$

possesses the independent solutions

$$y_1 = \cos x, \qquad y_2 = \sin x, \qquad y_3 = e^x.$$

The solutions y_1 and y_2 have infinitely many zeros on the interval $-\infty < x < +\infty$, while the solution y_3 has no zeros.

We next prove a theorem that compares the number of zeros of solutions of two different second-order equations.

Theorem 3. On an interval I let $u(x)$ and $v(x)$ be nontrivial solutions of the equations

$$y'' + f(x)y = 0 \tag{2.63}$$

$$y'' + g(x)y = 0, \tag{2.64}$$

respectively. On the interval I, let $g(x) \geq f(x)$, but $f(x) \not\equiv g(x)$. If x_1 and x_2 are successive zeros of $u(x)$ on the interval I, then $v(x)$ has at least one zero on the interval $x_1 < x < x_2$.

Proof. Since $u(x)$ does not change sign in the interval $x_1 < x < x_2$, we may assume, without loss of generality, that $u(x) > 0$ on this interval. For if $u(x) < 0$, we can simply replace $u(x)$ by the solution $-u(x)$, which has the same zeros. Now the Wronskian W, of v and u, is

$$W = vu' - v'u$$

and

$$\frac{dW}{dx} = vu'' - v''u.$$

Using the fact that u and v are solutions of the equations (2.63) and (2.64), respectively, we find that

$$\frac{dW}{dx} = [g(x) - f(x)]u(x)v(x). \tag{2.65}$$

Suppose that v does not vanish on the interval $x_1 < x < x_2$. Without loss of generality, we can assume that $v > 0$ on this interval; for if not, we can replace v by the solution $-v$, which has the same zeros. Then the function on the right-hand side of equation (2.65) is nonnegative on the interval $x_1 \le x \le x_2$. Therefore

$$\int_{x_1}^{x_2} \frac{dW}{dx}\, dx > 0,$$

so

$$W(x_2; v, u) - W(x_1; v, u) > 0$$

or

$$v(x_2)u'(x_2) - v'(x_2)u(x_2) - v(x_1)u'(x_1) + v'(x_1)u(x_1) > 0.$$

But $u(x_1) = u(x_2) = 0$, so this inequality becomes

$$v(x_2)u'(x_2) - v(x_1)u'(x_1) > 0. \tag{2.66}$$

The function $u'(x)$ cannot vanish at either x_1 or x_2, for if it did, then u and u' would both vanish at the same point, and u would be the trivial solution of equation (2.63). Since u is positive for $x_1 < x < x_2$, then necessarily $u'(x_1) > 0$ and $u'(x_2) < 0$. Also, $v(x_1) \ge 0$ and $v(x_2) \ge 0$. Therefore

$$v(x_2)u'(x_2) - v(x_1)u'(x_1) \le 0. \tag{2.67}$$

This evidently contradicts the inequality (2.66). Therefore our assumption that $v(x)$ did not vanish for $x_1 < x < x_2$ must be false, and we conclude that $v(x)$ has at least one zero on the interval $x_1 < x < x_2$.

If a solution $u(x)$ of equation (2.63) has N zeros on an interval where the inequality $g(x) \ge f(x)$ holds, then a solution $v(x)$ of equation (2.64) has at least $N - 1$ zeros on the same interval.

As an illustration of the use of this theorem, we shall prove that every nontrivial solution of the equation

$$y'' + x^2 y = 0 \tag{2.68}$$

has infinitely many zeros on the interval $1 \le x < +\infty$. For purposes of comparison, it is convenient to consider the equation

$$y'' + y = 0. \tag{2.69}$$

On the given interval, $x^2 \ge 1$. Since the solution $\sin x$ of equation (2.69) has zeros at the points $x = n\pi$, $n = 1, 2, 3, \ldots$, every nontrivial solution of equation (2.68) has at least one zero on each interval $n\pi < x < (n + 1)\pi$, $n = 1, 2, 3, \ldots$, and hence has infinitely many zeros on the interval $1 \le x < +\infty$.

In case we wish to investigate the zeros of the solutions of a second-order equation of the form

$$a_0(x)y'' + a_1(x)y' + a_2(x)y = 0, \tag{2.70}$$

we can first remove the first derivative term by means of the change of variable

$$y = w \exp\left(-\frac{1}{2} \int \frac{a_1}{a_0}\, dx\right) \tag{2.71}$$

as was shown in Section 2.3. The equation for w is

$$w'' + f(x)w = 0, \tag{2.72}$$

where

$$f(x) = \frac{a_2}{a_0} - \frac{1}{4}\frac{a_1{}^2}{a_0{}^2} - \frac{1}{2}\frac{a_1{}'a_0 - a_1 a_0{}'}{a_0{}^2} . \tag{2.73}$$

A zero of a solution of equation (2.72) is also a zero of the corresponding solution of equation (2.70) and vice versa, since the exponential factor in the transformation (2.71) does not vanish.

    Other, more general, comparison theorems for second-order equations are known. For statements and proofs of these theorems, the reader is referred to the books by Ince and by Coddington and Levinson listed at the end of Chapter 1.

2.4 EXERCISES

1. Verify Theorem 2 for two independent solutions of the equation

$$y'' + 2y' + 5y = 0.$$

2. Show that no nontrivial solution of the equation

$$y'' - 2y' + y = 0$$

has more than one zero on the interval $-\infty < x < +\infty$.

3. Show that every nontrivial solution of the equation

$$y'' + e^x y = 0$$

has infinitely many zeros on the interval $0 < x < +\infty$.

4. Show that a nontrivial solution of the equation

$$y'' - e^x y = 0$$

can have at most one zero on the interval $0 < x < +\infty$.

5. Show that a nontrivial solution of the equation

$$y'' - x^2 y = 0$$

can have at most two zeros on the interval $-\infty < x < +\infty$.

6. Show that every nontrivial solution of the equation

$$x^2 y'' + xy' + (x^2 - 1)y = 0$$

has infinitely many zeros on the interval $0 < x < +\infty$.

7. Let A and B be positive constants and let $f(x)$ be such that $A \leq f(x) \leq B$ on the interval $a \leq x \leq b$. Discuss the possible number of zeros of a nontrivial solution of the equation $y'' + f(x)y = 0$ on the interval (a, b). (Compare with the equations $y'' + Ay = 0$ and $y'' + By = 0$.)

REFERENCES

In addition to the references listed at the end of Chapter 1, the following are suggested:

1. Davis, H. T., *Introduction to Nonlinear Differential and Integral Equations.* Dover, New York, 1962.
2. Rainville, E. D., *Intermediate Differential Equations*, 2nd ed., Macmillan, New York, 1964.

CHAPTER **3**

COMPLEX VARIABLES

3.1 Introduction

It is possible to consider differential equations in which the independent variable is a complex rather than a real variable. It is not our intent in this book, however, to study "differential equations in the complex domain," as the subject is called. Rather we give an introduction to the theory of functions of a complex variable here because of its usefulness in the investigation of certain properties of functions of a real variable.

In particular, the problem of expanding a function in a power series can be best treated from the standpoint of complex variables, even when the independent variable of the function is real. The material presented in this chapter will be useful, but not essential, for an understanding of most of Chapter 4, which deals with series solutions of differential equations. In fact, only Section 4.9, which deals with complex exponents, requires a knowledge of series with complex terms.

3.2 Functions of a Complex Variable

A complex number $z = x + iy$ is essentially an ordered pair of real numbers (x, y). It is assumed that the reader is familiar with the laws of arithmetic for complex numbers. The real and imaginary parts, x and y, respectively, of a complex number z can be interpreted as the rectangular Cartesian coordinates of a point in a plane, called the *complex plane* (Figure 3.1). We shall therefore use the terms "complex number" and "point" interchangeably. In the coordinate system, the x and y axes are known as the *real and imaginary axes*, respectively.

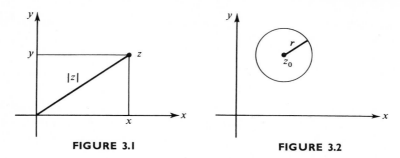

FIGURE 3.1   **FIGURE 3.2**

The *magnitude* of a complex number $z = x + iy$, written $|z|$, is defined to be the real number.

$$|z| = \sqrt{x^2 + y^2}.$$

Geometrically, the number $|z|$ represents the distance of the point z from the origin of the coordinate system (Figure 3.1). If $z_1 = x_1 + iy_1$ and $z_2 = x_2 + iy_2$ are two complex numbers, the quantity

$$|z_1 - z_2| = \sqrt{(x_1 - x_2)^2 + (y_1 - y_2)^2}$$

is the distance between the points z_1 and z_2. If z_0 is a fixed point and if r is a positive real number, then the locus of points z for which

$$|z - z_0| = r$$

is a circle with center z_0 and radius r (Figure 3.2). The points z for which

$$|z - z_0| < r$$

are those points inside the circle. Such a region is called a *neighborhood* of the point z_0.

A *function of a complex variable z* over a region D of the complex plane is a rule, or law, that assigns to every complex number $z = x + iy$ in D a complex number $w = u + iv$. The numbers w can be represented by points in a second complex plane with real u axis and imaginary v axis. We write

$$w = f(z), \qquad z \text{ in } D,$$

to denote a function defined over a region D. Examples of functions of a complex variable are

$$w = z^2 = (x^2 - y^2) + 2ixy, \qquad \text{all } z,$$

and

$$w = \frac{1}{z} = \frac{x}{x^2 + y^2} + i\,\frac{-y}{x^2 + y^2}, \qquad z \neq 0.$$

A function $w = f(z)$ is said to have the *limit* $L = a + ib$ as z approaches $z_0 = x_0 + iy_0$, written

$$\lim_{z \to z_0} f(z) = L, \tag{3.1}$$

if to every positive real number ε there corresponds a positive real number δ such that

$$|f(z) - L| < \varepsilon$$

whenever

$$0 < |z - z_0| < \delta.$$

Geometrically interpreted, statement (3.1) says that the points w can be made to lie in an arbitrarily small neighborhood of the point L in the complex w plane if z is restricted to a sufficiently small neighborhood of the point z_0 in the complex z plane (Figure 3.3).

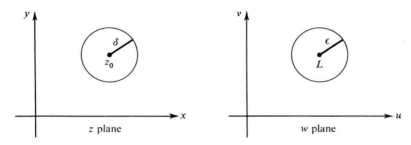

FIGURE 3.3

Since

$$|f(z) - L| = \sqrt{(u - a)^2 + (y - b)^2}$$

and

$$|z - z_0| = \sqrt{(x - x_0)^2 + (y - y_0)^2},$$

it is not hard to see that $f(z)$ has the limit L if, and only if, the real functions $u(x, y)$ and $v(x, y)$ have the real limits

$$\lim_{(x,y) \to (x_0,y_0)} u(x, y) = a, \qquad \lim_{(x,y) \to (x_0,y_0)} v(x, y) = b.$$

The *derivative* of a function $w = f(z)$ at a point z_0, written $f'(z_0)$, is defined to be

$$f'(z_0) = \lim_{z \to z_0} \frac{f(z) - f(z_0)}{z - z_0}, \tag{3.2}$$

if the limit exists. We use the symbols $f'(z)$ and dw/dz to denote the derivative of a function $w = f(z)$ at a general point z. The derivatives of many elementary functions of a complex variable can be calculated directly from the definition (3.2) in much the same way as derivatives of functions of a real variable are calculated. For example, the derivative of the function $w = \mathbf{z}^2$ at an arbitrary point z_0 is

$$\lim_{z \to z_0} \frac{z^2 - z_0^2}{z - z_0} = \lim_{z \to z_0} (z + z_0) = 2z_0.$$

We find also that

$$\frac{d}{dz}(c) = 0, \tag{3.3}$$

where c is a constant, and that

$$\frac{d}{dz}(z^n) = nz^{n-1}, \tag{3.4}$$

where n is any integer. The rules

$$\frac{d}{dz}[f(z) + g(z)] = f'(z) + g'(z),$$

$$\frac{d}{dz}[f(z)g(z)] = f'(z)g(z) + f(z)g'(z), \tag{3.5}$$

$$\frac{d}{dz}\frac{f(z)}{g(z)} = \frac{f'(z)g(z) - f(z)g'(z)}{[g(z)]^2}, \qquad g(z) \neq 0,$$

can be shown to hold for two differentiable functions $f(z)$ and $g(z)$. The chain rule formula,

$$\frac{d}{dz}f[g(z)] = f'[g(z)]g'(z), \tag{3.6}$$

also holds.

If a function $f(z)$ is differentiable at every point of some neighborhood N of a point z_0, the function is said to be *analytic* at z_0. (The function is also analytic at every point in N, since each point in N is the center of some disk that contains only points of N.) A function $f(z)$ is said to be analytic in a region D if it is analytic at every point of D. In particular, a polynomial function

$$P(z) = a_0z^n + a_1z^{n-1} + \cdots + a_n$$

is analytic in the entire complex plane, and a rational function $P(z)/Q(z)$, where $P(z)$ and $Q(z)$ are polynomials, is analytic except at the zeros of $Q(z)$.

It is shown in books on complex variables that a function $f(z)$ which is analytic in a region D possesses *derivatives of all orders* in D. Thus there is a sharp contrast between the class of functions of a complex variable that are analytic in a region and the class of functions of a real variable that are differentiable on an interval. There is no guarantee that a function of the latter class will possess a second or higher-order derivative at any point of the interval. However, the following facts should be noted. If the function $w = f(z)$ possesses a derivative at a point $z_0 = x_0 + i0$ on the real axis, then the real limit

$$\lim_{x \to x_0} \frac{f(x) - f(x_0)}{x - x_0}$$

exists. Thus the function $f(x)$ of the real variable x that coincides with $f(z)$ on the real axis possesses a derivative at the point x_0. If the function $f(z)$ is *analytic* at the point $z_0 = x_0 + i0$, then $f(x)$ possesses derivatives of all orders at x_0. This is one of the ways in which a knowledge of functions of a complex variable can be used to obtain information about functions of a real variable.

3.2 EXERCISES

1. (a) Find $|z|$ if

    (i) $z = -1 + i$,   (ii) $z = 3i$,   (iii) $z = 2 + 3i$.

(b) Show that $|z_1 z_2| = |z_1| |z_2|$ and that $|z_1/z_2| = |z_1|/|z_2|$ for every pair of complex numbers z_1 and z_2. ($z_2 \neq 0$ in the last case).

2. (a) Let O, P_1, P_2, and Q be the points in the plane that correspond to the complex numbers 0, z_1, z_2, and $z_1 + z_2$, respectively. Show that OQ is the diagonal of a parallelogram with sides OP_1 and OP_2.
(b) Show that $|z_1 + z_2| \leq |z_1| + |z_2|$ for every pair of complex numbers z_1 and z_2.

3. Given the functions $f(z) = z^2$, $g(x) = 2z + 3i$, find

    (a) $f(1 + i)$ (d) $g(1/i)$
    (b) $f(-i)$ (e) $f[g(z)]$
    (c) $g(1 - 2i)$ (f) $g[f(z)]$

4. Find the real part $u(x, y)$ and the imaginary part $v(x, y)$ of the given function:

    (a) $f(z) = z^3$ (c) $f(z) = 1/z^2$
    (b) $f(z) = 2z + 1 - 3i$ (d) $f(z) = |z|^2$

5. Describe the locus of points that satisfy the given conditions:

    (a) $|z - 2i| = 3$ (c) $1 < |z - 2 + i| < 2$
    (b) $|z + 1 - i| < 1$ (d) $0 < |z - 1| < 1$

6. Show that the limit which defines the derivative of a function $f(z)$ at a point z_0 can be written in the form

$$f'(z_0) = \lim_{h \to 0} \frac{f(z_0 + h) - f(z_0)}{h}.$$

7. If $F(z) = f(z) + g(z)$, show that $F'(z) = f'(z) + g'(z)$.

8. Use the definition of the derivative of a function to find $f'(z)$ if
    (a) $f(z) = z^3$,   (b) $f(z) = 1/z^2$,   (c) $f(z) = z^n$, n a positive integer.

9. If the function f possesses a derivative at a point z, show that

$$f'(z) = \lim_{\Delta x \to 0} \frac{f(z + \Delta x) - f(z)}{\Delta x} = \frac{\partial u}{\partial x} + i \frac{\partial v}{\partial x}$$

and also that

$$f'(z) = \lim_{\Delta y \to 0} \frac{f(z + i\Delta y) - f(z)}{i\Delta y} = \frac{\partial v}{\partial y} - i \frac{\partial u}{\partial y},$$

where Δx and Δy are real. Hence show that

$$\frac{\partial u}{\partial x} = \frac{\partial v}{\partial y} \qquad \text{and} \qquad \frac{\partial u}{\partial y} = -\frac{\partial v}{\partial x}$$

at each point where f is differentiable. These equations for u and v are called the Cauchy-Riemann equations. There is a sort of converse of this result. If the real functions $u(x, y)$ and $v(x, y)$ are continuous *along with their first partial derivatives* and satisfy the Cauchy-Riemann equations in a neighborhood of a point z, then it can be shown that the function of a complex variable $f(z) = u + iv$ is differentiable at the point.

10. By using the result of Problem 9, show that the function $f(z) = |z|^2$ does not possess a derivative at any point except possibly at $z = 0$. Then show that the derivative at $z = 0$ does exist and is equal to zero. Is $f(z)$ analytic at $z = 0$?

3.3 Complex Series

An *infinite sequence* of complex numbers is a function defined on the non-negative integers, with values

$$s_0, s_1, s_2, \ldots, s_n, \ldots. \tag{3.7}$$

We shall sometimes use the notation $\{s_n\}$, $n \geq 0$, to denote a sequence. We say that the sequence (3.7) *converges* to the limit $s = a + ib$ if

$$\lim_{n \to \infty} |s_n - s| = 0.$$

In this case we write

$$\lim_{n \to \infty} s_n = s.$$

If a sequence does not converge, it is said to *diverge*. If $s_n = a_n + ib_n$, then

$$|s_n - s| = \sqrt{(a_n - a)^2 + (b_n - b)^2},$$

so it is easy to see that the sequence (3.7) converges to s if, and only if, the two real sequences $\{a_n\}$ and $\{b_n\}$ converge to a and b, respectively.

An *infinite series* of complex numbers is an expression of the form

$$\sum_{n=0}^{\infty} c_n = c_0 + c_1 + c_2 + \cdots + c_n + \cdots, \tag{3.8}$$

where $c_n = a_n + ib_n$. Associated with the series (3.8) is the *sequence of partial sums*, $\{S_n\}$, where

$$S_0 = c_0$$

$$S_1 = c_0 + c_1$$

$$\cdots\cdots\cdots\cdots$$

$$S_n = c_0 + c_1 + \cdots + c_n$$

$$\cdots\cdots\cdots\cdots\cdots\cdots$$

The series (3.8) is said to converge to the sum S if, and only if, the sequence $\{S_n\}$ converges to the limit S. If the series does not converge, it is said to diverge. Since

$$S_n = (a_0 + a_1 + \cdots + a_n) + i(b_0 + b_1 + \cdots + b_n),$$

we see that the series (3.8) converges to $S = a + ib$ if, and only if, the real series

$$\sum_{n=0}^{\infty} a_n, \qquad \sum_{n=0}^{\infty} b_n \qquad (3.9)$$

converge to the sums a and b, respectively. If the series (3.8) converges, then

$$\lim_{n \to \infty} |c_n| = 0,$$

for $|c_n| = \sqrt{a_n^2 + b_n^2}$, and $\lim_{n \to \infty} a_n = \lim_{n \to \infty} b_n = 0$. Also, if the series (3.8) converges, its terms c_n are bounded; that is, there exists a positive real number M such that $|c_n| \leq M$ for all n. This property also follows from the corresponding property for real series.

Associated with the series (3.8) is the real series of absolute values,

$$\sum_{n=0}^{\infty} |c_n|. \qquad (3.10)$$

If the series (3.10) converges, the series (3.8) is said to be *absolutely convergent*. If a series is absolutely convergent, it is convergent. For we have

$$|a_n| \leq \sqrt{a_n^2 + b_n^2} = |c_n|, \qquad |b_n| \leq \sqrt{a_n^2 + b_n^2} = |c_n|,$$

so if the series (3.10) converges, then the real series (3.9) converge.

The *ratio test* is frequently useful in determining whether or not a given series converges. Suppose that the limit

$$\lim_{n \to \infty} \left| \frac{c_{n+1}}{c_n} \right| \qquad (3.11)$$

exists and is equal to the real number L. If $0 \leq L < 1$, then the series (3.10), and hence the series (3.8), converges. If $L > 1$ (or if $|c_{n+1}/c_n| \to +\infty$), then $|c_n| \to +\infty$, so both the series (3.10) and (3.8) diverge.

A series of functions,

$$\sum_{n=0}^{\infty} f_n(z),$$

is said to converge in a region D of the complex plane if it converges at every point of D. The sum of a series of functions that converges in a region D is a function defined on D.

3.3   EXERCISES

1. Determine whether or not the given sequence converges. If it converges, find the limit.

$$\text{(a)} \quad s_n = \frac{n - 2i}{n^2} \qquad n \geq 1$$

$$\text{(b)} \quad s_n = \frac{2n}{n + 1} - \frac{3in}{n + 2} \qquad n \geq 0$$

$$\text{(c)} \quad s_n = \frac{2n + (n^2 + 1)i}{n + 1} \qquad n \geq 0$$

2. If the sequences $\{\alpha_n\}$ and $\{\beta_n\}$, $n \geq 0$, converge to the limits α and β, respectively, show that the sequence $\{\alpha_n + \beta_n\}$ converges to the limit $\alpha + \beta$.

3. Determine whether or not the given series converges.

$$\text{(a)} \quad \sum_{n=0}^{\infty} \frac{1 + in^2}{n^2 + 1} \qquad\qquad \text{(c)} \quad \sum_{n=1}^{\infty} \left[\frac{(-1)^n}{n} + \frac{2i}{n^2} \right]$$

$$\text{(b)} \quad \sum_{n=1}^{\infty} \left(\frac{1}{n^2 + 1} - \frac{2i}{n^2} \right) \qquad \text{(d)} \quad \sum_{n=1}^{\infty} \left(\frac{1}{n^2} - \frac{2i}{n} \right).$$

4. Show that the series

$$\sum_{n=1}^{\infty} \frac{(-1)^n (1 + i)}{n}$$

is convergent, but not absolutely convergent.

5. If the series of complex terms

$$\sum_{n=0}^{\infty} \alpha_n, \qquad \sum_{n=0}^{\infty} \beta_n$$

are both convergent, with sums α and β, respectively, show that

$$\sum_{n=0}^{\infty} (\alpha_n + \beta_n) = \alpha + \beta.$$

6. A series of the form

$$\sum_{n=0}^{\infty} z^n,$$

where z is any complex number, is called a *geometric series*.

(a) Show that the series diverges if $|z| \geq 1$.

(b) Let $S_n(z) = 1 + z + z^2 + \cdots + z^n$ be the nth partial sum of the series. Show that

$$S_n - zS_n = 1 - z^{n+1},$$

and hence that

$$S_n = \frac{1 - z^{n+1}}{1 - z}, \qquad z \neq 1.$$

(c) Show that

$$\sum_{n=0}^{\infty} z^n = \frac{1}{1 - z}, \qquad |z| < 1.$$

7. Prove the ratio test. Suggestion: if $0 \leq L < 1$, let r be a positive number such that $L < r < 1$. Then there is a positive integer N such that $|c_{n+1}/c_n| < r$ when $n \geq N$. If $L > 1$, let R be a positive number such that $1 < R < L$. Then there is a positive integer N such that $|c_{n+1}/c_n| > R$ when $n \geq N$.

8. Given the series

$$\sum_{n=0}^{\infty} c_n,$$

suppose that the limit

$$\lim_{n \to \infty} \sqrt[n]{|c_n|}$$

exists and is equal to L. Show that the series converges if $L < 1$ and diverges if $L > 1$. (This test for convergence is called the *root test*.)

3.4 Power Series

An infinite series of functions of the special form

$$\sum_{n=0}^{\infty} c_n (z - z_0)^n,$$

where the quantities c_n and z_0 are complex constants, is called a *power series*. The point z_0 is called the *point of expansion* of the series, and the constants c_n are called the *coefficients* of the series.

A power series always converges at its point of expansion, since all but the first term of the series are zero there. It may converge *only* at this point. It may converge for all values of z. It is shown in books on advanced calculus†

---

† See, for example, the book by Protter and Morrey, Reference 4, at the end of this chapter.

that if neither of these two situations occurs, then there exists a positive real number R such that the series converges at each point inside the circle $|z - z_0| = R$ and diverges at each point outside the circle. The circle is called the *circle of convergence* of the series and the number R is called the *radius of convergence*. At a point on the circle itself, the series may, or may not, converge. In the two extreme situations mentioned earlier, it is customary to write $R = 0$ and $R = +\infty$, respectively. The following examples serve to illustrate the various possibilities. In each case, the radius of convergence can be determined by using the ratio test.

EXAMPLE 1. The series

$$\sum_{n=0}^{\infty} n! \, (z - 2i)^n$$

converges only at the point of expansion $z_0 = 2i$, so $R = 0$.

EXAMPLE 2. The series

$$\sum_{n=0}^{\infty} \frac{(z + 1 - i)^n}{n!}$$

converges for all z, so $R = +\infty$.

EXAMPLE 3. The series

$$\sum_{n=0}^{\infty} \frac{z^n}{n}$$

has radius of convergence $R = 1$. At the points $z = -1$ and $z = 1$, which are on the circle itself, the series converges and diverges, respectively.

We now state, without proof, some additional properties of power series. We consider first two power series, with radii of convergence R_1 and R_2, respectively. Let

$$f(z) = \sum_{n=0}^{\infty} a_n(z - z_0)^n, \qquad |z - z_0| < R_1,$$

$$g(z) = \sum_{n=0}^{\infty} b_n(z - z_0)^n, \qquad |z - z_0| < R_2. \tag{3.12}$$

Let $r = \min(R_1, R_2)$. Then it can be shown that

$$f(z) + g(z) = \sum_{n=0}^{\infty} (a_n + b_n)(z - z_0)^n, \qquad |z - z_0| < r, \tag{3.13}$$

and that

$$f(z)g(z) = \sum_{n=0}^{\infty} c_n(z - z_0)^n, \qquad |z - z_0| < r, \tag{3.14}$$

where

$$c_n = \sum_{k=0}^{n} a_k b_{n-k} = \sum_{k=0}^{n} a_{n-k} b_k \tag{3.15}$$

$$= a_0 b_n + a_1 b_{n-1} + a_2 b_{n-2} + \cdots + a_n b_0.$$

In this last formula, it should be noted that c_n is the sum of $n + 1$ products, in each of which the sum of the subscripts is n.

A power series can be differentiated term by term. More precisely, if

$$f(z) = \sum_{n=0}^{\infty} a_n(z - z_0)^n, \qquad |z - z_0| < R, \tag{3.16}$$

then it can be shown that $f'(z)$ exists and that

$$f'(z) = \sum_{n=1}^{\infty} na_n(z - z_0)^{n-1} = \sum_{n=0}^{\infty} (n + 1)a_{n+1}(z - z_0)^n \tag{3.17}$$

for $|z - z_0| < R$. It follows from this fact that $f(z)$ is analytic in the region $|z - z_0| < R$. Since the series (3.17) for $f'(z)$ is also a power series, we can differentiate again to obtain a power series for $f''(z)$, and so on.

Power series can be used to define functions of a complex variable. We define the functions e^z, $\cos z$, and $\sin z$ as

$$e^z = \sum_{n=0}^{\infty} \frac{z^n}{n!}, \tag{3.18}$$

$$\cos z = \sum_{n=0}^{\infty} \frac{(-1)^n z^{2n}}{(2n)!}, \tag{3.19}$$

$$\sin z = \sum_{n=1}^{\infty} \frac{(-1)^n z^{2n-1}}{(2n - 1!)} \tag{3.20}$$

for all z. (Each of the above series converges for all z, as can be verified by means of the ratio test.) These three functions have been defined in such a way that when z is real, they coincide with their real counterparts e^x, $\cos x$, $\sin x$, respectively. Each of the complex functions of z is analytic for all z. The truth of the relationship

$$e^{iz} = \cos z + i \sin z \tag{3.21}$$

follows from the power series definitions of the functions involved. The identities

$$\cos z = \frac{e^{iz} + e^{-iz}}{2}, \qquad \sin z = \frac{e^{iz} - e^{-iz}}{2i} \tag{3.22}$$

can be derived from formula (3.21). It is left as an exercise to show that the definition (3.18) of e^z agrees with the definition given in Chapter 1.

3.4 EXERCISES

1. Find the radius of convergence of the given power series. Draw a graph showing the circle of convergence.

(a) $\displaystyle\sum_{n=0}^{\infty} \frac{n^2}{n+1} z^n$

(d) $\displaystyle\sum_{n=0}^{\infty} \frac{100^n (z-2)^n}{n^n}$

(b) $\displaystyle\sum_{n=0}^{\infty} \frac{(z+i)^n}{2^n (n+1)}$

(e) $\displaystyle\sum_{n=1}^{\infty} \frac{n^n z^n}{n+1}$

(c) $\displaystyle\sum_{n=1}^{\infty} \frac{(-1)^n (z-1+i)^n}{n \log n}$

(f) $\displaystyle\sum_{n=1}^{\infty} \frac{n^n z^n}{n!}$

2. Let $f(z)$ and $g(z)$ be defined by the given series. Find a series for $f(z) + g(z)$ and for $f(z)g(z)$.

(a) $\displaystyle f(z) = \sum_{n=0}^{\infty} (z+1)^n, \qquad g(z) = \sum_{n=0}^{\infty} (2-n)(z+1)^n, \qquad |z+1| < 1$

(b) $\displaystyle f(z) = g(z) = \sum_{n=0}^{\infty} z^n, \qquad |z| < 1$

(c) $\displaystyle f(z) = \sum_{n=1}^{\infty} nz^n, \qquad g(z) = \sum_{n=1}^{\infty} \frac{z^n}{n}, \qquad |z| < 1$

3. Show that the series which define the functions e^z, $\cos z$, and $\sin z$ converge for all z.

4. Show that

$$\frac{d}{dz} e^z = e^z, \qquad \frac{d}{dz} \cos z = -\sin z, \qquad \frac{d}{dz} \sin z = \cos z$$

5. Show that

$$e^{iz} = \cos z + i \sin z$$

and that

$$e^z = e^x(\cos y + i \sin y), \qquad z = x + iy$$

6. (a) If the power series

$$\sum_{n=0}^{\infty} c_n (z - z_0)^n$$

converges at a point z_1, where $z_1 \neq z_0$, show that the series converges absolutely for $|z - z_0| < |z_1 - z_0|$.

(b) If the power series in part (a) diverges at a point z_2, show that it diverges for $|z - z_0| > |z_2 - z_0|$.

7. The hyperbolic functions $\cosh z$ and $\sinh z$ are defined by means of the formulas

$$\cosh z = \frac{e^z + e^{-z}}{2}, \qquad \sinh z = \frac{e^z - e^{-z}}{2}$$

for all z. Show that

$$\cosh z = \sum_{n=0}^{\infty} \frac{z^{2n}}{(2n)!}, \qquad \sinh z = \sum_{n=1}^{\infty} \frac{z^{2n-1}}{(2n-1)!}$$

for all z.

8. Show that

$$\cos z = \cos(x + iy) = \cos x \cosh y - i \sin x \sinh y,$$

$$\sin z = \sin(x + iy) = \sin x \cosh y + i \cos x \sinh y.$$

9. Prove DeMoivre's theorem, which states that

$$(\cos \theta + i \sin \theta)^n = \cos n\theta + i \sin n\theta,$$

for every nonnegative integer n.

3.5 Taylor Series

Suppose that a function $f(z)$ can be represented by a power series in some neighborhood of the point z_0, that is, that

$$f(z) = \sum_{n=0}^{\infty} c_n(z - z_0)^n, \qquad |z - z_0| < r. \tag{3.23}$$

Setting $z = z_0$ in this equation, we see that

$$c_0 = f(z_0).$$

Since

$$f'(z) = \sum_{n=1}^{\infty} nc_n(z - z_0)^{n-1}, \qquad |z - z_0| < r,$$

we see, upon setting $z = z_0$, that

$$c_1 = f'(z_0).$$

By continuing this process, we find that

$$c_n = \frac{f^{(n)}(z_0)}{n!}, \qquad n = 0, 1, 2, \dots. \tag{3.24}$$

Thus if $f(z)$ is representable by a power series with point of expansion z_0, the coefficients in that power series must be given by the formula (3.24).

On the other hand, if a function $f(z)$ is analytic at the point z_0, its derivatives of all orders exist at z_0, and we can write down the power series

$$\sum_{n=0}^{\infty} \frac{f^{(n)}(z_0)}{n!} (z - z_0)^n. \tag{3.25}$$

The series (3.25) is called the *Taylor series* for $f(z)$ at z_0. The question now arises as to whether the Taylor series for $f(z)$ actually converges to $f(z)$ at any point other than z_0 itself. An answer to this question is given by the following theorem, a proof of which can be found in any book on complex variables.

Theorem 1. Let $f(z)$ be analytic in the neighborhood $|z - z_0| < r$ of the point z_0. Then the Taylor series for $f(z)$ at the point z_0 converges to $f(z)$, at least for $|z - z_0| < r$.

Although this theorem is about functions of a complex variable, it is also useful in establishing the validity of Taylor series expansions of functions of a real variable. A classic example is furnished by the function

$$f(x) = \frac{1}{1 + x^2}, \qquad -\infty < x < -\infty.$$

The function of a complex variable,

$$f(z) = \frac{1}{1 + z^2},$$

is analytic except at the points $z = i$ and $z = -i$. Taking $z_0 = 0$ as our point of expansion, we see that the largest neighborhood of z_0 in which $f(z)$ is analytic is the neighborhood $|z| < 1$. The Taylor series for $f(z)$ at $z_0 = 0$ is

$$\sum_{n=0}^{\infty} (-1)^n z^{2n};$$

according to Theorem 1, it converges to $f(z)$ for $|z| < 1$. (It diverges for $z > 1$, as can be verified by means of the ratio test.) We therefore have

$$f(x) = \frac{1}{1 + x^2} = \sum_{n=0}^{\infty} (-1)^n x^{2n}, \qquad -1 < x < 1.$$

There is no general theorem, such as Theorem 1, for functions of a real variable. In the real domain, the validity of every Taylor series expansion must be considered separately. In fact, a function $F(x)$ of a real variable is *defined* to be analytic at a point x_0 if, and only if, it has a Taylor series at x_0 which converges to $F(x)$ in some interval $|x - x_0| < r$, where $r > 0$. Even the assumption that $F(x)$ possesses derivatives of all orders in an interval I is not sufficient to guarantee that $F(x)$ is analytic at a point of I. On the other hand, suppose that a function $F(x)$ of the real variable x *is* analytic at a point $x = x_0$, so that

$$F(x) = \sum_{n=0}^{\infty} a_n (x - x_0)^n, \qquad |x - x_0| < r.$$

Then the series of complex terms,

$$\sum_{n=0}^{\infty} a_n (z - x_0)^n,$$

defines a function $F(z)$ of a complex variable that is analytic in the region $|z - x_0| < r$ and that coincides with $F(x)$ on the interval $|x - x_0| < r$ of the real axis. Thus the theory of analytic functions of a complex variable can always be brought to bear to yield information about analytic functions of a real variable.

3.5 EXERCISES

1. Find the Taylor series for the given function at the indicated point by calculating the derivatives of the function. Find the region in which the series converges to the function.

   (a) $f(z) = z^3 + 2z,$ $\quad z_0 = 2i$ $\quad$ (c) $f(z) = e^{2z},$ $\quad z_0 = 0$
   (b) $f(z) = 1/z,$ $\quad z_0 = 1$ $\quad$ (d) $f(z) = \sin z,$ $\quad z_0 = \pi/4$

2. Show that the function $f(z) = 1/(1 - z)$ possesses the Taylor series

$$\frac{1}{1 - z} = \sum_{n=0}^{\infty} z^n$$

   at $z_0 = 0$, valid for $|z| < 1$.

3. By using the result of Problem 2, find the Taylor series expansion of the given function about the indicated point. Find the region of the complex plane in which the series converges to the function.

   (a) $f(z) = \dfrac{1}{1 + 2z},$ $\quad z_0 = 0$ $\quad$ (c) $f(z) = \dfrac{z}{1 - z^3},$ $\quad z_0 = 0$

   (b) $f(z) = \dfrac{1}{z},$ $\quad z_0 = 1$ $\quad$ (d) $f(z) = \dfrac{1}{(z - 2)(z + 1)},$ $\quad z_0 = 0$

4. Find, by any means, the Taylor series for the given function $f(x)$ of the real variable x at the indicated point. Find the interval in which the series converges to the function.

   (a) $f(x) = \dfrac{1}{x^2 + 4},$ $\quad x_0 = 0$ $\quad$ (c) $f(x) = \dfrac{e^{-x}}{x + 1},$ $\quad x_0 = 0.$

   (b) $f(x) = \dfrac{x + 1}{x - 2},$ $\quad x_0 = -1$

REFERENCES

1. Churchill, R. V., *Complex Variables and Applications*. McGraw-Hill, New York, 1960.
2. Knopp, K., *Theory of Functions*. Dover, New York, 1945.
3. Pennisi, L. L., *Elements of Complex Variables*. Holt, Rinehart, and Winston, New York, 1963.
4. Protter, M. H. and Morrey, C. B., *Modern Mathematical Analysis*. Addison-Wesley, Reading, Mass. ,1964.
5. Titchmarsh, E. C., *The Theory of Functions*. Oxford, New York, 1950.

CHAPTER **4**

SERIES SOLUTIONS

4.1 Introduction

In Chapter 1, we saw that a solution of any linear first-order equation can be expressed in terms of integrals of quantities that depend in a simple way on the coefficients of the equation. With regard to higher-order equations, we saw that those equations with constant coefficients and those of Cauchy type possess solutions that can be expressed explicitly in terms of elementary functions. In Chapter 2, we saw that in a few other cases the solutions of a linear equation can be expressed in terms of integrals of known quantities. This can be done, for example, when the operator of the equation can be factored, or when one nontrivial solution of a second-order equation is known. However, relatively few differential equations permit such simple methods of solution. For instance, the seemingly innocent equation

$$y'' + xy = 0$$

defies all our efforts.

There are, however, fairly large classes of differential equations whose solutions can be expressed either in terms of power series or else as simple combinations of power series and elementary functions. It is with such classes of equations that we shall be concerned in this chapter, We shall restrict ourselves primarily to second-order equations for the sake of simplicity, although general theories for equations of arbitrary order are well-known. The so-called series solutions yield information about solutions only near the point of expansion, in general. They show which, if any, solutions are finite at the point of expansion, and which, if any, become infinite there. The series may also be useful for the numerical tabulation of solutions near the point of expansion.

We shall present here only a few definitions and results concerning real power series. A *real power series* is a series of functions, of the form

$$\sum_{n=0}^{\infty} a_n(x - x_0)^n,$$

where the quantities a_n and x_0 are real constants and x is a real variable. The point x_0 is called the *point of expansion* of the series and the constants a_n are called the *coefficients* of the series. A function $f(x)$ is said to be *analytic* at the point x_0 if it can be represented by a power series, with point of expansion x_0, in some interval of the form $|x - x_0| < r$, where $r > 0$. If a function $f(x)$ is analytic $x = x_0$, we have

$$f(x) = \sum_{n=0}^{\infty} a_n(x - x_0)^n, \qquad |x - x_0| < r, \tag{4.1}$$

where

$$a_n = \frac{f^{(n)}(x_0)}{n!}, \qquad n = 0, 1, 2, \ldots . \tag{4.2}$$

The series (4.1), with coefficients (4.2), is called the *Taylor series* for $f(x)$ at $x = x_0$.

4.2   Solutions at an Ordinary Point

If, at a point $x = x_0$, each of the coefficient functions $a_i(x)$, $1 \le i \le n$, of the linear homogeneous differential equation

$$y^{(n)} + a_1(x)y^{(n-1)} + \cdots + a_{n-1}(x)y' + a_n(x)y = 0 \tag{4.3}$$

is analytic, then the point x_0 is said to be an *ordinary point* for the differential equation. If not all the coefficients are analytic at x_0, then x_0 is said to be a *singular point* for the equation. In the special case of an equation with constant coefficients, obviously every point is an ordinary point. In the case of an equation of the Cauchy type,

$$y^{(n)} + \frac{1}{x} b_1 y^{(n-1)} + \cdots + \frac{1}{x^{n-1}} b_{n-1} y' + \frac{1}{x^n} b_n y = 0,$$

the point $x = 0$ is a singular point, but every other point is an ordinary point.

Suppose that x_0 is an ordinary point for the equation (4.3), and that each of the functions $a_i(x)$ is represented by its Taylor series at x_0 in the interval $|x - x_0| < r$, where $r > 0$. Then it turns out that every solution of the equation (on an interval that contains x_0) is analytic at x_0 and is represented by its Taylor series at least for $|x - x_0| < r$. Roughly speaking, if the coefficients of a linear homogeneous differential equation are analytic at a point, then all of its solutions are analytic at that point. This is certainly true for an equation with constant coefficients. For its solutions are linear combinations of functions of the form

$$x^k e^{ax} \cos bx, \qquad x^k e^{ax} \sin bx,$$

where k is a nonnegative integer, and such functions are analytic at every point.

In the next section, we shall give a proof of the statement made at the beginning of the last paragraph, for second-order equations. Meanwhile, let us examine a method by which the coefficients in the power series expansions of the solutions can be calculated. We shall illustrate the procedure by means of an example.

In the differential equation

$$y'' + xy' + 3y = 0, \tag{4.4}$$

every point is an ordinary point, since the coefficients $a_1(x) = x$ and $a_2(x) = 3$ are polynomials. In order to be specific, we shall consider the point $x = 0$, and shall endeavor to find the solution that satisfies the initial conditions

$$y(0) = A_0, \qquad y'(0) = A_1, \tag{4.5}$$

where A_0 and A_1 are constants. Assuming that this solution is analytic at $x = 0$, it must possess a power series expansion of the form

$$y = \sum_{n=0}^{\infty} A_n x^n = A_0 + A_1 x + A_2 x^2 + \cdots, \tag{4.6}$$

where A_0 and A_1 are the same constants that appear in the initial conditions (4.5). Differentiating the series (4.6), we have

$$y' = \sum_{n=1}^{\infty} n A_n x^{n-1}, \qquad y'' = \sum_{n=2}^{\infty} n(n-1) A_n x^{n-2}. \tag{4.7}$$

Upon substituting the series (4.6) and (4.7) into the equation (4.4) we obtain the condition

$$\sum_{n=2}^{\infty} n(n-1) A_n x^{n-2} + \sum_{n=1}^{\infty} n A_n x^n + 3 \sum_{n=0}^{\infty} A_n x^n = 0. \tag{4.8}$$

We want to combine the three series in the left-hand member of this equation into a single power series. In order to combine the like powers of x, it is convenient to make a change in the index of summation in the first series. If we let $k = n - 2$, or $n = k + 2$, then as n ranges over the set of integers $2, 3, 4, \ldots$, k ranges over the set of integers $0, 1, 2, \ldots$. We can therefore write

$$\sum_{n=2}^{\infty} n(n-1) A_n x^{n-2} = \sum_{k=0}^{\infty} (k+2)(k+1) A_{k+2} x^k.$$

The index of summation in any series is a "dummy index." That is, the sum of a series does not depend on the symbol used for the index, which takes on certain integral values, successively. Thus the series above is exactly the same as the series

$$\sum_{n=0}^{\infty} (n + (n + 2)(n + 1)A_{n+2}x^n.$$

Equation (4.8) can now be written as

$$\sum_{n=0}^{\infty} (n + 2)(n + 1)A_{n+2}x^n + \sum_{n=1}^{\infty} nA_n x^n + \sum_{n=0}^{\infty} 3A_n x^n = 0. \qquad (4.9)$$

The first and third series here start with constant terms, whereas the second series begins with a term that involves the first power of x. Collecting the two constant terms, and combining like powers of x in the three series, we have

$$(2A_2 + 3A_0) + \sum_{n=1}^{\infty} [(n + 1)(n + 2)A_{n+2} + (n + 3)A_n]x^n = 0. \quad (4.10)$$

But the power series expansion of the zero function at any point has all its coefficients equal to zero. Therefore $2A_2 + 3A_0 = 0$, and

$$(n + 1)(n + 2)A_{n+2} + (n + 3)A_n = 0 \qquad (4.11)$$

for $n \geq 1$. (It happens that this relation also holds for $n = 0$.) This relation is called the *recurrence relation* for the coefficients A_n. A function that is analytic at $x = 0$ is a solution of the differential equation if, and only if, its power series coefficients satisfy this relation.

Let us write the recurrence relation in the form

$$A_{n+2} = -\frac{n + 3}{(n + 1)(n + 2)} A_n, \qquad n \geq 0.$$

We see that, given A_0 and A_1, we can express $A_2, A_4, A_6, \ldots$, in terms of A_0 and $A_3, A_5, A_7, \ldots$, in terms of A_1. For the first few coefficients, we have

$$A_2 = -\frac{3}{2} A_0,$$

$$A_4 = -\frac{5}{3 \cdot 4} A_2 \quad \frac{3 \cdot 5}{2 \cdot 3 \cdot 4} A_0,$$

$$\cdots \cdots \cdots \cdots \cdots \cdots \cdots \cdots \cdots$$

$$A_3 = -\frac{4}{2 \cdot 3} A_1,$$

$$A_5 = -\frac{6}{4 \cdot 5} A_3 = \frac{4 \cdot 6}{2 \cdot 3 \cdot 4 \cdot 5} A_1,$$

$$\cdots \cdots \cdots \cdots \cdots \cdots \cdots \cdots \cdots$$

Looking at the expressions for A_2 and A_4, it seems reasonable to conjecture that

$$A_{2m} = (-1)^m \frac{1 \cdot 3 \cdot 5 \cdots (2m+1)}{(2m)!} A_0 = (-1)^m \frac{(2m+1)}{2^m m!} A_0 \qquad (4.12)$$

for $m \geq 1$. (It happens that the formula is valid for $m = 0$ also.) The validity of this formula can be established by mathematical induction. Similarly, we find that for the coefficients with odd indices,

$$A_{2m+1} = (-1)^m \frac{4 \cdot 6 \cdot 8 \cdots (2m+2)}{(2m+1)!} A_1 = (-1)^m \frac{2^m (m+1)!}{(2m+1)!} A_1 \qquad (4.13)$$

for $m \geq 1$. (The last member of this equation is equal to A_1 when $m = 0$.)

Actually, each of the infinite series in the expression

$$y = A_0 \sum_{m=0}^{\infty} (-1)^m \frac{2m+1}{2^m m!} x^{2m} + A_1 \sum_{m=0}^{\infty} (-1)^m \frac{2^m(m+1)!}{(2m+1)!} x^{2m+1} \qquad (4.14)$$

converges for all x, as can be verified by applying the ratio test. Therefore the function defined by equation (4.14) *is* analytic at $x = 0$. It satisfies the initial conditions $y(0) = A_0$, $y'(0) = A_1$. It is also a solution of the differential equation for all x, since its power series coefficients satisfy the recurrence relation (4.11). Therefore the function (4.14) is the unique solution of the initial value problem on the interval $-\infty < x < +\infty$. If A_0 and A_1 are allowed to be arbitrary constants, the expression (4.14) represents the general solution of the differential equation.

4.3   Analyticity of Solutions at an Ordinary Point

We shall prove the following theorem.

Theorem 1.   Let the functions $P(x)$ and $Q(x)$ be analytic at $x = x_0$ and be represented by their Taylor series at x_0 for $|x - x_0| < R$. Then the initial value problem

$$Ly \equiv y'' + P(x)y' + Q(x)y = 0, \qquad |x - x_0| < R,$$

$$y(x_0) = A_0, \qquad y'(x_0) = A_1 \qquad (4.15)$$

possesses a (unique) solution that is analytic at x_0 and is represented by its Taylor series at x_0 for $|x - x_0| < R$.

Before proving the theorem, we remark that the general method of proof will be similar to the procedure used in the example of the previous section. We shall show that a function which is analytic at x_0 is a solution of the initial value problem if, and only if, the coefficients in its power series expansion satisfy a certain recurrence relation. We shall then show that the series whose coefficients satisfy the recurrence relation actually converges. The convergent series will therefore represent an analytic function that is the solution of the initial value problem. In the example, we were fortunate in being able to find explicit formulas [(4.12) and (4.13)] for the coefficients that satisfied the recurrence relation. These formulas enabled us to prove that the series with these coefficients converge. In the general case, it will not be possible to find explicit formulas for the coefficients, so we shall have to establish the convergence of the series in a different way.

Proof. Let

$$P(x) = \sum_{n=0}^{\infty} P_n(x - x_0)^n, \qquad Q(x) = \sum_{n=0}^{\infty} Q_n(x - x_0)^n, \qquad |x - x_0| < R. \quad (4.16)$$

Let $y(x)$ be a function that is analytic at $x = x_0$, with Taylor series

$$y(x) = \sum_{n=0}^{\infty} A_n(x - x_0)^n, \tag{4.17}$$

where A_0 and A_1 are the constants given in the initial conditions. Then

$$y'(x) = \sum_{n=1}^{\infty} nA_n(x - x_0)^{n-1} = \sum_{n=0}^{\infty} (n + 1)A_{n+1}(x - x_0)^n,$$

$$y''(x) = \sum_{n=2}^{\infty} n(n - 1)A_n(x - x_0)^{n-2} = \sum_{n=0}^{\infty} (n + 1)(n + 2)A_{n+2}(x - x_0)^n,$$

and

$$P(x)y'(x) = \sum_{n=0}^{\infty} \left(\sum_{k=0}^{n} (k + 1)A_{k+1}P_{n-k} \right)(x - x_0)^n,$$

$$Q(x)y(x) = \sum_{n=0}^{\infty} \left(\sum_{k=0}^{n} A_kQ_{n-k} \right)(x - x_0)^n.$$

The function $L[y(x)]$ is analytic at $x = x_0$ and

$$Ly = \sum_{n=0}^{\infty} \left[(n + 1)(n + 2)A_{n+2} + \sum_{k=0}^{n} (k + 1)A_{k+1}P_{n-k} + \sum_{k=0}^{n} A_kQ_{n-k} \right](x - x_0)^n. \tag{4.18}$$

We see from this equation that $y(x)$ is a solution of the differential equation if, and only if, its coefficients A_n satisfy the recurrence relation

$$A_{n+2} = \frac{-1}{(n + 1)(n + 2)} \left[\sum_{k=0}^{n} (k + 1)A_{k+1}P_{n-k} + \sum_{k=0}^{n} A_kQ_{n-k} \right], \qquad n \geq 0. \quad (4.19)$$

By making a shift in the index n (we replace n by $n - 2$), we can write this relation in the form

$$A_n = \frac{-1}{n(n - 1)} \left[\sum_{k=0}^{n-2} (k + 1)A_{k+1}P_{n-k-2} + \sum_{k=0}^{n-2} A_kQ_{n-k-2} \right], \qquad n \geq 2. \quad (4.20)$$

If A_0 and A_1 are given, this relation actually specifies each coefficient with index ≥ 2 uniquely in terms of A_0 and A_1. We shall now show that the series with these coefficients converges for $|x - x_0| < R$.

Let x_1 be an arbitrary, but fixed, number in the interval $|x - x_0| < R$. Let r be a positive number such that $|x_1 - x_0| < r < R$. Since the series (4.16) for $P(x)$ and $Q(x)$ converge when $x = x_0 + r$, there exists a positive constant M such that

$$|P_n| \le \frac{M}{r^n}, \qquad |Q_n| \le \frac{M}{r^n}, \qquad n \ge 0. \tag{4.21}$$

Then, from the recurrence relation (4.20) we see that

$$|A_n| \le \frac{M}{n(n-1)} \left[\sum_{k=0}^{n-2} \frac{(k+1)|A_{k+1}|}{r^{n-k-2}} + \sum_{k=0}^{n-2} \frac{|A_k|}{r^{n-k-2}} \right], \qquad n \ge 2. \tag{4.22}$$

We now define a sequence of positive numbers B_n in the following way. Let B_0 and B_1 be positive numbers such that

$$B_0 \ge |A_0|, \qquad B_1 \ge |A_1|.$$

(We can take $B_0 = |A_0| + 1$, $B_1 = |A_1| + 1$, for example.) The remaining terms of the sequence are defined according to the formula

$$B_n = \frac{M}{n(n-1)} \left[\sum_{k=0}^{n-2} \frac{(k+1)|A_{k+1}|}{r^{n-k-2}} + \sum_{k=0}^{n-1} \frac{|A_k|}{r^{n-k-2}} \right], \qquad n \ge 2. \tag{4.23}$$

It should be noted that for $n \ge 2$ the expression for B_n is exactly the same as the right-hand member of the inequality (4.22), except for the additional term $r|A_{n-1}|$ in the second group of terms in brackets in formula (4.23). Therefore,

$$|A_n| \le B_n, \qquad n \ge 0. \tag{4.24}$$

For the $(n+1)$st term in the sequence $\{B_n\}$ we have

$$B_{n+1} = \frac{M}{n(n+1)} \left[\sum_{k=0}^{n-1} \frac{(k+1)|A_{k+1}|}{r^{n-k-1}} + \sum_{k=0}^{n} \frac{|A_k|}{r^{n-k-1}} \right].$$

If the terms in this expression are grouped properly, it can be shown that

$$B_{n+1} = \frac{n-1}{n+1} \frac{1}{r} B_n + \frac{M}{n(n+1)} (n+r)|A_n|, \qquad n \ge 2, \tag{4.25}$$

and hence that

$$\frac{B_{n+1}}{B_n} = \frac{n-1}{n+1} \frac{1}{r} + M \frac{n+r}{n(n+1)} \frac{|A_n|}{B_n}, \qquad n \ge 2. \tag{4.26}$$

Since $|A_n|/B_n \le 1$, $n \ge 0$, we have

$$\lim_{n \to \infty} \frac{B_{n+1}}{B_n} = \frac{1}{r}. \tag{4.27}$$

The power series

$$\sum_{n=0}^{\infty} B_n (x - x_0)^n$$

therefore converges absolutely for $|x - x_0| < r$. In particular, it converges absolutely for $x = x_1$. Since

$$|A_n(x_1 - x_0)^n| \le |B_n(x_1 - x_0)^n|, \qquad n \ge 0,$$

the series

$$\sum_{n=0}^{\infty} A_n(x - x_0)^n \tag{4.28}$$

converges for $x = x_1$. But since x_1 was an arbitrary point of the interval $|x - x_0| < R$, the series converges at every point of this interval.

We have shown that the power series (4.28), whose coefficients satisfy the recurrence relation (4.20), converges for $|x - x_0| < R$ to a function which is analytic at $x = x_0$. But we have also shown that a function that is analytic at $x = x_0$ is a solution of the initial value problem if, and only if, its power series coefficients satisfy the relation (4.20). Therefore, the function defined by the power series (4.28) is a solution of the initial value problem on the interval $|x - x_0| < R$. By Theorem 1 of Chapter 1, it is the only solution.

In proving the existence of an analytic solution of the initial value problem, we have derived a formula, formula (4.19), that can be used to calculate the coefficients in the power series expansion of the solution. In a specific problem, however, it is probably easier to determine the coefficients by substituting a series of the form (4.17) directly into the differential equation, rather than by using the general formula. Also, for the purpose of calculating the coefficients of a power series solution, it may be more convenient to write the differential equation in the form

$$p(x)y'' + q(x)y' + r(x)y = 0 \tag{4.29}$$

instead of the form (4.15). For example, in finding power series solutions of the differential equation

$$y'' + \frac{2x}{x^2 - 1} y' - \frac{1}{x - 1} y = 0 \tag{4.30}$$

at $x = 0$, it is convenient to multiply through by $x^2 - 1$ and deal with the equation

$$(x^2 - 1)y'' + 2xy' - (x + 1)y = 0, \tag{4.31}$$

whose coefficients are polynomials. Any power series that satisfies equation (4.31) formally also satisfies equation (4.30) formally, and vice versa. Convergence of any formal power series solution of equation (4.31) is therefore guaranteed, at least for $|x| < 1$.

In concluding our discussion of solutions at an ordinary point, it seems worthwhile to state as a theorem the following result for the general nth-order homogeneous equation.

Theorem 2. Let each of the functions $a_i(x)$, $1 \le i \le n$, be analytic at

$x = x_0$ and be represented by its Taylor series at $x = x_0$ for $|x - x_0| < R$. Then the initial value problem

$$y^{(n)} + a_1(x)y^{(n-1)} + \cdots + a_n(x)y = 0,$$

$$y^{(j)}(x_0) = k_j, \qquad 0 \le j \le n - 1,$$

possesses a (unique) solution that is analytic at $x = x_0$ and is represented by its Taylor series at x_0 for $|x - x_0| < R$.

4.3 EXERCISES

1. Determine which points are ordinary points and which points are singular points for the given differential equation:

   (a) $y'' + e^x y' + (2x^2 - 1)y = 0$

   (b) $y'' + \dfrac{x + 1}{(x + 2)(x - 3)} y' + \dfrac{\cos x}{x^2} y = 0$

   (c) $(x + 1)^2 (2x - 1)y'' - 2xy' + (x^2 - 1)y = 0$

2. Verify that the point $x = 0$ is an ordinary point for the given differential equation, and express the general solution in the form of power series about this point. What can you deduce about the interval of convergence of the series solutions from an examination of the coefficients in the differential equation?

   (a) $y'' + xy = 0$ (d) $y'' + (1 - x)y' - y = 0$
   (b) $y'' - xy' + 2y = 0$ (e) $y'' - e^x y = 0$
   (c) $(x^2 - 1)y'' + 3xy' + y = 0$

3. Let the point $x = x_0$, where $x_0 \ne 0$, be an ordinary point for the equation

   (A) $$\frac{d^2 y}{dx^2} + P(x)\frac{dy}{dx} + Q(x)y = 0$$

   Show that the change of independent variable $t = x - x_0$ leads to a differential equation

   (B) $$\frac{d^2 y}{dt^2} + p(t)\frac{dy}{dt} + q(t)y = 0$$

   for which the point $t = 0$ is an ordinary point. Show that the function

   $$y = \sum_{n=0}^{\infty} A_n t^n, \qquad |t| < r,$$

   is a solution of equation (B) if, and only if, the corresponding function

   $$y = \sum_{n=0}^{\infty} A_n (x - x_0)^n, \qquad |x - x_0| < r,$$

   is a solution of equation (A).

4. Verify that the given differential equation has an ordinary point at the indicated point, and express the general solution of the equation in terms of power series about this point. Discuss the interval of convergence of the series. Use the result of Problem 3 if you wish.

(a) $y'' + 2(x - 1)y' - y = 0$, $x_0 = 1$
(b) $xy'' + 2y' + y = 0$, $x_0 = -1$
(c) $(x^2 - 4x + 5)y'' + (x - 2)y' + y = 0$, $x_0 = 2$

5. Let the function $P(x)$ be analytic at $x = x_0$, and be represented by its Taylor series at x_0 for $|x - x_0| < r$. Show that the initial value problem

$$\frac{dy}{dx} + P(x)y = 0, \qquad y(x_0) = A_0,$$

possesses a solution on the interval $|x - x_0| < r$ that is analytic at x_0 and is represented by its Taylor series on the interval.

6. Let the functions $P(x)$, $Q(x)$, and $f(x)$ be analytic at $x = x_0$, and be represented by their Taylor series at x_0 for $|x - x_0| < R$. Modify the proof of Theorem 1 to show that the problem

$$y'' + P(x)y' + Q(x)y = f(x), \qquad y(x_0) = A_0, \qquad y'(x_0) = A_1$$

possesses a solution that is analytic at $x = x_0$ and is represented by its Taylor series for $|x - x_0| < R$.

7. Express the general solution of the given equation in the form of power series about the point $x = 0$. By using the result of Problem 6, what can you say about the interval of convergence of the power series solutions?

(a) $y'' - xy' - y = e^x$ (b) $y'' - 2xy' - 2y = \dfrac{1}{1 - x}$

4.4   Regular Singular Points

If not all the coefficients in the differential equation

$$y^{(n)} + a_1(x)y^{(n-1)} + \cdots + a_{n-1}(x)y' + a_n(x)y = 0 \qquad (4.32)$$

are analytic at $x = x_0$, then x_0 is called a *singular point* for the differential equation. Singular points are further classified as to type. A singular point x_0 at which the functions

$$(x - x_0)a_1(x), \qquad (x - x_0)^2 a_2(x), \ldots, \qquad (x - x_0)^n a_n(x) \qquad (4.33)$$

are analytic is called a *regular singular point* of the equation. If a singular point x_0 is not a regular singular point, but there is a positive integer m such that the functions

$$(x - x_0)^m a_i(x), \qquad i = 1, 2, \ldots, n, \qquad (4.34)$$

are analytic at x_0, then the point x_0 is called an *irregular singular* point for the differential equation. If x_0 is a regular singular point of the second-order differential equation

$$y'' + a_1(x)y' + a_2(x)y = 0, \tag{4.35}$$

then the functions

$$p(x) = (x - x_0)a_1(x), \qquad q(x) = (x - x_0)^2 a_2(x) \tag{4.36}$$

are analytic at $x = x_0$. The equation may therefore be written in the form

$$y'' + \frac{p(x)}{x - x_0} y' + \frac{q(x)}{(x - x_0)^2} y = 0, \tag{4.37}$$

where $p(x)$ and $q(x)$ are analytic at $x = x_0$. In many applications, we are interested in solutions of an equation of the type (4.37) on an interval of the form (x_0, b) or (a, x_0). Of particular interest is the behavior of solutions and their derivatives as $x \to x_0$.

Simple examples of equations with regular singular points are provided by equations of the Cauchy type. A second-order equation of the Cauchy type is of the form

$$y'' + b_1 x^{-1} y' + b_2 x^{-2} y = 0, \tag{4.38}$$

where b_1 and b_2 are constants. Such an equation possesses a regular singular point at $x = 0$; every other point is an ordinary point. The specific equation

$$2x^2 y'' + 3xy' - y = 0 \tag{4.39}$$

possesses the general solution

$$y = C_1 x^{-1} + C_2 x^{1/2} \tag{4.40}$$

on the interval $0 < x < +\infty$. No solution of equation (4.39) can be represented by a power series with $x = 0$ as its point of expansion on any interval of the form $(0, b)$, $b > 0$. For if $\tilde{y}(x)$ is a function such that

$$\tilde{y}(x) = \sum_{n=0}^{\infty} a_n x^n, \qquad 0 < x < b,$$

then $\tilde{y}(x)$ and all its derivatives possess finite right-hand limits at $x = 0$. No function of the form (4.40) has this property.

We can say, then, that at a regular singular point, the solutions of a differential equation need not be analytic. In some instances there may be analytic solutions. For example, every solution of the equation

$$x^2 y'' - 2xy' + 2y = 0$$

is analytic at $x = 0$, since the general solution is

$$y = C_1 x + C_2 x^2.$$

Although an equation of the Cauchy type need not possess a solution that is analytic at the singular point $x = 0$, such an equation always possesses at least one solution of the form

$$y = x^s,$$

where the constant s need not be a nonnegative integer. Although we cannot expect every equation of the general form (4.37) to have quite such a simple solution, we shall presently see that every such equation does possess at least one solution of the form

$$y = (x - x_0)^s g(x),$$

where $g(x)$ is a function which is analytic at $x = x_0$.

4.4 EXERCISES

1. Locate and classify the singular points of the given differential equation:
   (a) $x^2(x + 2)y'' + xy' - (2x - 1)y = 0$
   (b) $(x - 1)^2(x + 3)y'' + (2x + 1)y' - y = 0$
   (c) $(2x + 1)x^2y'' - (x + 2)y' + 2e^x y = 0$
   (d) $(\sin x)y' - y = 0$

2. Show that there is no solution of the equation $x^2y'' - 2xy' + 2y = 0$ that satisfies the initial condition $y(0) = 1$ at the singular point $x = 0$.

3. Find all solutions of the equation $x^2y'' + xy' - y = 0$ on the interval $(0, +\infty)$ that are finite as $x \to 0$.

4. Show that the equation $xy'' + 3y' = 0$ possesses a solution that satisfies the conditions $y(0) = 2$, $y'(0) = k$ if, and only if, $k = 0$.

4.5 Solutions at a Regular Singular Point

Since there is no guarantee that any of the solutions of a differential equation are analytic at a regular singular point, we must look for solutions in a larger class of functions. Consideration of equations of the Cauchy type suggests that we consider functions of the form

$$y = (x - x_0)^s \sum_{n=0}^{\infty} A_n(x - x_0)^n, \tag{4.41}$$

where the exponent s need not be an integer. Such a function is the product of a function that is analytic at $x = x_0$ and a power of $(x - x_0)$. We may as well assume that $A_0 \neq 0$. For if $A_0 = 0$, and A_N is the first nonvanishing coefficient in the series, we have

$$y = (x - x_0)^s \sum_{n=N}^{\infty} A_n(x - x_0)^n$$

$$= (x - x_0)^{s+N}[A_N + A_{N+1}(x - x_0) + \cdots]$$

$$= (x - x_0)^r \sum_{n=0}^{\infty} B_n(x - x_0)^n,$$

where $r = s + N$, $B_n = A_{N+n}$, and $B_0 = A_N \neq 0$.

The exponent s and the coefficients A_n in the series (4.41) are to be determined by substituting the series into the differential equation and collecting the coefficients of like powers of $(x - x_0)$. The procedure, then, is similar to that used in calculating the coefficients of series solutions at an ordinary point.

Before we take up the general case, we shall consider a particular example for which the calculations are simple. The equation

$$2xy'' + y' - y = 0 \qquad (4.42)$$

has a regular singular point at $x = 0$. We shall seek solutions of the form

$$y = x^s \sum_{n=0}^{\infty} A_n x^n = \sum_{n=0}^{\infty} A_n x^{n+s}. \qquad (4.43)$$

Substitution of this series, and the series

$$y' = \sum_{n=0}^{\infty} (n + s)A_n x^{n+s-1}, \qquad y'' = \sum_{n=0}^{\infty} (n + s)(n + s - 1)A_n x^{n+s-2}$$

into the differential equation yields the condition

$$2 \sum_{n=0}^{\infty} (n + s)(n + s - 1)A_n x^{n+s-1} + \sum_{n=0}^{\infty} (n + s)A_n x^{n+s-1} - \sum_{n=0}^{\infty} A_n x^{n+s} = 0.$$

The first two series in the left-hand member of this equation begin with terms that involve x^{s-1}, while the third series begins with a term that involves x^s. If we isolate the two terms that involve the lowest power of x and replace the index of summation n in the first two series by $n + 1$, we can write the above equation as

$$[2s(s - 1) + s]A_0 x^{s-1} + 2 \sum_{n=0}^{\infty} (n + s + 1)(n + s)A_{n+1} x^{n+s}$$
$$+ \sum_{n=0}^{\infty} (n + s + 1)A_{n+1} x^{n+s} - \sum_{n=0}^{\infty} A_n x^{n+s} = 0.$$

It is now easy to combine like powers of x in the three series. Upon doing this, we obtain the equation

$$s(2s - 1)A_0 x^{s-1} + \sum_{n=0}^{\infty} [(n + s + 1)(2n + 2s + 1)A_{n+1} - A_n]x^{n+s} = 0. \qquad (4.44)$$

If the equation (4.42) possesses a solution of the form (4.43), then the exponent s and the coefficients A_i must be such that

$$s(2s - 1) = 0 \qquad (4.45)$$

(since $A_0 \neq 0$), and

$$(n + s + 1)(2n + 2s + 1)A_{n+1} = A_n, \qquad n \geq 0. \qquad (4.46)$$

The equation (4.45) has two roots, $s_1 = \tfrac{1}{2}$ and $s_2 = 0$, so there are two possible values for s to consider. These two numbers are called the *exponents* of the differential equation at the regular singular point $x = 0$.

We consider first the value $s_1 = \frac{1}{2}$. For this value of s, the recurrence relation (4.46) yields the formula

$$A_{n+1} = \frac{1}{(n+1)(2n+3)} A_n, \qquad n \geq 0. \tag{4.47}$$

From this formula we find that

$$A_1 = \frac{1}{1 \cdot 3} A_0, \qquad A_2 = \frac{1}{2 \cdot 5} A_1 = \frac{1}{(1 \cdot 2)(3 \cdot 5)} A_n,$$

and in general,

$$A_n = \frac{1}{n! \; 1 \cdot 3 \cdot 5 \cdots (2n+1)} A_0 = \frac{2^n}{(2n+1)!} A_0, \; n \geq 0. \tag{4.48}$$

Taking $A_0 = 1$, we obtain the formal† series solution

$$y_1(x) = x^{1/2} \sum_{n=0}^{\infty} \frac{2^n}{(2n+1)!} x^n. \tag{4.49}$$

Actually, the power series that multiplies $x^{1/2}$ converges for all x, as can be shown by the ratio test. Therefore the function $y_1(x)$ that is defined by formula (4.49) is a real solution of the differential equation on the interval $0 < x < +\infty$.

We now consider the second possible value for s, the value $s_2 = 0$. In this case the recurrence relation (4.46) yields the formula

$$A_{n+1} = \frac{1}{(n+1)(2n+1)} A_n, \qquad n \geq 0. \tag{4.50}$$

We find that

$$A_1 = \frac{1}{1 \cdot 1} A_0, \qquad A_2 = \frac{1}{2 \cdot 3} A_1 = \frac{1}{(1 \cdot 2)(1 \cdot 3)} A_0,$$

and in general,

$$A_n = \frac{1}{n! \; [1 \cdot 3 \cdot 5 \cdots (2n-1)]} A_0 = \frac{2^n}{(2n)!} A_0, \; n \geq 0. \tag{4.51}$$

Taking $A_0 = 1$, we obtain a second formal series solution,

$$y_2(x) = \sum_{n=0}^{\infty} \frac{2^n}{(2n)!} x^n. \tag{4.52}$$

† We call the series a *formal* solution because we do not yet know that it converges.

This series also converges for all x, and defines a second solution of the differential equation on the interval $0 < x < +\infty$.

The two solutions (4.49) and (4.52) are linearly independent on the interval $0 < x < +\infty$. For if

$$C_1 y_1(x) + C_2 y_2(x) = 0, \qquad 0 < x < +\infty,$$

we see, upon letting $x \to 0+$, that $C_2 = 0$. But then $C_1 = 0$ also, since $y_1(x)$ is a nontrivial solution.

In this example, we were fortunate in being able to find *two* independent solutions of the form (4.43). This does not always happen. For example, the equation

$$x^2 y'' - xy' + y = 0$$

has the general solution

$$y = C_1 x + C_2 x \log x, \qquad 0 < x < +\infty.$$

Only one solution is of the form (4.43). In the general case, to be discussed in the next section, we shall see that there always exists *one* solution of the form (4.41). In some cases, however, any second independent solution involves the function $\log x$ and is not of the form (4.41).

4.6. The Method of Frobenius

We now consider the general second-order differential equation with a regular singular point,

$$y'' + \frac{P(x)}{x - x_0} y' + \frac{Q(x)}{(x - x_0)^2} y = 0, \tag{4.53}$$

where $P(x)$ and $Q(x)$ are analytic at $x = x_0$. Let

$$P(x) = \sum_{n=0}^{\infty} P_n (x - x_0)^n, \qquad Q(x) = \sum_{n=0}^{\infty} Q_n (x - x_0)^n, \qquad |x - x_0| < R. \tag{4.54}$$

If the equation has a solution of the form

$$y = \sum_{n=0}^{\infty} A_n (x - x_0)^{n+s}, \qquad A_0 \neq 0, \tag{4.55}$$

then

$$\frac{Q(x)}{(x - x_0)^2} y = (x - x_0)^{s-2} \left(\sum_{n=0}^{\infty} A_n (x - x_0)^n \right) \left(\sum_{n=0}^{\infty} Q_n (x - x_0)^n \right)$$

$$= \sum_{n=0}^{\infty} \left(\sum_{k=0}^{n} A_k Q_{n-k} \right) (x - x_0)^{n+s-2},$$

$$\frac{P(x)}{x - x_0} y' = (x - x_0)^{s-2} \left(\sum_{n=0}^{\infty} (n + s) A_n (x - x_0)^n \right) \left(\sum_{n=0}^{\infty} P_n (x - x_0)^n \right)$$

$$= \sum_{n=0}^{\infty} \left(\sum_{k=0}^{n} (k+s)A_k P_{n-k} \right)(x-x_0)^{n+s-2},$$

and

$$y'' = \sum_{n=0}^{\infty} (n+s)(n+s-1)A_n(x-x_0)^{n+s-2}.$$

Upon substituting these quantities into the differential equation (4.53) and combining terms with like powers of $(x-x_0)$, we obtain the relation

$$\sum_{n=0}^{\infty} \left\{ (n+s)(n+s-1)A_n + \sum_{k=0}^{n} [(k+s)P_{n-k} + Q_{n-k}]A_k \right\}(x-x_0)^{n+s-2} = 0.$$
(4.56)

The coefficient of the lowest power of $x-x_0$ (which corresponds to the value $n=0$ in the series) is $f(s)A_0$, where

$$f(s) = s(s-1) + sP_0 + Q_0 = s^2 + (P_0 - 1)s + Q_0.$$
(4.57)

Since $A_0 \neq 0$, the possible values for s are those values which are the roots of the *indicial equation*

$$f(s) = 0.$$
(4.58)

These two roots, which we denote by s_1 and s_2, are called the *exponents* of the differential equation at the regular singular point $x = x_0$.

The coefficients A_i in the series (4.55) must satisfy the recurrence relation

$$(n+s)(n+s-1)A_n + \sum_{k=0}^{n} [(k+s)P_{n-k} + Q_{n-k}]A_k = 0, \qquad n \geq 1. \quad (4.59)$$

By collecting the terms which involve A_n, we can write this relation in the form

$$[(n+s)(n+s-1) + (n+s)P_0 + Q_0]A_n$$

$$= -\sum_{k=0}^{n-1} [(k+s)P_{n-k} + Q_{n-k}]A_k = 0, \qquad n \geq 1. \quad (4.60)$$

We can write this relation more briefly as

$$f(s+n)A_n = \sum_{k=0}^{n-1} C(k, n, s)A_k, \qquad n \geq 1, \quad (4.61)$$

where

$$f(s+n) = (s+n-s_1)(s+n-s_2), \qquad n \geq 1, \quad (4.62)$$

and the quantities $C(k, n, s)$ depend on the coefficients P_i and Q_i, but not on the coefficients A_i. If, for a given value of s, say s_1 or s_2, the quantities $f(s+n)$, $n \geq 1$, *do not vanish*, then each of the coefficients $A_1, A_2, A_3, \ldots$, is determined (in terms of A_0) by the relation (4.61).

Let us first take up the case where the exponents s_1 and s_2 are *real* and *distinct*. We denote the larger of the two exponents by s_1. Now

$$f(s_1 + n) = (s_1 + n - s_1)(s_1 + n - s_2) = n[n + (s_1 - s_2)], \qquad n \geq 1,$$

and so $f(s_1 + n) \neq 0$ for $n \geq 1$. Thus the differential equation always possesses a formal series solution of the form

$$y_1(x) = (x - x_0)^{s_1} \sum_{n=0}^{\infty} A_n(x - x_0)^n, \qquad (4.63)$$

corresponding to the larger exponent s_1. It can be shown that the power series in formula (4.63) actually converges, at least for $|x - x_0| < R$, and that the function $y_1(x)$ is a solution of the differential equation, at least for $x_0 < x < x_0 + R$. The proof is similar to the proof of Theorem 1, and is left as an exercise.

Considering now the smaller exponent s_2, we see that

$$f(s_2 + n) = (s_2 + n - s_1)(s_2 + n - s_2) = n[n - (s_1 - s_2)], \qquad n \geq 1.$$

If the difference $s_1 - s_2$ is not a positive integer, then $f(s_2 + n) \neq 0$ for $n \geq 1$, and we obtain a second series solution of the form

$$y_2(x) = (x - x_0)^{s_2} \sum_{n=0}^{\infty} A_n(x - x_0)^n, \qquad (4.64)$$

corresponding to the exponent s_2. In this case also, the power series converges and $y_2(x)$ is a solution of the differential equation, at least for $x_0 < x < x_0 + R$.

However, if $s_1 - s_2 = N$, where N is a positive integer, then $f(s_2 + n) = 0$, when, and only when, $n = s_1 - s_2 = N$. In this case, equation (4.61) becomes, for $n = N$,

$$0 \cdot A_N = \sum_{k=0}^{N-1} C(k, N, s_2) A_k. \qquad (4.65)$$

Unless it happens that the right-hand member of this equation is zero, it is impossible to find a number A_N that satisfies this equation, and no formal series solution of the form (4.64) exists. If it does happen that the right-hand member of equation (4.65) is zero, then this equation has the form

$$0 \cdot A_N = 0,$$

and *any* value for A_N will do. (In particular, we can choose $A_N = 0$.) In this case we again obtain a series solution of the form (4.64).

As an illustration of this last-mentioned situation, let us consider the equation.

$$xy'' + 3y' - x^2 y = 0,$$

which has a regular singular point at $x = 0$. Seeking solutions of the form

$$y = x^s \sum_{n=0}^{\infty} A_n x^n, \qquad A_0 \neq 0,$$

we find, after some calculation, that the indicial equation is

$$s(s + 2) = 0,$$

and that the coefficients A_i must satisfy the conditions

$$(s + 1)(s + 3)A_1 = 0,$$

$$(s + 2)(s + 4)A_2 = 0,$$

and

$$(n + s + 3)(n + s\,5)A_{n+3} = A_n, \qquad n \geq 0.$$

The exponents are $s_1 = 0$ and $s_2 = -2$. For the larger exponent s_1, we have

$$A_1 = 0$$

$$A_2 = 0$$

$$A_{n+3} = \frac{A_n}{(n + 3)(n + 5)}, \qquad n \geq 0.$$

All the coefficients A_i vanish except those whose subscripts are multiples of three. We have

$$A_3 = \frac{1}{3 \cdot 5} A_0$$

$$A_6 = \frac{1}{6 \cdot 8} A_3 = \frac{1}{(3 \cdot 6)(5 \cdot 8)} A_0$$

and in general,

$$A_{3m} = \frac{1}{(3 \cdot 6 \cdot 9 \cdots 3m)[5 \cdot 8 \cdot 11 \cdots (3m + 2)]} A_0$$

$$= \frac{1}{3^m m! \, [5 \cdot 8 \cdot 11 \cdots (3m + 2)]} A_0.$$

The solution which corresponds to the exponent s_1 is

$$y_1 = 1 + \sum_{m=1}^{\infty} \frac{x^{3m}}{3^m m! \, [5 \cdot 8 \cdot 11 \cdots (3m + 2)]}.$$

For the smaller exponent $s_2 = -2$, we have

$$A_1 = 0$$

$$0 \cdot A_2 = 0$$

$$A_{n+3} = \frac{A_n}{(n + 1)(n + 3)}, \qquad n \geq 0.$$

(Note that A_2 is the critical coefficient, since $N = 2$ in this example.) Here A_2 is arbitrary, and we may choose $A_2 = 0$. A solution that corresponds to the exponent s_2 is found to be

$$y_2 = x^{-2}\left[1 + \sum_{m=1}^{\infty} \frac{x^{3m}}{3^m m! \, [1 \cdot 4 \cdot 7 \cdots (3m - 2)]}\right]. \qquad (4.66)$$

In treating the general second-order equation with a regular singular point at $x = x_0$, we used the general form (4.53), in which the coefficient of y'' is 1. It was convenient to do this, because then we had to deal with only two arbitrary functions, $P(x)$ and $Q(x)$. For purposes of actually calculating a series solution, it may be more convenient, in some cases, to write the equation in the form

$$p(x)y'' + \frac{q(x)}{x - x_0} y' + \frac{r(x)}{(x - x_0)^2} y = 0, \qquad (4.67)$$

where $p(x) \neq 1$. Since a series of the form (4.55) which formally satisfies one equation also formally satisfies the other, we can substitute the expression (4.55) into equation (4.67) in order to determine solutions.

4.6   EXERCISES

1. Verify that the given differential equation has a regular singular point at $x = 0$, and express the general solution in terms of series of the Frobenius type.

(a) $2x^2 y'' + 3xy' - (x + 1)y = 0$ (c) $(3x^2 + x^3)y'' - xy' + y = 0$

(b) $2xy'' + (3 - x)y' - y = 0$ (d) $2xy'' + (1 - x)y' + xy = 0$

2. If the equation

$$\frac{d^2 y}{dx^2} + P(x)\frac{dy}{dx} + Q(x)y = 0$$

has a regular singular point at $x = x_0$, where $x_0 \neq 0$, verify that the change of variable $t = x - x_0$ leads to an equation

$$\frac{d^2 y}{dt^2} + p(t)\frac{dy}{dt} + q(t)y = 0,$$

which has a regular singular point at $t = 0$.

3. Verify that the given equation has a regular singular point at the indicated point, and express the general solution of the equation in terms of series of the Frobenius type. Use the result of Problem 2.

(a) $(1 - x^2)y'' + y' + 2y = 0, \qquad x = -1$

(b) $(x - 2)(5 - x)y'' + 2y' + 2y = 0, \qquad x = 2.$

4. Verify that the given equation has a regular singular point at $x = 0$, and find all solutions of the Frobenius type.

(a) $x^2 y'' + x(1 + x)y' - y = 0$ (d) $x^2 y'' - 2x^2 y' + (4x - 2)y = 0$

(b) $xy'' + (3 + x^2)y' + 2xy = 0$ (e) $xy'' - y = 0$

(c) $(x + x^2)y'' - 2y' - 2y = 0$

5. Let the exponents s_1 and s_2 of the equation (4.53) be real, with $s_1 > s_2$. Let the functions $P(x)$ and $Q(x)$ be represented by their Taylor series at

$x = x_0$ for $|x - x_0| < R$. Prove that the power series involved in the formal solution

$$y_1 = (x - x_0)^{s_1} \sum_{n=0}^{\infty} A_n(x - x_0)^n$$

actually converges for $|x - x_0| < R$, and hence that the formal solution is an actual solution. Prove that when $s_1 - s_2$ is not an integer, the formal solution that corresponds to the exponent s_2 is an actual solution. Use the method of proof employed in Theorem 1.

6. Assume that the exponents s_1 and s_2 of equation (4.53) are such that $s_1 - s_2 = N$, where N is a positive integer, but that a formal solution of the form

$$y_2 = (x - x_0)^{s_2} \sum_{n=0}^{\infty} A_n(x - x_0)^n$$

nevertheless exists. Prove that the power series involved in the formal solution actually converges, and hence that the formal solution is an actual solution. Suggestion: in modifying the proof of Theorem 1, let $B_n = |A_n|$ for $0 \le n \le N$, and use the recurrence relation to define B_n when $n > N$.

7. Let the functions $P(x)$, $Q(x)$, and $f(x)$ be analytic at $x = x_0$. Show that the equation

$$(x - x_0)^2 y'' + (x - x_0)P(x)y' + Q(x)y = (x - x_0)^\alpha f(x)$$

possesses at least a formal solution of the form

$$y = (x - x_0)^\alpha \sum_{n=0}^{\infty} A_n(x - x_0)^n$$

whenever the constant α is such that neither $\alpha - s_1$ nor $\alpha - s_2$ is a positive integer. Show, by means of an example, that the equation may still possibly have a solution of the given form even when α does not satisfy these conditions.

4.7 The Case of Equal Exponents

When the exponents, s_1 and s_2, of the differential equation (4.53) are equal, we can find only one solution of the form (4.55). In order to get some idea as to how a second independent solution can be found, suppose we look at a Cauchy equation whose exponents are equal. Let the equation be

$$Ly \equiv y'' + x^{-1}b_1 y' + x^{-2}b_2 y = 0, \tag{4.68}$$

where b_1 and b_2 are real constants, Seeking a solution of the form $y = x^s$, we have

$$L(x^s) \equiv [s(s - 1) + b_1 s + b_2]x^{s-2}. \tag{4.69}$$

The exponents of the equation (4.68) are the roots of the indicial equation

$$s(s - 1) + b_1 s + b_2 \equiv (s - s_1)(s - s_2) = 0. \tag{4.70}$$

If $s_1 = s_2$, then

$$L(x^s) \equiv (s - s_1)^2 x^{s-2}. \tag{4.71}$$

Evidently $L(x^{s_1}) \equiv 0$, so $y_1(x) = x^{s_1}$ is one solution of the equation. It is not hard to see that a second solution is given by the formula

$$y_2(x) = \left[\frac{\partial}{\partial s} x^s \right]_{s=s_1} = x^{s_1} \log x. \tag{4.72}$$

For we have

$$L \left[\frac{\partial}{\partial s} x^s \right]_{s=s_1} = \left[\frac{\partial}{\partial s} (Lx^s) \right]_{s=s_1}$$

$$= \left\{ \frac{\partial}{\partial s} [(s - s_1)^2 x^s] \right\}_{s=s_1}$$

$$= 0.$$

The first step in the above manipulation simply involves a change in the order of taking derivatives with respect to x and s.

Let us now consider a general equation,

$$Ly \equiv y'' + \frac{P(x)}{x - x_0} y' + \frac{Q(x)}{(x - x_0)^2} y = 0, \tag{4.73}$$

whose exponents at $x = x_0$ are equal. Let

$$y(x, s) = (x - x_0)^s \sum_{n=0}^{\infty} A_n(s)(x - x_0)^n, \tag{4.74}$$

where the coefficients $A_n(s)$ are functions of s that are to be determined. As in the previous section, we find that

$$Ly(x, s) \equiv f(s)A_0(x - x_0)^{s-2}$$
$$+ \sum_{n=1}^{\infty} \left\{ f(s + n)A_n(s) + \sum_{k=0}^{n-1} [(k + s)P_{n-k} + Q_{n-k}]A_k(s) \right\}(x - x_0)^{n+s-2}, \tag{4.75}$$

where now

$$f(s) = (s - s_1)^2 \tag{4.76}$$

and

$$f(s + n) = (s + n - s_1)^2, \qquad n \geq 1. \tag{4.77}$$

The functions (4.77) do not vanish for $|s - s_1| < 1$. Therefore, we can define coefficients $A_n(s)$, $n \geq 1$, in terms of A_0 (which we take to be a fixed, nonzero constant, independent of s) by means of the recurrence relation

$$A_n(s) = \frac{-1}{(s + n - s_1)^2} \sum_{k=0}^{n-1} [(k + s)P_{n-k} + Q_{n-k}]A_k(s), \qquad n \geq 1. \tag{4.78}$$

The functions $A_n(s)$ that are so defined are rational functions of s and are analytic for $|s - s_1| < 1$.

Let us assume that the coefficients $A_n(s)$ in the series (4.74) have been chosen in the manner described above. Then, from formula (4.75), we see that

$$Ly(x, s) = A_0(s - s_1)^2(x - x_0)^{s-2}. \tag{4.79}$$

Evidently $Ly(x, s_1) = 0$, and the function

$$y_1(x) = y(x, s_1) = (x - x_0)^{s_1} \sum_{n=0}^{\infty} A_n(s_1)(x - x_0)^n \tag{4.80}$$

is one solution of the equation $Ly = 0$. We shall now show that the quantity

$$y_2(x) = \left[\frac{\partial}{\partial s} y(x, s)\right]_{s=s_1} \tag{4.81}$$

is a second (formal) solution of the equation. We have

$$L\left[\frac{\partial}{\partial s} y(x, s)\right]_{s=s_1} = \left[\frac{\partial}{\partial s} Ly(x, s)\right]_{s=s_1}$$

$$= \left\{\frac{\partial}{\partial s} [A_0(s - s_1)^2(x - x_0)^{s-2}]\right\}_{s=s_1}$$

$$= 0,$$

where in the first step we have switched the order of differentiation with respect to x and s.

To see the form of the solution $y_2(x)$, we differentiate the series (4.74) with respect to s and then set $s = s_1$. We have

$$y_2(x) = (x - x_0)^{s_1} \sum_{n=0}^{\infty} A_n(s_1)(x - x_0)^n \log(x - x_0)$$

$$+ (x - x_0)^{s_1} \sum_{n=1}^{\infty} A_n'(s_1)(x - x_0)^n$$

or

$$y_2(x) = y_1(x) \log(x - x_0) + (x - x_0)^{s_1} \sum_{n=1}^{\infty} A_n'(s_1)(x - x_0)^n, \tag{4.82}$$

where $y_1(x)$ is the solution (4.80). It can be shown that the power series in the expression for $y_2(x)$ converges and that $y_2(x)$ is a solution of the differential equation, at least for $x_0 < x < x_0 + R$. It is left as an exercise to show that $y_1(x)$ and $y_2(x)$ are linearly independent.

Let us now consider, as an example of an equation with equal exponents, the equation

$$Ly \equiv x^2 y'' + 3xy' + (1 - x)y = 0. \tag{4.83}$$

Setting

$$y(x, s) = \sum_{n=0}^{\infty} A_n(s)x^{n+s},$$

we find that

$$Ly(x, s) = (s + 1)^2 A_0 x^s + \sum_{n=0}^{\infty} [(n + s + 2)^2 A_{n+1} - A_n] x^{n+s+1}.$$

The indicial equation is $(s + 1)^2 = 0$, and the exponents are $s_1 = s_2 = -1$. We choose the coefficients $A_n(s)$ to satisfy the recurrence relation

$$(n + s + 2)^2 A_{n+1}(s) = A_n(s), \qquad n \geq 0.$$

Then

$$A_1(s) = \frac{A_0}{(s + 2)^2}, \qquad A_2(s) = \frac{A_1(s)}{(s + 3)^2} = \frac{A_0}{(s + 2)^2 (s + 3)^2},$$

and in general,

$$A_n(s) = \frac{A_0}{(s + 2)^2 (s + 3)^2 \cdots (s + n + 1)^2}, \qquad n \geq 1. \qquad (4.84)$$

Setting $s = s_1 = -1$, we have

$$A_n(-1) = \frac{A_0}{1^2 \cdot 2^2 \cdots n^2} = \frac{A_0}{(n!)^2}.$$

Taking $A_0 = 1$, we obtain the solution

$$y_1(x) = x^{-1} \sum_{n=0}^{\infty} \frac{x^n}{(n!)^2}.$$

In order to obtain a second solution, we need to compute the derivatives $A_n'(-1)$. It is convenient to do this by logarithmic differentiation. From formula (4.84) we have

$$\log A_n(s) = \log A_0 - 2[\log(s + 2) + \log(s + 3) + \cdots + \log(s + n + 1)].$$

Differentiating with respect to s, we have

$$\frac{A_n'(s)}{A_n(s)} = -2 \left[\frac{1}{s + 2} + \frac{1}{s + 3} + \cdots + \frac{1}{s + n + 1} \right].$$

Then

$$\frac{A_n'(-1)}{A_n(-1)} = -2 \left[1 + \frac{1}{2} + \cdots + \frac{1}{n} \right],$$

or

$$A_n'(-1) = -2 \frac{\phi(n)}{(n!)^2}, \qquad n \geq 1,$$

where we use the notation

$$\phi(n) = 1 + \frac{1}{2} + \frac{1}{3} + \cdots + \frac{1}{n}. \qquad (4.85)$$

From the general formula (4.82), we see that a second solution of the equation (4.83) is

$$y_2(x) = y_1(x) \log x - 2x^{-1} \sum_{n=1}^{\infty} \frac{\phi(n)}{(n!)^2} x^n.$$

The second solution could also have been determined by substituting an expression of the form

$$y = y_1(x) \log x + x^{-1} \sum_{n=1}^{\infty} B_n x^n \qquad (4.86)$$

into the differential equation. The coefficients B_n can be determined by collecting the like powers of x and equating the coefficient of each power of x to zero. This method, however, does not so readily yield a general formula for the coefficients B_n.

4.7 EXERCISES

1. Prove that the solutions (4.80) and (4.82) are linearly independent on the interval $x_0 < x < x_0 + R$.

2. Verify that the point $x = 0$ is a regular singular point of the given differential equation and find the general solution by using the methods described in this section.

   (a) $xy'' + y' + y = 0$
   (b) $(x^2 + x^3)y'' + (x^2 - x)y' + y = 0$
   (c) $(x^2 + x^3)y'' - (x^2 + x)y' + y = 0$
   (d) $x^2 y'' + 5xy' + (4 - x)y = 0$

3. Let the functions $P(x)$ and $Q(x)$ in the equation (4.73) be represented by their Taylor series at $x = x_0$ for $|x - x_0| < R$. Let $y_1(x)$ and $y_2(x)$ be the formal solutions that are defined by equations (4.80) and (4.82), respectively. It is known (Exercise 5, Section 4.6) that the power series

   $$\sum_{n=0}^{\infty} A_n(s_1)(x - x_0)^n$$

   converges for $|x - x_0| < R$. A proof that the series

   $$\sum_{n=0}^{\infty} A_n{}'(s_1)(x - x_0)^n, \qquad (1)$$

   which appears in the formula for $y_2(x)$, also converges for $|x - x_0| < R$ can be accomplished in the following manner:
   (a) Deduce from the recurrence relation (4.78) that

   $$A_n{}'(s_1) = \frac{1}{n^3} \sum_{k=0}^{n-1} [(2k + 2s_1 - n)P_{n-k} + Q_{n-k}]A_k(s_1)$$

   $$- \frac{1}{n^2} \sum_{k=0}^{n-1} [(k + s_1)P_{n-k} + Q_{n-k}]A_k{}'(s_1), \qquad n \geq 1.$$

(b) Let r be any positive number such that $0 < r < R$. Show that there exists a positive constant M such that

$$|P_m| \leq \frac{M}{r^m}, \qquad |Q_m| \leq \frac{M}{r^m}, \qquad |A_m(s_1)| \leq \frac{M}{r^m}, \qquad m \geq 0.$$

(c) Show that $|A_n'(s_1)| \leq B_n$, $n \geq 1$, where

$$B_n = \frac{M^2}{n^2 r^n}(2n + 2|s_1| + 1) + \frac{M}{n^2} \sum_{k=0}^{n-1} \frac{k + |s_1| + 1}{r^{n-k}} |A_k'(s_1)|$$

and

$$B_{n+1} = \left(\frac{n}{n+1}\right)^2 \frac{1}{r} B_n + \frac{M(n + |s_1| + 1)}{(n+1)^2 r} |A_n'(s_1)| + \frac{2M^2}{(n+1)^2 r^{n+1}}.$$

(d) Show that

$$B_n = \frac{2M^2}{nr^n} + \alpha_n, \qquad n \geq 1,$$

where $\alpha_n \geq 0$, and hence that

$$\frac{B_{n+1}}{B_n} = \frac{1}{r}\left(\frac{n}{n+1}\right)^2 + \frac{M(n + |s_1| + 1)}{(n+1)^2 r}\frac{|A_n'(s_1)|}{B_n} + \beta_n,$$

where

$$|\beta_n| \leq \frac{n}{(n+1)^2}\frac{1}{r}.$$

(e) Show that

$$\lim_{n \to \infty} \frac{B_{n+1}}{B_n} = \frac{1}{r}.$$

Deduce from this fact that the series (1) converges for $|x - x_0| < R$.
(f) Verify that $y_2(x)$ is a solution of the differential equation.

4.8 When the Exponents Differ by a Positive Integer

In the case when $s_1 - s_2 = N$, N a positive integer, the differential equation

$$Ly = y'' + \frac{P(x)}{x - x_0} y' + \frac{Q(x)}{(x - x_0)^2} y = 0 \tag{4.87}$$

may possess either one or two solutions of the form (4.55). (In the case of a Cauchy equation, there are always two such solutions.) In any case, there is always one solution,

$$y_1(x) = (x - x_0)^{s_1} \sum_{n=0}^{\infty} A_n(s_1)(x - x_0)^n, \tag{4.88}$$

of the form (4.55) which corresponds to the exponent s_1.

We now consider the case where the equation (4.87) possesses only one solution of the form (4.55). As in the previous section, let

$$y(x, s) = (x - x_0)^s \sum_{n=0}^{\infty} A_n(s)(x - x_0)^n. \tag{4.89}$$

Then

$$Ly(x, s) = f(s)A_0(x - x_0)^{s-2}$$
$$+ \sum_{n=0}^{\infty} \left\{ f(s + n)A_n(s) + \sum_{k=0}^{n-1} [(k + s)P_{n-k} + Q_{n-k}]A_k(s) \right\} (x - x_0)^{s+n-2}, \tag{4.90}$$

where

$$f(s) = (s - s_1)(s - s_2) = (s - s_2 - N)(s - s_2) \tag{4.91}$$

and

$$f(s + n) = (s + n - s_2 - N)(s + N - s_2), \qquad n \geq 1. \tag{4.92}$$

The function

$$f(s + N) = (s - s_2)(s + N - s_2)$$

vanishes when $s = s_2$; it is the only one of the function (4.92) to do so.

Let us choose the coefficients $A_n(s)$ so that they satisfy the recurrence relation

$$f(s + n)A_n(s) = - \sum_{k=0}^{n-1} [(k + s)P_{n-k} + Q_{n-k}]A_k(s), \qquad n \geq 1. \tag{4.93}$$

Then the functions $A_1(s)$, $A_2(s)$, ..., $A_{N-1}(s)$ are analytic at $s = s_2$. The functions $A_n(s)$, with $n \geq N$, are rational functions of s that contain the factor $s - s_2$ in their denominators; they may become infinite as s approaches s_2. However, the functions

$$B_n(s) = (s - s_2)A_n(s), \qquad n \geq 1, \tag{4.94}$$

are analytic at $s = s_2$ and satisfy the recurrence relation (4.93), not only for s near s_2 but also for s equal to s_2.

Let

$$\tilde{y}(x, s) = (s - s_2)y(x, s) = (x - x_0)^s \sum_{n=0}^{\infty} B_n(s)(x - x_0)^n. \tag{4.95}$$

Then, from equation (4.90), we see that

$$L\tilde{y}(x, s) = A_0(s - s_2)f(s)(x - x_0)^{s-2} = A_0(s - s_1)(s - s_2)^2(x - x_0)^{s-2}. \tag{4.96}$$

Because of the occurence of the factor $(s - s_2)^2$ in the last expression, it follows that each of the quantities

$$\tilde{y}_1(x) = \tilde{y}(x, s_2) \tag{4.97}$$

$$y_2(x) = \left[\frac{\partial}{\partial s} \tilde{y}(x, s) \right]_{s=s_2} \tag{4.98}$$

formally satisfies the differential equation.

We now examine the forms of these two formal solutions. Since $B_n(s_2) = 0$ for $0 \leq n \leq N - 1$, the solution $\tilde{y}_1(x)$ has the form

$$\tilde{y}_1(x) = (x - x_0)^{s_2} \sum_{n=N}^{\infty} B_n(s_2)(x - x_0)^n$$

$$= (x - x_0)^{s_2 + N} \sum_{n=0}^{\infty} B_{n+N}(s_2)(x - x_0)^n$$

$$= (x - x_0)^{s_1} \sum_{n=0}^{\infty} B_{n+N}(s_2)(x - x_0)^n.$$

Thus $\tilde{y}_1(x)$ must be simply a multiple of the solution $y_1(x)$ given in formula (4.88). In fact,

$$\tilde{y}_1(x) = \frac{B_N(s_2)}{A_0} y_1(x). \tag{4.99}$$

The solution $y_2(x)$ is obtained by setting $s = s_2$ in the formula

$$\frac{\partial}{\partial s} y(x, s) = \frac{\partial}{\partial s} \left[(x - x_0)^s \sum_{n=0}^{\infty} B_n(s)(x - x_0)^n \right]$$

$$= (x - x_0)^s \sum_{n=0}^{\infty} B_n(s)(x - x_0)^n \log(x - x_0)$$

$$+ (x - x_0)^s \sum_{n=0}^{\infty} B_n'(s)(x - x_0)^n. \tag{4.100}$$

We have

$$y_2(x) = \tilde{y}_1(x) \log(x - x_0) + (x - x_0)^{s_2} \sum_{n=0}^{\infty} B_n'(s_2)(x - x_0)^n$$

or

$$y_2(x) = \frac{B_N}{A_0} y_1(x) \log(x - x_0) + (x - x_0)^{s_2} \sum_{n=0}^{\infty} B_n'(s_2)(x - x_0)^n. \tag{4.101}$$

Here again, it can be shown that the power series in the expression for $y_2(x)$ converges and that $y_2(x)$ is a solution of the differential equation, at least for $x_0 < x < x_0 + R$.

As an example, let us consider the equation

$$Ly = xy'' + 2y' - y = 0. \tag{4.102}$$

Writing

$$y(x, s) = x^s \sum_{n=0}^{\infty} A_n(s)x^n, \tag{4.103}$$

we find that

$$Ly(x, s) = s(s + 1)A_0 x^{s-1} + \sum_{n=0}^{\infty} [(n + s + 1)(n + s + 2)A_{n+1} - A_n]x^{n+s}.$$

The exponents for equation (4.102) are $s_1 = 0$ and $s_2 = -1$; the recurrence relation for the coefficients A_n is

$$(n + s + 1)(n + s + 2)A_{n+1}(s) = A_n(s), \qquad n \geq 0.$$

From this relation we find that

$$A_1(s) = \frac{A_0}{(s + 1)(s + 2)}, \qquad A_2(s) = \frac{A_0}{(s + 1)(s + 2)^2(s + 3)},$$

and in general

$$A_n(s) = \frac{A_0}{(s + 1)(s + 2)^2(s + 3)^2 \cdots (s + n)^2(s + n + 1)}, \qquad n \geq 2. \quad (4.104)$$

Setting $s = s_1 = 0$ in these formulas, we find that

$$A_n(s_1) = \frac{A_0}{1 \cdot 2^2 \cdot 3^3 \cdots n^2(n + 1)} = \frac{A_0}{n!\,(n + 1)!}, \qquad n \geq 0.$$

Therefore a solution of equation (4.102) which corresponds to the exponent $s_1 = 0$ is

$$y_1(x) = \sum_{n=0}^{\infty} \frac{x^n}{n!\,(n + 1)!}. \quad (4.105)$$

The function $A_1(s)$ ($N = 1$ in this example) becomes infinite as s approaches $s_2 = -1$, because of the factor $(s + 1)$ in its denominator. Hence equation (4.102) does not possess a second solution of the form (4.103) corresponding to the exponent s_2. The second solution is therefore logarithmic.

The functions

$$B_0(s) = (s + 1)A_0$$

$$B_1(s) = (s + 1)A_1(s) = \frac{A_0}{s + 2}$$

$$B_n(s) = (s + 1)A_n(s) = \frac{A_0}{(s + 2)^2(s + 3)^2 \cdots (s + n)^2(s + n + 1)}, \qquad n \geq 2,$$

are analytic at $s = s_2 = -1$. Routine calculation shows that

$$B_0'(-1) = A_0, \qquad B_1'(-1) = -A_0,$$

$$B_n'(-1) = -\frac{\phi(n - 1) + \phi(n)}{(n - 1)!\,n!}, \qquad n \geq 2,$$

where $\phi(n)$ is defined by formula (4.85). Choosing $A_0 = 1$, we obtain the solution

$$y_2(x) = y_1(x) \log x - x^{-1}\left[1 - x - \sum_{n=2}^{\infty} \frac{\phi(n - 1) + \phi(n)}{(n - 1)!\,n!} x^n\right], \quad (4.106)$$

where $y_1(x)$ is given by formula (4.105).

This second solution (4.106) could also have been found by substituting an expression of the form

$$y = y_1(x) \log x + x^{-1}\sum_{n=0}^{\infty} C_n x^n \quad (4.107)$$

into equation (4.102) and determining the coefficients C_n. However, it is difficult to find a general formula for C_n using this method.

4.8   EXERCISES

1. Prove that the solutions $y_1(x)$ and $y_2(x)$, which are given by formulas (4.88) and (4.101), respectively, are linearly independent on the interval $x_0 < x < x_0 + R$.

2. Verify that the point $x = 0$ is a regular singular point for the given equation, and express the general solution in terms of series.

   (a) $xy'' - y = 0$ (c) $xy'' - xy' - y = 0$
   (b) $xy'' - y' + y = 0$ (d) $x^2y'' + xy' - (2x + 1)y = 0$

3. This problem deals with the convergence of the power series that appears in the formula (4.101) for $y_2(x)$.

   (a) Deduce from the recurrence relation (4.93) that

   $$B_n'(s_2) = \frac{-1}{n(n - N)} \sum_{k=0}^{n-1} [(k + s_2)P_{n-k} + Q_{n-k}]B_k'(s_2)$$

   $$+ \frac{2n + N}{n^2(n - N)^2} \sum_{k=0}^{n-1} [(k + s_2)P_{n-k} + Q_{n-k}]B_k(s_2)$$

   $$- \frac{1}{n(n - N)} \sum_{k=0}^{n-1} P_{n-k}B_k(s_2), \qquad n > N.$$

   (b) Let r be any number such that $0 < r < R$. Show that there exists a positive constant M such that

   $$|P_m| \leq \frac{M}{r^m}, \qquad |Q_m| \leq \frac{M}{r^m}, \qquad |B_k(s_2)| \leq \frac{M}{r^m}, \qquad m \geq 0.$$

   (c) Let $C_n = |B_n'(s_2)|$, $0 \leq n \leq N$,
   and let

   $$C_n = \frac{M}{n(n - N)} \sum_{k=0}^{n-1} \frac{k + |s_2| + 1}{r^{n-k}} |B_k'(s_2)|$$

   $$+ \frac{2n^2 + (2 + N)n + N(2|s_2| + 1)}{2n(n - N)r^n} M^2, \qquad n > N.$$

   Show that $|B_n'(s_2)| \leq C_n$, $n \geq 0$.

   (d) Show that

   $$\lim_{n \to \infty} \frac{C_{n+1}}{C_n} = \frac{1}{r}.$$

   Deduce from this fact that the series in question converges for $|x - x_0| < R$

   (e) Verify that $y_2(x)$ is a solution of the differential equation.

4.9 Complex Exponents

We consider a differential equation

$$y'' + \frac{P(x)}{x} y' + \frac{Q(x)}{x^2} y = 0 \tag{4.108}$$

with a regular singular point at $x = 0$. (An equation with a regular singular point at $x = x_0$, where $x_0 \neq 0$, can be put in the form (4.108) by means of a change of variable. See Exercise 2, Section 4.6.) Since the coefficients in the equation are real, the indicial equation

$$s^2 + (P_0 - 1)s + Q_0 = 0$$

has real coefficients. Thus if $s_1 = a + ib$ is a complex exponent, the other exponent will be its complex conjugate, that is, $s_2 = a - ib$. The difference $s_1 - s_2 = 2ib$ cannot be an integer, so the equation possesses formal solutions that involve no logarithmic terms.

Let

$$Y_1(x) = x^{a+ib} \sum_{n=0}^{\infty} A_n x^n \tag{4.109}$$

be the formal solution that corresponds to the exponent s_1. The coefficients A_n will in general be complex numbers. Assuming that the power series in formula (4.109) actually converges, and that $Y_1(x)$ is actually a solution of the equation (4.108) on the interval $0 < x < R$, then the function

$$\overline{Y}_1(x) = x^{a-ib} \sum_{n=0}^{\infty} \overline{A}_n x^n$$

is also a solution. It is a solution that corresponds to the exponent s_2.

Let us write

$$A_n = a_n + ib_n, \qquad \overline{A}_n = a_n - ib_n, \qquad n \geq 0,$$

where a_n and b_n are real constants, and let

$$Y_1(x) = y_1(x) + iy_2(x),$$

where $y_1(x)$ and $y_2(x)$ are real-valued functions. Since

$$x^{a+ib} = x^a[\cos(b \log x) + i \sin(b \log x)], \qquad x > 0,$$

we have

$$y_1(x) = x^a \left[\cos(b \log x) \sum_{n=0}^{\infty} a_n x^n - \sin(b \log x) \sum_{n=0}^{\infty} b_n x^n \right]$$

$$y_2(x) = x^a \left[\cos(b \log x) \sum_{n=0}^{\infty} b_n x^n + \sin(b \log x) \sum_{n=0}^{\infty} a_n x^n \right]. \tag{4.110}$$

These functions are *real* solutions of the differential equation for $0 < x < R$.

Let us now establish the linear independence of y_1 and y_2. Since

$$y_1 = \tfrac{1}{2}(Y_1 + \overline{Y}_1), \qquad y_2 = \frac{1}{2i}(Y_1 - \overline{Y}_1),$$

it follows that if Y_1 and $\overline{Y}_1$ are linearly independent with respect to the set of complex numbers, then y_1 and y_2 will be linearly independent with respect to the set of real numbers. The Wronskian of Y_1 and $\overline{Y}_1$ is found to be of the form

$$W(x; Y_1, \overline{Y}_1) = -2ib|A_0|^2 x^{2a-1}[1 + xg(x)],$$

where $g(x)$ is analytic at $x = 0$. Evidently the Wronskian does not vanish when x is sufficiently small. Hence Y_1 and $\overline{Y}_1$ are linearly independent, and so are y_1 and y_2.

As an example of a differential equation with complex exponents, let us consider the equation

$$x^2 y'' + xy' + (1 - x)y = 0. \tag{4.111}$$

Substitution of a series of the form

$$y = x^s \sum_{n=0}^{\infty} A_n x^n$$

into this equation yields the relation

$$(s^2 + 1)A_0 x^s + \sum_{n=0}^{\infty} \{[(n + s + 1)^2 + 1]A_{n+1} - A_n\}x^{n+s+1} = 0.$$

The exponents are $s_1 = i$ and $s_2 = -i$. The recurrence relation is

$$[(n + s + 1)^2 + 1]A_{n+1} = A_n, \qquad n \geq 0.$$

Setting $s = s_1 = i$ in this relation, we have

$$A_{n+1} = \frac{1}{(n + 1 + i)^2 + 1} A_n = \frac{(n + 1) - 2i}{(n + 1)[(n + 1)^2 + 4]} A_n, \qquad n \geq 0.$$

Taking $A_0 = 1 + i$ (A_0 can be any complex number other than zero), we find that

$$A_1 = \frac{3 - i}{2}, \qquad A_2 = \frac{1 - 2i}{20}, \qquad A_3 = \frac{-1 - 8i}{780}.$$

Taking real and imaginary parts, we have

$$a_0 = 1, \qquad a_1 = \tfrac{3}{5}, \qquad a_2 = \tfrac{1}{20}, \qquad a_3 = -\tfrac{1}{780},$$

$$b_0 = 1, \qquad b_1 = -\tfrac{1}{5}, \qquad b_2 = -\tfrac{1}{10}, \qquad b_3 = -\tfrac{2}{195}.$$

Two real solutions of equation (4.111) are

$$y_1 = \cos(\log x)[1 + \tfrac{3}{5}x + \tfrac{1}{20}x^2 + \cdots] - \sin(\log x)[1 - \tfrac{1}{5}x - \tfrac{1}{10}x^2 + \cdots],$$

$$y_2 = \cos(\log x)[1 - \tfrac{1}{5}x - \tfrac{1}{10}x^2 + \cdots] + \sin(\log x)[1 + \tfrac{3}{5}x + \tfrac{1}{20}x^2 + \cdots].$$

4.9 EXERCISES

1. Express the general solution in terms of power series at $x = 0$.

(a) $x^2y'' + (x^2 - x)y' + 2y = 0$
(b) $x^2y'' + xy' + (4 - x)y = 0$
(c) $x^2y'' + (3x - x^2)y' + (5 - x)y = 0$
(d) $(x^2 - x^3)y'' - 3xy' + 5y = 0$

2. Carry out the details in the derivation of the formula for the Wronskian $W(x; Y_1, \overline{Y}_1)$.

3. Let the functions $P(x)$ and $Q(x)$ in equation (4.108) be represented by their Taylor series at $x = 0$ for $|x| < R$. Prove that the complex power series in the formula (4.109) for $Y_1(x)$ converges for $|x| < R$, and that $Y_1(x)$ is a solution of the differential equation for $0 < x < R$.

4.10   The Point at Infinity

In some instances, it may be desired to find the behavior of solutions of a differential equation as the independent variable x becomes infinite, rather than near some finite point. If we make the change of variable

$$x = \frac{1}{t}, \tag{4.112}$$

then as t tends to zero through positive (negative) values, x becomes positively (negatively) infinite. The change of variable (4.112) in the equation

$$\frac{d^2y}{dx^2} + P(x)\frac{dy}{dx} + Q(x)y = 0 \tag{4.113}$$

leads to the equation

$$\frac{d^2y}{dt^2} + p(t)\frac{dy}{dt} + q(t)y = 0, \tag{4.114}$$

where

$$p(t) = \frac{2}{t} - \frac{1}{t^2}P\left(\frac{1}{t}\right), \qquad q(t) = \frac{1}{t^4}Q\left(\frac{1}{t}\right). \tag{4.115}$$

If equation (4.114) has an ordinary point at $t = 0$, then equation (4.113) is said to have an ordinary point at infinity. Similarly, if equation (4.114) has a regular (irregular) singular point at $t = 0$, then equation (4.113) is said to have a regular (irregular) singular point at infinity.

For purposes of illustration, let us attempt to find series solutions of the equation

$$(1 - x^2)\frac{d^2y}{dx^2} - x\frac{dy}{dx} + y = 0 \tag{4.116}$$

which are valid for large values of $|x|$. After the transformation (4.112), this equation becomes

$$(t^4 - t^2)\frac{d^2 y}{dt^2} + (2t^3 - t)\frac{dy}{dt} + y = 0. \tag{4.117}$$

Equation (4.117) has a regular singular point at $t = 0$. Applying the method of Frobenius, we find that the exponents at $t = 0$ are $s_1 = 1$ and $s_2 = -1$, and that corresponding solutions are

$$Y_1(t) = \sum_{n=0}^{\infty} \frac{(2n)!}{2^{2n} n!\,(n+1)!}\, t^{2n+1}, \qquad Y_2(t) = t^{-1}. \tag{4.118}$$

(Here it happens that we have two nonlogarithmic solutions, even though the exponents differ by an integer.) Replacing t by $1/x$ in the formulas (4.118), we obtain the solutions

$$y_1(x) = \sum_{n=0}^{\infty} \frac{(2n)!}{2^{2n} n!\,(n+1)!}\, x^{-2n-1}, \qquad y_2(x) = x, \tag{4.119}$$

of the original equation (4.116). Since the series for $Y_1(t)$ converges for $|t| < 1$, the series for $y_1(x)$ converges for $|x| > 1$.

4.10   EXERCISES

1. Find and classify, if possible, all singular points of the given differential equation. Include any singularity at infinity.

   (a) $x^4 y'' + x^3(x+2)y' + y = 0$
   (b) $(x+1)^2 y'' + (x+1)y' - y = 0$
   (c) $(x-2)y'' + y' - xy = 0$
   (d) $y'' + ay' + by = 0$, a and b constants.
   (e) $y'' + e^x y = 0$

2. Let us introduce the symbol $0(x^m)$ as a general symbol for a function $f(x)$ which is such that $f(x)/x^m$ is bounded when $|x|$ is sufficiently large. If the differential equation

   $$y'' + P(x)y' + Q(x)y = 0$$

   has a regular singular point at infinity, show that $P(x) = 0(x^{-1})$ and that $Q(x) = 0(x^{-2})$. If the equation has an ordinary point at infinity, show that $P(x) = 2/x + 0(x^{-2})$ and that $Q(x) = 0(x^{-4})$.

3. Verify that the point at infinity is either an ordinary point or a regular singular point for the given equation. Express the general solution in terms of series which converge for large $|x|$.

   (a) $x^4 y'' + 2(x^3 - x)y' + y = 0$
   (b) $x^3 y'' + (x^2 - x)y' + (2 - x)y = 0$
   (c) $2x^3 y'' + x^2 y' - (x+1)y = 0$

4. (a) Verify that the differential equation

$$xy'' - (x + 1)y = 0$$

has an irregular singular point at infinity.

(b) Show that the equation possesses *formal* solutions of the forms

$$y = x^{1/2}e^x \sum_{n=0}^{\infty} A_n x^{-n}, \qquad y = x^{-1/2}e^{-x} \sum_{n=0}^{\infty} B_n x^{-n},$$

but that both of the series involved *diverge* for all values of x.

REFERENCES

1. Copson, E. T., *An Introduction to the Theory of Functions of a Complex Variable.* Oxford, London, 1935.
2. Hildebrand, F. B., *Advanced Calculus for Applications.* Prentice-Hall, Englewood Cliffs, New Jersey, 1962.
3. Piaggio, H. T. H., *Differential Equations.* G. Bell, London, 1952.
4. Rainville, E. D., *Intermediate Differential Equations*, 2nd ed. Macmillan, New York, 1964.

CHAPTER 5

BESSEL FUNCTIONS

5.1 The Gamma Function

In our study of Bessel functions, the main object of our interest in this chapter, we shall need to know certain properties of the function $\Gamma(x)$, where

$$\Gamma(x) = \int_0^\infty t^{x-1} e^{-t} \, dt, \qquad x > 0. \tag{5.1}$$

This function is called the *gamma function*. It should be noted that the variable t in the integrand of (5.1) is a "dummy" variable of integration, and that the value of the integral depends only on the value of the variable x. The integral is improper, first of all because the interval of integration is infinite. However, the factor e^{-t} tends to zero sufficiently rapidly as t becomes infinite, so that convergence at the upper limit is insured no matter what value x may have. At the lower limit, $t = 0$, the factor e^{-t} tends to 1, and the factor t^{x-1} becomes infinite whenever $x < 1$. In order to obtain convergence of the integral at the lower limit, it is necessary to restrict x to the interval $x > 0$.

We shall now establish two important properties of the gamma function. These properties are

$$\Gamma(1) = 1 \tag{5.2}$$

and

$$\Gamma(x + 1) = x\Gamma(x), \qquad x > 0. \tag{5.3}$$

To prove property (5.2), we simply set $x = 1$ in formula (5.1) and integrate. Thus we have

$$\Gamma(1) = \int_0^\infty e^{-t} \, dt = 1.$$

To establish property (5.3), we replace x by $x + 1$ in formula (5.1) and integrate by parts. Thus

$$\Gamma(x + 1) = \int_0^\infty t^x e^{-t}\, dt = \left[-t^x e^{-t} \right]_0^\infty + x \int_0^\infty t^{x-1} e^{-t}\, dt.$$

The integrated part vanishes and the remaining term is $x\Gamma(x)$.

Combining properties (5.2) and 5.3), we see that

$$\Gamma(2) = 1 \cdot \Gamma(1) = 1$$

$$\Gamma(3) = 2 \cdot \Gamma(2) = 1 \cdot 2$$

$$\Gamma(4) = 3 \cdot \Gamma(3) = 1 \cdot 2 \cdot 3.$$

It can be verified by mathematical induction that

$$\Gamma(n + 1) = n! \tag{5.4}$$

where n is a nonnegative integer.

The derivation of another useful fact, namely that

$$\Gamma(\tfrac{1}{2}) = \sqrt{\pi}, \tag{5.5}$$

is left as an exercise.

Formula (5.1) defines the gamma function only when $x > 0$. We shall define the gamma function for negative values of x in the following way. First, let us write formula (5.3) in the form

$$\Gamma(x) = \frac{\Gamma(x + 1)}{x}. \tag{5.6}$$

We have proven that this formula holds when $x > 0$. However, since $\Gamma(x + 1)$ is defined when $x > -1$, we may use formula (5.6) to define $\Gamma(x)$ for x in the interval $-1 < x < 0$. Also, since

$$\Gamma(x + 1) = \frac{\Gamma(x + 2)}{x + 1} \tag{5.7}$$

when $x > -1$, we may write

$$\Gamma(x) = \frac{\Gamma(x + 2)}{x(x + 1)} \tag{5.8}$$

for $x > 0$. But since $\Gamma(x + 2)$ is defined for $x > -2$, we may use formula (5.8) to define $\Gamma(x)$ for $-2 < x < 0$, $x \neq -1$. Continuing this process, we have

$$\Gamma(x) = \frac{\Gamma(x + k)}{x(x + 1)(x + 2) \cdots (x + k - 1)} \tag{5.9}$$

for any positive integer k and for $x > 0$. We use this formula to define $\Gamma(x)$ for $-k < x < 0$, $x \neq -1, -2, \ldots, -k + 1$. By defining $\Gamma(x)$ in this way for negative x, we insure that formula (5.3) holds for all values of x other than

$x = 0, -1, -2, \ldots$. Evidently $\Gamma(x)$ becomes infinite when x tends to zero or to a negative integral value. The graph of $\Gamma(x)$ is shown in Figure 5.1.

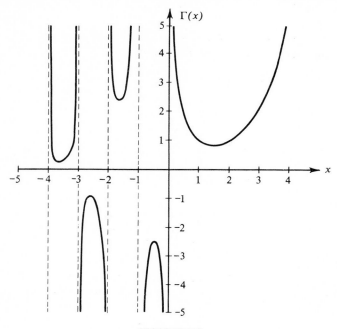

FIGURE 5.1

The function $1/\Gamma(x)$ is defined except at the points $x = -N$, $N = 0, 1, 2, \ldots$. However, as $x \to -N$,

$$\lim_{x \to -N} \frac{1}{\Gamma(x)} = 0.$$

Therefore the function

$$f(x) = \begin{cases} \dfrac{1}{\Gamma(x)}, & x \neq -N \\ 0, & x = -N \end{cases} \tag{5.10}$$

is defined and continuous for all x. We shall therefore adopt the convention that

$$\frac{1}{\Gamma(-N)} = 0. \tag{5.11}$$

From the definition (5.1) we find, by differentiation under the integral sign, that

$$\Gamma'(x) = \int_0^\infty t^{x-1} e^{-t} \log t \, dt \qquad (x > 0) \tag{5.12}$$

Let us define the function $\psi(x)$ as

$$\psi(x) = \frac{\Gamma'(x+1)}{\Gamma(x+1)} = \frac{d}{dx} \log \Gamma(x+1) \qquad (x > -1). \qquad (5.13)$$

Since

$$\Gamma(x+1) = x\Gamma(x) \qquad (x > 0)$$

and

$$\Gamma'(x+1) = x\Gamma'(x) + \Gamma(x) \qquad (x > 0)$$

we have

$$\psi(x) = \frac{\Gamma'(x)}{\Gamma(x)} + \frac{1}{x}$$

or

$$\psi(x) = \psi(x-1) + \frac{1}{x} \qquad (x > 0). \qquad (5.14)$$

If n is a positive integer, we have

$$\psi(n) = \psi(n-1) + \frac{1}{n}$$

$$= \psi(n-2) + \frac{1}{n-1} + \frac{1}{n}$$

$$= \psi(n-3) + \frac{1}{n-2} + \frac{1}{n-1} + \frac{1}{n} \qquad (n > 2).$$

By repeated application of formula (5.14), we find that

$$\psi(n) = \psi(0) + 1 + \frac{1}{2} + \frac{1}{3} + \cdots + \frac{1}{n-1} + \frac{1}{n}. \qquad (5.15)$$

The quantity

$$\psi(0) = \frac{\Gamma'(1)}{\Gamma(1)} = \Gamma'(1) = \int_0^\infty e^{-t} \log t \, dt \qquad (5.16)$$

is a negative constant, which we denote by $-\gamma$. The positive constant $\gamma = 0.57721 \cdots$ is known as Euler's constant. It can be shown that

$$\gamma = \lim_{n \to \infty} \left(1 + \frac{1}{2} + \frac{1}{3} + \cdots \frac{1}{n} - \log n \right). \qquad (5.17)$$

If we introduce the notation

$$\phi(n) = 1 + \frac{1}{2} + \frac{1}{3} + \cdots + \frac{1}{n}, \qquad (5.18)$$

then

$$\psi(n) = \frac{\Gamma'(n+1)}{\Gamma(n+1)} = -\gamma + \phi(n). \qquad (5.19)$$

5.1 EXERCISES

1. Given that $\Gamma(\frac{1}{2}) = \sqrt{\pi}$, find

  (a) $\Gamma(\frac{3}{2})$ (b) $\Gamma(\frac{5}{2})$ (c) $\Gamma(-\frac{1}{2})$ (d) $\Gamma(-\frac{3}{2})$

2. If α is not zero or a negative integer, verify that

$$\frac{\Gamma(\alpha + n)}{\Gamma(\alpha)} = \alpha(\alpha + 1)(\alpha + 2) \cdots (\alpha + n - 1),$$

where n is a positive integer.

3. From the definition (5.1), we have

$$\Gamma(\tfrac{1}{2}) = \int_0^\infty t^{-1/2} e^{-t} \, dt.$$

Show that the change of variable $t = u^2$ leads to the representation

$$\Gamma(\tfrac{1}{2}) = 2 \int_0^\infty e^{-u^2} \, du.$$

4. Using the result of Problem 3, we have

$$[\Gamma(\tfrac{1}{2})]^2 = 4\left(\int_0^\infty e^{-u^2} \, du\right)\left(\int_0^\infty e^{-v^2} \, dv\right) = 4 \int_0^\infty \int_0^\infty e^{-(u^2 + v^2)} \, du \, dv$$

where the last expression on the right may be interpreted as a double integral. Changing to polar coordinates r and θ, where

$$u = r \cos \theta, \qquad v = r \sin \theta,$$

show that

$$[\Gamma(\tfrac{1}{2})]^2 = 4 \int_0^{\pi/2} \int_0^\infty e^{-r^2} r \, dr \, d\theta = \pi$$

and hence that

$$\Gamma(\tfrac{1}{2}) = \sqrt{\pi}.$$

5. Show that

$$\Gamma(x) = 2 \int_0^\infty e^{-u^2} u^{2x-1} \, du, \qquad x > 0.$$

6. The beta function $B(x, y)$ may be defined as

$$B(x, y) = \int_0^1 t^{x-1}(1 - t)^{y-1} \, dt, \qquad x > 0, y > 0.$$

Show that

$$B(x, y) = \frac{\Gamma(x)\Gamma(y)}{\Gamma(x + y)}, \qquad x > 0, y > 0.$$

Suggestion: start with the expression

$$\Gamma(x)\Gamma(y) = \left(2 \int_0^\infty e^{-u^2} u^{2x-1} \, du\right)\left(2 \int_0^\infty e^{-v^2} v^{2y-1} \, dv\right).$$

Write the product of the two integrals as a double integral, and then change to polar coordinates. Then write the resulting double integral as the product of two single integrals.

5.2 Bessel's Equation

The differential equation

$$x^2 y'' + x y' + (x^2 - \alpha^2) y = 0, \tag{5.20}$$

where α is a constant, is known as *Bessel's equation* of order α. We shall assume that α is real. Then, without loss of generality, we can also assume that $\alpha \geq 0$, since only the quantity α^2 appears in the equation.

Bessel's equation has a regular singular point at $x = 0$, and series solutions of the equation can be found by the methods of Chapter 4. Bessel's equation arises in the process of solving certain partial differential equations of mathematical physics. Because of the importance of these applications, we shall consider the solutions of equation (5.20) in some detail. The solutions of equation (5.20) are called *Bessel functions* of order α.

As an example of an application that gives rise to Bessel functions, let us consider the problem of finding the temperature distribution in a solid right circular cylinder. Let the cylinder be described by means of the inequalities $0 \leq r \leq c$, $0 \leq z \leq h$, where $r = \sqrt{x^2 + y^2}$ and c and h are positive constants. Suppose that the temperature depends only on the quantities r and t, where t represents time, and that it can be represented by a function of the form $u(r, t)$. Then it can be shown that $u(r, t)$ must satisfy the partial differential equation

$$\frac{\partial u}{\partial t} = k \left(\frac{\partial^2 u}{\partial r^2} + \frac{1}{r} \frac{\partial u}{\partial r} \right), \tag{5.21}$$

where the constant k is called the thermal diffusivity of the material. One procedure for solving this equation is to look for solutions of the form $u = R(r)T(t)$, that is, solutions that are the product of a function of r and a function of t, Anticipating results brought out in Chapter 11, let us assume that the time-dependent function $T(t)$ is a decreasing exponential function, of the form $T(t) = e^{-\lambda k t}$, where λ is a positive constant. If the expression $u = R(r)e^{-\lambda k t}$ is to satisfy the equation (5.21), we must have

$$-\lambda k R e^{-\lambda k t} = k \left(R'' + \frac{1}{r} R' \right) e^{-\lambda k t}.$$

Thus the function $R(r)$ must be a solution of the ordinary differential equation

$$r R'' + R' - \lambda R = 0.$$

The change of variable $s = \sqrt{\lambda} \, r$ leads us to the differential equation

$$s \frac{d^2 R}{ds^2} + \frac{dR}{ds} - R = 0,$$

which is Bessel's equation of order zero. Bessel functions of other orders arise when we assume that the temperature in the cylinder depends in a more complicated way on the space variables x, y, and z.

Let us now investigate the solutions of equation (5.20). Seeking a solution of the form

$$y = x^s \sum_{n=0}^{\infty} A_n x^n,$$

we find that

$$x^2 y'' + xy' + (x^2 - \alpha^2)y = (s^2 - \alpha^2)A_0 x^s + [(s+1)^2 - \alpha^2]A_1 x^{s+1}$$

$$+ \sum_{n=0}^{\infty} \{[(n+s+2)^2 - \alpha^2]A_{n+2} + A_n\} x^{n+s+2}.$$

Equation of the coefficients of the various powers of x to zero gives the indicial equation

$$s^2 - \alpha^2 = (s - \alpha)(s + \alpha) = 0 \qquad (5.22)$$

and the relations

$$[(s+1)^2 - \alpha^2]A_1 = 0 \qquad (5.23)$$

$$(n+s+2+\alpha)(n+s+2-\alpha)A_{n+2} = -A_n, \qquad n \geq 0. \qquad (5.24)$$

The exponents of the equation at $x = 0$ are therefore $s_1 = \alpha$ and $s_2 = -\alpha$. Taking first $s = s_1 = \alpha$, we see that the coefficients A_n must be such that

$$(2\alpha + 1)A_1 = 0 \qquad (5.25)$$

$$(n+2)(n+2+2\alpha)A_{n+2} = -A_n, \qquad n \geq 0. \qquad (5.26)$$

From these relations we see that the coefficients with odd subscripts must all vanish, that is,

$$A_1 = A_3 = A_5 = \cdots A_{2m+1} = \cdots = 0. \qquad (5.27)$$

For the coefficients with even subscripts we have

$$A_2 = -\frac{A_0}{2 \cdot (2 + 2\alpha)}$$

$$A_4 = -\frac{A_2}{4 \cdot (4 + 2\alpha)} = \frac{A_0}{2 \cdot 4(2 + 2\alpha)(4 + 2\alpha)}$$

$$A_{2m} = \frac{(-1)^m A_0}{2 \cdot 4 \cdots (2m)(2 + 2\alpha)(4 + 2\alpha) \cdots 2m + 2\alpha)} \qquad (5.28)$$

$$= \frac{(-1)^m A_0}{2^{2m} m! \, (1 + \alpha)(2 + \alpha) \cdots (m + \alpha)}, \qquad m \geq 1.$$

Thus a solution of Bessel's equation is

$$y_1(x) = A_0 x^\alpha \sum_{m=0}^{\infty} \frac{(-1)^m x^{2m}}{2^{2m} m! \, (1 + \alpha)(2 + \alpha) \cdots (m + \alpha)}. \qquad (5.29)$$

Choosing

$$A_0 = \frac{1}{2^\alpha \Gamma(\alpha + 1)},$$

we obtain a specific solution called the *Bessel function* of the first kind of order α and denoted by the symbol $J_\alpha(x)$. We find that

$$J_\alpha(x) = \sum_{m=0}^{\infty} \frac{(-1)^m (x/2)^{2m+\alpha}}{m! \, \Gamma(m + \alpha + 1)}. \tag{5.30}$$

The power series involved converges for all x. We note that $J_\alpha(x)$ is finite at $x = 0$. In fact, $J_0(0) = 1$ and $J_\alpha(0) = 0$ for $\alpha > 0$. We shall see presently that the only solutions of Bessel's equation that are finite at $x = 0$ are those which are constant multiples of $J_\alpha(x)$. It can be shown that every nontrivial solution of Bessel's equation has infinitely many zeros on the interval $0 < x < +\infty$. The graphs of $J_0(x)$ and $J_1(x)$ are shown in Figure 5.2.

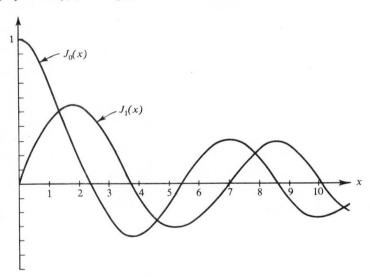

FIGURE 5.2

For the second exponent $s = s_2 = -\alpha$, the relations (5.23) and (5.24) become

$$(1 - 2\alpha)A_1 = 0 \tag{5.31}$$

$$(n + 2)(n + 2 - 2\alpha)A_{n+2} = -A_n, \qquad n \geq 0. \tag{5.32}$$

These relations are the same as the relations (5.25) and (5.26) except that α in the former is replaced by $-\alpha$.

The difference $s_1 - s_2 = 2\alpha$ is an integer whenever α is half an integer. When this is not the case, we obtain a second solution of the form (5.29), except that α is replaced by $-\alpha$. When α is half an *odd* integer, that is, $\alpha = (2N + 1)/2$, then $s_1 - s_2 = 2N + 1$. If $\alpha = \frac{1}{2}$, that is, $N = 0$, formula (5.31) becomes

$$0 \cdot A_1 = 0,$$

so A_1 is arbitrary. Choosing $A_1 = 0$, we find that all the coefficients with odd subscripts are zero. If $N > 0$, formula (5.32) becomes, for $n = 2N + 1$,

$$0 \cdot A_{2N+3} = -A_{2N+1}.$$

Since $A_1 = A_3 = \cdots = A_{2N+1} = 0$, the coefficient A_{2N+3} is arbitrary and we choose it to be zero. The coefficients with odd subscripts will again all be zero. Thus, except when α is half an even integer, that is, *except when α is an integer*, we obtain a second solution of Bessel's equation which is of the same form as (5.29) except that α is replaced by $-\alpha$. If we choose

$$A_0 = \frac{1}{2^{-\alpha}\Gamma(1 - \alpha)},$$

we obtain a specific solution that is of the same form as the solution (5.30), except that α is replaced by $-\alpha$. This solution, denoted by $J_{-\alpha}(x)$, is

$$J_{-\alpha}(x) = \sum_{m=0}^{\infty} \frac{(1-)^m (x/2)^{2m-\alpha}}{m! \, \Gamma(m - \alpha + 1)}. \tag{5.33}$$

Since $J_{-\alpha}(x)$ becomes infinite as $x \to 0$, the solutions $J_\alpha(x)$ and $J_{-\alpha}(x)$ and $J_{-\alpha}(x)$ are linearly independent on the interval $0 < x < +\infty$.

Let us define $J_{-N}(x)$, where N is zero or a positive integer, by formally setting $\alpha = N$ in formula (5.33). Then

$$J_{-N}(x) = \sum_{m=0}^{\infty} \frac{(-1)^m (x/2)^{2m-N}}{m! \, \Gamma(m - N + 1)}.$$

But since $1/\Gamma(m - N + 1) = 0$ when $m = 0, 1, 2, \ldots, N - 1$, we have

$$J_{-N}(x) = \sum_{m=N}^{\infty} \frac{(-1)^m (x/2)^{2m-N}}{m! \, \Gamma(m - N + 1)} = (-1)^N \sum_{k=0}^{\infty} \frac{(-1)^k (x/2)^{2k+N}}{k! \, \Gamma(k + N + 1)}$$

where we have made the shift of index $m = k + N$ to obtain the last expression on the right. Thus

$$J_{-N}(x) = (-1)^N J_N(x). \tag{5.34}$$

When α is a nonnegative integer N, the functions $J_N(x)$ and $J_{-N}(x)$ are both solutions of Bessel's equation of order N, but they are not linearly independent.

When α is a nonnegative integer N, a second solution of Bessel's equation will be of the form

$$y_2(x) = (A \log x + B) J_N(x) + x^{-N} \sum_{n=0}^{\infty} c_n x^n, \tag{5.35}$$

where $A \neq 0$. We shall discuss a particular second solution in Section 5.3.

5.2 EXERCISES

1. Show that

(a) $J_0(0) = 1$ and $J_\alpha(0) = 0$ when $\alpha > 0$.

(b) $J_1'(0) = \frac{1}{2}$ and $J_\alpha'(0) = 0$ when $\alpha > 1$.

2. When n is a nonnegative integer, show that

$$\frac{d^n}{dx^n} J_n(x)\bigg|_{x=0} = \frac{1}{2^n}.$$

3. Using the series definition of $J_\alpha(x)$, calculate the following quantities to three decimal places:

(a) $J_0(0.2)$　　(b) $J_1(0.6)$　　(c) $J_{-1}(0.4)$

4. Explain why the only solutions of Bessel's equation on the interval $(0, +\infty)$ that are finite as $x \to 0$ are those that are constant multiples of $J_\alpha(x)$.

5. (a) Verify that

$$J_0(x) = \frac{2}{\pi} \int_0^{\pi/2} \cos(x \sin t)\, dt.$$

Suggestion: show that the function represented by the integral satisfies Bessel's equation of order zero, and that it has the value 1 at $x = 0$.

(b) Deduce from the formula of part (a) that $|J_0(x)| \le 1$, $x \ge 0$.

6. (a) Show that the change of variable $y = x^{-1/2}u$ allows Bessel's equation to be written in the form

$$u'' + f(x)u = 0, \qquad f(x) = 1 + \frac{1 - 4\alpha^2}{4x^2}.$$

(b) Show that there exists a positive number x_0 such that $f(x) > \frac{1}{2}$ whenever $x \ge x_0$. Then, using the methods of Section 2.4, show that every solution of this equation has infinitely many zeros on the interval $(0, +\infty)$. Hence, show that every solution of Bessel's equation has infinitely many zeros on this interval.

5.3　Bessel Functions of the Second and Third Kinds

When α is not an integer, the functions $J_\alpha(x)$ and $J_{-\alpha}(x)$ are independent solutions of Bessel's equation on the interval $0 < x < +\infty$. The general solution of the equation is therefore

$$y = C_1 J_\alpha(x) + C_2 J_{-\alpha}(x). \tag{5.36}$$

For nonintegral α, the function

$$Y_\alpha(x) = \frac{(\cos \alpha\pi)J_\alpha(x) - J_\alpha(x)}{\sin \alpha\pi} \tag{5.37}$$

is also a solution of Bessel's equation, since it is a linear combination of J_α and $J_{-\alpha}$. The functions $J_\alpha(x)$ and $Y_\alpha(x)$ are linearly independent, so the expression

$$y = C_1 J_\alpha(x) + C_2 Y_\alpha(x) \tag{5.38}$$

is also the general solution of Bessel's equation.

The function (5.37) is not defined when α is an integer N, since in this case it has the indeterminate form $0/0$. However, the limit as $\alpha \to N$ does exist, and we define

$$Y_N(x) = \lim_{\alpha \to N} Y_\alpha(x). \tag{5.39}$$

Applying L'Hospital's rule, we find that

$$Y_N(x) = \frac{1}{\pi} \left[\frac{\partial}{\partial \alpha} J_\alpha(x) - (-1)^N \frac{\partial}{\partial \alpha} J_{-\alpha}(x) \right]_{\alpha = N}. \tag{5.40}$$

This limiting process leads to a second solution of Bessel's equation of the form (5.35). We shall carry out the derivation for the case $N = 0$ only.

From the definitions (5.30) and (5.33), we find that

$$\frac{\partial}{\partial \alpha} J_\alpha(x) = \sum_{m=0}^\infty \frac{(-1)^m (x/2)^{2m+\alpha}}{m! \, \Gamma(m + \alpha + 1)} \left[\log \frac{x}{2} - \psi(m + \alpha) \right] \tag{5.41}$$

$$\frac{\partial}{\partial \alpha} J_{-\alpha}(x) = \sum_{m=0}^\infty \frac{(-1)^m (x/2)^{2m-\alpha}}{m! \, \Gamma(m - \alpha + 1)} \left[-\log \frac{x}{2} + \psi(m - \alpha) \right] \tag{5.42}$$

where $\psi(x)$ is defined by formula (5.13). Setting $\alpha = 0$ and substituting into formula (5.40), we have

$$Y_0(x) = \frac{2}{\pi} \left[J_0(x) \log \frac{x}{2} - \sum_{m=0}^\infty \frac{(-1)^m \psi(m)(x/2)^{2m}}{(m!)^2} \right]. \tag{5.43}$$

Since $\psi(m) = -\gamma + \phi(m)$, we have

$$Y_0(x) = \frac{2}{\pi} \left[J_0(x)\left(\gamma + \log \frac{x}{2}\right) - \sum_{m=0}^\infty \frac{(-1)^m \phi(m)(x/2)^{2m}}{(m!)^2} \right]. \tag{5.44}$$

The derivation in the general case is more difficult. We shall content ourselves with a statement of the final result, which is

$$Y_N(x) = \frac{2}{\pi} \left[J_N(x)\left(\gamma + \log \frac{x}{2}\right) - \frac{1}{2} \sum_{m=0}^{N-1} \frac{(N - m - 1)! \, (x/2)^{2m-N}}{m!} \right.$$

$$\left. - \frac{1}{2} \sum_{m=0}^\infty \frac{(-1)^m [\phi(m) + \phi(m + N)](x/2)^{2m+N}}{m! \, (m + N)!} \right]. \tag{5.45}$$

It should be noted that $Y_N(x)$ becomes infinite as $x \to 0$. When $\alpha = N$, the general solution of Bessel's equation is

$$y = C_1 J_N(x) + C_2 Y_N(x). \tag{5.46}$$

The function $Y_\alpha(x)$ is known as *Weber's Bessel function of the second kind*. There are, of course, infinitely many ways of defining a second solution of Bessel's equation when $\alpha = N$. Our choice amounts to choosing $A = 2/\pi$ and $B = (2/\pi)(\gamma - \log 2)$ in formula (5.35). This choice is often convenient because of the fact that $J_\alpha(x)$ and $Y_\alpha(x)$ exhibit a certain similarity of behavior as x becomes infinite.

The *Bessel functions of the third kind* are the complex solutions of Bessel's equation that are defined by the relations

$$H_\alpha^{(1)}(x) = J_\alpha(x) + i Y_\alpha(x) \tag{5.47}$$

$$H_\alpha^{(2)}(x) = J_\alpha(x) - i Y_\alpha(x). \tag{5.48}$$

These functions are also known as the *Hankel functions of the first and second kinds*. They are sometimes convenient choices for solutions because of the behaviors they exhibit for large x.

Because of their importance in applications, the Bessel functions have been tabulated for various values of x and α. Tables of Bessel functions can be found in Reference 2. For many practical purposes, a differential equation or other problem can be regarded as solved when its solutions can be expressed in terms of Bessel functions. The same is true, of course, when the solutions can be expressed in terms of any tabulated function, including the elementary trigonometric and exponential functions.

5.3   EXERCISES

1. Evaluate the limits:

(a) $\lim\limits_{x \to 0} [x^{-\alpha} J_\alpha(x)]$ (b) $\lim\limits_{x \to 0} [x^\alpha Y_\alpha(x)]$.

2. If $u(x)$ and $v(x)$ are any two solutions of Bessel's equation of order α, show that $x W(x; u, v) = C$, where C is a constant that may depend on α. In particular, show that

(a) $W(x; J_\alpha, J_{-\alpha}) = -\dfrac{2}{x} \dfrac{1}{\Gamma(\alpha)\Gamma(1-\alpha)}$,   (b) $W(x; J_\alpha, Y_\alpha) = \dfrac{2}{\pi x}$.

3. The derivation of the expression (5.44) for $Y_0(x)$ was only formal, since we did not justify the termwise differentiation of the series for $J_\alpha(x)$ with respect to α. This operation can be justified by using results from advanced calculus. However, it is also possible to derive a second solution of Bessel's equation of order zero by using the methods of Chapter 4. By using these methods, derive a second solution of the form

$$J_0(x) \log x - \sum_{m=0}^{\infty} B_m x^m.$$

Then use your result to show that the expression (5.44) is actually a solution of Bessel's equation of order zero.

5.4 Properties of Bessel Functions

The Bessel function of the first kind has been defined for all α by means of the formula

$$J_\alpha(x) = \sum_{m=0}^{\infty} \frac{(-1)^m (x/2)^{2m+\alpha}}{2^m m! \, \Gamma(m+\alpha+1)} \, . \tag{5.49}$$

The Bessel functions of the first kind satisfy the two differential recurrence relations

$$\frac{d}{dx}\left[x^\alpha J_\alpha(x)\right] = x^\alpha J_{\alpha-1}(x) \tag{5.50}$$

$$\frac{d}{dx}\left[x^{-\alpha} J_\alpha(x)\right] = -x^{-\alpha} J_{\alpha+1}(x). \tag{5.51}$$

We shall verify the first of these relations, leaving the verification of the second as an exercise. We have, from the definition (5.49)

$$\frac{d}{dx}\left[x^\alpha J_\alpha(x)\right] = \frac{d}{dx}\sum_{m=0}^{\infty} \frac{(-1)^m x^{2m+2\alpha}}{2^{2m+\alpha} m! \, \Gamma(m+\alpha+1)}$$

$$= \sum_{m=0}^{\infty} \frac{(-1)^m x^{2m+2\alpha-1}}{2^{2m+\alpha-1} m! \, \Gamma(m+\alpha)}$$

$$= x^\alpha \sum_{m=0}^{\infty} \frac{(-1)^m (x/2)^{2m+\alpha-1}}{m! \, \Gamma(m+\alpha)}$$

$$= x^\alpha J_{\alpha-1}(x).$$

By carrying out the differentiations in the left-hand members of the equations (5.50) and (5.51), we find that these relations can be written as

$$J_\alpha'(x) = J_{\alpha-1}(x) - \frac{\alpha}{x} J_\alpha(x) \tag{5.52}$$

$$J_\alpha'(x) = -J_{\alpha+1}(x) + \frac{\alpha}{x} J_\alpha(x). \tag{5.53}$$

Adding these equations, we obtain the formula

$$2J_\alpha'(x) = J_{\alpha-1}(x) - J_{\alpha+1}(x). \tag{5.54}$$

Subtracting the equations (5.52) and (5.53), we obtain the pure recurrence relation

$$J_{\alpha+1}(x) = \frac{2\alpha}{x} J_\alpha(x) - J_{\alpha-1}(x). \tag{5.55}$$

This relation implies that every function $J_\alpha(x)$ can be expressed in terms of the functions $J_p(x)$, where $0 \le p < 2$. In particular, every function $J_N(x)$ of integral order can be expressed in terms of $J_0(x)$ and $J_1(x)$.

The Bessel functions of the second and third kinds satisfy the same recurrence relations as do the functions of the first kind. That is, each of the formulas (5.50)–(5.55) remains valid if the symbol J is replaced by any one of the symbols Y, $H^{(1)}$, or $H^{(2)}$ throughout. Let us first verify that the functions of the second kind satisfy a relation of the form (5.50), that is, that

$$\frac{d}{dx}\left[x^\alpha Y_\alpha(x)\right] = x^\alpha Y_{\alpha-1}(x). \tag{5.56}$$

By definition,

$$Y_\alpha(x) = \frac{(\cos \alpha\pi)J_\alpha(x) - J_{-\alpha}(x)}{\sin \alpha\pi}, \qquad \alpha \neq N.$$

From formulas (5.50) and (5.51) we have

$$\frac{d}{dx}\left[z^\alpha J_\alpha(x)\right] = x^\alpha J_{\alpha-1}(x)$$

$$\frac{d}{dx}\left[x^\alpha J_{-\alpha}(x)\right] = -x^\alpha J_{-\alpha+1}(x)$$

respectively. Then

$$\frac{d}{dx}\left[x^\alpha Y_\alpha(x)\right] = \frac{(\cos \alpha\pi)(d/dx)[x^\alpha J_\alpha(x)] - (d/dx)[x^\alpha J_{-\alpha}(x)]}{\sin \alpha\pi}$$

$$= \frac{(\cos \alpha\pi)x^\alpha J_{\alpha-1}(x) + x^\alpha J_{-\alpha+1}(x)}{\sin \alpha\pi}$$

$$= x^\alpha \frac{\cos(\alpha - 1)\pi J_{\alpha-1}(x) - J_{-\alpha+1}(x)}{\sin(\alpha - 1)\pi}$$

$$= x^\alpha Y_{\alpha-1}(x).$$

Formula (5.56) is therefore valid for nonintegral α. It must also be valid in the limit as $\alpha \to N$.

The formula

$$\frac{d}{dx}\left[x^{-\alpha}Y_\alpha(x)\right] = -x^{-\alpha}Y_{\alpha+1}(x), \tag{5.57}$$

which corresponds to formula (5.51), can be verified in the same way. The relations that corresponds to the relations (5.52)–(5.55) follow from the formulas (5.56) and (5.57). Since the real and imaginary parts of the Hankel functions satisfy relations of the forms (5.50)–(5.55), it can easily be verified that the Hankel functions themselves satisfy the same relations.

By the notation

$$f(x) \sim g(x) \qquad (x \to x_0) \tag{5.58}$$

we mean that there exists a function $h(x)$ such that

$$f(x) = g(x)[1 + h(x)]$$

when x is sufficiently close to x_0, and such that

$$\lim_{x \to x_0} h(x) = 0.$$

It can be shown that the following relations are valid as $x \to +\infty$.

$$H_\alpha^{(1)}(x) \sim \sqrt{\frac{2}{\pi x}} \exp\left[i\left(x - \frac{\pi}{4} - \frac{\alpha\pi}{2}\right)\right]$$

$$H_\alpha^{(2)}(x) \sim \sqrt{\frac{2}{\pi x}} \exp\left[-i\left(x - \frac{\pi}{4} - \frac{\alpha\pi}{2}\right)\right]. \qquad (5.59)$$

From these relations it can be shown that

$$J_\alpha(x) = \sqrt{\frac{2}{\pi x}} \left[\cos\left(x - \frac{\pi}{4} - \frac{\alpha\pi}{2}\right) + F(x)\right]$$

$$Y_\alpha(x) = \sqrt{\frac{2}{\pi x}} \left[\sin\left(x - \frac{\pi}{4} - \frac{\alpha\pi}{2}\right) + G(x)\right] \qquad (5.60)$$

where

$$\lim_{x \to +\infty} F(x) = \lim_{x \to +\infty} G(x) = 0. \qquad (5.61)$$

The second solution of Bessel's equation, $Y_\alpha(x)$, was defined in a manner to exhibit the behavior shown here.

5.4 EXERCISES

1. Verify the identity

$$\frac{d}{dx}\left[x^{-\alpha}J_\alpha(x)\right] = -x^{-\alpha}J_{\alpha+1}(x).$$

Also, show from this relation that

$$\frac{d}{dx}\left[x^\alpha J_{-\alpha}(x)\right] = -x^\alpha J_{1-\alpha}(x).$$

2. Verify that

$$\frac{d}{dx}\left[x^{-\alpha}Y_\alpha(x)\right] = -x^{-\alpha}Y_{\alpha+1}(x).$$

3. Express $Y_3(x)$ in terms of $Y_0(x)$ and $Y_1(x)$.

4. Express $J_2'(x)$ in terms of $J_0(x)$ and $J_1(x)$.

5. If λ is a constant, show that

$$\frac{d}{dx}J_\alpha(\lambda x) = \lambda J_{\alpha-1}(\lambda x) - \frac{\alpha}{x}J_\alpha(\lambda x)$$

$$= -\lambda J_{\alpha+1}(\lambda x) + \frac{\alpha}{x}J_\alpha(\lambda x).$$

6. Verify the following formulas:

(a) $\int x^{\alpha+1} J_{\alpha}(x)\, dx = x^{\alpha+1} J_{\alpha+1}(x) + C$

(b) $\int x^{1-\alpha} J_{\alpha}(x)\, dx + x^{1-\alpha} J_{\alpha-1}(x) + C$

7. The problem is to show that every solution of Bessel's equation approaches zero as x becomes positively infinite. Suppose that $\tilde{y}(x)$ is a solution of Bessel's equation on the interval $(0, +\infty)$. Then the function $\tilde{u}(x) = x^{1/2}\tilde{y}(x)$ is a solution of the equation

$$u'' + \left(1 + \frac{1 - 4\alpha^2}{x^2}\right) u = 0, \qquad 0 < x < +\infty.$$

Consequently $\tilde{u}(x)$ is a solution of the *nonhomogeneous* equation

$$u'' + u = \frac{4\alpha^2 - 1}{x^2}\tilde{u}(x), \qquad 0 < x < +\infty.$$

Let x_0 be any fixed positive number such that $x_0 > |4\alpha^2 - 1|$, and let $x \geq x_0$. Application of the method of variation of parameters shows that

$$\tilde{u}(x) = c \sin(x - k) + (4\alpha^2 - 1) \int_{x_0}^{x} \frac{\sin(x - t)}{t^2}\tilde{u}(t)\, dt,$$

where c and k are constants. Let $m(x) = \max_{x_0 \leq t \leq x} |\tilde{u}(t)|$. Then

$$m(x) \leq |c| + |4\alpha^2 - 1|m(x) \int_{x_0}^{x} t^{-2}\, dt$$

or

$$m(x) \leq \frac{c}{1 - |4\alpha^2 - 1|(1/x_0 - 1/x)}.$$

Letting $x \to +\infty$, we find that $|\tilde{u}(x)| \leq M$, $x \geq x_0$, where

$$M = \frac{|c|x_0}{x_0 - |4\alpha^2 - 1|}.$$

Hence $|\tilde{y}(x)| \leq M x^{-1/2}$ when $x \geq x_0$, and so $\tilde{y}(x) \to 0$ as $x \to +\infty$.

5.5 Modified Bessel Functions

The differential equation

$$x^2 y'' + xy' - (x^2 + \alpha^2)y = 0 \tag{5.62}$$

is known as the *modified Bessel's equation* of order α. The resemblance to Bessel's equation is apparent. Application of the method of Frobenius shows that the exponents of the equation at $x = 0$ are $s_1 = \alpha$ and $s_2 = -\alpha$. A particular solution which corresponds to the exponent s_1 is found to be

$$I_\alpha(x) = \sum_{m=0}^\infty \frac{(x/2)^{2m+\alpha}}{m!\,\Gamma(m+\alpha+1)}. \tag{5.63}$$

This function is called the *modified Bessel function of the first kind of order* α.

If we make the formal change of variable $t = ix$ in equation (5.62), we find that it becomes

$$t^2 \frac{d^2 y}{dt^2} + t\frac{dy}{dt} + (t^2 - \alpha^2)y = 0, \tag{5.64}$$

which is Bessel's equation of order α. From the definition (5.49) we have, formally,

$$\begin{aligned} J_\alpha(t) = J_\alpha(ix) &= \sum_{m=0}^\infty \frac{(-1)^m (ix/2)^{2m+\alpha}}{m!\,\Gamma(m+\alpha+1)} \\ &= i^\alpha \sum_{m=0}^\infty \frac{(x/2)^{2m+\alpha}}{m!\,\Gamma(m+\alpha+1)} \\ &= i^\alpha I_\alpha(x). \end{aligned}$$

Thus

$$I_\alpha(x) = i^{-\alpha} J_\alpha(ix). \tag{5.65}$$

The treatment here is only formal because we have restricted ourselves to functions of real variables. However, when both x and t are allowed to be complex, the analysis can be justified by the theory of functions of a complex variable.

When α is not an integer, a second solution of equation (5.62), which corresponds to the exponent $-\alpha$, is found to be

$$I_{-\alpha}(x) = \sum_{m=0}^\infty \frac{(x/2)^{2m-\alpha}}{m!\,(m-\alpha+1)}. \tag{5.66}$$

This solution becomes infinite as $x \to 0$. For nonintegral α, the function

$$K_\alpha(x) = \frac{\pi}{2} \frac{I_{-\alpha}(x) - I_\alpha(x)}{\sin \alpha\pi} \tag{5.67}$$

is also a solution. A second solution of equation (5.62), when α is an integer N, may be defined as

$$K_N(x) = \lim_{\alpha \to N} K_\alpha(x). \tag{5.68}$$

This second solution is of the form

$$(A \log x + B)I_N(x) + x^{-N} \sum_{m=0}^\infty c_m x^m \tag{5.69}$$

where $A \neq 0$. It becomes infinite as $x \to 0$. The function $K_\alpha(x)$ is known as the *modified Bessel function* of the second kind of order α. When α is not an integer, the general solution of equation (5.62) is

$$y = C_1 I_\alpha(x) + C_2 I_{-\alpha}(x). \tag{5.70}$$

The expression

$$y = C_1 I_\alpha(x) + C_2 K_\alpha(x) \tag{5.71}$$

is the general solution whether or not α is an integer.

5.5 EXERCISES

1. Show that

(a) $W(x; I_\alpha, I_{-\alpha}) = -\dfrac{2}{x} \dfrac{1}{\Gamma(\alpha)\Gamma(1 - \alpha)}$

(b) $W(x; I_\alpha, K_\alpha) = -\dfrac{1}{x}$

2. (a) Show that when N is an integer,

$$K_N(x) = \tfrac{1}{2}(-1)^N \left[\frac{\partial}{\partial \alpha} I_{-\alpha}(x) - \frac{\partial}{\partial \alpha} I_\alpha(x) \right]_{\alpha = N}$$

(b) Show that

$$K_0(x) = -\left(\gamma + \log \frac{x}{2} \right) I_0(x) + \sum_{m=1}^{\infty} \frac{\phi(m)(x/2)^{2m}}{(m!)^2}$$

3. Show that

(a) $\dfrac{d}{dx}\left[x^\alpha I_\alpha(x) \right] = x^\alpha I_{\alpha-1}(x)$ (b) $\dfrac{d}{dx}\left[x^{-\alpha} I_\alpha(x) \right] = x^{-\alpha} I_{\alpha+1}(x)$

4. Using the results of Problem 3, show that

(a) $I_\alpha'(x) = I_{\alpha-1}(x) - \dfrac{\alpha}{x} I_\alpha(x)$ (c) $I_{\alpha-1}(x) - I_{\alpha+1}(x) = \dfrac{2\alpha}{x} I_\alpha(x)$

(b) $I_\alpha'(x) = I_{\alpha+1}(x) + \dfrac{\alpha}{x} I_\alpha(x)$ (d) $I_\alpha'(x) = \tfrac{1}{2}[I_{\alpha-1}(x) + I_{\alpha+1}(x)]$

5. Show that

(a) $\dfrac{d}{dx}[x^\alpha K_\alpha(x)] = -x^\alpha K_{\alpha-1}(x)$ (b) $\dfrac{d}{dx}[x^{-\alpha} K_\alpha(x)] = -x^{-\alpha} K_{\alpha+1}(x)$

5.6 Other Forms for Bessel's Equation

Starting with Bessel's equation in the form

$$t^2 \frac{d^2 u}{dt^2} + t \frac{du}{dt} + (t^2 - \alpha^2)u = 0, \tag{5.72}$$

let us make the variable changes

$$t = ax^r, \qquad y = x^s u, \tag{5.73}$$

where a, r, and s are constants. Then

$$\frac{du}{dt} = \frac{d}{dx}(x^{-s}y)\frac{dx}{dt} = \frac{x^{-r-s}}{ar}\left(x\frac{dy}{dx} - sy\right)$$

$$\frac{d^2u}{dt^2} = \frac{x^{-2r-s}}{a^2r^2}\left[x^2\frac{d^2y}{dx^2} + (1 - r - 2s)x\frac{dy}{dx} + s(r+s)y\right]$$

and equation (5.72) becomes

$$x^2\frac{d^2y}{dx^2} + (1 - 2s)x\frac{dy}{dx} + [(s^2 - r^2\alpha^2) + a^2r^2x^{2r}]y = 0. \tag{5.74}$$

The general solution of equation (5.74) is

$$y = x^s[C_1 J_\alpha(ax^r) + C_2 Y_\alpha(ax^r)]. \tag{5.75}$$

When α is not an integer, the general solution is

$$y = x^s[C_1 J_\alpha(ax^r) + C_2 J_{-\alpha}(ax^r)]. \tag{5.76}$$

If a is a pure imaginary number, that is, $a = ia_1$, where a_1 is real, the general solution is

$$y = x^s[C_1 I_\alpha(a_1 x^r) + C_2 K_\alpha(a_1 x^r)]. \tag{5.77}$$

When α is not an integer, the general solution is also

$$y = x^s[C_1 I_\alpha(a_1 x^r) + C_2 I_{-\alpha}(a_1 x^r)]. \tag{5.78}$$

As a first example, let us consider the differential equation

$$y'' + xy = 0. \tag{5.79}$$

In order to compare this equation with the general equation (5.74), let us multiply through by x^2 to obtain the form

$$x^2 y'' + x^3 y = 0. \tag{5.80}$$

If this equation is of the form (5.74), we must have

$$1 - 2s = 0, \qquad s^2 - r^2\alpha^2 = 0, \qquad a^2r^2 = 1, \qquad 2r = 3.$$

But these conditions are satisfied if

$$r = \tfrac{3}{2}, \qquad s = \tfrac{1}{2}, \qquad \alpha = \tfrac{1}{3}, \qquad a = \tfrac{2}{3}.$$

Therefore the general solution of equation (5.79) is

$$y = x^{1/2}[C_1 J_{1/3}(\tfrac{2}{3}x^{3/2}) + C_2 J_{-1/3}(\tfrac{2}{3}x^{3/2})]. \tag{5.81}$$

As a second example, let us consider the differential equation

$$y'' + y = 0, \tag{5.82}$$

for which the general solution is known to be

$$y = C_1 \cos x + C_2 \sin x.$$

But the equation

$$x^2 y'' + x^2 y = 0$$

is of the form (5.74), with

$$s = \tfrac{1}{2}, \qquad r = 1, \qquad \alpha = \tfrac{1}{2}, \qquad a = 1.$$

Therefore, each of the functions

$$x^{1/2} J_{1/2}(x), \qquad x^{1/2} J_{-1/2}(x) \tag{5.83}$$

is a solution of equation (5.82). Hence there exist constants A, B, C, and D such that

$$x^{1/2} J_{1/2}(x) = A \cos x + B \sin x \tag{5.84}$$

and

$$x^{1/2} J_{-1/2}(x) = C \cos x + D \sin x. \tag{5.85}$$

The series expansion of the function on the left in equation (5.84) is

$$x^{1/2} J_{1/2}(x) = \frac{1}{2^{1/2}\Gamma(\frac{3}{2})} x - \frac{1}{2^{5/2}\Gamma(\frac{5}{2})} x^3 + \cdots \tag{5.86}$$

Since only odd powers of x are involved, we must have $A = 0$. Since

$$\sin x = x - \tfrac{1}{6}x^3 + \cdots,$$

we must have

$$B = \frac{1}{2^{1/2}\Gamma(\frac{3}{2})} = \frac{\sqrt{2}}{\Gamma(\frac{1}{2})} = \sqrt{\frac{2}{\pi}}.$$

Therefore

$$J_{-1/2}(x) = \sqrt{\frac{2}{\pi x}} \sin x. \tag{5.87}$$

Similarly, it can be shown that

$$J_{-1/2}(x) = \sqrt{\frac{2}{\pi x}} \cos x. \tag{5.88}$$

The recurrence relation (5.55) enables us to express any function of the form $J_{(2N+1)/2}(x)$, where N is an integer, in terms of the two functions (5.86) and (5.87). Thus all solutions of Bessel's equation can be expressed in terms of elementary functions when the order is half an odd integer. It can also be shown that

$$I_{1/2}(x) = \sqrt{\frac{2}{\pi x}} \sinh x, \tag{5.89}$$

$$I_{-1/2}(x) = \sqrt{\frac{2}{\pi x}} \cosh x. \tag{5.90}$$

5.6 EXERCISES

Express the general solution of the given equation in terms of Bessel functions:

1. $y'' + x^2 y = 0$

2. $4x^2 y'' + (1 + 4x)y = 0$

3. $x^2 y'' + 5xy' + (3 + 4x^2)y = 0$

4. $x^2 y'' + 5xy' + (9x^6 - 12)y = 0$

5. $y'' - xy = 0$

6. $xy'' - 3y' - 9x^5 y = 0$

7. $xy'' + 3y' - 2y = 0$

8. $x^2 y'' - xy' - (3 + 4x^2)y = 0$

9. Express the following quantities in terms of elementary functions.

    (a) $J_{5/2}(x)$ (b) $J_{-3/2}(x^2)$ (c) $Y_{1/2}(x)$ (d) $I_{3/2}(x)$ (e) $I_{-3/2}(x)$

REFERENCES

1. Copson, E. T., *An Introduction to the Theory of Functions of a Complex Variable*. Oxford, London, 1935.
2. Jahnke, E., Emde, F., and Losch, F., *Tables of Higher Functions*. McGraw-Hill, New York, 1960.
3. Watson, G. N., *A Treatise on the Theory of Bessel Functions*. Macmillan, New York, 1945.
4. Whittaker, E. T., and Watson, G. N., *Modern Analysis*. Cambridge, London, 1958.

CHAPTER **6**

ORTHOGONAL POLYNOMIALS

6.1 Orthogonal Functions

Let there be assigned on an interval $a < x < b$ a real positive function $w(x)$. Let $f(x)$ and $g(x)$ be two real functions defined on the interval. The *inner product* of $f(x)$ and $g(x)$ with respect to the *weight function* $w(x)$ on the interval (a, b) is defined to be

$$(f, g) = \int_a^b w(x)f(x)g(x)\, dx. \tag{6.1}$$

The interval of integration may be infinite in extent. In any case, it is assumed that f, g, and w are such that the integral (6.1) exists. It can be verified readily that

$$(f, g) = (g, f), \tag{6.2a}$$

that

$$(f, g + h) = (f, g) + (f, h), \tag{6.2b}$$

and that

$$(cf, g) = c(f, g), \tag{6.2c}$$

where c is a real constant. The symbol (f, g) does not show what the weight function is or what interval is involved. This information must be given in any specific case.

The inner product of a function $f(x)$ with itself,

$$(f, f) = \int_a^b w(x)[f(x)]^2\, dx,$$

is nonnegative, since $w(x) > 0$ for $a < x < b$. We define the *norm* of a function $f(x)$, written $\|f\|$, to be

$$\|f\| = (f, f)^{1/2} = \left(\int_a^b w(x)[f(x)]^2\, dx \right)^{1/2}. \tag{6.3}$$

If $f(x)$ is continuous on the interval $a \le x \le b$, its norm is zero if, and only if, $f(x) \equiv 0$. It should be noted that the norm of a function depends on the specified interval and weight function.

If the inner product of $f(x)$ and $g(x)$ is zero,

$$(f, g) = 0, \tag{6.4}$$

then $f(x)$ and $g(x)$ are said to be *orthogonal* with respect to the weight function $w(x)$ on the interval $a < x < b$. In the special case when $w(x) = 1$, the functions are said to be *simply orthogonal* on the interval $a < x < b$.

A sequence of functions $\{f_n(x)\}$ is called an *orthogonal set* of functions (or a set of orthogonal functions) if the functions are pairwise orthogonal, that is, if

$$(f_m, f_n) = 0, \qquad m \ne n. \tag{6.5}$$

A sequence of polynomials $\{\phi_n(x)\}$, $n = 0, 1, 2, \ldots$, where $\phi_n(x)$ is of degree n, is called a *simple set of polynomials*. In this chapter we shall be concerned with simple sets of *orthogonal* polynomials. These sets of orthogonal polynomials arise in various ways. We shall show, under certain conditions, that given any interval and a positive weight function on that interval, there exists a corresponding set of orthogonal polynomials. We shall also see that the polynomials of an orthogonal set may arise as solutions of a family of differential equations containing a parameter.

Eigenvalue problems, which are discussed in Chapter 7, are another important source of sets of orthogonal functions, not necessarily polynomials. In Chapter 8 we shall see that under certain conditions an arbitrary function $f(x)$ can be expanded in an infinite series of the functions of an orthogonal set. Such series are called *Fourier series*. Finally, in Chapter 11, we shall use our knowledge of Fourier series and orthogonal functions to obtain solutions to some boundary-value problems of mathematical physics.

6.1 EXERCISES

1. (a) Show that the set of functions $\{\sin n\pi x/c\}$, $n = 1, 2, 3, \ldots$, is simply orthogonal on the interval $0 < x < c$. Find the norms of the functions.
   (b) Show that the set of functions $\{\cos n\pi x/c\}$, $n = 0, 1, 2, \ldots$, is simply orthogonal on the interval $0 < x < c$. Find the norms of the functions.

2. Let the functions $\phi_n(x)$ be orthogonal on the interval $a < x < b$ with respect to a positive weight function $w(x)$. Show that the functions $\psi_n(x) = \sqrt{w(x)}\, \phi_n(x)$ are simply orthogonal on the same interval.

3. Let the functions $\phi_n(x)$ be orthogonal with respect to a weight function $w(x)$ on the interval $-1 < x < 1$. Find a linear change of variable, of the form $x = Az + B$, such that the functions $\psi_n(z) = \phi_n(Az + B)$ will be orthogonal on the interval $a < z < b$ with respect to the weight function $W(z) = w(Az + B)$.

4. Let the weight function $w(x)$ be real and positive on the interval $a < x < b$. If

$$f(x) = u_1(x) + iv_1(x)$$

and

$$g(x) = u_2(x) + iv_2(x)$$

are complex functions of the real variable x, the inner product (f, g) of f and g is defined to be

$$(f, g) = \int_a^b w(x)f(x)\bar{g}(x)\, dx,$$

where the bar denotes the complex conjugate. Show that

(a) $(f, g) = \overline{(g, f)}$

(b) $(f, g + h) = (f, g) + (f, h)$, $(f + g, h) = (f, h) + (g, h)$

If c is a complex constant, show that

(c) $(cf, g) = c(f, g)$, $(f, cg) = \bar{c}(f, g)$

5. Show that, for a complex function $f(x)$, the quantity (f, f) is real and nonnegative. The norm of a complex function is defined to be

$$\|f\| = (f, f)^{1/2}.$$

6.2 An Existence Theorem for Orthogonal Polynomials

We shall eventually prove the existence of a set of orthogonal polynomials which corresponds to a given interval and a given positive weight function. First, however, we must derive some properties of polynomials that will be needed in the proof.

Theorem 1. Let $\{\phi_n(x)\}$ be a simple set of polynomials and let $Q_m(x)$ be an arbitrary polynomial of arbitrary degree m. Then $Q_m(x)$ is a linear combination of the polynomials $\phi_0(x)$, $\phi_1(x)$, $\dots$, $\phi_m(x)$.

Proof. We shall prove the theorem by induction. If $Q_0(x)$ is any constant (that is, any polynomial of degree zero) and if $C = Q_0/\phi_0$, then $Q_0(x) = C\phi_0(x)$. Thus the theorem is true for $m = 0$. Suppose that the theorem is true for $m \le k$, where k is any nonnegative integer. Let $Q_{k+1}(x)$ be any polynomial of degree $k + 1$,

$$Q_{k+1}(x) = A_{k+1}x^{k+1} + A_k x^k + \cdots + A_0,$$

where $A_{k+1} \ne 0$. Let

$$\phi_{k+1}(x) = a_{k+1}x^{k+1} + a_k x^k + \cdots + a_0,$$

where $a_{k+1} \neq 0$. If we choose $C_{k+1} = A_{k+1}/a_{k+1}$, then $Q_{k+1}(x) - C_{k+1}\phi_{k+1}(x)$ is a polynomial of degree $\leq k$. By hypothesis, we have

$$Q_{k+1}(x) - C_{k+1}\phi_{k+1}(x) = C_0\phi_0(x) + C_1\phi_1(x) + \cdots + C_k\phi_k(x)$$

or

$$Q_{k+1}(x) = \sum_{j=0}^{k+1} C_j\phi_j(x).$$

Thus if the theorem is true for $m \leq k$ it is true for $m = k + 1$. Since it is true for $m = 0$, it is true for every nonnegative integer m.

Theorem 2.   A simple set of polynomials $\{\phi_n(x)\}$ is an orthogonal set with respect to the weight function $w(x)$ on the interval $a < x < b$ if, and only if,

$$(\phi_n, x^m) = \int_a^b w(x)\phi_n(x)x^m dx = 0 \qquad m = 0, 1, 2, \ldots, n - 1, \tag{6.6}$$

for every positive integer n.

Proof.   We first show that if condition (6.6) holds, then the $\{\phi_n\}$ is orthogonal. Let $\phi_n(x)$ and $\phi_m(x)$ be two distinct polynomials of the set, and suppose that $n > m$. Let

$$\phi_m(x) = a_m x^m + a_{m-1}x^{m-1} + \cdots + a_0.$$

Then

$$(\phi_n, \phi_m) = a_m(\phi_n, x^m) + a_{m-1}(\phi_n x^{m-1}) + \cdots + a_0(\phi_n, 1) = 0,$$

so the polynomials are orthogonal.

Next we show that if the set $\{\phi_n\}$ is orthogonal, then the condition (6.6) is satisfied. Let n be any positive integer and let m be any integer such that $0 \leq m < n$. By Theorem 1, there exist constants $C_0, C_1, \ldots, C_m$ such that

$$x^m = C_0\phi_0(x) + C_1\phi_1(x) + \cdots + C_m\phi_m(x).$$

Then

$$(\phi_n, x^m) = C_0(\phi_n, \phi_0) + C_1(\phi_n, \phi_1) + \cdots + C_m(\phi_n, \phi_m) = 0.$$

Thus condition (6.6) is satisfied.

We are now ready to prove a basic existence theorem for orthogonal polynomials.

Theorem 3.   Let the function $w(x)$ be positive and continuous† on the interval $a < x < b$ and let $w(x)$ be such that each of the integrals

$$M_n = \int_a^b w(x)x^n \, dx, \qquad n = 0, 1, 2, \ldots, \tag{6.7}$$

exists (either a or b or both may be infinite). Then there exists a simple set of

---

† These restrictions on $w(x)$ can be relaxed, but they are satisfactory for our purposes.

polynomials that is orthogonal with respect to $w(x)$ on the interval $a < x < b$. Each polynomial of the set is unique except for a constant factor.

Proof. We shall show that for every positive integer n there exists a polynomial $\phi_n(x)$, of degree n, such that

$$(\phi_n, x^m) = \int_a^b w(x)\phi_n(x)x^m \, dx = 0, \qquad m = 0, 1, 2, \ldots, n-1. \qquad (6.8)$$

If $\phi_0(x)$ is assigned any nonzero constant value, the set $\{\phi_n(x)\}$, $n = 0, 1, 2, \ldots$, will be an orthogonal set, by Theorem 2.

We shall show that for every positive integer n, there exist constants $C_0, C_1, \ldots, C_n$, with $C_n \neq 0$, such that the polynomial

$$\phi_n(x) = C_0 + C_1 x + \cdots + C_{n-1} x^{n-1} + C_n x^n \qquad (6.9)$$

satisfies the conditions (6.8). Using the notation (6.7), these conditions can be written as

$$M_0 C_0 + M_1 C_1 + \cdots + M_{n-1} C_{n-1} = -M_n C_n$$

$$M_1 C_0 + M_2 C_1 + \cdots + M_n C_{n-1} \quad = -M_{n+1} C_n \qquad (6.10)$$

$$\cdots\cdots\cdots\cdots\cdots\cdots\cdots\cdots\cdots\cdots\cdots\cdots\cdots\cdots$$

$$M_{n-1} C_0 + M_n C_1 + \cdots + M_{2n-2} C_{n-1} = -M_{2n-1} C_n.$$

If the determinant

$$\Delta_n = \begin{vmatrix} M_0 & M_1 & \cdots & M_{n-1} \\ M_1 & M_2 & \cdots & M_n \\ \cdots\cdots\cdots\cdots\cdots\cdots\cdots \\ M_{n-1} & M_n & \cdots & M_{2n-2} \end{vmatrix} \qquad (6.11)$$

is not zero, the ratios C_k/C_n, $k = 0, 1, 2, \ldots, n-1$, are uniquely determined. In this case the polynomial $\phi_n(x)$ is uniquely determined except for a constant factor. For if C_n is assigned any nonzero value, the remaining coefficients C_k are uniquely determined multiples of C_n.

We now show that Δ_n cannot be zero. To do this we shall assume that $\Delta_n = 0$ and show that this assumption leads to a contradiction. If we set $C_n = 0$ in the system (6.10), the resulting *homogeneous* system has a vanishing determinant and therefore possesses a nontrivial solution. This means that there exists a polynomial $Q_{n-1}(x)$ of degree $\leq n - 1$ and not identically zero, such that

$$(Q_{n-1}, x^m) = 0, \qquad m = 0, 1, 2, \ldots, n-1. \qquad (6.12)$$

But this means that $Q_{n-1}(x)$ is orthogonal to every polynomial of degree $\leq n - 1$. In particular, it must be orthogonal to itself, so that

$$(Q_{n-1}, Q_{n-1}) = \int_a^b w(x)[Q_{n-1}(x)]^2 \, dx = 0.$$

But this is impossible, since $w(x)$ is positive for $a < x < b$. Therefore our assumption that $\Delta_n = 0$ must be false, and we must have $\Delta_n \neq 0$. This concludes the proof.

Theorem 3 actually gives us a method for the construction of any finite number of the polynomials of an orthogonal set. For purposes of illustration, let us construct the first few orthogonal polynomials of the set which corresponds to the weight function $w(x) = \sqrt{x}$ on the interval $0 < x < 1$. If we choose $\phi_0(x) = 1$ and choose the coefficient of x^n in $\phi_n(x)$ to be unity, then the polynomials are uniquely determined. The polynomials $\phi_1(x)$ and $\phi_2(x)$ are of the forms

$$\phi_1(x) = x + a, \qquad \phi_2(x) = x^2 + bx + c.$$

The constant a is determined by the requirement that

$$(\phi_1, 1) = \int_0^1 \sqrt{x}\,(x + a)\,dx = \tfrac{2}{5} + \tfrac{2}{3}a = 0.$$

Hence $a = -\tfrac{3}{5}$ and

$$\phi_1(x) = x - \tfrac{3}{5}.$$

The constants b and c are determined by the requirements that

$$(\phi_2, 1) = \int_0^1 \sqrt{x}\,(x^2 + bx + c)\,dx = \tfrac{2}{7} + \tfrac{2}{5} + \tfrac{2}{3}c = 0$$

$$(\phi_2, x) = \int_0^1 x^{3/2}(x^2 + bx + c)\,dx = \tfrac{2}{9} + \tfrac{2}{7}b + \tfrac{2}{5}c = 0.$$

We find that $b = -10/9$, $c = 5/21$, and so

$$\phi_2(x) = x^2 - \frac{10}{9}x + \frac{5}{21}.$$

This method is laborious and does not provide a general formula for the polynomial ϕ_n of arbitrary degree n.

6.2   EXERCISES

1. Let the polynomials $\phi_n(x)$ be orthogonal with respect to the given weight function on the given interval. Find $\phi_0(x)$, $\phi_1(x)$, and $\phi_2(x)$. (Take the coefficient of x^n in ϕ_n to be one.)

(a) $w(x) = 1$, $0 < x < 1$ (c) $w(x) = e^{-x}$, $0 < x < +\infty$
(b) $w(x) = x$, $0 < x < 1$ (d) $w(x) = x\,e^{-x}$, $0 < x < +\infty$

2. Let $\{\phi_n(x)\}$ be a simple set of orthogonal polynomials relative to the weight function $w(x)$ on the interval (a, b). If

$$\phi_n(x) = a_n x^n + a_{n-1} x^{n-1} + \cdots + a_0,$$

show that

$$\int_a^b w(x) x^n \phi_n(x)\,dx = \frac{1}{a_n} \int_a^b w(x)[\phi_n(x)]^2\,dx.$$

3. Let $\{\phi_n(x)\}$ be a simple set of orthogonal polynomials relative to the weight function $w(x)$ on the interval (a, b). Show that

$$\int_a^b w(x)\phi_n(x)\, dx = 0, \qquad n = 1, 2, 3, \ldots.$$

4. An infinite sequence of continuous functions $f_1, f_2, f_3, \ldots$, is said to be linearly independent on an interval $[a, b]$ if, for every positive integer k, the functions $f_1, f_2, \ldots, f_k$ are linearly independent on $[a, b]$. If the sequence $\{f_n\}$ is linearly independent, prove that there exists a sequence $\{g_n\}$, where

$$g_n = a_{n1}f_1 + a_{n2}f_2 + \cdots + a_{nn}f_n, \qquad n \geq 1,$$

such that the sequence $\{g_n\}$ is orthogonal on (a, b). (The function g_n is a linear combination of the functions $f_1, f_2, \ldots, f_n$.) Suggestion: let

$$g_1 = f_1, \qquad g_2 = f_2 - \frac{(g_1, f_2)}{(g_1, g_1)}\, g_1,$$

$$g_3 = f_3 - \frac{(g_1, f_3)}{(g_1, g_1)}\, g_1 - \frac{(g_2, f_3)}{(g_2, g_2)}\, g_2.$$

Use induction.

5. Using the definition of Problem 4, prove that the sequence $\{x^n\}$, $n = 0, 1, 2, \ldots$, is linearly independent on every interval of the form $[a, b]$.

6. Use the results of Problems 4 and 5 to prove Theorem 3.

6.3 Some Properties of Orthogonal Polynomials

In the discussion of this section, we assume that the weight function $w(x)$ is continuous and positive on the interval $a < x < b$ and that the integrals

$$M_n = \int_a^b w(x)x^n\, dx, \qquad n = 0, 1, 2, \ldots,$$

all exist.

Theorem 4. Let $\{\phi_n(x)\}$ be a set of orthogonal polynomials and let $Q_m(x)$ be an arbitrary polynomial of arbitrary degree m. Then

$$Q_m(x) = C_0\phi_0(x) + C_1\phi_1(x) + \cdots + C_m\phi_m(x), \tag{6.13}$$

where

$$C_k = \frac{(Q_m, \phi_k)}{\|\phi_k\|^2}, \qquad k = 0, 1, 2, \ldots, m. \tag{6.14}$$

Proof. By Theorem 1, we know that there exist constants C_i such that

$$Q_m(x) = \sum_{i=1}^m C_i\phi_i(x).$$

Multiplying both sides of this equation by $w(x)\phi_k(x)$, where k is an arbitrary integer such that $0 \le k \le m$, and integrating from a to b, we have

$$(Q_m, \phi_k) = C_0(\phi_0, \phi_k) + C_1(\phi_1, \phi_k) + \cdots + C_m(\phi_m, \phi_k).$$

Since $(\phi_i, \phi_k) = 0$ when $i \ne k$, we have

$$(Q_m, \phi_k) = C_k(\phi_k, \phi_k) = C_k\|\phi_k\|^2.$$

Since $\|\phi_k\| \ne 0$, we can solve for C_k to obtain the formula (6.14).

Theorem 5. The polynomials $\phi_n(x)$ of an orthogonal set satisfy a recurrence relation of the form

$$x\phi_n(x) = A_n\phi_{n+1}(x) + B_n\phi_n(x) + C_n\phi_{n-1}(x), \qquad n \ge 1, \qquad (6.15)$$

where A_n, B_n, and C_n are constants that may depend on n.

Proof. Since $x\phi_n(x)$ is a polynomial of degree $n + 1$, we have, by Theorem 4,

$$x\phi_n(x) = \sum_{k=1}^{n+1} a_{n,k}\phi_k(x),$$

where

$$a_{n,k} = \frac{(x\phi_n, \phi_k)}{\|\phi_k\|^2} = \frac{(\phi_n, x\phi_k)}{\|\phi_k\|^2}, \qquad k = 0, 1, 2, \ldots, n + 1.$$

Since $x\phi_k(x)$ is a polynomial of degree $k + 1$, we have $a_{n,k} = 0$ for $k + 1 < n$ or $k < n - 1$. Setting $A_n = a_{n+1,n}$, $B_n = a_{n,n}$, and $C_n = a_{n-1,n}$, we obtain the relation (6.15). Evidently A_n can never be zero, for if it were, the right-hand member of (6.15) would be a polynomial of degree $\le n$. It can also be shown that C_n is never zero (Exercise 2).

Theorem 6. The nth degree polynomial $\phi_n(x)$ of an orthogonal set has n real distinct zeros, all of which lie in the interval $a < x < b$.

Proof. The polynomial $\phi_0(x)$ is a nonzero constant, and of course has no zeros. For $n > 0$, we have

$$(\phi_n, 1) = \int_a^b w(x)\phi_n(x)\, dx = 0.$$

Since $w(x) > 0$ for $a < x < b$, $\phi_n(x)$ changes sign at at least one point in this interval. Let $x_1, x_2, \ldots, x_m$ be the points in the interval $a < x < b$ where $\phi_n(x)$ changes sign. Then $m \le n$, for $\phi_n(x)$ can have at most n distinct zeros. Suppose that $m < n$. The polynomial

$$\psi_m(x) = (x - x_1)(x - x_2) \cdots (x - x_m)$$

also changes sign at each of the points $x_1, x_2, \ldots, x_m$, and only at those points, so the product $\phi_n(x)\psi_m(x)$ does not change sign at all for $a < x < b$. But

$$(\phi_n, \psi_m) = \int_a^b w(x)\phi_n(x)\psi_m(x)\, dx = 0,$$

since $\psi_m(x)$ is of degree m, where $m < n$. This is impossible, so we must conclude that $m = n$. Thus $\phi_n(x)$ must change sign at n distinct points in the interval $a < x < b$, and so $\phi_n(x)$ has n real distinct zeros in this interval.

6.3 EXERCISES

1. Show that the polynomials $\psi_n(x) = x^{2n}$, $n = 0, 1, 2, \ldots$, are orthogonal with respect to the weight function $w(x) = x$ on the interval $(-2, 2)$. Note that $\psi_n(x)$ does not, in general, have n distinct zeroes in the interval of orthogonality. Is this a contradiction of Theorem 6? Explain.

2. Let $\{\phi_n(x)\}$ be a simple set of orthogonal polynomials, with positive weight function. Prove that $(x\phi_n, \phi_{n-1}) \neq 0$ for $n \geq 1$. Hence prove that $C_n \neq 0$, $n \geq 1$, in the recurrence relation (6.15).

3. Let the functions $u_1(x), u_2(x), \ldots, u_n(x)$ be defined and continuous on the interval $[a, b]$. Let $(f, g) = \int_a^b fg\, dx$. Prove that the functions $u_i(x)$ are linearly dependent on $[a, b]$ if, and only if, the determinant

$$D_n = \begin{vmatrix} (u_1, u_1) & (u_1, u_2) & \cdots & (u_1, u_n) \\ (u_2, u_1) & (u_2, u_2) & \cdots & (u_2, u_n) \\ \multicolumn{4}{c}{\cdots\cdots\cdots\cdots\cdots\cdots\cdots\cdots\cdots\cdots\cdots\cdots} \\ (u_n, u_1) & (u_n, u_2) & \cdots & (u_n, u_n) \end{vmatrix}$$

is zero. Suggestion: if the functions u_i are linearly dependent, there exist constants C_i, not all zero, such that

$$(C_1 u_1 + C_2 u_2 + \cdots + C_n u_n, u_i) = 0, \qquad i = 1, 2, \ldots, n.$$

The determinant of this system for the constants C_i is D_n. Conversely, if $D_n = 0$, show that there exist constants C_i, not all zero, such that

$$\|C_1 u_1 + C_2 u_2 + \cdots + C_n u_n\|^2 = 0.$$

6.4 Generating Functions

A function of two variables $F(x, t)$ is said to be a *generating function* for the set of functions $\{f_n(x)\}$, $n \geq 0$, if

$$F(x, t) = \sum_{n=0}^{\infty} f_n(x)t^n. \tag{6.16}$$

We also say that the functions $f_n(x)$ are *generated* by the function $F(x, t)$.

The series in equation (6.16) need not coverge for all x and t. We shall only require that it converge for $|t| < r$, where r is any positive constant, and for x in some interval I.

Generating functions for many important sets of orthogonal polynomials are known. In these cases, the generating function provides a convenient method for deriving some of the important properties of the set. We shall illustrate the procedure for the set of polynomials known as the Legendre polynomials in the next section. In doing this, we shall have need of two theorems.

Theorem 7. Let the function $f(u)$ be analytic at $u = 0$, with power series expansion

$$f(u) = \sum_{n=0}^{\infty} a_n u^n, \qquad |u| < R. \tag{6.17}$$

Let the function $g(z)$ be analytic at $z = 0$, with $g(0) = 0$. Suppose that

$$g(z) = \sum_{n=1}^{\infty} b_n z^n, \qquad |z| < r, \tag{6.18}$$

and that $|g(z)| < R$ for $|z| < r$. Then the function $F(z) = f[g(z)]$ is analytic at $z = 0$, and is represented by its power series expansion

$$F(z) = \sum_{n=0}^{\infty} c_n z^n \tag{6.19}$$

for $|z| < r$. Furthermore, the series (6.19) for $F(z)$ can be obtained by substituting the series (6.18) into the series (6.17) for u, and collecting terms that involve like powers of z.

A proof of this theorem or its equivalent can be found in many books on advanced calculus.†

Suppose that a function $F(x, t)$ is analytic in t at $t = 0$ for each x in an interval I, so that

$$F(x, t) = \sum_{n=0}^{\infty} f_n(x) t^n, \qquad |t| < r, \qquad x \text{ in } I. \tag{6.20}$$

Then by the rule for differentiating an ordinary power series, we have

$$\frac{\partial F(x, t)}{\partial t} = \sum_{n=1}^{\infty} n f_n(x) t^{n-1}, \qquad |t| < r, \qquad x \text{ in } I. \tag{6.21}$$

The following question now arises: assuming that $\partial F(x, t)/\partial x$ exists, when is it true that

$$\frac{\partial F(x, t)}{\partial x} = \sum_{n=0}^{\infty} f_n'(x) t^n \ ? \tag{6.22}$$

† See, for example, page 256 of the book by Olmstead, Reference 3 at the end of this chapter.

A set of sufficient conditions for the termwise differentiation of the series (6.20) with respect to x is given by the following theorem.

Theorem 8.   Let $F(x, t)$ and $\partial F(x, t)/\partial x$ be analytic in t at $t = 0$ for x in an interval I, so that

$$F(x, t) = \sum_{n=0}^{\infty} f_n(x)t^n, \tag{6.23}$$

$$\frac{\partial F(x, t)}{\partial x} = \sum_{n=0}^{\infty} g_n(x)t^n \tag{6.24}$$

for $|t| < r$ and for x in I. Furthermore, let the partial derivatives of $F(x, t)$ of all orders exist and be continuous for $|t| < r$ and for x in I. Then the derivatives $f_n'(x)$ exist and $g_n(x) = f_n'(x)$ for x in I and $n \geq 0$.

Proof.   The assumption about the continuity of the partial derivatives of $F(x, t)$ insures that the order of differentiation does not matter. Thus

$$\frac{\partial^2 F(x, t)}{\partial t\, \partial x} = \frac{\partial^2 F(x, t)}{\partial x\, \partial t}, \qquad \frac{\partial^3 F(x, t)}{\partial t^2\, \partial x} = \frac{\partial^3 F(x, t)}{\partial x\, \partial t^2},$$

and so on. Now from equation (6.23) we have

$$f_n(x) = n! \left[\frac{\partial^n F(x, t)}{\partial t^n} \right]_{t=0},$$

and from equation (6.24) we have

$$g_n(x) = n! \left[\frac{\partial^{n+1} F(x, t)}{\partial t^n \partial x} \right]_{t=0}.$$

Then $f_n'(x)$ exists and

$$f_n'(x) = n! \frac{\partial}{\partial x} \left[\frac{\partial^n F(x, t)}{\partial t^n} \right]_{t=0} = n! \left[\frac{\partial^{n+1} F(x, t)}{\partial t^n\, \partial x} \right]_{t=0} = g_n(x).$$

6.5 Legendre Polynomials

We shall consider the set of functions generated by the function

$$F(x, t) = (1 - 2xt + t^2)^{-1/2}. \tag{6.25}$$

In order to obtain the expansion of $F(x, t)$ in powers of t, we first write

$$F(x, t) = (1 - u)^{-1/2}, \tag{6.26}$$

where

$$u(x, t) = 2xt - t^2, \tag{6.27}$$

and expand F in a power series in u. The binomial series

$$(1 + z)^\alpha = 1 + \sum_{m=1}^{\infty} \frac{\alpha(\alpha - 1)(\alpha - 2) \cdots (\alpha - m + 1)}{m!} z^m \tag{6.28}$$

converges for $|z| < 1$, for every real number α. (When α is a nonnegative integer, the series is finite and converges for all z.) Then

$$F(x, t) = 1 + \sum_{m=1}^{\infty} \frac{(-\frac{1}{2})(-\frac{1}{2} - 1)(-\frac{1}{2} - 2) \cdots (-\frac{1}{2} - m + 1)(-u)^m}{m!}$$

$$= 1 + \sum_{m=1}^{\infty} \frac{1 \cdot 3 \cdot 5 \cdots (2m - 1)}{2^m m!} u^m \qquad (6.29)$$

$$= \sum_{m=0}^{\infty} \frac{(2m)!}{2^{2m} m!} u^m$$

whenever $|u| = |2xt - t^2|$ is less than one. In particular, the expansion is valid when $|x| \le 1$ and $|t| < \sqrt{2} - 1$, for then

$$|u| \le 2|x||t| + |t|^2 < 1.$$

Each of the quantities $u^m = (2xt - t^2)^m$ in equation (6.29) can be expanded in a finite power series in t,

$$u^m = \sum_{j=0}^{m} \frac{(-1)^j m! (2x)^{m-j}}{j! (m-j)!} t^{m+j} \qquad (6.30)$$

valid for all x and t. Hence

$$F(x, t) = \sum_{m=0}^{\infty} \left[\sum_{j=0}^{m} \frac{(-1)^j (2m)! (2x)^{m-j}}{2^{2m} m! j! (m-j)!} t^{m+j} \right], \qquad (6.31)$$

for $|x| \le 1$ and $|t| < \sqrt{2} - 1$. According to Theorem 7, $F(x, t)$ is analytic in t at $t = 0$, and is represented by its Maclaurin series in t for $|x| \le 1$ and $|t| < \sqrt{2} - 1$.

The Maclaurin series can be obtained by collecting the terms in formula (6.31) with like powers of t. In order to accomplish this, let us consider rectangular coordinates j and m in a plane, as in Figure 6.1. The values

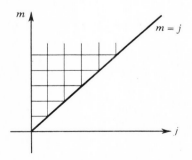

FIGURE 6.1

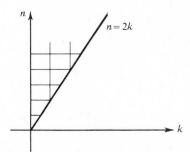

FIGURE 6.2

assumed by the indices j and m in the series (6.31) correspond to the points with integer coordinates in the region of the jm plane that is described by means of the inequalities

$$0 \le j \le m, \qquad m \ge 0. \tag{6.32}$$

This region is shown in Figure 6.1. If we introduce new indices of summation k and n by means of the equations

$$k = j, \qquad n = m + j \tag{6.33a}$$

$$j = k, \qquad m = n - k, \tag{6.33b}$$

the corresponding region in the kn plane is described by the inequalities

$$0 \le k \le n - k, \qquad n - k \ge 0, \tag{6.34}$$

or equivalently, by the inequalities

$$0 \le k \le \frac{n}{2}, \qquad n \ge 0. \tag{6.35}$$

This region is shown in Figure 6.2.

For any real number α, we use the symbol $[\alpha]$ to denote the largest integer N such that $N \le \alpha$. For instance,

$$[\tfrac{5}{4}] = 1, \qquad [\pi] = 3, \qquad [-\tfrac{5}{3}] = -2.$$

Since n and k are integers when m and j are integers, we actually have

$$0 \le k \le \left[\frac{n}{2} \right] \tag{6.36}$$

for the new indices n and k.

If we introduce the new indices n and k in the series (6.31) by means of the formulas (6.33b), and collect the terms with like powers of t, we find that

$$F(x, t) = \sum_{n=0}^{\infty} \left[\sum_{k=0}^{[n/2]} \frac{(-1)^k (2n - 2k)! \, x^{n-2k}}{2^n (n - k)! \, k! \, (n - 2k)!} \right] t^n \tag{6.37}$$

for $|x| \le 1$ and $|t| < \sqrt{2} - 1$.

The coefficient of t^n in the above series is a polynomial in x of degree n; we denote it by the symbol $P_n(x)$. Then

$$F(x, t) = (1 - 2xt + t^2)^{-1/2} = \sum_{n=0}^{\infty} P_n(x) t^n, \tag{6.38}$$

where

$$P_n(x) = \sum_{k=0}^{[n/2]} \frac{(-1)^k (2n - 2k)! \, x^{n-2k}}{2^n (n - k)! \, k! \, (n - 2k)!}. \tag{6.39}$$

The polynomials $P_n(x)$ are called the *Legendre polynomials*.

A few properties of these polynomials are easily found. We see from formula (6.39) that $P_n(x)$ involves only even powers of x when n is even and only odd powers when n is odd. The first two Legendre polynomials are found, from formula (6.39), to be

$$P_0(x) = 1, \qquad P_1(x) = x. \tag{6.40}$$

Since

$$F(1, t) = \sum_{n=0}^{\infty} P_n(1)t^n \tag{6.41}$$

and also

$$F(1, t) = (1 - 2t + t^2)^{-1/2} = \frac{1}{1 - t} = \sum_{n=0}^{\infty} t^n, \tag{6.42}$$

we can see by comparing coefficients of like powers of t that

$$P_n(1) = 1. \tag{6.43}$$

An alternative formula for the Legendre polynomials is the *Rodrigues formula*

$$P_n(x) = \frac{1}{2^n n!} \frac{d^n}{dx^n} (x^2 - 1)^n. \tag{6.44}$$

In order to verify the validity of this formula, let us expand the function $(x^2 - 1)^n$ in a binomial series,

$$(x^2 - 1)^n = \sum_{k=0}^{n} \frac{(-1)^k n!}{k!\,(n - k)!} x^{2n - 2k} \tag{6.45}$$

and differentiate n times. Since

$$\frac{d^n}{dx^n} x^r = \begin{cases} \dfrac{r!}{(n - r)!}, & n \leq r \\[2mm] 0, & n > r \end{cases}$$

we have

$$\frac{d^n}{dx^n} (x^2 - 1)^n = \sum_{k=0}^{[n/2]} \frac{(-1)^k n!\,(2n - 2k)!}{k!\,(n - k)!\,(n - 2k)!} x^{n - 2k}. \tag{6.46}$$

Comparing the right-hand member of this equation with the expression in formula (6.39), we see that

$$\frac{d^n}{dx^n} (x^2 - 1)^n = 2^n n!\, P_n(x).$$

6.5 EXERCISES

1. Let

$$F(t) = \sum_{m=0}^{\infty} \left(\sum_{j=0}^{m} \alpha_{j,m} t^{m+j} \right).$$

Show that the rearrangement of terms that corresponds to the change of indices

$$k = j, \qquad n = m + j$$

leads to the formula

$$F(t) = \sum_{n=0}^{\infty} \left(\sum_{k=0}^{[n/2]} \alpha_{k,n-k} \right) t^n.$$

2. Let

$$F(t) = \sum_{m=0}^{\infty} \left(\sum_{j=0}^{\infty} \alpha_{j,m} t^{m+j} \right).$$

Show that the rearrangement of terms that corresponds to the change of indices

$$k = j, \qquad n = m + j$$

leads to the formula

$$F(t) = \sum_{n=0}^{\infty} \left(\sum_{k=0}^{n} \alpha_{k,n-k} \right) t^n.$$

3. Prove that

$$P_n(-1) = (-1)^n, \qquad P_{2n+1}(0) = 0, \qquad P_{2n}(0) = \frac{(-1)^n (2n)!}{2^{2n}(n!)^2}.$$

4. Let $f(x)$ possess a continuous nth-order derivative on the interval $[-1, 1]$. Show that

$$\int_{-1}^{1} f(x) P_n(x) \, dx = \frac{(-1)^n}{2^n n!} \int_{-1}^{1} (x^2 - 1)^n f^{(n)}(x) \, dx.$$

6.6 Properties of Legendre Polynomials

The generating function

$$F(x, t) = (1 - 2xt + t^2)^{-1/2} \tag{6.47}$$

for the Legendre polynomials has as its first partial derivatives

$$\frac{\partial F(x, t)}{\partial t} = (x - t)(1 - 2xt + t^2)^{-3/2} \tag{6.48}$$

$$\frac{\partial F(x, t)}{\partial x} = t(1 - 2xt + t^2)^{-3/2}. \tag{6.49}$$

From the formulas (6.47) and (6.48) we see that

$$(1 - 2xt + t^2)\frac{\partial F}{\partial t} = (x - t)F. \tag{6.50}$$

Substituting the series

$$F(x, t) = \sum_{n=0}^{\infty} P_n(x) t^n, \qquad \frac{\partial F(x, t)}{\partial t} = \sum_{n=1}^{\infty} n P_n(x) t^{n-1} \tag{6.51}$$

into this equation, we find that

$$\sum_{n=1}^{\infty} nP_n(x)t^{n-1} - 2x \sum_{n=1}^{\infty} nP_n(x)t^n + \sum_{n=1}^{\infty} nP_n(x)t^{n+1}$$

$$= x \sum_{n=0}^{\infty} P_n(x)t^n - \sum_{n=0}^{\infty} P_n(x)t^{n+1}. \quad (6.52)$$

By shifting indices we may write this equation as

$$\sum_{n=1}^{\infty} nP_n(x)t^{n-1} - 2x \sum_{n=2}^{\infty} (n-1)P_{n-1}(x)t^{n-1} + \sum_{n=2}^{\infty} (n-2)P_{n-2}(x)t^{n-1}$$

$$= x \sum_{n=1}^{\infty} P_{n-1}(x)t^{n-1} - \sum_{n=2}^{\infty} P_{n-2}(x)t^{n-1}$$

or

$$[P_1(x) - xP_0(x)] + \sum_{n=2}^{\infty} [nP_n(x) - x(2n-1)P_{n-1}(x)$$

$$+ (n-1)P_{n-2}(x)]t^{n-1} = 0.$$

Consequently the Legendre polynomials must satisfy the pure recurrence relation

$$nP_n(x) = (2n-1)xP_{n-1}(x) - (n-1)P_{n-2}(x), \qquad n \geq 2. \quad (6.53)$$

Given that $P_0(x) = 1$ and $P_1(x) = x$, this relation can be used to calculate polynomials of higher order. The first few Legendre polynomials are found to be

$$P_0(x) = 1$$
$$P_1(x) = x$$
$$P_2(x) = \tfrac{1}{2}(3x^2 - 1)$$
$$P_3(x) = \tfrac{1}{2}(5x^3 - 3x) \qquad\qquad (6.54)$$
$$P_4(x) = \tfrac{1}{8}(35x^4 - 30x^2 + 3)$$
$$P_5(x) = \tfrac{1}{8}(63x^5 - 70x^3 + 15x).$$

Going back to formulas (6.47) and (6.49), we see that the generating function $F(x, t)$ also satisfies the partial differential equation

$$(x - t)\frac{\partial F(x, t)}{\partial x} - t\frac{\partial F(x, t)}{\partial t} = 0. \quad (6.55)$$

Since $F(x, t)$ satisfies the hypotheses of Theorem 8, we have

$$\frac{\partial F(x, t)}{\partial x} = \sum_{n=0}^{\infty} P_n{}'(x)t^n, \qquad |x| < 1, |t| < \sqrt{2} - 1 \quad (6.56)$$

Substituting this series and the first of the series (6.51) into equation (6.55), we find that

$$\sum_{n=0}^{\infty} xP_n'(x)t^n - \sum_{n=0}^{\infty} P_n'(x)t^{n+1} - \sum_{n=1}^{\infty} nP_n(x)t^n = 0,$$

or

$$\sum_{n=0}^{\infty} xP_n'(x)t^n - \sum_{n=1}^{\infty} P_{n-1}'(x)t^n - \sum_{n=1}^{\infty} nP_n(x)t^n = 0$$

or

$$xP_0'(x) + \sum_{n=1}^{\infty} [xP_n'(x) - P_{n-1}'(x) - nP_n(x)]t^n = 0.$$

Thus the Legendre polynomials are seen to satisfy the differential recurrence relation

$$xP_n'(x) = P_{n-1}'(x) + nP_n(x), \qquad n \geq 1. \tag{6.57}$$

The recurrence relations (6.53) and (6.57) can be used to derive an equation that involves only $P_n(x)$ and its derivatives. Differentiation of the recurrence relation (6.53) yields the relation

$$nP_n'(x) = (2n-1)xP_{n-1}'(x) + (2n-1)P_{n-1}(x) - (n-1)P_{n-2}'(x), \qquad (n \geq 2). \tag{6.58}$$

From formula (6.57) we have

$$P_{n-1}'(x) = xP_n'(x) - nP_n(x), \qquad n \geq 1. \tag{6.59}$$

and

$$P_{n-2}'(x) = xP_{n-1}'(x) - (n-1)P_{n-1}(x)$$
$$= x^2 P_n'(x) - nxP_n(x) - (n-1)P_{n-1}(x), \qquad n \geq 2. \tag{6.60}$$

Substituting these expressions for $P_{n-1}'(x)$ and $P_{n-2}'(x)$ into equation (6.58) and simplifying, we have

$$P_n'(x) = x^2 P_n'(x) - nxP_n(x) + nP_{n-1}(x), \qquad n \geq 2. \tag{6.61}$$

Differentiating this equation, we have

$$P_n''(x) = x^2 P_n''(x) + (2-n)xP_n'(x) - nP_n(x) + nP_{n-1}'(x), \qquad n \geq 2. \tag{6.62}$$

Using formula (6.59) to eliminate $P_{n-1}'(x)$, we find that

$$(1 - x^2)P_n''(x) - 2xP_n'(x) + n(n+1)P_n(x) = 0. \tag{6.63}$$

This equation, as derived, is valid for $n \geq 2$. However, in view of the fact that $P_0(x) = 1$ and $P_1(x) = x$, it is seen to be valid for $n = 0$ and $n = 1$ also.

The differential equation

$$(1 - x^2)\frac{d^2 y}{dx^2} - 2x\frac{dy}{dx} + \alpha(\alpha + 1)y = 0 \tag{6.64}$$

is known as Legendre's equation of order α. Evidently when α is a nonnegative integer n, one solution of the equation is the polynomial $P_n(x)$. The differential equation (6.64) can be written in the form

$$\frac{d}{dx}\left[(1-x^2)\frac{dy}{dx}\right] + \alpha(\alpha+1)y = 0. \tag{6.65}$$

6.6 EXERCISES

1. The zeros of $P_n(x)$ lie on the interval $(-1, 1)$. Calculate the zeros of the functions $P_1(x)$, $P_2(x)$, and $P_3(x)$.

2. Draw, on the same figure, the graphs of the functions $P_i(x)$, $0 \le i \le 3$ for $-1 \le x \le 1$.

3. Verify that the generating function $F(x, t)$ satisfies the equation

$$(1 - 2xt + t^2)F_x = tF.$$

From this equation, deduce the recurrence relation

$$P'_{n+2}(x) - 2xP'_{n+1}(x) + P_n'(x) = P_{n+1}(x), \qquad n \ge 0.$$

4. Deduce the recurrence relation derived in Problem 3 from the relations (6.53) and (6.57).

5. Verify that the generating function $F(x, t)$ satisfies the equation

$$(1 - t^2)F_x - 2t^2F_t = tF.$$

From this equation, derive the relation

$$P'_{n+2}(x) - P_n'(x) = 2(n + 3)P_{n+1}(x), \qquad n \ge 0.$$

6. Calculate the polynomials $P_2(x)$, $P_3(x)$ and $P_4(x)$ from the recurrence relation (6.53).

6.7 Orthogonality

That the Legendre polynomials are simply orthogonal over the interval $-1 < x < 1$ can be established from the differential equation (6.65). If m and n are distinct nonnegative integers, we have

$$\frac{d}{dx}[(1 - x^2)P_n'(x)] + n(n + 1)P_n(x) = 0 \tag{6.66a}$$

and

$$\frac{d}{dx}[(1 - x^2)P_m'(x)] + m(m + 1)P_m(x) = 0. \tag{6.66b}$$

Multiplying the first equation through by $P_m(x)$ and the second by $P_n(x)$ and subtracting, we have

$$[n(n + 1) - m(m + 1)]P_m(x)P_n(x) \tag{6.67}$$

$$= P_n(x) \frac{d}{dx} [(1 - x^2)P_m'(x)] - P_m(x) \frac{d}{dx} [(1 - x^2)P_n'(x)].$$

This equation can be written in the form

$$(n - m)(n + m + 1)P_m(x)P_n(x) = \frac{d}{dx} \{(1 - x^2)[P_n(x)P_m'(x) - P_m(x)P_n'(x)]\}. \tag{6.68}$$

Integrating both sides of this equation with respect to x from -1 to 1, we have

$$(n - m)(n + m + 1) \int_{-1}^{1} P_m(x)P_n(x)\, dx$$

$$= \{(1 - x^2)[P_n(x)P_m'(x) - P_m(x)P_n'(x)]\}_{-1}^{1} = 0. \tag{6.69}$$

Since $m \neq n$, we have

$$\int_{-1}^{1} P_m(x)P_n(x)\, dx = 0. \tag{6.70}$$

We next derive a formula for the quantities

$$C_n = \|P_n(x)\|^2 = \int_{-1}^{1} [P_n(x)]^2\, dx. \tag{6.71}$$

From the the recurrence relation (6.53), we have

$$P_n(x) = \frac{2n - 1}{n} xP_{n-1}(x) - \frac{n - 1}{n} P_{n-2}(x), \qquad n \geq 2. \tag{6.72}$$

Therefore

$$C_n = \int_{-1}^{1} P_n(x) \left[\frac{2n - 1}{n} xP_{n-1}(x) - \frac{n - 1}{n} P_{n-2}(x) \right] dx, \tag{6.73}$$

and because of the orthogonality property (6.70),

$$C_n = \frac{2n - 1}{n} \int_{-1}^{1} xP_n(x)P_{n-1}(x)\, dx, \qquad n \geq 2. \tag{6.74}$$

From the recurrence relation (6.53), we also have that

$$xP_n(x) = \frac{1}{2n - 1} [(n + 1)P_{n+1}(x) + nP_{n-1}(x)], \qquad n \geq 1. \tag{6.75}$$

Substituting this expression for $xP_n(x)$ into formula (6.74) and using the orthogonality property (6.70), we find that

$$C_n = \frac{2n - 1}{2n + 1} \int_{-1}^{1} [P_{n-1}(x)]^2 \, dx, \qquad (6.76)$$

or

$$C_n = \frac{2n - 1}{2n + 1} C_{n-1}, \qquad n \geq 2. \qquad (6.77)$$

Since $P_0(x) = 1$ and $P_1(x) = x$, we have

$$C_0 = \int_{-1}^{1} dx = 2, \qquad C_1 = \int_{-1}^{1} x^2 \, dx = \frac{2}{3}. \qquad (6.78)$$

Making use of formula (6.77), we find that

$$C_2 = \frac{3}{5} C_1 \frac{2}{3} \frac{3}{5} = \frac{2}{5}$$

$$C_3 = \frac{5}{7} C_2 \frac{2}{5} \frac{5}{7} = \frac{2}{7}.$$

It is easy to show, by using mathematical induction, that

$$C_n = \frac{2}{2n + 1}, \qquad n \geq 0. \qquad (6.79)$$

6.7 EXERCISES

1. Let the functions $p_n{}^m(x)$, where m and n are nonnegative integers with $0 \leq m \leq n$, be defined by means of the relation

$$p_n{}^m(x) = \frac{d^m}{dx^m} p_n(x).$$

By differentiating the equation (6.63) m times, show that $p_n{}^m(x)$ is a solution of the equation

$$(1 - x^2)y'' - 2(m + 1)xy' + (n - m)(n + m + 1)y = 0.$$

2. Show that the functions $p_i{}^m(x)$ and $p_j{}^m(x)$ (see Problem 1), where $i \neq j$, are orthogonal with respect to the weight function $(1 - x^2)^m$ on the interval $(-1, 1)$.

3. The functions

$$P_n{}^m(x) = (1 - x^2)^{m/2} p_n{}^m(x) = (1 - x^2)^{m/2} \frac{d^m}{dx^m} P_n(x), \qquad 0 \leq m \leq n,$$

are called *associated Legendre functions*. Show that the functions $P_i{}^m(x)$ and $P_j{}^m(x)$, $i \neq j$, are simply orthogonal on the interval $(-1, 1)$. Show that the function $P_n{}^m(x)$ is a solution of the differential equation

$$(1 - x^2)y'' - 2xy' + \left[n(n + 1) - \frac{m^2}{1 - x^2}\right]y = 0.$$

4. Prove that

$$\int_{-1}^{1} [P_n{}^m(x)]^2 \, dx = \frac{2}{2n + 1} \frac{(n + m)!}{(n - m)!}.$$

Suggestion: use integration by parts, and make use of the differential equation satisfied by $P_n{}^m(x)$.

5. Show that the function $P_n{}^m(\cos \phi)$ is a solution of the equation

$$\frac{d}{d\phi}\left(\sin \phi \frac{dy}{d\phi}\right) + \left[n(n + 1)\sin \phi - \frac{m^2}{\sin \phi}\right]y = 0$$

on the interval $0 < \phi < \pi$.

6.8 Legendre's Differential Equation

The differential equation

$$(1 - x^2)\frac{d^2 y}{dx^2} - 2x\frac{dy}{dx} + \alpha(\alpha + 1)y = 0, \qquad (6.80)$$

where α is a real constant, is known as Legendre's equation of order α. We can assume without loss of generality that $\alpha \geq -\frac{1}{2}$. For if $\alpha < -\frac{1}{2}$, we can set $\beta = -\alpha - 1$, and then $\alpha(\alpha + 1) = \beta(\beta + 1)$, where $\beta > -\frac{1}{2}$.

When α is a nonnegative integer n, we have seen that one solution of equation (6.80) is the Legendre polynomial $P_n(x)$ of degree n. Let us now consider the differential equation for general α.

Legendre's equation has regular singular points at $x = 1$ and $x = -1$. If we make the change of variable $t = 1 - x$, the point $x = 1$ corresponds to $t = 0$ and the differential equation becomes

$$t(2 - t)\frac{d^2 y}{dt^2} + 2(1 - t)\frac{dy}{dt} + \alpha(\alpha + 1)y = 0. \qquad (6.81)$$

This equation has a regular singular point at $t = 0$, with both exponents equal to zero. By the methods of Chapter 4, two independent solutions are found to be

$$u_1 = 1 + \sum_{m=1}^{\infty} \frac{[(\alpha + 1)(\alpha + 2) \cdots (\alpha + m)][(-\alpha)(1 - \alpha) \cdots (m - 1 - \alpha)]}{2^m(m!)^2} t^m$$

$$(6.82)$$

$$u_2 = u_1 \log t + \sum_{m=1}^{\infty} a_m t^m. \qquad (6.83)$$

In terms of the variable x, these solutions are

$$u_1(x) = 1 + \sum_{m=1}^{\infty} \frac{[(\alpha+1)(\alpha+2)\cdots(\alpha+m)][(-\alpha)(1-\alpha)\cdots(m-1-\alpha)]}{2^m(m!)^2}(1-x)^m$$

(6.84)

$$u_2(x) = u_1(x)\log(1-x) + \sum_{m=1}^{\infty} a_m(1-x)^m.$$

(6.85)

The function $u_1(x)$ has the value 1 at $x = 1$ for all α. When α is not an integer, the series for $u_1(x)$ is infinite and converges for $|x - 1| < 2$. When α is a nonnegative integer n, the series (6.84) is finite and $u_1(x)$ is a polynomial of degree n. There is no other polynomial solution of Legendre's equation when $\alpha = n$, and so

$$P_n(x) = 1 + \sum_{m=1}^{n} \frac{[(n+1)(n+2)\cdots(n+m)][(-n)(1-n)\cdots(m-1-n)]}{2^m(m!)^2}(1-x)^m$$

(6.86)

or

$$P_n(x) = \sum_{m=0}^{n} \frac{(-1)^m(m+n)!}{2^m(m!)^2(n-m)!}(1-x)^m.$$

(6.87)

The solution $u_2(x)$ becomes infinite as $x \to 1$, for all α. It can be shown (Exercise 4) that when α is not an integer, the solution $u_1(x)$ becomes infinite as $x \to -1$. Thus Legendre's equation has a solution that is finite at both $x = 1$ and $x = -1$ only when α is an integer n. In this case, the only solutions that are finite at $x = 1$ and $x = -1$ are those which are multiples of $P_n(x)$. This fact is of interest in applications that give rise to Legendre's equation.

If we take the series solution (6.87) as our definition of the Legendre polynomial of degree n, we can use Theorem 5 to obtain a recurrence relation. According to this theorem, there exist constants A_n, B_n, and C_n such that

$$xP_n(x) = A_nP_{n+1}(x) + B_nP_n(x) + C_nP_{n-1}(x)$$

or

$$A_nP_{n+1}(x) + (1-x)P_n(x) + (B_n-1)P_n(x) + C_nP_{n-1}(x) = 0, \qquad n \equiv 1. \quad (6.88)$$

By comparing coefficients of $(1-x)^{n+1}$, $(1-x)^n$, and $(1-x)^0$, we find, after some calculation, that

$$A_n = \frac{n+1}{2n+1}, \qquad B_n = 0, \qquad C_n = \frac{n}{2n+1}$$

and hence the recurrence relation is

$$(n+1)P_{n+1}(x) = x(2n+1)P_n(x) - nP_{n-1}(x), \qquad n \geq 1. \quad (6.89)$$

This relation may be seen to be equivalent to the relation (6.53), which was derived from the generating function.

The Legendre polynomials are also characterized, except for constant factors, as the polynomials $\{\phi_n(x)\}$ which are orthogonal with respect to the weight function $w(x) = 1$ on the interval $-1 < x < 1$. The differential equation (6.63) which is satisfied by $\phi_n(x)$ can be derived from this orthogonality condition as follows: let

$$I = \int_{-1}^{1} \frac{d}{dx}\left[(1 - x^2)\frac{d}{dx}\,\phi_n(x)\right]Q(x)\,dx, \tag{6.90}$$

where $Q(x)$ is any polynomial of degree $\leq n - 1$. Integrating by parts, we have

$$I = [(1 - x^2)\phi_n'(x)Q(x)]_{-1}^{1} - \int_{-1}^{1} (1 - x^2)\phi_n'(x)Q'(x)\,dx,$$

where the integrated part vanishes. Integrating by parts again, we have

$$I = -[(1 - x^2)\phi_n(x)Q'(x)]_{-1}^{1} + \int_{-1}^{1} \phi_n(x)\frac{d}{dx}[(1 - x^2)Q'(x)]\,dx.$$

The integrated part vanishes, and since the quantity

$$\frac{d}{dx}[(1 - x^2)Q'(x)]$$

is a polynomial of degree $\leq n - 1$, we have $I = 0$.

Since the quantity

$$\frac{d}{dx}[(1 - x^2)\phi_n'(x)]$$

in the integrand in formula (6.90) is a polynomial of degree n, and since it is orthogonal to every polynomial of degree $< n$, it must be a constant multiple of $\phi_n(x)$. Thus, there is a constant A_n such that

$$\frac{d}{dx}[(1 - x^2)\phi_n'(x)] = A_n\phi_n(x). \tag{6.91}$$

If we write

$$\phi_n(x) = a_n x^n + a_{n-1}x^{n-1} + \cdots + a_0,$$

and compare the coefficients of x^n on both sides of this equation, we find that $A_n = -n(n + 1)$, and hence

$$\frac{d}{dx}\left[(1 - x^2)\frac{d}{dx}\,\phi_n(x)\right] + n(n + 1)\phi_n(x) = 0. \tag{6.92}$$

This is Legendre's equation of order n.

This process for finding the differential equation from the weight function can be generalized somewhat. See Exercise 6 below, and also Exercises 7 and 8 of Section 6.10.

6.8 EXERCISES

1. Express the polynomial $Q(x) = x^3 + 2x^2 = 2$ in terms of Legendre polynomials.

2. Derive the formula

$$\|P_n\|^2 = \int_{-1}^{1} [P_n(x)]^2 \, dx = \frac{2}{2n + 1}$$

by using the Rodrigues formula (6.44) and repeated integration by parts.

3. Let $P_\alpha(x)$ be the solution of Legendre's differential equation, which is finite at $x = 1$, with $P_\alpha(1) = 1$. Show that a second solution of Legendre's equation is

$$P_\alpha(x) \int \frac{dx}{(1 - x^2)[P_\alpha(x)]^2}.$$

4. In Section 6.8 it was shown that Legendre's equation possessed solutions of the form

$$u_1(x) = \sum_{m=0}^{\infty} A_m(1 - x)^m, \qquad (A_0 = 1)$$

$$u_2(x) = u_1(x) \log (1 - x) + \sum_{m=1}^{\infty} B_m(1 - x)^m$$

where the power series converge for $|x - 1| < 2$.
(a) Show that Legendre's equation also possesses solutions of the form

$$v_1(x) = \sum_{m=0}^{\infty} A_m(1 + x)^m$$

$$v_2(x) = v_1(x) \log (1 + x) + \sum_{m=1}^{\infty} B_m(1 + x)^m,$$

where the power series converge for $|x + 1| < 2$.
(b) Show that, when α is not an integer, the solution $u_1(x)$ becomes infinite as $x \to -1$. One method is outlined by the following remarks. For $|x| < 1$. there exist constants C_1 and C_2 such that

$$u_1(x) = C_1 v_1(x) + C_2 v_2(x).$$

If $C_2 \neq 0$, then $u_1(x)$ becomes infinite as $x \to -1$. Suppose that $C_2 = 0$. Then $C_1 = 1$, since $u_1(0) = v_1(0)$. Hence $u_1(x) = v_1(x)$. But from the series for $u_1(x)$ and $v_1(x)$ it can be seen that $u_1(-x) = v_1(x)$, so that $u_1(x)$ is an even function. But then the odd derivatives of $u_1(x)$ must vanish at $x = 0$. This is not true, as an examination of the series expressions for these derivatives reveals. Hence $C_2 \neq 0$, and $u_1(x)$ becomes infinite as $x \to -1$.

5. (a) Show that the change of variable $x = \cos \phi$ transforms Legendre's equation into the equation

$$\frac{d^2 y}{d\phi^2} + \frac{dy}{d\phi} \cot \phi + \alpha(\alpha + 1)y = 0.$$

(b) Show that this equation has nontrivial solutions that are finite at $\phi = 0$, π when, and only when α is an integer n, and that these solutions are of the form $C_n P_n(\cos \phi)$, where C_n is an arbitrary constant.

6. Let $\{\phi_n(x)\}$ be the set of orthogonal polynomials that corresponds to the positive weight function $w(x)$ on the finite interval $a < x < b$. Let $w(x)$ be of the form

$$w(x) = (x - a)^\alpha (b - x)^\beta,$$

where $\alpha > -1$, $\beta > -1$.

(a) Show that

$$\int_b^a \frac{d}{dx} [(x - a)(x - b)\phi_n'(x)w(x)]Q(x)\, dx = 0$$

for every polynomial $Q(x)$ of degree less than n.

(b) Show that $\phi_n(x)$ satisfies the second-order differential equation

$$(x - a)(x - b)\phi_n'' + [(2 + \alpha + \beta)x - a(1 + \beta) - b(1 + \alpha)]\phi_n'$$
$$= [n^2 + (\alpha + \beta + 1)n]\phi_n.$$

7. Polynomial sets that are orthogonal over the interval $-1 < x < 1$ with respect to weight functions of the form $w(x) = (1 - x)^\alpha (1 + x)^\beta$, $\alpha, \beta > -1$, are known as *Jacobi polynomials*. Show that the polynomial of degree n of such a set satisfies the differential equation

$$(1 - x^2)y'' + [(\beta - \alpha) - (\alpha + \beta + 2)x]y' + n(\alpha + \beta + n + 1)y = 0.$$

8. In the example that follows the proof of Theorem 3, we found the first few polynomials of the orthogonal set that corresponds to the weight function $w(x) = \sqrt{x}$ on the interval $0 < x < 1$.

(a) Show that the nth-degree polynomial of this set satisfies the differential equation

$$2(x^2 - x)y'' + (5x - 3)y' - n(2n + 3)y = 0.$$

(b) Show that the differential equation of (a) above possesses the polynomial solution

$$\phi_n(x) =$$

$$1 - \sum_{k=0}^{n} \frac{n(2n + 3)[5 - n(2n + 3)] \cdots [(k - 1)(2k + 1) - n(2n + 3)]}{k!\, 1 \cdot 3 \cdot 5 \cdots (2k + 1)} x^k$$

(c) Show that the polynomials of part (b) are orthogonal with respect to the weight function $w(x) = \sqrt{x}$ on the interval $0 < x < 1$.

6.9 Tchebycheff Polynomials

Sets of orthogonal polynomials that are orthogonal on the interval $-1 < x < 1$ with respect to weight functions of the form

$$w(x) = (1 - x)^\alpha (1 + x)^\beta, \qquad \alpha > -1, \beta > -1, \qquad (6.93)$$

are known as *Jacobi polynomials*. (It is necessary to restrict the constants α and β in order that the integrals

$$\int_{-1}^{1} w(x) x^m \, dx, \qquad m = 0, 1, 2, \ldots,$$

all exist.) The Legendre polynomials are a special class of Jacobi polynomials, with $\alpha = \beta = 0$.

General treatments of Jacobi polynomials can be found in the references by Jackson, Rainville, and Szego. Here we shall be concerned with two particular classes of Jacobi polynomials. The *Tchebycheff polynomials of the first kind* have the weight function $w(x) = (1 - x^2)^{-1/2}$ and correspond to the case $\alpha = \beta = -\frac{1}{2}$. The *Tchebycheff polynomials of the second kind* have the weight function $w(x) = (1 - x^2)^{1/2}$ and correspond to the case $\alpha = \beta = \frac{1}{2}$. Generating functions for these polynomial sets are known, and their properties can be derived much in the same way as for the Legendre polynomials. However, we shall leave this approach to the exercises. Here we shall adopt a different procedure based on a special relationship between the Tchebycheff polynomials and certain trigonometric functions. We shall need the following lemma.

Lemma. Let n be any nonnegative integer. Then there exist polynomials $T_n(x)$ and $S_n(x)$, of degree n, such that

$$\cos n\theta = T_n(\cos \theta) \qquad (6.94)$$

$$\sin(n + 1)\theta = \sin \theta S_n(\cos \theta). \qquad (6.95)$$

Proof. By DeMoivre's theorem,

$$\cos n\theta + i \sin n\theta = (\cos \theta + i \sin \theta)^n \qquad (6.96)$$

for every nonnnegative integer n. Expanding the right-hand member of this equation by the use of the binomial theorem, we have

$$\cos n\theta + i \sin n\theta = \sum_{k=0}^{n} C(n, k)(i \sin \theta)^k (\cos \theta)^{n-k}, \qquad (6.97)$$

where the quantities

$$C(n, k) = \frac{n!}{k! \, (n - k)!}$$

are the binomial coefficients. We now equate real and imaginary parts in equation (6.97). The real terms in the sum on the right in this equation correspond to the even values of k. When $k = 2m$, $m = 0, 1, 2, \ldots, [n/2]$, then

$$(i \sin \theta)^k = (i \sin \theta)2^m = (-1)^m(1 - \cos^2 \theta)^m.$$

Equating real parts in equation (6.97), we have

$$\cos n\theta = \sum_{m=0}^{[n/2]} (-1)^m C(n, 2m)(1 - \cos^2 \theta)^m (\cos \theta)^{n-2m}. \tag{6.98}$$

The right-hand member of this equation is a polynomial of degree n in $\cos \theta$, which we denote by $T_n(\cos \theta)$. Then

$$\cos n\theta = T_n (\cos \theta), \tag{6.99}$$

where

$$T_n(x) = \sum_{m=0}^{[n/2]} (-1)^m \frac{n!}{(2m)! (n - 2m)!} (1 - x^2)^m x^{n-2m}. \tag{6.100}$$

We note that

$$T_n(1) = \cos 0 = 1, \qquad n = 0, 1, 2, \ldots. \tag{6.101}$$

The imaginary terms in the sum on the right in equation (6.97) correspond to the odd values of k. When $k = 2m + 1$, $m = 0, 1, 2, \ldots, [(n - 1)/2]$,

$$(i \sin \theta)^k = (i \sin \theta)^{2m+1} = (-1)^m i \sin \theta(1 - \cos^2 \theta)^m.$$

Equating imaginary parts in equation (6.97), we have

$$\sin n\theta = \sin \theta \sum_{m=0}^{[(n-1)/2]} (-1)^m C(n, 2m + 1)(1 - \cos^2 \theta)^m (\cos \theta)^{n-2m-1}. \tag{6.102}$$

The sum on the right is a polynomial of degree $n - 1$ in $\cos \theta$. We denote it by $S_{n-1}(\cos \theta)$. Then

$$\sin n\theta = \sin \theta S_{n-1}(\cos \theta) \tag{6.103}$$

and

$$\sin (n + 1)\theta = \sin \theta S_n(\cos \theta), \tag{6.104}$$

where

$$S_n(x) = \sum_{m=0}^{[n/2]} (-1)^m \frac{(n + 1)!}{(2m + 1)! (n - 2m)!} (1 - x^2)^m x^{n-2m}. \tag{6.105}$$

We note that

$$S_n(1) = \lim_{\theta \to 0} \frac{\sin(n + 1)\theta}{\sin \theta} = n + 1. \tag{6.106}$$

Theorem 9. The polynomial set $\{T_n(x)\}$ is orthogonal on the interval $-1 < x < 1$ with respect to the weight function $(1 - x^2)^{-1/2}$. The polynomial set $\{S_n(x)\}$ is orthogonal on the same interval with respect to the weight function $(1 - x^2)^{1/2}$. Furthermore

$$\|T_0\|^2 = \pi, \|T_n\|^2 = \frac{\pi}{2}, n = 1, 2, 3, \ldots, \qquad \text{and} \qquad \|S_n\|^2 = \frac{\pi}{2}, n = 0, 1, 2, \ldots.$$

Proof. First let us consider the quantities

$$(T_m, T_n) = \int_{-1}^{1} \frac{1}{\sqrt{1 - x^2}} T_m(x) T_n(x) \, dx. \tag{6.107}$$

Making the change of variable $x = \cos \theta$, where $0 \le \theta \le \pi$, we have

$$(T_m, T_n) = \int_{0}^{\pi} T_m(\cos \theta) T_n(\cos \theta) \, d\theta. \tag{6.108}$$

By virtue of property (6.99),

$$(T_m, T_n) = \int_{0}^{\pi} \cos m\theta \cos n\theta \, d\theta. \tag{6.109}$$

Direct integration shows that

$$(T_m, T_n) = \begin{cases} 0, & m \ne n \\ \dfrac{\pi}{2}, & m = n \ne 0 \\ \pi, & m = n = 0. \end{cases} \tag{6.110}$$

For the polynomials $S_n(x)$ we have

$$(S_m, S_n) = \int_{-1}^{1} \sqrt{1 - x^2} S_m(x) S_n(x) \, dx \tag{6.111}$$

$$= \int_{0}^{\pi} \sin^2 \theta \, S_m(\cos \theta) S_n(\cos \theta) \, d\theta$$

where again we have set $x = \cos \theta$, $0 \le \theta \le \pi$. In view of formula (6.104), we can write

$$(S_m, S_n) = \int_{0}^{\pi} \sin(m + 1)\theta \sin(n + 1)\theta \, d\theta. \tag{6.112}$$

Direct integration shows that

$$(S_m, S_n) = \begin{cases} 0, & m \ne n \\ \dfrac{\pi}{2}, & m = n. \end{cases} \tag{6.113}$$

We now define the Tchebycheff polynomials of the first and second kinds to be the polynomials $\{T_n(x)\}$ and $\{S_n(x)\}$, respectively. The polynomials of the first kind must satisfy a recurrence relation of the form

$$x T_n(x) = A_n T_{n+1}(x) + B_n(x) + C_n T_{n-1}(x),$$

according to Theorem 5. Setting $x = \cos \theta$, and using property (6.99), we see that this relation can be written in the form

$$\cos n\theta \cos \theta = A_n \cos(n + 1)\theta + B_n \cos n\theta + C_n \cos(n - 1)\theta.$$

From the trigonometric identity

$$\cos n\theta \cos \theta = A_n \cos(n+1)\theta + B_n \cos n\theta + C_n \cos(n-1)\theta$$

we see that $A_n = C_n = \frac{1}{2}$, $B_n = 0$. Hence the Tchebycheff polynomials of the first kind satisfy the recurrence relation

$$2xT_n(x) = T_{n+1}(x) + T_{n-1}(x), \qquad n \geq 1. \tag{6.114}$$

In a similar fashion, it can be shown that the Tchebycheff polynomials of the second kind satisfy the recurrence relation

$$2xS_n(x) = S_{n+1}(x) + S_{n-1}(x), \qquad n \geq 1. \tag{6.115}$$

The function $\cos n\theta$ is a solution of the differential equation

$$\frac{d^2 y}{d\theta^2} + n^2 y = 0. \tag{6.116}$$

Therefore the change of variable $x = \cos \theta$ leads to a differential equation that is satisfied by $T_n(x)$. Since

$$\frac{dy}{d\theta} = \frac{dy}{dx}\frac{dx}{d\theta} = -\frac{dy}{dx}\sin \theta$$

and

$$\frac{d^2 y}{d\theta^2} = \frac{d^2 y}{dx^2}\sin^2\theta - \frac{dy}{dx}\cos \theta = (1-x^2)\frac{d^2 y}{dx^2} - x\frac{dy}{dx},$$

this differential equation is

$$(1-x^2)\frac{d^2 y}{dx^2} - x\frac{dy}{dx} + n^2 y = 0. \tag{6.117}$$

It is left as an exercise to show that the polynomial $S_n(x)$ satisfies the differential equation

$$(1-x^2)\frac{d^2 y}{dx^2} - 3x\frac{dy}{dx} + n(n+2)y = 0. \tag{6.118}$$

6.9 EXERCISES

1. Derive the recurrence relation (6.115) for the polynomials $S_n(x)$, using the formula (6.104).

2. Derive the differential equation (6.118) that is satisfied by $S_n(x)$, using the formula (6.104).

3. The generating function for the Tchebycheff polynomials of the first kind is

$$F(x, t) = \frac{1 - xt}{1 - 2xt + t^2}.$$

From the generating function derive:

(a) The formula for $T_n(x)$
(b) The recurrence relation (6.114)
(c) The differential equation (6.117)

4. (a) Show that when α is a nonnegative integer n, the differential equation

$$(1 - x^2)y'' - xy' + \alpha^2 y = 0$$

possesses a polynomial solution $y = T_n(x)$ of degree n, with $y(1) = 1$. Find an explicit formula for $T_n(x)$ in terms of powers of $(x - 1)$.
(b) Show that the polynomials $T_n(x)$ of part (a) are orthogonal with respect to the weight function $w(x) = (1 - x^2)^{-1/2}$ on the interval $-1 < x < 1$.
(c) Find the recurrence relation that is satisfied by the polynomials $T_n(x)$. Use the general formula (6.15).

5. The generating function for the Tchebycheff polynomials of the second kind is

$$G(x, t) = \frac{1}{1 - 2xt + t^2}.$$

From this generating function, derive:

(a) The formula (6.105) for $S_n(x)$
(b) The recurrence relation (6.115)
(c) The differential equation (6.118)

6. (a) Show that when α is a nonnegative integer n, the differential equation

$$(1 - x^2)y'' - 3xy' + \alpha(\alpha + 2)y = 0$$

possesses a polynomial solution $y = S_n(x)$, of degree n, with $y(1) = n + 1$. Obtain an explicit formula for $S_n(x)$ in terms of powers of $(x - 1)$.
(b) Show that the polynomials $S_n(x)$ of part (a) are orthogonal with respect to the weight function $w(x) = (1 - x^2)^{1/2}$ on the interval $-1 < x < 1$.
(c) Find the recurrence relation which is satisfied by the polynomials $S_n(x)$, making use of the general formula (6.15).

7. (a) Show that

$$T_0(x) = 1, \quad T_1(x) = x, \quad T_2(x) = 2x^2 - 1, \quad T_3(x) = 4x^3 - 3x$$
$$T_4(x) = 8x^4 - 8x^2 + 1, \quad T_5(x) = 16x^5 - 20x^3 + 5x.$$

(b) Show that

$$S_0(x) = 1, \quad S_1(x) = 2x, \quad S_2(x) = 4x^2 - 1, \quad S_3(x) = 8x^3 - 4x$$
$$S_4(x) = 16x^4 - 12x^2 + 1, \quad S_5(x) = 32x^5 - 32x^3 + 6x.$$

6.10   Other Sets of Orthogonal Polynomials

In addition to the Jacobi polynomials, two other sets of orthogonal polynomials seem worthy of mention in an introductory treatment. These are the Laguerre and Hermite polynomials. Both sets have an infinite interval of orthogonality. The Laguerre polynomials $L_n(x)$ are orthogonal with respect to the weight function $w(x) = e^{-x}$ on the interval $0 < x < +\infty$. The Hermite polynomials $H_n(x)$ are orthogonal with respect to the weight function $w(x) = e^{-x^2}$ on the interval $-\infty < x < +\infty$.

In the table below are listed, for convenience of reference, some of the basic properties of these and the previously discussed sets of orthogonal polynomials. The derivations of these properties are left as exercises. The reader should be warned that various authors use slightly different definitions for polynomial sets bearing the same name. However, the polynomials of two such sets usually differ only by constant factors, and by a linear change of dependent variable.

Table of Orthogonal Polynomials

I. Legendre Polynomials

$$P_n(x) = \sum_{k=0}^{[n/2]} \frac{(-1)^k (2n - 2k)!}{2^n (n - k)!\, k!\, (n - 2k)!} x^{n - 2k}$$

(a) Interval: $-1 < x < 1$.
(b) Weight function: $w(x) = 1$.
(c) Generating function:

$$(1 - 2xt + t^2)^{-1/2} = \sum_{n=0}^{\infty} P_n(x) t^n$$

(d) Recurrence relation:

$$nP_n(x) = (2n - 1)xP_{n-1}(x) - (n - 1)P_{n-2}(x) \qquad (n > 2)$$

(e) Differential equation:

$$(1 - x^2)P_n''(x) - 2xP_n'(x) + n(n + 1)P_n(x) = 0$$

(f) Rodrigues formula:

$$P_n(x) = \frac{1}{2^n n!} \frac{d^n}{dx^n} (x^2 - 1)^n$$

(g) Norm:

$$\|P_n\|^2 = \int_{-1}^{1} [P_n(x)]^2 \, dx = \frac{2}{2n + 1} \qquad (n \geq 0)$$

2. Tchebycheff Polynomials of the First Kind

$$T_n(x) = \sum_{k=0}^{[n/2]} \frac{n!\, x^{n - 2k}(x^2 - 1)^k}{(2k)!\, (n - 2k)!} = \cos\,(n \cos^{-1} x)$$

(a) Interval: $-1 < x < 1$.
(b) Weight function: $w(x) = (1 - x^2)^{-1/2}$.
(c) Generating function:

$$\frac{1 - xt}{1 - 2xt + t^2} = \sum_{n=0}^{\infty} T_n(x)t^n.$$

(d) Recurrence relation:

$$T_n(x) = 2xT_{n-1}(x) - T_{n-2}(x) \qquad (n \geq 2).$$

(e) Differential equation:

$$(1 - x^2)T_n''(x) - xT_n'(x) + n^2 T_n(x) = 0.$$

(f) Norm:

$$\|T_n\|^2 = \int_{-1}^{1} \frac{[T_n(x)]^2}{\sqrt{1 - x^2}}\, dx = \begin{cases} \pi, & n = 0 \\ \dfrac{\pi}{2}, & n \geq 1 \end{cases}$$

3. Tchebycheff Polynomials of the Second Kind

$$S_n(x) = \sum_{k=0}^{[n/2]} \frac{(n + 1)!\, x^{n-2k}(x^2 - 1)^k}{(2k + 1)!\,(n - 2k)!} = \frac{\sin[(n + 1)\cos^{-1} x]}{\sqrt{1 - x^2}}$$

(a) Interval: $-1 < x < 1$.
(b) Weight function: $w(x) = (1 - x^2)^{1/2}$.
(c) Generating function:

$$\frac{1}{1 - 2xt + t^2} = \sum_{n=0}^{\infty} S_n(x)t^n.$$

(d) Recurrence relation:

$$S_n(x) = 2xS_{n-1}(x) - S_{n-2}(x) \qquad (n \geq 2).$$

(e) Differential equation:

$$(1 - x^2)S_n''(x) - 3xS_n'(x) + n(n + 2)S_n(x) = 0.$$

(f) Norm:

$$\|S_n\|^2 = \int_{-1}^{1} \sqrt{1 - x^2}[S_n(x)]^2 = \frac{\pi}{2}, \qquad (n \geq 0).$$

4. Laguerre Polynomials

$$L_n(x) = \sum_{k=0}^{n} \frac{(-1)^k n!\, x^k}{(k!)^2(n - k)!}$$

(a) Interval: $0 < x < +\infty$.

(b) Weight function: $w(x) = e^{-x}$

(c) Generating function:

$$\frac{1}{1-t} \exp\left(\frac{-xt}{1-t}\right) = \sum_{n=0}^{\infty} L_n(x) t^n$$

(d) Recurrence relation:

$$nL_n(x) = (2n - 1 - x)L_{n-1}(x) - (n-1)L_{n-2}(x) \qquad (n \geq 2).$$

(e) Differential equation:

$$xL_n''(x) + (1 - x)L_n'(x) + nL_n(x) = 0.$$

(f) Rodrigues formula:

$$L_n(x) = \frac{1}{n!} e^x \frac{d^n}{dx^n}(x^n e^{-x}).$$

(g) Norm:

$$\|L_n\|^2 = \int_0^{\infty} e^{-x}[L_n(x)]^2 \, dx = 1 \qquad (n \geq 0).$$

5. Hermite Polynomials

$$H_n(x) = \sum_{k=0}^{[n/2]} \frac{(-1)^k n! (2x)^{n-2k}}{k!(n-2k)!}$$

(a) Interval: $-\infty < x < +\infty$.

(b) Weight function: $w(x) = e^{-x^2}$

(c) Generating function:

$$\exp(2xt - t^2) = \sum_{n=0}^{\infty} \frac{H_n(x)}{n!} t^n.$$

(d) Recurrence relation:

$$H_n(x) = 2xH_{n-1}(x) - 2(n-1)H_{n-2}(x) \qquad (n \geq 2).$$

(e) Differential equation:

$$H_n''(x) - 2xH_n'(x) + 2nH_n(x) = 0.$$

(f) Rodrigues formula:

$$H_n(x) = (-1)^n e^{x^2} \frac{d^n}{dx^n} e^{-x^2}.$$

(g) Norm:

$$\|H_n\|^2 = \int_{-\infty}^{+\infty} e^{-x^2}[H_n(x)]^2 \, dx = 2^n n! \sqrt{\pi} \qquad (n \geq 0).$$

6.10 EXERCISES

1. Starting with the generating function

$$F(x, t) = \frac{1}{1 - t} \exp\left[\frac{-xt}{1 - t}\right]$$

for the Laguerre polynomials, derive the properties of these polynomials that are listed in the table.

2. (a) Show that when α is a nonnegative integer n, the differential equation

$$xy'' + (1 - x)y' + \alpha y = 0$$

possesses a polynomial solution $y = L_n(x)$ of degree n, with $y(0) = 1$. Obtain an explicit formula for $L_n(x)$ in terms of powers of x.
(b) Show that the polynomials $L_n(x)$ of (a) above are orthogonal with respect to the weight function $w(x) = e^{-x}$ on the interval $0 < x < +\infty$.
(c) Derive the recurrence relation for the polynomials $L_n(x)$, using the general formula (6.15).

3. Show that

$$L_0(x) = 1, \quad L_1(x) = 1 - x, \quad L_2(x) = 1 - 2x + \tfrac{1}{2}x^2,$$

$$L_3(x) = 1 - 3x + \tfrac{3}{2}x^2 - \tfrac{1}{6}x^3,$$

$$L_4(x) = 1 - 4x + 3x^2 - \tfrac{3}{2}x^3 + \tfrac{1}{24} x^4$$

$$L_5(x) = 1 - 5x + 5x^2 - \tfrac{5}{3}x^3 + \tfrac{5}{24}x^4 - \tfrac{1}{120}x^5.$$

4. Starting with the generating relation

$$\exp(2xt - t^2) = \sum_{n=0}^{\infty} \frac{H_n(x)}{n!} t^n,$$

derive the properties of the Hermite polynomials $H_n(x)$ that are listed in the table.

5. (a) Show that when α is a nonnegative integer n, the differential equation

$$y'' - 2xy' + 2\alpha y = 0$$

possesses a polynomial solution $y = H_n(x)$, of degree n.
(b) Show that the polynomials $H_n(x)$ are orthogonal with respect to the weight function $w(x) = \exp(-x^2)$ on the interval $-\infty < x < +\infty$.

6. Show that

$$H_0(x) = 1, \quad H_1(x) = 2x, \quad H_2(x) = 4x^2 - 2, \quad H_3(x) = 8x^3 - 12x,$$

$$H_4(x) = 16x^4 - 48x^2 + 12, \quad H_5(x) = 32x^5 - 160x^3 + 120x.$$

7. Let $\{\phi_n(x)\}$ be the polynomial set that corresponds to the positive weight function $w(x)$ on the infinite interval $a < x < +\infty$. Let $w(x)$ be of the form

$$w(x) = ce^{-\alpha x}(x - a)^\beta,$$

where $c > 0$, $\alpha > 0$, and $\beta > -1$.

(a) Show that

$$\int_a^\infty \frac{d}{dx}[(x - a)\phi_n{}'(x)w(x)]Q(x)\,dx = 0$$

for every polynomial $Q(x)$ of degree less than n.

(b) Show that $\phi_n(x)$ satisfies the differential equation

$$(x - a)\phi_n'' + (a\alpha + \beta + 1 - \alpha x)\phi_n{}' = [n^2 - (\alpha + 1)n]\phi_n.$$

8. Let $\{\phi_n(x)\}$ be the polynomial set that corresponds to the positive weight function $w(x)$ on the interval $-\infty < x < +\infty$. Let $w(x)$ be of the form

$$w(x) = ce^{-\alpha x^2 + \beta x},$$

where $c > 0$, $\alpha > 0$.

(a) Show that

$$\int_{-\infty}^\infty \frac{d}{dx}[\phi_n{}'(x)w(x)]Q(x)\,dx = 0$$

for every polynomial $Q(x)$ of degree less than n.

(b) Show that $\phi_n(x)$ satisfies the differential equation

$$\phi_n'' + (\beta - 2\alpha x)\,\phi_n{}' = n(n - 2\alpha - 1)\phi_n.$$

REFERENCES

1. Jackson, D., *Fourier Series and Orthogonal Polynomials*, Carus Mathematical Monograph No. 6. The Mathematical Association of America, 1941.
2. MacRobert, T. M., *Spherical Harmonics*. Dover, New York, 1948.
3. Olmsted, S. M. H., *Real Variables*. Appleton, New York, 1956.
4. Rainville, E. D., *Special Functions*. Macmillan, New York, 1960.
5. Sansone, G., *Orthogonal Functions*. Interscience, New York, 1959.
6. Szego, G., *Orthogonal Polynomials*, American Mathematical Society Colloquium Publications, vol. 23. New York, 1939.

CHAPTER 7

EIGENVALUE PROBLEMS

7.1   Introduction

Eigenvalue problems arise in a number of different areas of mathematics. In order to introduce the notion of an eigenvalue problem in the area of ordinary differential equations, let us consider a second-order linear homogeneous differential equation

$$a_0(x, \lambda)\frac{d^2 y}{dx^2} + a_1(x, \lambda)\frac{dy}{dx} + a_2(x, \lambda)y = 0 \tag{7.1}$$

on an interval $a \leq x \leq b$. At least one of the coefficients $a_i(x, \lambda)$ is assumed to depend on a parameter λ as well as on the independent variable x. In addition to satisfying the differential equation (7.1), we shall require that our unknown function $y(x)$ also satisfy linear homogeneous *boundary conditions* of the form

$$\begin{aligned}
\alpha_{11}y(a) + \alpha_{12}y'(a) + \alpha_{13}y(b) + \alpha_{14}y'(b) &= 0 \\
\alpha_{21}y(a) + \alpha_{22}y'(a) + \alpha_{23}y(b) + \alpha_{24}y'(b) &= 0.
\end{aligned} \tag{7.2}$$

The quantities α_{ij} are specific real constants. We note that the boundary conditions involve the values of y and its first derivative at the two endpoints a and b of the interval $a \leq x \leq b$, in general.

The differential equation (7.1) and the boundary conditions (7.2) constitute an *eigenvalue problem*. Evidently the trivial solution $y = 0$ of the differential equation also satisfies the boundary conditions. We may ask whether there are any values of the parameter λ for which the differential equation possesses a *nontrivial* solution that satisfies the boundary conditions. Such a value of λ is called an *eigenvalue* of the problem. A corresponding nontrivial solution is called an *eigenfunction*.

The above problem can be generalized in a number of ways. For instance, the coefficients α_{ij} which appear in the boundary conditions can depend on the parameter λ, instead of being fixed constants. Also, the number of boundary conditions need not be equal to two, although this is the case in most applications. In an eigenvalue problem associated with a linear homogeneous differential equation of arbitrary order n, each linear homogeneous boundary condition may involve the values of the unknown function and its first $n-1$ derivatives at the two points a and b. In this chapter we shall be concerned almost entirely with second-order eigenvalue problems with two boundary conditions.

Let us now consider some specific examples of eigenvalue problems.

EXAMPLE 1. We consider first the eigenvalue problem that consists of the differential equation

$$\frac{d^2 y}{dx^2} + \lambda y = 0 \qquad (7.3)$$

on the interval $0 \le x \le c$, and the boundary conditions

$$y(0) = 0, \qquad y(c) = 0. \qquad (7.4)$$

For real λ, it is convenient to consider the three cases $\lambda > 0$, $\lambda = 0$, and $\lambda < 0$ separately, because the solutions of the differential equation have different forms in these three cases.

For $\lambda > 0$, let $\lambda = k^2$, where $k > 0$. Then the differential equation (7.3) becomes

$$\frac{d^2 y}{dx^2} + k^2 y = 0.$$

The general solution is

$$y = C_1 \cos kx + C_2 \sin kx,$$

where C_1 and C_2 are arbitrary constants. The condition $y(0) = 0$ requires that $C_1 = 0$. Thus, if a nontrivial solution exists, it must be of the form

$$y = C_2 \sin kx.$$

The condition $y(c) = 0$ requires that

$$C_2 \sin kc = 0.$$

This condition is satisfied if we choose $C_2 = 0$, but in this event we obtain only the trivial solution $y = 0$. However, the condition is also satisfied, regardless of the value of C_2, if we choose k to have any one of the values

$$k_n = \frac{n\pi}{c}, \qquad n = 1, 2, 3, \ldots.$$

The corresponding values of λ are

$$\lambda_n = k_n^2 = \left(\frac{n\pi}{c}\right)^2, \qquad n = 1, 2, 3, \ldots. \qquad (7.5)$$

These numbers are eigenvalues of the problem. The functions

$$y_n(x) = \sin k_n x = \sin \frac{n\pi x}{c}, \qquad n = 1, 2, 3, \dots \qquad (7.6)$$

are corresponding eigenfunctions. Here we have taken the arbitrary constant C_2 to be equal to one. Actually C_2 can have any nonzero value.

When $\lambda = 0$, equation (7.3) becomes

$$\frac{d^2 y}{dx^2} = 0.$$

The general solution is

$$y = C_1 + C_2 x.$$

The condition $y(0) = 0$ requires that $C_1 = 0$, so that

$$y = C_2 x.$$

The condition $y(c) = 0$ is satisfied if, and only if, $C_2 = 0$. Thus, when $\lambda = 0$, the only solution of the differential equation that satisfies the boundary conditions is the trivial solution $y = 0$. Hence $\lambda = 0$ is not an eigenvalue of the problem.

When $\lambda < 0$, let $\lambda = -k^2$, where $k > 0$. Then equation (7.3) becomes

$$\frac{d^2 y}{dx^2} - k^2 y = 0.$$

The general solution is

$$y = C_1 \cosh kx + C_2 \sinh kx.$$

The condition $y(0) = 0$ requires that $C_1 = 0$, so that

$$y = C_2 \sinh kx.$$

The condition $y(c) = 0$ requires that

$$C_2 \sinh kc = 0.$$

But $\sinh kc > 0$ for $k > 0$, so we must have $C_2 = 0$. Hence the only solution that satisfies the boundary conditions is the trivial solution, and so the problem has no negative eigenvalues.

If we admit complex solutions, the possibility of the existence of complex eigenvalues arises. Later on, however, we shall show that for a certain class of eigenvalue problems, of which Example 1 is a special case, no complex eigenvalues exist. Hence the only eigenvalues of the problem of Example 1 are given by formula (7.5). In each of the examples which follow, it also turns out that no complex eigenvalues exist.

EXAMPLE 2. We consider the same differential equation as in Example 1,

$$\frac{d^2 y}{dx^2} + \lambda y = 0, \qquad (7.7)$$

but this time with the boundary conditions

$$y'(0) = 0, \qquad y'(c) = 0. \tag{7.8}$$

When $\lambda > 0$, we let $\lambda = k^2$, where $k > 0$. Then

$$y = C_1 \cos kx + C_2 \sin kx$$

and

$$y' = -kC_1 \sin kx + kC_2 \cos kx.$$

The condition $y'(0) = 0$ requires that $C_2 = 0$, so that

$$y = C_1 \cos kx, \qquad y' = -kC_1 \sin kx.$$

The condition $y'(c) = 0$ requires that

$$-kC_1 \sin kc = 0.$$

This condition is satisfied if k has one of the values

$$k_n = \frac{n\pi}{c}, \qquad n = 1, 2, 3, \ldots,$$

that is, if λ has one of the values

$$\lambda_n = \left(\frac{n\pi}{c}\right)^2, \qquad n = 1, 2, 3, \ldots.$$

The corresponding eigenfunctions are

$$y_n(x) = \cos \frac{n\pi x}{c}, \qquad n = 1, 2, 3, \ldots.$$

When $\lambda = 0$, the general solution of the differential equation is

$$y = C_1 + C_2 x.$$

Then

$$y' = C_2.$$

The condition $y'(0)$ requires that $C_2 = 0$. But then $y'(x) \equiv 0$, so the condition $y'(c) = 0$ is also satisfied. The constant C_1 is arbitrary. Thus $\lambda_0 = 0$ is an eigenvalue of the problem, and a corresponding eigenfunction is

$$y_0(x) = 1.$$

When $\lambda < 0$, let $\lambda = -k^2$, where $k > 0$. The general solution of the differential equation is

$$y = C_1 \cosh kx + C_2 \sinh kx,$$

and

$$y' = kC_1 \sinh kx + kC_2 \cosh kx.$$

The condition $y'(0) = 0$ requires that $C_2 = 0$, so that

$$y = C_1 \cosh kx, \qquad y' = kC_1 \sinh kx.$$

The condition $y'(c) = 0$ requires that

$$kC_1 \sinh kc = 0,$$

and so C_1 must be zero also. But then $y = 0$, so the eigenvalue problem has no negative eigenvalues.

The eigenvalues of the problem are therefore the numbers

$$\lambda_n = \left(\frac{n\pi}{c}\right)^2, \qquad n = 0, 1, 2, \ldots, \tag{7.9}$$

and the corresponding eigenfunctions are the functions

$$y_n(x) = \cos \frac{n\pi x}{c}, \qquad n = 0, 1, 2, \ldots. \tag{7.10}$$

EXAMPLE 3.   As another example of an eigenvalue problem, we consider the fourth-order differential equation

$$\frac{d^4 y}{dx^4} + \lambda \frac{d^2 y}{dx^2} = 0, \tag{7.11}$$

with the boundary conditions

$$y(0) = 0, \qquad y''(0) = 0 \tag{7.12a}$$

$$y(1) = 0, \qquad y'(1) = 0. \tag{7.12b}$$

As in the previous examples, it is convenient to consider the cases $\lambda > 0$, $\lambda = 0$, and $\lambda < 0$ separately. When $\lambda > 0$, we let $\lambda = k^2$, where $k > 0$. The differential equation

$$\frac{d^4 y}{dx^4} + k^2 \frac{d^2 y}{dx^2} = 0$$

possesses the general solution

$$y = C_1 \cos kx + C_2 \sin kx + C_3 + C_4 x.$$

The first two derivatives are

$$y' = k(-C_1 \sin kx + C_2 \cos kx) + C_4$$

$$y'' = -k^2(C_1 \cos kx + C_2 \sin kx).$$

The boundary conditions (7.12a) require that

$$C_1 + C_3 = 0, \qquad C_1 = 0.$$

Thus $C_1 = C_3 = 0$, and

$$y = C_2 \sin kx + C_4 x$$

$$y' = kC_2 \cos kx + C_4.$$

The boundary conditions (7.12b) require that

$$C_2 \sin k + C_4 = 0$$

$$C_2 k \cos k + C_4 = 0. \tag{7.13}$$

This system of equations for C_2 and C_4 has a nontrivial solution if, and only if, the determinant

$$\begin{vmatrix} \sin k & 1 \\ k \cos k & 1 \end{vmatrix} = \sin k - k \cos k$$

vanishes. Thus k must satisfy the equation

$$\tan k = k. \tag{7.14}$$

Although we cannot give an explicit formula for the positive roots of this equation, the fact that an infinite number of roots does exist can be seen from the graphs of the functions k and $\tan k$ in Figure 7.1. If we denote the

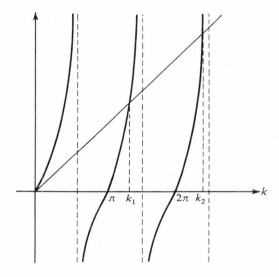

FIGURE 7.1

nth positive root of the quation (7.14) by k_n, then the corresponding eigenvalues of the problem are

$$\lambda_n = k_n{}^2, \qquad n = 1, 2, 3, \dots . \tag{7.15}$$

When $k = k_n$, the two equations (7.12) are equivalent, and either one can be used to eliminate one of the constants C_2 or C_4. Taking the first equation, we have

$$C_2 = -\frac{C_4}{\sin k_n}$$

where C_4 is arbitrary. Then as eigenfunctions, we have

$$y_n(x) = -C_4 \left[\frac{\sin k_n x}{\sin k_n} - x \right].$$

If we choose $C_4 = -\sin k_n$, then

$$y_n(x) = \sin k_n x - x \sin k_n, \qquad n = 1, 2, 3, \ldots . \qquad (7.16)$$

It is a routine matter to show that when $\lambda \leq 0$ the differential equation (7.11) possesses no nontrivial solutions that satisfy the boundary conditions. Thus all the eigenvalues and eigenfunctions of the problem are given by formulas (7.15) and (7.16).

7.1 EXERCISES

1. Find all real eigenvalues, and also find the corresponding eigenfunctions.

(a) $y'' + \lambda y = 0,$ $\quad 0 \leq x \leq \pi,$ $\quad y(0) = 0,$ $\quad y'(\pi) = 0$
(b) $y'' + \lambda y = 0,$ $\quad 0 \leq x \leq 1,$ $\quad y(0) - y'(0) = 0,$ $\quad y(1) - y'(1) = 0$
(c) $y'' + \lambda y = 0,$ $\quad 0 \leq x \leq 1,$ $\quad y'(0) = 0,$ $\quad y(1) + y'(1) = 0$
(d) $y'' + \lambda y = 0,$ $\quad 0 \leq x \leq 1,$ $\quad y'(0) + 2y'(1) = 0,$ $\quad y(1) = 0$
(e) $y'' + 2y' + (\lambda + 1)y = 0,$ $\quad 0 \leq x \leq \pi,$ $\quad y(0) = 0,$ $\quad y(\pi) = 0$
(f) $x^2 y'' - xy' + (\lambda + 1)y = 0,$ $\quad 1 \leq x \leq e,$ $\quad y(1) = 0,$ $\quad y(e) = 0$
(g) $y^{(4)} - \lambda y = 0,$ $\quad 0 \leq x \leq 1,$ $\quad y'(0) = y'''(0) = y'(1) = y'''(1) = 0$
(h) $y^{(4)} + \lambda y'' = 0,$ $\quad 0 \leq x \leq 1,$ $\quad y(0) = y'(0) = y(1) = y''(1) = 0$

2. Consider the partial differential equation

$$\frac{\partial^2 u}{\partial x^2} = \frac{\partial u}{\partial t}$$

for a function $u(x, t)$, subject to the boundary conditions $u(0, t) = 0$, $u(1, t) = 0$.

(a) Show that if the differential equation possesses a solution of the form $u(x, t) = X(x)T(t)$, then

$$\frac{X''(x)}{X(x)} = \frac{T'(t)}{T(t)} = -\lambda,$$

where λ is a constant. Hence show that $X(x)$ and $T(t)$ must be solutions of the ordinary differential equations $X'' + \lambda X = 0$, $T' + \lambda T = 0$, respectively.
(b) Let $X(x)$ be an eigenfunction of the problem $X'' + \lambda X = 0$, $X(0) = 0$, $X(1) = 0$, and let $T(t)$ be a solution of the corresponding equation $T' + \lambda T = 0$. Verify that the product $X(x)T(t)$ satisfies the original partial differential equation and the boundary conditions. Show that each of the functions $u_n(x, t) = \exp(-n^2\pi^2 t)\sin n\pi x$, $n = 1, 2, 3, \ldots$, is a solution of the original problem.

3. Consider the partial differential equation for a function $u(x, t)$,

$$Au_{xx} + Bu_{xt} + Cu_{tt} + Du_x + Eu_t = 0,$$

where A, B, C, D, and E are constants, with $A \neq 0$. Let $u(x, t)$ also be required to satisfy the boundary conditions

$$\alpha u(0, t) + \beta u_x(0, t) = 0, \qquad \gamma u(1, t) + \delta u_x(1, t) = 0,$$

where α, β, γ, and δ are constants.

(a) Show that if the equation possesses a solution of the form $u(x, t) = X(x)T(t)$, then

$$\frac{AX'' + (B + D)X'}{X} = -\frac{CT'' + (B + E)T'}{T} = -\lambda,$$

where λ is a constant.

(b) Let $X(x)$ be an eigenfunction of the problem

$$AX'' + (B + D)X' + \lambda X = 0, \qquad \alpha X(0) + \beta X'(0) = 0,$$

$$\gamma X(1) + \delta X'(1) = 0,$$

and let $T(t)$ be a solution of the corresponding equation

$$CT'' + (B + E)T' - \lambda T = 0.$$

Verify that the product $X(x)T(t)$ is a solution of the original problem.

7.2 The Adjoint Equation

In the remainder of this chapter we shall restrict out attention to eigenvalue problems associated with a certain class of second-order differential equations. Although a theory for equations of arbitrary order is well known, a presentation of this theory requires considerable knowledge of matrix algebra. We shall therefore confine our study to second-order problems. Treatments of the general case are given in the books by Coddington and Levinson and by Miller listed among the references at the end of the chapter.

Let L be the second-order differential operator that is defined by means of the relation

$$Ly \equiv a_0(x)y'' + a_1(x)y' + a_2(x)y. \tag{7.17}$$

Let I be a specific interval, $a \leq x \leq b$. We assume that the functions $a_0''(x)$, $a_1'(x)$, and $a_2(x)$ are continuous on I. If $u(x)$ and $v(x)$ are any two functions that possess two continuous derivatives on I, we have

$$\int_a^x vLu \, dx = \int_a^x [(a_0v)u'' + (a_1v)u' + (a_2v)u] \, dx, \qquad a \leq x \leq b. \tag{7.18}$$

Using integration by parts, we find that

$$\int_a^x (a_1 v) u' \, dx = [(a_1 v) u]_a^x - \int_a^x (a_1 v)' u \, dx,$$

$$\int_a^x (a_0 v) u'' \, dx = [(a_0 v) u']_a^x - \int_a^x (a_0 v)' u' \, dx$$

$$= [(a_0 v) u' - (a_0 v)' u]_a^x + \int_a^x (a_0 v)'' u \, dx.$$

From these relations and the relation (7.18), we see that

$$\int_a^x v L u \, dx = [(a_0 v) u' - (a_0 v)' u + (a_1 v) u]_a^x + \int_a^x [(a_0 v)'' - (a_1 v)' + a_2 v] u \, dx.$$
(7.19)

If the second-order differential operator L^* is defined by means of the relation

$$L^* v \equiv (a_0 v)'' - (a_1 v)' + a_2 v \equiv a_0 v'' + (2a_0' - a_1) v' + (a_0'' - a_1' + a_2 v),$$
(7.20)

then equation (7.19) may be written as

$$\int_a^x (v L u - u L^* v) \, dx = [a_0 (u'v - uv') + (a_1 - a_0') uv]_a^x.$$
(7.21)

The operator L^* is called the *adjoint operator* corresponding to the operator L. It is not hard to verify that the adjoint of the operator L^* is the operator L. Thus each of the operators L and L^* is the adjoint of the other.

The operator L is said to be *self-adjoint* if, and only if, the corresponding coefficients of the operators L and L^* are identical. From formulas (7.17) and (7.20) we see that the operator L is self-adjoint if, and only if,

$$2a_0' - a_1 = a_1$$

and

$$a_0'' - a_1' + a_2 = a_2.$$

These conditions are satisfied if, and only if,

$$a_1 = a_0'.$$
(7.22)

Thus, if L is self-adjoint, we have

$$L y = a_0 y'' + a_0' y' + a_2 y = (a_0 y')' + a_2 y.$$
(7.23)

As we shall see, the condition that a differential operator be self-adjoint is of considerable significance in the theory of eigenvalue problems.

A differential equation $L y = 0$ is said to be self-adjoint if the operator L is self-adjoint. Any second-order differential equation

$$a_0 y'' + a_1 y' + a_2 y = 0$$

can be put in self-adjoint from by multiplying through by the quantity

$$\frac{1}{a_0} \exp\left(\int \frac{a_1}{a_0} dx \right); \tag{7.24}$$

for then the differential equation assumes the form

$$(py')' + qy = 0,$$

where

$$p = \exp\left(\int \frac{a_1}{a_0} dx \right), \qquad q = \frac{a_2}{a_0} \exp\left(\int \frac{a_1}{a_0} dx \right).$$

Going back to equation (7.21) and differentiating both members with respect to x, we obtain the relation

$$vLu - uL^*v = \frac{d}{dx} \left[a_0(u'v - uv') + (a_1 - a_0')uv \right]. \tag{7.25}$$

This relation is known as *Lagrange's identity* for the second-order operator L. The expression in brackets on the right is called the *bilinear concomitant* of the functions u and v. Putting $x = b$ in equation (7.21), we obtain *Green's identity*,

$$\int_a^b (vLu - uL^*v)\, dx = \left[a_0(u'v - uv') + (a_1 - a_0')uv \right]_a^b. \tag{7.26a}$$

In the special but important case when the operator L is self-adjoint, Green's identity becomes

$$\int_a^b (vLu - uLv)\, dx = \left[a_0(u'v - uv') \right]_a^b. \tag{7.26b}$$

7.2 EXERCISES

1. The adjoint of the differential operator

$$L = a_0 D^2 + a_1 D + a_2$$

was defined to be the operator

$$L^* = a_0 D^2 + (2a_0' - a_1)D + (a_0'' - a_1' + a_2).$$

Show that the adjoint of the operator L^* is the operator L, that is, that $L^{**} = L$.

2. (a) The differential equation $Lu \equiv a_0 u'' + a_1 u' + a_2 u = 0$ is said to be *exact* if, and only if, it can be written in the factored form

$$Lu \equiv D(b_0 D + b_1)u = 0.$$

Prove that the differential equation is exact if, and only if,

$$a_0'' - a_1' + a_2 = 0.$$

(b) If a differential equation is not exact, there is still the possibility that it can be put in exact form by multiplying through by some function $v(x)$. If such a function exists, it is called an *integrating factor* for the equation. Prove that a function $v(x)$ is an integrating factor for the equation $Lu = 0$ if, and only if, it is a nontrivial solution of the adjoint equation $L^*v = 0$.

3. Put the given differential equation in self-adjoint form:

(a) $x^2 y'' + xy' + (x^2 - 1)y = 0$
(b) $y'' + ay' + by = 0$, a and b constants
(c) $xy'' + (1 - x)y' + y = 0$
(d) $y'' - 2xy' + y = 0$.

4. Let $v_1(x)$ and $v_2(x)$ be linearly independent solutions of the equation

$$L^*v \equiv (a_0 v)'' - (a_1 v)' + a_2 v = 0.$$

Prove that the functions

$$u_i(x) = a_0 v_i e^{-\int a_1/a_0 \, dx}, \qquad i = 1, 2,$$

are linearly independent solutions of the equation

$$Lu = a_0 u'' + a_1 u' + a_2 u = 0.$$

5. Show that Green's identity for the self-adjoint operator

$$L = p(x)D^2 + p'(x)D + q(x)$$

can be written in the form

$$\int_a^b (vLu - uLv) \, dx = p(a)W(a; u, v) - p(b)W(b; u, v),$$

where $W(x; u, v)$ is the Wronskian of $u(x)$ and $v(x)$.

6. Let $u(x)$ and $v(x)$ possess continuous nth-order derivatives on the interval $[a, b]$, and let the function $a_{n-j}(x)$, $j = 0, 1, \ldots, n$, possess a continuous derivative of order j on $[a, b]$.
(a) Show that, for $1 \le j \le n$,

$$\int_a^b a_{n-j} v u^{(j)} \, dx = \left[\sum_{m=0}^{j-1} (-1)^m (a_{n-j} v)^{(m)} u^{(j-1-m)} \right]_a^b + (-1)^j \int_a^b u(a_{n-j} v)^{(j)} \, dx.$$

(b) Let

$$Lu = \sum_{j=0}^n a_{n-j} u^{(j)} = a_0 u^{(n)} + a_1 u^{(n-1)} + \cdots + a_{n-1} u' + a_n u.$$

Show that

$$\int_a^b vLu \, dx = \left[\sum_{j=1}^n \sum_{m=0}^{j-1} (-1)^m (a_{n-j} v)^{(m)} u^{(j-1-m)} \right]_a^b + \int_a^b uL^*v \, dx,$$

where

$$L^*v = \sum_{j=0}^{n} (-1)^j (a_{n-j}v)^{(j)}$$

$$= (-1)^n (a_0 v)^{(n)} + (-1)^{n-1}(a_1 v)^{(n-1)} + \cdots + a_n v.$$

The operator L^* is defined to be the adjoint of the operator L. It can be shown that the adjoint of the operator L^* is L.

7.3 Boundary Operators

Let $u(x)$ be any function that is differentiable for $a \le x \le b$. We define a *boundary operator* U by means of the relation

$$U(u) = \alpha_1 u(a) + \alpha_2 u'(a) + \alpha_3 u(b) + \alpha_4 u'(b), \tag{7.27}$$

where α_1, α_2, α_3, and α_4 are real constants. We shall adopt the notation

$$u_1 = u(a), \qquad u_2 = u'(a), \qquad u_3 = u(b), \qquad u_4 = u'(b) \tag{7.28}$$

and write

$$U(u) = \alpha_1 u_1 + \alpha_2 u_2 + \alpha_3 u_3 + \alpha_4 u_4. \tag{7.29}$$

An equation of the form

$$U(u) = 0$$

is a *boundary condition* for the function $u(x)$.

In case $\alpha_1 = \alpha_2 = \alpha_3 = \alpha_4 = 0$, we call U the zero operator, and write $U = 0$. Let us now consider two boundary operators U_1 and U_2, where

$$U_1(u) = \alpha_1 u_1 + \alpha_2 u_2 + \alpha_3 u_3 + \alpha_4 u_4$$
$$U_2(u) = \beta_1 u_1 + \beta_2 u_2 + \beta_3 u_3 + \beta_4 u_4. \tag{7.30}$$

The operators U_1 and U_2 are said to be *equal*, written $U_1 = U_2$, if, and only if, $\alpha_i = \beta_i$, $i = 1, 2, 3, 4$. The *sum* of the operators U_1 and U_2, written $U_1 + U_2$, is defined to be the operator given by the formula

$$(U_1 + U_2)(u) = (\alpha_1 + \beta_1)u_1 + (\alpha_2 + \beta_2)u_2 + (\alpha_3 + \beta_3)u_3 + (\alpha_4 + \beta_4)u_4.$$

If c is any real constant, we define cU_1 to be the operator such that

$$(cU_1)(u) = (c\alpha_1)u_1 + (c\alpha_2)u_2 + (c\alpha_3)u_3 + (c\alpha_4)u_4.$$

The difference $U_1 - U_2$ is defined to be the $U_1 + (-1)U_2$.

Let us now consider a set of m boundary operators $U_1, U_2, \ldots, U_m$, where

$$U_i(u) = \alpha_{i1}u_1 + \alpha_{i2}u_2 + \alpha_{i3}u_3 + \alpha_{i4}u_4, \qquad i = 1, 2, 3, \ldots, m. \tag{7.31}$$

The operators are said to be *linearly dependent* if there exist constants $C_1, C_2, \ldots, C_m$, not all zero, such that

$$C_1 U_1 + C_2 U_2 + \cdots + C_m U_m = 0. \tag{7.32}$$

If a set of boundary operators is linearly dependent, then at least one of the operators can be expressed as a linear combination of the others. If, for instance, $C_1 \neq 0$ in the relation (7.32), then any function that satisfies the boundary conditions

$$U_2(u) = 0, \ U_3(u) = 0, \ \ldots, \ U_m(u) = 0$$

must also satisfy the boundary condition

$$U_1(u) = 0.$$

A set of operators that is not linearly dependent is said to be *linearly independent*.

In the case when $m = 4$, the condition

$$C_1 U_1 + C_2 U_2 + C_3 U_3 + C_4 U_4 = 0 \tag{7.33}$$

is equivalent to the conditions

$$C_1 \alpha_{11} + C_2 \alpha_{21} + C_3 \alpha_{31} + C_4 \alpha_{41} = 0$$

$$C_1 \alpha_{12} + C_2 \alpha_{22} + C_3 \alpha_{32} + C_4 \alpha_{42} = 0$$

$$C_1 \alpha_{13} + C_2 \alpha_{23} + C_3 \alpha_{33} + C_4 \alpha_{43} = 0 \tag{7.34}$$

$$C_1 \alpha_{14} + C_2 \alpha_{24} + C_3 \alpha_{34} + C_4 \alpha_{44} = 0.$$

Hence the operators U_1, U_2, U_3, U_4 are linearly dependent if, and only if, the determinant

$$\Delta = \begin{vmatrix} \alpha_{11} & \alpha_{12} & \alpha_{13} & \alpha_{14} \\ \alpha_{21} & \alpha_{22} & \alpha_{23} & \alpha_{24} \\ \alpha_{31} & \alpha_{32} & \alpha_{33} & \alpha_{34} \\ \alpha_{41} & \alpha_{42} & \alpha_{43} & \alpha_{44} \end{vmatrix} \tag{7.35}$$

vanishes.

In the case of two operators, U_1 and U_2, the condition

$$C_1 U_1 + C_2 U_2 = 0 \tag{7.36}$$

is equivalent to the conditions

$$C_1 \alpha_{11} + C_2 \alpha_{21} = 0$$

$$C_1 \alpha_{12} + C_2 \alpha_{22} = 0$$

$$C_1 \alpha_{13} + C_2 \alpha_{23} = 0 \tag{7.37}$$

$$C_1 \alpha_{14} + C_2 \alpha_{24} = 0.$$

If the operators U_1 and U_2 are linearly dependent, each *pair* of equations for

C_1 and C_2 must have a nontrivial solution, and so each of the second-order determinants

$$\begin{vmatrix} \alpha_{1i} & \alpha_{2i} \\ \alpha_{1j} & \alpha_{2j} \end{vmatrix} = \begin{vmatrix} \alpha_{1i} & \alpha_{1j} \\ \alpha_{2i} & \alpha_{2j} \end{vmatrix} \qquad i \neq j, \tag{7.38}$$

must vanish. Conversely, if each of the determinants (7.38) vanishes, it can be shown (Exercise 3) that the operators U_1 and U_2 are linearly dependent. Thus if U_1 and U_2 are linearly independent, at least one of the determinants (7.38) does not vanish.

7.3 EXERCISES

1. If

$$U_1(u) = 2u(0) - u'(0) + u(1) + 3u'(1)$$

$$U_2(u) = u(0) - 2u(1) + u'(1),$$

find

(a) $U_1(x^2)$ (b) $U_2(\sin \pi x)$ (c) $(U_1 - 2U_2)(3x + 2)$.

2. If

$$U_1(u) = u(0) - u'(1), \qquad U_2(u) = u'(0) - u(1),$$

determine whether or not the following functions satisfy the boundary conditions $U_1(u) = 0$ and $U_2(u) = 0$.

(a) $u(x) = 2\pi \cos 2\pi x + \sin 2\pi x$ (b) $u(x) = \sin 3\pi x$

3. Let the boundary operators U_1 and U_2 be given by the relations

$$U_1(u) = \alpha_{11}u_1 + \alpha_{12}u_2 + \alpha_{13}u_3 + \alpha_{14}u_4$$

$$U_2(u) = \alpha_{21}u_1 + \alpha_{22}u_2 + \alpha_{23}u_3 + \alpha_{24}u_4 .$$

(a) Show that the operator equation $C_1U_1 + C_2U_2 = 0$ is equivalent to the system of algebraic equations

$$C_1\alpha_{11} + C_2\alpha_{21} = 0$$

$$C_1\alpha_{12} + C_2\alpha_{22} = 0$$

$$C_1\alpha_{13} + C_2\alpha_{23} = 0$$

$$C_1\alpha_{14} + C_2\alpha_{24} = 0.$$

(b) If U_1 and U_2 are linearly dependent, show that each of the determinants

$$A_{ij} = \begin{vmatrix} \alpha_{1i} & \alpha_{1j} \\ \alpha_{2i} & \alpha_{2j} \end{vmatrix}, \qquad i \neq j, \qquad i, j = 1, 2, 3, 4$$

must vanish.

(c) Show that if $A_{ij} = 0$, $i \neq j$, $i, j = 1, 2, 3, 4$, then U_1 and U_2 are linearly dependent. Suggestion: consider first the pair of equations

$$C_1\alpha_{11} + C_2\alpha_{21} = 0,$$

$$C_1\alpha_{12} + C_2\alpha_{22} = 0.$$

If α_{11}, α_{21}, α_{12}, α_{22} are all zero, then C_1 and C_2 need only constitute a nontrivial solution of the remaining pair of equations. Suppose then that these quantities are not all zero. Show that a pair of values C_1 and C_2 that satisfies the above pair of equations also satisfies each of the remaining equations.

4. Determine whether or not the boundary operators are linearly independent:

(a) $U_1(u) = u_1 - 3u_3 + u_4$, $U_2(u) = u_1 + u_3 - 2u_4$
(b) $U_1(u) = u_1 - 3u_2 - 2u_4$, $U_2 \quad = -2u_1 + 6u_2 + 4u_4$
(c) $U_1(u) = u_1 - u_2 + u_4$, $U_2(u) = u_1 + u_2 + 2u_3$
    $U_3(u) = 2u_2 - u_3 + u_4$, $U_4(u) = 3u_1 + u_2 + u_3 + 3u_4$
(d) $U_1(u) = 2u_1 - u_2 + 2u_4$, $U_2(u) = u_1 + u_2 + u_3$
    $U_3(u) = u_2 - u_3 - u_4$, $U_4(u) = u_1 - u_3$

5. If U_1, U_2, U_3, U_4 are linearly independent boundary operators for a given interval $a \leq x \leq b$, prove that every boundary operator for this interval can be expressed as a linear combination of U_1, U_2, U_3, and U_4.

7.4 Self-Adjoint Eigenvalue Problems

Let L be a second-order differential operator such that

$$Ly \equiv a_0(x)y'' + a_1(x)y' + a_2(x)y. \tag{7.39}$$

We shall consider eigenvalue problems of the special form

$$Ly = -\lambda r(x)y, \qquad a \leq x \leq b, \tag{7.40}$$

$$U_1(y) \equiv \alpha_{11}y(a) + \alpha_{12}y'(a) + \alpha_{13}y(b) + \alpha_{14}y'(b) = 0$$
$$U_2(y) \equiv \alpha_{21}y(a) + \alpha_{22}y'(a) + \alpha_{23}y(b) + \alpha_{24}y'(b) = 0, \tag{7.41}$$

where U_1 and U_2 are linearly independent boundary operators, and $a_0(x) > 0$, $r(x) > 0$ on $[a, b]$.

Let us denote by B the class of all functions that possess continuous second derivatives on the interval $[a, b]$, and that satisfy the boundary conditions (7.41). Any eigenfunction of the above problem must belong to the class B; it must also satisfy the differential equation (7.42) for some value of the parameter λ.

The eigenvalue problem (7.40), (7.41) is said to be *self-adjoint* if

$$\int_a^b (vLu - uLv)\, dx = 0 \tag{7.42}$$

for every pair of functions $u(x)$ and $v(x)$ that belong to the class B. We shall presently investigate the consequences of the assumption that an eigenvalue problem is self-adjoint. First, however, it should be pointed out that the assumption of self-adjointness imposes certain restrictions on the operator L and on the boundary conditions. The condition imposed on the operator L is given by the following theorem:

Theorem 1.　If the eigenvalue problem (7.40), (7.41) is self-adjoint, then the operator L is self-adjoint.

Proof.　Let

$$v(x) = (x - a)^2(x - b)^2, \qquad a \le x \le b.$$

Then

$$v(a) = v'(a) = v(b) = v'(b) = 0$$

and $v(x)$ belongs to the class B. If $u(x)$ is any function of the class B, we have

$$\int_a^b (vLu - uL^*v)\, dx = 0, \tag{7.43}$$

by Green's identity. Subtracting the equations (7.42) and (7.43), we see that

$$\int_a^b u(L^*v - Lv)\, dx = 0 \tag{7.44}$$

for every function $u(x)$ in B. We claim that

$$L^*v - Lv = 0, \qquad a \le x \le b. \tag{7.45}$$

To prove this, let $g(x) = L^*v - Lv$, and suppose that $g(x_0) \ne 0$, where $a < x_0 < b$. Then there is an interval (c, d) containing x_0 and contained in (a, b), on which $g(x)$ does not vanish. Let

$$u(x) = \begin{cases} 0, & a \le x < c, \\ (x - c)^3(x - d)^3, & c \le x \le d. \\ 0, & d < x \le b. \end{cases}$$

Then $u(x)$ belongs to B and

$$\int_a^b u(x)g(x)\, dx = \int_c^d u(x)g(x)\, dx = 0.$$

But this is impossible, since $u(x)g(x)$ does not change sign on (c, d). Hence $g(x) = 0$ for $a < x < b$. Since $g(x)$ is continuous on $[a, b]$, we have $g(a) = g(b) = 0$ also. A similar argument applies in the case $g(a) \ne 0$ and the case $g(b) \ne 0$.

We have shown that

$$g(x) = L^*v - Lv = 2a(x)v' + a'(x)v = 0, \qquad a \le x \le b,$$

where

$$a(x) = a_0'(x) - a_1(x).$$

Then

$$g(x)v(x) = 2avv' + a'v^2 = (av^2)' = 0,$$

so av^2 is a constant. Since $v(a) = 0$, we have $av^2 = 0$ for $a \leq x \leq b$. Consequently, $a(x) = 0$ for $a \leq x \leq b$, so the operator L is self-adjoint.

In order to see what the self-adjointness assumption requires of the boundary conditions, we shall need the following two lemmas.

Lemma 1. Let k_1, k_2, k_3, and k_4 be any four real numbers. Then there exists a function $f(x)$ that possesses a continuous second derivative on the interval $[a, b]$ and for which

$$f(a) = k_1, \qquad f'(a) = k_2, \qquad f(b) = k_3, \qquad f'(b) = k_4. \qquad (7.46)$$

Proof. Consider a function of the form

$$f(x) = C_0 + C_1 x + C_2 x^2 + C_3 x^3,$$

where the quantities C_i are constants. The requirement that $f(x)$ is to satisfy the four conditions (7.46) leads to a system of four linear algebraic equations for the four constants C_i. A little calculation shows that the determinant of this system does not vanish. (The details are left as an exercise.) Hence it is always possible to choose the constants C_i so that $f(x)$ satisfies the conditions (7.46). Since $f(x)$ is a polynomial, it possesses derivatives of all orders.

Lemma 2. Let $W(x; u, v)$ denote the Wronskian of the functions $u(x)$ and $v(x)$. Then $W(a; u, v) = 0$ for every pair of functions u and v in B if, and only if,

$$\begin{vmatrix} \alpha_{13} & \alpha_{14} \\ \alpha_{23} & \alpha_{24} \end{vmatrix} = 0, \qquad (7.47)$$

and $W(b; u, v) = 0$ for every pair of functions u and v in B if, and only if,

$$\begin{vmatrix} \alpha_{11} & \alpha_{12} \\ \alpha_{21} & \alpha_{22} \end{vmatrix} = 0. \qquad (7.48)$$

Proof. Suppose first that $W(a; u, v) = 0$ for every pair of functions u and v in B. Let us assume that the condition (7.47) does not hold—that is, that $\alpha_{13}\alpha_{24} - \alpha_{21}\alpha_{14} \neq 0$. Then there exist constants r_1, r_2, s_1, s_2 such that

$$\alpha_{13}r_1 + \alpha_{14}r_2 = -\alpha_{11} \qquad \alpha_{13}s_1 + \alpha_{14}s_2 = -\alpha_{12}$$

$$\alpha_{23}r_1 + \alpha_{24}r_2 = -\alpha_{21} \qquad \alpha_{13}s_1 + \alpha_{24}s_2 = -\alpha_{22}. \qquad (7.49)$$

According to Lemma 1, there exist functions $u(x)$ and $v(x)$, with continuous second derivatives on $[a, b]$, such that

$$u(a) = 1, \qquad u'(a) = 0, \qquad u(b) = r_1, \qquad u'(b) = r_2$$
$$v(a) = 0, \qquad v'(a) = 1, \qquad v(b) = s_1, \qquad v'(b) = s_2. \tag{7.50}$$

Because of the equations (7.49), these functions $u(x)$ and $v(x)$ belong to B. But $W(a; u, v) = 1 \neq 0$, which is a contradiction. Consequently the condition (7.47) holds.

Conversely, suppose that the condition (7.47) holds. Then there exist constants C_1 and C_2, not both zero, such that

$$C_1\alpha_{13} + C_2\alpha_{14} = 0$$
$$C_1\alpha_{23} + C_2\alpha_{24} = 0. \tag{7.51}$$

For any function $u(x)$ in B we have

$$\alpha_{11}u(a) + \alpha_{12}u'(a) + \alpha_{13}u(b) + \alpha_{14}u'(b) = 0$$
$$\alpha_{21}u(a) + \alpha_{22}u'(a) + \alpha_{23}u(b) + \alpha_{34}u'(b) = 0. \tag{7.52}$$

Multiplying through in the first of these equations by C_1, and in the second by C_2, and adding, we find that

$$(C_1\alpha_{11} + C_2\alpha_{21})u(a) + (C_1\alpha_{12} + C_2\alpha_{22})u'(a) = 0.$$

Similarly, we find that

$$(C_1\alpha_{11} + C_2\alpha_{21})v(a) + (C_1\alpha_{12} + C_2\alpha_{22})v'(a) = 0$$

for every function $v(x)$ in B. If $W(a; u, v) \neq 0$, then

$$C_1\alpha_{11} + C_2\alpha_{21} = 0$$
$$C_1\alpha_{12} + C_2\alpha_{22} = 0. \tag{7.53}$$

But these conditions, together with the conditions (7.51), imply that the boundary conditions are linearly dependent. Consequently $W(a; u, v) = 0$ for every pair of functions $u(x)$ and $v(x)$ in B.

The proof that $W(b; u, v) = 0$ for all u and v in B if, and only if, the condition (7.48) is satisfied is left as an exercise.

We are now ready to prove the following important theorem.

Theorem 2. The eigenvalue problem (7.40), (7.41) is self-adjoint if, and only if,

(a) the operator L is self-adjoint

and

(b)
$$\frac{\begin{vmatrix} \alpha_{11} & \alpha_{12} \\ \alpha_{21} & \alpha_{22} \end{vmatrix}}{a_0(a)} = \frac{\begin{vmatrix} \alpha_{13} & \alpha_{14} \\ \alpha_{23} & \alpha_{24} \end{vmatrix}}{a_0(b)}.$$

Proof. If L is self-adjoint, then Green's identity becomes

$$\int_a^b (vLu - uLv)\, dx = a_0(b)W(b; u, v) - a_0(a)W(a; u, v). \qquad (7.54)$$

If $u(x)$ and $v(x)$ satisfy the boundary conditions, then the matrix equation

$$\begin{pmatrix} \alpha_{11} & \alpha_{12} \\ \alpha_{21} & \alpha_{22} \end{pmatrix}\begin{pmatrix} u_1 & v_1 \\ u_2 & v_2 \end{pmatrix} = -\begin{pmatrix} \alpha_{13} & \alpha_{14} \\ \alpha_{23} & \alpha_{24} \end{pmatrix}\begin{pmatrix} u_3 & v_3 \\ u_4 & v_4 \end{pmatrix} \qquad (7.55)$$

holds. Upon taking determinants, we have

$$\begin{vmatrix} \alpha_{11} & \alpha_{12} \\ \alpha_{21} & \alpha_{22} \end{vmatrix} W(a; u, v) = \begin{vmatrix} \alpha_{13} & \alpha_{14} \\ \alpha_{23} & \alpha_{24} \end{vmatrix} W(b; u, v). \qquad (7.56)$$

Suppose first that the problem (7.40), (7.41) is self-adjoint. Then L is self-adjoint, and from formula (7.54) we have that

$$a_0(a)W(a; u, v) = a_0(b)W(b; u, v) \qquad (7.57)$$

for all u and v in B. If there exists a pair of functions u and v in B for which $W(a; u, v) \neq 0$, then condition (b) follows immediately from equations (7.56) and (7.57). If there is no such pair of functions in B, then by Lemma 2,

$$\begin{vmatrix} \alpha_{11} & \alpha_{12} \\ \alpha_{21} & \alpha_{22} \end{vmatrix} = \begin{vmatrix} \alpha_{13} & \alpha_{14} \\ \alpha_{23} & \alpha_{24} \end{vmatrix} = 0,$$

so the condition (b) is still satisfied.

Conversely, suppose that the conditions (a) and (b) are satisfied. Let u and v by any pair of functions in B. If

$$\alpha_{11}\alpha_{22} - \alpha_{21}\alpha_{12} \neq 0,$$

the conditions (b) and (7.56) imply that the condition (7.57) is satisfied, and so the problem is self-adjoint. If

$$\alpha_{11}\alpha_{22} - \alpha_{21}\alpha_{12} = 0,$$

then

$$\alpha_{13}\alpha_{24} - \alpha_{23}\alpha_{14} = 0$$

also, and

$$W(a; u, v) = W(b; u, v) = 0$$

for all u and v in B. In this case the condition (7.57) is still satisfied, and the problem is self-adjoint.

Let us now test some specific eigenvalue problems for self-adjointness, using the criterion of Theorem 2.

EXAMPLE 1.

$$y'' + \lambda y = 0, \qquad 0 \leq x \leq 1,$$
$$y(0) = 3y'(0) - y'(1) = 0,$$
$$y'(0) + y(1) = 0.$$

In this problem, $Ly = y''$, so the operator L is self-adjoint. Also

$$\frac{\begin{vmatrix} \alpha_{11} & \alpha_{12} \\ \alpha_{21} & \alpha_{22} \end{vmatrix}}{a_0(0)} = \frac{\begin{vmatrix} 1 & -3 \\ 0 & 1 \end{vmatrix}}{1} = 1 = \frac{\begin{vmatrix} 0 & -1 \\ 1 & 1 \end{vmatrix}}{1} = \frac{\begin{vmatrix} \alpha_{13} & \alpha_{14} \\ \alpha_{23} & \alpha_{24} \end{vmatrix}}{a_0(1)},$$

so the eigenvalue problem is self-adjoint.

EXAMPLE 2.

$$y'' + \lambda y = 0, \qquad 0 \le x \le 1,$$
$$y(0) - y'(1) = 0,$$
$$y'(0) - y(1) = 0.$$

Although the operator L is self-adjoint, the eigenvalue problem is not self-adjoint, because

$$\frac{\begin{vmatrix} \alpha_{11} & \alpha_{12} \\ \alpha_{21} & \alpha_{22} \end{vmatrix}}{a_0(0)} = \frac{\begin{vmatrix} 1 & 0 \\ 0 & 1 \end{vmatrix}}{1} = 1$$

and

$$\frac{\begin{vmatrix} \alpha_{13} & \alpha_{14} \\ \alpha_{23} & \alpha_{24} \end{vmatrix}}{a_0(1)} = \frac{\begin{vmatrix} 0 & -1 \\ -1 & 0 \end{vmatrix}}{1} = -1.$$

EXAMPLE 3.   A problem of the form

$$[p(x)y']' + [\lambda r(x) + q(x)]y = 0, \qquad a \le x \le b,$$
$$\alpha y(a) + \beta y'(a) = 0,$$
$$\gamma y(b) + \delta y'(b) = 0.$$

is said to have *separated boundary conditions*. Such a problem is self-adjoint, because

$$\frac{\begin{vmatrix} \alpha_{11} & \alpha_{12} \\ \alpha_{21} & \alpha_{22} \end{vmatrix}}{p(a)} = \frac{\begin{vmatrix} \alpha & \beta \\ 0 & 0 \end{vmatrix}}{p(a)} = 0 = \frac{\begin{vmatrix} 0 & 0 \\ \gamma & \delta \end{vmatrix}}{p(b)} = \frac{\begin{vmatrix} \alpha_{13} & \alpha_{14} \\ \alpha_{23} & \alpha_{24} \end{vmatrix}}{p(b)}.$$

7.4 EXERCISES

1. Determine whether or not the given eigenvalue problem is self-adjoint:

(a) $y'' + \lambda y = 0, \qquad 0 \le x \le 1,$
    $y(0) + 2y'(0) + 2y(1) = 0,$
    $y(0) + y(1) - y'(1) = 0.$

(b) $(x^2y')' + (\lambda e^x + x)y = 0,$ $\qquad 1 \le x \le 2,$
$2y(1) + y'(1) + 2y(2) + y'(2) = 0,$
$y(1) + y'(1) - 2y(2) + y'(2) = 0.$
(c) $y'' + y' + (1 + \lambda)y = 0,$ $\qquad 0 \le x \le 1,$
$y(0) = 0,$
$y(1) = 0.$
(d) $(xy')' + (\lambda x^2 + 2)y = 0,$ $\qquad 1 \le x \le 2,$
$y(1) - y'(1) - y'(2) = 0,$
$y(1) + y(2) + y'(2) = 0.$

2. Two pairs of boundary conditions are said to be equivalent if every function that satisfies the first pair of conditions also satisfies the second, and vice-versa. If U_1 and U_2 are such that

$$\begin{vmatrix} \alpha_{11} & \alpha_{12} \\ \alpha_{21} & \alpha_{22} \end{vmatrix} = \begin{vmatrix} \alpha_{13} & \alpha_{14} \\ \alpha_{23} & \alpha_{24} \end{vmatrix} = 0,$$

show that the boundary conditions $U_1(y) = 0,$ $U_2(y) = 0$ are equivalent to a pair of conditions of the form

$$\alpha y(a) + \beta y'(a) = 0, \qquad \gamma y(b) + \delta y'(b) = 0.$$

3. Complete the proof of Lemma 2.
Problems 4, 5, and 6 form a sequence, and should be done in order.

4. (a) Let U_1 and U_2 be linearly independent boundary operators. Show that there exist operators U_3 and U_4 such that the operators $U_1,$ $U_2,$ $U_3,$ U_4 are linearly independent.
(b) Let $U_1,$ $U_2,$ $U_3,$ U_4 be linearly independent boundary operators. Let $u(x)$ be differentiable on $[a, b]$. Show that there exists a unique set of constants $A_{ij},$ $1 \le i, j \le 4$, independent of $u(x)$, such that

$$u_i = \sum_{j=1}^{4} A_{ij}U_j(u), \qquad i = 1, 2, 3, 4.$$

5. (a) Let $U_1,$ $U_2,$ $U_3,$ U_4 be linearly independent boundary operators. Let $u(x)$ and $v(x)$ be any two functions that possess continuous second derivatives on $[a, b]$. Show that there exists a unique set of linearly independent boundary operators $V_1,$ $V_2,$ $V_3,$ V_4, independent of u and v, such that

$$\int_a^b (vLu - uL^*v)\, dx = U_1(u)V_4(v) + U_2(u)V_3(v) + U_3(u)V_2(v) + U_4(u)V_1(v).$$

(b) Let the operators $U_i,$ $i = 1, 2, 3, 4$, be as in part (a) above, and let $\tilde{U}_3,$ $\tilde{U}_4$ be a pair of operators, not identical with $U_3,$ U_4, such that $U_1,$ $U_2,$ $\tilde{U}_3,$ $\tilde{U}_4$ are linearly independent. Let $\tilde{V}_1,$ $\tilde{V}_2,$ $\tilde{V}_3,$ $\tilde{V}_4$ be the associated set of operators. Show that there exist constants m_1, m_2, n_1, n_2 such that

$$\tilde{V}_1 = m_1 V_1 + m_2 V_2, \qquad \tilde{V}_2 = n_1 V_1 + n_2 V_2.$$

In other words, show that the pair of boundary conditions $\tilde{V}_1(y) = 0$, $\tilde{V}_1(y) = 0$ is equivalent to the pair of conditions $V_1(y) = 0$, $V_2(y) = 0$.

6. The eigenvalue problem

$$L^*y = -\lambda r(x)y, \qquad V_1(y) = 0, \qquad V_2(y) = 0$$

is called the *adjoint* of the problem

$$Ly = -\lambda r(x)y, \qquad U_1(y) = 0, \qquad U_2(y) = 0.$$

Prove that the latter problem is self-adjoint if, and only if, the operator L is self-adjoint and the conditions $U_1(y) = 0$, $U_2(y) = 0$ are equivalent to the conditions $V_1(y) = 0$, $V_2(y) = 0$.

7. Let $y_1(x, \lambda)$ and $y_2(x, \lambda)$ be linearly independent solutions of the differential equation $Ly = -\lambda r(x)y$ on the interval $[a, b]$. Show that λ is an eigenvalue of the problem

$$Ly = -\lambda r(x)y, \qquad U_1(y) = 0, \qquad U_2(y) = 0$$

if, and only if, the determinant

$$\begin{vmatrix} U_1(y_1) & U_1(y_2) \\ U_2(y_1) & U_2(y_2) \end{vmatrix}$$

vanishes.

8. Show that an eigenvalue $\lambda = \lambda_0$ of the problem

$$Ly = -\lambda r(x)y, \qquad U_1(y) = 0, \qquad U_2(y) = 0$$

is also an eigenvalue of the adjoint problem

$$L^*y = -\lambda r(x)y, \qquad V_1(y) = 0, \qquad V_1(y) = 0.$$

Suggestion: let $u_0(x)$ be an eigenfunction of the original problem which corresponds to the eigenvalue λ_0. Let $v_1(x)$ and $v_2(x)$ be linearly independent solutions of the differential equation $L^*y = -\lambda_0 r(x)y$. Show that

$$U_3(u_0)V_2(v_1) + U_4(u_0)V_1(v_1) = 0$$

$$U_3(u_0)V_2(v_2) + U_4(u_0)V_1(v_2) = 0,$$

and deduce from this that

$$\begin{vmatrix} V_1(v_1) & V_1(v_2) \\ V_2(v_1) & V_2(v_2) \end{vmatrix} = 0.$$

7.5   Properties of Self-Adjoint Problems

In this section we shall restrict our attention to self-adjoint problems of the form

$$Ly = [p(x)y']' + q(x)y = -\lambda r(x)y, \qquad a \le x \le b, \tag{7.58}$$

$$U_1(y) = 0, \qquad U_2(y) = 0. \tag{7.59}$$

Here it is assumed that $p(x) > 0$, $r(x) > 0$ on $[a, b]$, and of course the boundary conditions are assumed to be such that the condition (b) of Section 7.4 is satisfied. It should be recalled that if $u(x)$ and $v(x)$ are any two functions that possess two continuous derivatives on $[a, b]$ and satisfy the boundary conditions, then

$$\int_a^b (vLu - uLv)\, dx = 0. \tag{7.60}$$

We shall make use of this property to prove two important results for self-adjoint problems.

Theorem 3.   Let λ_1 and λ_2 be distinct eigenvalues of the problem (7.58), (7.59), and let $y_1(x)$ and $y_2(x)$ be corresponding eigenfunctions. Then $y_1(x)$ and $y_2(x)$ are orthogonal† with respect to the weight function $r(x)$ on the interval (a, b).

Proof.   We have

$$Ly_1 = -\lambda_1 r(x)y_1, \qquad Ly_2 = -\lambda_2 r(x)y_2.$$

Multiplying through in the first of these equations by y_2 and in the second by y_1, and subtracting, we have

$$y_2 Ly_1 - y_1 Ly_2 = (\lambda_2 - \lambda_1)r(x)y_1 y_2.$$

Integrating from a to b, we have

$$(\lambda_2 - \lambda_1) \int_a^b r(x)y_1 y_2\, dx = \int_a^b (y_2 Ly_1 - y_1 Ly_2)\, dx = 0,$$

since y_1 and y_2 satisfy the boundary conditions (7.59). Since $\lambda_1 \ne \lambda_2$, we have

$$\int_a^b r(x)y_1 y_2\, dx = 0.$$

Theorem 4.   The self-adjoint problem (7.58), (7.59) has no complex eigenvalues.

Proof.   Let us suppose that the problem does have a complex eigenvalue

---

† See Section 6.1 for the definition of orthogonality.

$\lambda_0 = \alpha_0 + i\beta_0$, where $\beta_0 \neq 0$. Let $y_0(x) = u_0(x) + iv_0(x)$ be a corresponding eigenfunction. Then

$$Ly_0(x) = \frac{d}{dx}\left[p(x)\frac{dy_0(x)}{dx}\right] + q(x)y_0(x) = -\lambda_0 r(x)y_0(x).$$

Taking complex conjugates, and remembering that $p(x)$, $q(x)$, and $r(x)$ are real functions, we have

$$L\bar{y}_0(x) = \frac{d}{dx}\left[p(x)\frac{d\bar{y}_0(x)}{dx}\right] + q(x)\bar{y}_0(x) = -\bar{\lambda}_0 r(x)\bar{y}_0(x).$$

The function $y_0(x)$ satisfies the conditions

$$U_1(y_0) = 0, \qquad U_2(y_0) = 0.$$

Taking complex conjugates, and remembering that the operators U_1 and U_2 have real coefficients, we have

$$\overline{U_1(y_0)} = U_1(\bar{y}_0) = 0, \qquad \overline{U_2(y_0)} = U_2(\bar{y}_0) = 0.$$

Thus the function $\bar{y}_0(x) = u_0(x) - iv_0(x)$ is also an eigenfunction of the problem, corresponding to the eigenvalue $\bar{\lambda}_0 = \alpha_0 - i\beta_0$. But then

$$(\lambda_0 - \bar{\lambda}_0)\int_a^b r(x)y_0(x)\bar{y}_0(x)\,dx = 0,$$

or

$$2i\beta_0 \int_a^b r(x)|y_0(x)|^2\,dx = 0.$$

But this is impossible, since $\beta_0 \neq 0$, and since $y_0(x)$ is a *nontrivial* solution of the differential equation. We conclude that the problem can have no complex eigenvalues.

Examples 1 and 2 of Section 7.1 involved self-adjoint problems. The theory of the present section explains why these problems can have no complex eigenvalues.

Theorem 4 says that if a self-adjoint problem has any eigenvalues, they must be real. It does not guarantee that any eigenvalues exist. However, it can be shown† that a self-adjoint problem does possess infinitely many eigenvalues, and that these eigenvalues can be arranged to form a sequence,

$$\lambda_1, \lambda_2, \ldots, \lambda_n, \ldots.$$

According to Theorem 3, eigenfunctions corresponding to distinct eigenvalues are orthogonal, and so to the sequence of eigenvalues there corresponds a sequence of orthogonal functions. Such sequences will be discussed further in Chapter 8.

† A proof is given in Coddington and Levinson (see References).

There is no corresponding general theorem about the existence of eigen-values for non-self-adjoint problems. Also, the eigenvalues of a non-self-adjoint problem that do exist need not be real. We shall illustrate some of the possible situations by means of some examples.

EXAMPLE 1.   The problem

$$y'' + \lambda y = 0,$$

$$y'(0) + 2y'(1) = 0, \qquad y(1) = 0$$

is non-self-adjoint. The reader can easily verify that no real eigenvalues exist. However, the problem does possess the complex eigenvalues

$$\lambda_n = [(2n - 1)\pi + i \cosh^{-1}2]^2, \qquad n = 0, \pm1, \pm2, \dots .$$

EXAMPLE 2.   For the non-self-adjoint problem

$$y'' + \lambda y = 0,$$

$$y(0) - y(1) = 0,$$

$$y'(0) + y'(1) = 0,$$

every value of λ, real and complex, is an eigenvalue.

EXAMPLE 3.   The non-self-adjoint problem

$$y'' + \lambda y = 0,$$

$$2y(0) - y(1) = 0,$$

$$2y'(0) + y(1) = 0$$

possesses no eigenvalues, real or complex.

7.5 EXERCISES

1. Verify that the given problem is self-adjoint, and find the eigenvalues and eigenfunctions. Verify, by direct integration, that eigenfunctions which correspond to distinct eigenvalues are orthogonal.

   (a) $y'' + \lambda y = 0, \qquad 0 \le x \le c,$
       $y(0) = 0,$
       $y(c) = 0.$
   (b) $y'' + \lambda y = 0, \qquad 0 \le x \le c,$
       $y'(0) = 0,$
       $y'(c) = 0.$
   (c) $(e^{2x}y')' + e^{2x}(\lambda + 1)y = 0, \qquad 0 \le x \le \pi,$
       $y(0) = 0,$
       $y(\pi) = 0.$

(d) $\left(\dfrac{1}{x}y'\right)' + \dfrac{\lambda + 1}{x^3}y = 0, \qquad 1 \le x \le e,$

$$y(1) = 0,$$
$$y(e) = 0.$$

2. Verify that the eigenvalue problem in Example 3 has no real eigenvalues.

3. Verify that every real number is an eigenvalue for the problem of Example 2.

4. Let λ_1 and λ_2 be distinct eigenvalues of the (not necessarily self-adjoint) problem

$$Ly = -\lambda r(x)y, \qquad U_1(y) = 0, \qquad U_2(y) = 0. \tag{1}$$

According to Exercise 8, Section 7.4, λ_1 and λ_2 are also eigenvalues of the adjoint problem

$$L^*y = -\lambda r(x)y, \qquad V_1(y) = 0, \qquad V_2(y) = 0. \tag{2}$$

Let $u_1(x)$ be an eigenfunction of the problem (1) that corresponds to λ_1, and let $v_2(x)$ be an eigenfunction of the adjoint problem that corresponds to $\lambda = \lambda_2$. Show that

$$\int_a^b r(x)u_1(x)v_2(x)\,dx = 0.$$

5. In the differential equation

$$\frac{d}{dx}\left[p(x)\frac{dy}{dx}\right] + [\lambda r(x) + q(x)]y = 0,$$

let $p(x) > 0$, $r(x) > 0$ for $a \le x \le b$.
(a) Let us make a change of independent variable of the form

$$t = \int_a^x f(x)\,dx, \qquad f(x) > 0 \quad \text{for} \quad a \le x \le b.$$

Then $d/dx = f(x)\,d/dt$. Show that the differential equation takes on the form

$$\frac{d^2y}{dt^2} + \frac{(pf)'}{(pf)}\frac{dy}{dt} + \left[\lambda\frac{r}{f^2p} + \frac{q}{f^2p}\right]y = 0, \tag{3}$$

where the prime denotes differentiation with respect to t. Show that the choice

$$f(x) = \left[\frac{r(x)}{p(x)}\right]^{1/2}$$

leads to the differential equation

$$\frac{d^2y}{dt^2} + \frac{1}{2}\frac{(rp)'}{rp}\frac{dy}{dt} + \left(\lambda + \frac{q}{r}\right)y = 0.$$

(b) Making a change of dependent variable $y = g(t)w$, show that the differential equation (3) becomes

$$gw'' + \left[2g' + \tfrac{1}{2}\frac{(rp)'}{rp}g\right]w' + \left[\left(\lambda + \frac{q}{r}\right)g + g'' + \tfrac{1}{2}\frac{(rp)'}{rp}g'\right]w = 0.$$

Show that the choice $g = (rp)^{-1/4}$ makes the coefficient of w' vanish, and that the differential equation takes on the form

$$\frac{d^2w}{dt^2} + [\lambda + Q(t)]w = 0 \tag{4}$$

where

$$Q(t) = -\tfrac{7}{16}(rp)^{-2}[(rp)']^2 - \tfrac{1}{4}(rp)^{-1}(rp)''.$$

The equation (4) is called the *Liouville normal form* for the original differential equation.

(c) Show that under the transformations of parts (a) and (b) above, the eigenvalue problem

$$\frac{d}{dx}\left[p(x)\frac{dy}{dx}\right] + [\lambda r(x) + q(x)]y = 0 \tag{5}$$

$$U_i(y) = \alpha_{i1}y(a) + \alpha_{i2}y'(a) + \alpha_{i3}y(b) + \alpha_{i4}y'(b) = 0, \qquad i = 1, 2,$$

takes on the form

$$\frac{d^2w}{dt^2} + [\lambda + Q(t)]w = 0, \qquad 0 \le t \le c, \tag{6}$$

$$\tilde{U}_i(w) = \beta_{i1}w(0) + \beta_{i2}w'(0) + \beta_{i3}w(c) + \beta_{i4}w'(c) = 0, \qquad i = 1, 2,$$

where

$$c = \int_a^b \left[\frac{r(x)}{p(x)}\right]^{1/2} dx.$$

(d) Let the problem (5) be self-adjoint, let λ_1 and λ_2 be distinct eigenvalues, and let $y_1(x)$ and $y_2(x)$ be corresponding eigenvalues. Show that the functions

$$w_i(t) = (rp)^{1/4}y_i(x), \qquad i = 1, 2,$$

are simply orthogonal on the interval $0 < t < c$.

(e) Is the problem (6) self-adjoint?

7.6 Some Special Types of Self-Adjoint Problems

We have seen that eigenvalue problems may be classified as self-adjoint or non-self-adjoint. Among the self-adjoint problems, we shall consider further two special types.

We first consider self-adjoint problems of the form

$$\frac{d}{dx}\left[p(x)\frac{dy}{dx}\right] + [\lambda r(x) + q(x)]y = 0, \qquad (7.61)$$

$$\alpha y(a) + \beta y'(a) = 0$$
$$\gamma y(b) + \delta y'(b) = 0, \qquad (7.62)$$

where α, β, γ, and δ are real constants. It sould be noted that the one boundary condition involves the values of y and y' at $x = a$ only, while the other boundary condition involves the values of y and y' at $x = b$ only. For this reason, the problem is said to have *separated boundary conditions*.

We assume that $p'(x)$, $q(x)$, and $r(x)$ are continuous and that $p(x) > 0$, $r(x) > 0$ for $a \le x \le b$. (If $p(x)$ and $r(x)$ have opposite signs, we can simply set $\lambda = -\mu$ to obtain a problem of this type.) As for any self-adjoint problem, the eigenvalues of the problem (7.61), (7.62) are real, and eigenfunctions which correspond to distinct eigenvalues are orthogonal with respect to the weight function $r(x)$ on the interval $a < x < b$.

In addition, it can be shown† that the problem (7.61), (7.62) possesses an infinite sequence of real eigenvalues

$$\lambda_0 < \lambda_1 < \lambda_2 < \cdots < \lambda_n < \cdots, \qquad (7.63)$$

such that

$$\lim_{n \to +\infty} \lambda_n = +\infty.$$

Thus the problem possesses at most a finite number of negative eigenvalues. If the additional requirements

$$\alpha\beta \le 0, \qquad \gamma\delta \ge 0 \qquad (7.64)$$

$$q(x) \le 0, \qquad a \le x \le b$$

it can be shown that no negative eigenvalues exist (Exercise 3 below).

We now prove the following result for problems with separated boundary conditions.

Theorem 5. An eigenfunction of the problem (7.61), (7.62) is unique except for a constant factor.

Proof. Let λ_0 be an eigenvalue of the problem and suppose that $y = u(x)$ and $y = v(x)$ are both eigenfunctions corresponding to $\lambda = \lambda_0$. We shall show that $u(x)$ and $v(x)$ are linearly dependent on the interval $a \le x \le b$, and hence that $v(x)$ is simply a constant multiple of $u(x)$.

† The references listed at the end of this chapter contain proofs of this result.

The functions $u(x)$ and $v(x)$ are both solutions of the differential equation

$$p(x)\frac{d^2y}{dx^2} + p'(x)\frac{dy}{dx} + [\lambda_0 r(x) + q(x)]y = 0.$$

According to Abel's formula (Section 1.6) we have

$$p(x)W(x; u, v) = C,$$

where C is a constant and $W(x; u, v)$ is the Wronskian of $u(x)$ and $v(x)$. If the Wronskian vanishes at one point of the interval $a \leq x \leq b$, it must vanish at every point. The functions $u(x)$ and $v(x)$ both satisfy the boundary conditions (7.62). From the first of these conditions we have

$$\alpha u(a) + \beta u'(a) = 0$$

$$\alpha v(a) + \beta v'(a) = 0.$$

Since α and β are not both zero, we must have

$$\begin{vmatrix} u(a) & u'(a) \\ v(a) & v'(a) \end{vmatrix} = W(a; u, v) = 0.$$

Then $W(x; u, v) \equiv 0$, so $u(x)$ and $v(x)$ are linearly dependent. Hence there exists a constant k such that $v(x) = ku(x)$.

It can be shown that the eigenfunction $y_n(x)$, which corresponds to the eigenvalue λ_n in the sequence (7.63), possesses exactly n zeros on the interval $a < x < b$.

We also consider problems of the form

$$\frac{d}{dx}\left[p(x)\frac{dy}{dx}\right] + [\lambda r(x) + q(x)]y = 0, \tag{7.65}$$

$$\begin{aligned} y(a) &= y(b), \\ y'(a) &= y'(b), \end{aligned} \tag{7.66}$$

where

$$p(a) = p(b). \tag{7.67}$$

Such a problem is self-adjoint, and is said to have *periodic boundary conditions*. We again assume that $p'(x)$, $q(x)$, and $r(x)$ are continuous and that $p(x) > 0$, $r(x) > 0$ for $a \leq x \leq b$. It can be shown that such a problem possesses an infinite sequence of real eigenvalues

$$\lambda_0 < \lambda_1 < \cdots < \lambda_n < \cdots$$

such that

$$\lim_{n \to +\infty} \lambda_n = +\infty.$$

However, to each eigenvalue there may correspond either one or two linearly independent eigenfunctions.

As an example, we consider the problem

$$y'' + \lambda y = 0,$$

$$y(-c) = y(c), \qquad y'(-c) = y'(c).$$

Here $p(x) = 1$, so the condition (7.67) is satisfied. When $\lambda = 0$, the general solution of the differential equation is

$$y = C_1 + C_2 x.$$

The boundary conditions require that

$$C_1 - C_2 c = C_1 + C_2 c, \qquad C_2 = C_2 .$$

Then C_2 must be zero, but C_1 is arbitrary. Thus $\lambda_0 = 0$ is an eigenvalue with one independent eigenfunction

$$y_0(x) = 1.$$

When $\lambda = k^2$, $k > 0$, the general solution of the differential equation is

$$y = C_1 \cos kx + C_2 \sin kx.$$

The boundary conditions require that

$$C_1 \cos kc - C_2 \sin kc = C_1 \cos kc + C_2 \sin kc$$

$$C_1 \sin kc + C_2 \cos kc = -C_1 \sin kc + C_2 \cos kc$$

or

$$C_1 \sin kc = 0$$

$$C_2 \sin kc = 0.$$

In order to have a nontrivial solution k must have one of the values

$$k_n = \frac{n\pi}{c}, \qquad n = 1, 2, 3, \dots .$$

But for such a value of k, both C_1 and C_2 are arbitrary. Therefore, to each eigenvalue

$$\lambda_n = k_n^2 = \left(\frac{n\pi}{c}\right)^2, \qquad n = 1, 2, 3, \dots ,$$

there corresponds the eigenfunctions

$$y_n(x) = A_n \cos \frac{n\pi x}{c} + B_n \sin \frac{n\pi x}{c} ,$$

where A_n and B_n are not both zero, but are otherwise arbitrary. Thus, to each of the eigenvalues there correspond two linearly independent eigenfunctions. If $u(x)$ and $v(x)$ are any two functions that are linearly independent on an interval $[a, b]$, it is always possible to choose two linear combinations of $u(x)$ and $v(x)$ that are orthogonal on (a, b). For instance, let

$$f(x) = u(x), \qquad g(x) = v(x) - ku(x),$$

where

$$k = \frac{(u, v)}{\|u\|^2} = \frac{\int_a^b r(x)u(x)v(x)\, dx}{\int_a^b r(x)[u(x)]^2\, dx}.$$

Then

$$(f, g) = (u, v) - k\|u\|^2 = 0,$$

so $f(x)$ and $g(x)$ are orthogonal.

If two independent eigenfunctions correspond to one eigenvalue, we can find two independent eigenfunctions that are orthogonal to each other. Every eigenfunction for that eigenvalue is simply a linear combination of the two orthogonal eigenfunctions.

In the example above, the eigenfunctions $\cos(n\pi x/c)$, $\sin(n\pi x/c)$, which both correspond to the eigenvalue λ_n, are orthogonal on the interval $(-c, c)$ for each $n \geq 1$. Therefore the set of eigenfunctions

$$\left\{ 1, \cos\frac{n\pi x}{c}, \sin\frac{n\pi x}{c} \right\}, \qquad n \geq 1,$$

is an orthogonal set, with weight function $r(x) = 1$, on the interval $(-c, c)$.

7.6 EXERCISES

1. Show that the boundary conditions

$$U_1(y) = \alpha_{11}y_1 + \alpha_{12}y_2 + \alpha_{13}y_3 + \alpha_{14}y_4 = 0$$

$$U_2(y) = \alpha_{21}y_1 + \alpha_{22}y_2 + \alpha_{23}y_3 + \alpha_{24}y_4 = 0$$

are equivalent to a set of separated boundary conditions if, and only if,

$$\begin{vmatrix} \alpha_{11} & \alpha_{12} \\ \alpha_{21} & \alpha_{22} \end{vmatrix} = \begin{vmatrix} \alpha_{13} & \alpha_{14} \\ \alpha_{23} & \alpha_{24} \end{vmatrix} = 0.$$

2. Theorem 5 can be generalized as follows. Let the boundary conditions of a problem that is not necessarily self-adjoint be such that either (or both) of the determinants

$$\begin{vmatrix} \alpha_{11} & \alpha_{12} \\ \alpha_{21} & \alpha_{22} \end{vmatrix}, \qquad \begin{vmatrix} \alpha_{13} & \alpha_{14} \\ \alpha_{23} & \alpha_{24} \end{vmatrix}$$

vanishes. Then if $y_1(x)$ and $y_2(x)$ are eigenfunctions of the problem that correspond to the same eigenvalue, they are linearly dependent. Prove this statement.

3. (a) Let $y(x)$ satisfy the conditions $\alpha y(a) + \beta y'(a) = 0$, $\gamma y(b) + \delta y'(b) = 0$. If $\alpha \beta \leq 0$ and $\gamma \delta \geq 0$, show that $y(a)y'(a) \geq 0$ and $y(b)y'(b) \leq 0$.

(b) Let λ_0 be an eigenfunction of the problem (7.63), (7.64), and let $y_0(x)$ be a corresponding eigenfunction. Show that

$$\lambda_0 \int_a^b r(y_0)^2 \, dx = \int_a^b p(y_0')^2 \, dx - \int_a^b q(y_0)^2 \, dx$$
$$+ p(a)y_0(a)y_0'(a) - p(b)y_0(b)y_0'(b).$$

Suggestion: multiply through in the equation for y_0 by y_0 and integrate by parts.

(c) If $\alpha \beta \leq 0$, $\gamma \delta \geq 0$, and $q(x) \leq 0$ on $[a, b]$, show that $\lambda_0 \geq 0$.

4. Why can the problem (7.65)–(7.67) not have more than two independent eigenfunctions associated with a particular eigenvalue?

5. Let $y_1(x, \lambda)$ and $y_2(x, \lambda)$ be the solutions of equation (7.65) for which

$$y_1(a,\lambda) = 1, \quad y_1'(a,\lambda) = 0, \quad y_2(a,\lambda) = 0, \quad y'_2(a,\lambda) = 1.$$

If λ_0 is an eigenvalue of the problem (7.65)–(7.67), show that there exist two independent eigenfunctions if, and only if,

$$y_1'(b,\lambda_0) = y_2(b,\lambda_0) = 0, \quad y_1(b,\lambda_0) = y_2'(b,\lambda_0) = 1.$$

7.7 Singular Problems

In the preceding discussion, we have dealt with problems associated with a differential equation of the form

$$\frac{d}{dx}\left[p(x) \frac{dy}{dx} \right] + [\lambda r(x) + q(x)]y = 0 \qquad (7.68)$$

on an interval $a \leq x \leq b$. In each case, it was assumed that $p'(x)$, $q(x)$, and $r(x)$ were continuous and that $p(x) \neq 0$ for $a \leq x \leq b$. Suppose now that $p'(x)$, $q(x)$, and $r(x)$ are continuous and that $p(x) \neq 0$ for $a < x < b$, but that at $x = a$, or $x = b$, or both, one or more of the following events occurs:

(a) $p(x)$ vanishes

(b) One or more of the functions $p(x)$, $q(x)$, $r(x)$ becomes infinite.

Eigenvalue problems associated with such a differential equation are said to be *singular*.† Many physically important eigenvalue problems are of this type.

For a *nonsingular* self-adjoint problem on an interval $a \leq x \leq b$, the relation

$$\int_a^b (vLu - uLv) \, dx = p(b)[u'(b)v(b) - u(b)v'(b)]$$
$$- p(a)[u'(a)v(a) - u(a)v'(a)] \qquad (7.69)$$
$$= 0$$

---

† Eigenvalue problems on an *infinite* interval are also said to be singular.

holds for all functions $u(x)$, $v(x)$ with two continuous derivatives that satisfy the boundary conditions. It is this property that insures the orthogonality of the eigenfunctions.

Let us now consider a problem with a singularity at the end point $x = a$. If δ is a small positive number, we have

$$\int_{a+\delta}^{b} (vLu - uLv)\, dx = p(b)[u'(b)v(b) - u(b)v'(b)]$$

$$- p(a + \delta)[u'(a + \delta)v(a + \delta) - u(a + \delta)v'(a + \delta)] \qquad (7.70)$$

for functions $u(x)$, $v(x)$, which possess two continuous derivatives on the interval $a < x \le b$. If we impose conditions on $u(x)$ and $v(x)$ which insure that

$$\lim_{x \to a+} p(x)[u'(x)v(x) - u(x)v'(x)] = 0 \qquad (7.71\mathrm{a})$$

$$p(b)[u'(b)v(b) - u(b)v'(b)] = 0, \qquad (7.71\mathrm{b})$$

then the property

$$\int_{a}^{b} (vLu - uLv)\, dx = 0 \qquad (7.72)$$

again holds. For instance, if $p(a) = 0$, the conditions

$$y(x) \text{ and } y'(x) \text{ finite as } x \to a+ \qquad (7.73)$$

$$\gamma y(b) + \delta y'(b) = 0$$

insure that the equalities (7.71) hold.

The case of a singularity at the end point $x = b$ can be treated by working on an interval $a \le x \le b - \delta$, and then letting $\delta \to 0$. If $p(b) = 0$, the boundary conditions

$$\alpha y(a) + \beta y'(a) = 0 \qquad (7.74)$$

$$y(x) \text{ and } y'(x) \text{ finite as } x \to b-$$

insure that

$$\int_{a}^{b} (vLu - uLv)\, dx = 0$$

for functions $u(x)$, $v(x)$ that satisfy these conditions.

If $p(a)$ and $p(b)$ are both zero, the boundary conditions

$$y(x) \text{ and } y'(x) \text{ finite as } x \to a+$$
$$y(x) \text{ and } y'(x) \text{ finite as } x \to b- \qquad (7.75)$$

are appropriate.

Singular eigenvalue problems with the property that

$$\int_{a}^{b} (vLu - uLv)\, dx = 0$$

for all functions $u(x)$, $v(x)$ which satisfy the boundary conditions are said to be self-adjoint. For such problems, eigenfunctions that correspond to distinct eigenvalues are orthogonal with respect to $r(x)$ on the interval $a < x < b$. If $r(x) \neq 0$ for $a < x < b$, then all eigenvalues of such a problem are real, just as in the nonsingular case.

In the next section we shall discuss some specific singular problems that are of importance in applications.

7.8 Some Important Singular Problems

As a first example of a singular eigenvalue problem, let us consider the differential equation

$$[(1 - x^2)y']' + \lambda y = 0 \tag{7.76}$$

on the interval $-1 < x < 1$ with the boundary conditions

$$y, y' \text{ finite as } x \to -1 + \tag{7.77}$$

$$y, y' \text{ finite as } x \to 1 - \quad .$$

In the differential equation, $p(x) = 1 - x^2$ vanishes at $x = 1$ and $x = -1$. The boundary conditions insure the orthogonality of the eigenfunctions with respect to $r(x) = 1$ on the interval $-1 < x < 1$. Also, since $r(x) \neq 0$ on this interval, all eigenvalues are real.

The equation (7.76) is Legendre's equation. This equation possesses solutions that are finite at both $x = 1$ and $x = -1$ when, and only when,

$$\lambda = \lambda_n = n(n + 1), \qquad n = 0, 1, 2, \dots . \tag{7.78}$$

The corresponding eigenfunctions are

$$y_n(x) = P_n(x), \qquad n = 0, 1, 2, \dots , \tag{7.79}$$

where $P_n(x)$ is the Legendre polynomial of degree n. Properties of these functions were discussed in Chapter 6. We state again, for purposes of reference, the property

$$\int_{-1}^{1} [P_n(x)]^2 \, dx = \frac{2}{2n + 1}, \qquad n = 0, 1, 2, \dots . \tag{7.80}$$

As a second example of a singular eigenvalue problem, we consider the differential equation

$$x^2 y'' + xy' + (\lambda x^2 - \alpha^2)y = 0 \tag{7.81}$$

on an interval $0 < x \leq c$, with the boundary conditions

$$y, y' \text{ finite as } x \to 0 + \tag{7.82}$$

$$y(c) = 0.$$

Here α is assumed to be a fixed real constant. The differential equation (7.81) is not self-adjoint as it stands, but it can be put in self-adjoint form by multiplying through by $1/x$. The result is

$$(xy')' + \left(\lambda x - \frac{\alpha^2}{x}\right)y = 0. \tag{7.83}$$

Comparing this equation with the standard form (7.68), we see that

$$p(x) = x, \qquad q(x) = -\frac{\alpha^2}{x}, \qquad r(x) = x.$$

Because $p(0) = 0$, and also because $q(x)$ becomes infinite as $x \to 0$, the problem (7.81), (7.82) is singular. However, the boundary conditions (7.82) insure the orthogonality of the eigenfunctions on the interval $0 < x < c$ with respect to $r(x) = x$. All eigenvalues are real.

In order to determine the eigenvalues, let us consider the three cases $\lambda > 0$, $\lambda = 0$, and $\lambda < 0$ separately. When $\lambda > 0$, let $\lambda = k^2$, where $k > 0$. Then the general solution of the differential equation is

$$y = C_1 J_\alpha(kx) + C_2 Y_\alpha(kx),$$

where J_α and Y_α are Bessel functions of the first and second kinds, respectively. The requirement that y and y' be finite as $x \to 0+$ necessitates that $C_2 = 0$. Then

$$y = C_1 J_\alpha(kx).$$

The condition at $x = c$ requires that

$$C_1 J_\alpha(kc) = 0.$$

If μ_n is the nth positive root of the equation

$$J_\alpha(\mu) = 0, \tag{7.84}$$

then k must have one of the values

$$k_n = \frac{\mu_n}{c}, \qquad n = 1, 2, 3, \dots . \tag{7.85}$$

The values

$$\lambda_n = k_n{}^2 = \left(\frac{\mu_n}{c}\right)^2, \qquad n = 1, 2, 3, \dots , \tag{7.86}$$

are eigenvalues of the problem, and the corresponding eigenfunctions are

$$y_n(x) = J_\alpha(k_n x), \qquad n = 1, 2, 3, \dots . \tag{7.87}$$

When $\lambda = 0$, the differential equation (7.81) has the form

$$x^2 y'' + xy' - \alpha^2 y = 0.$$

This is an equation of the Cauchy type, with general solution

$$y = C_1 x_\alpha + C_2 x^{-\alpha}, \qquad \alpha > 0$$

$$y = C_1 + C_2 \log x, \qquad \alpha = 0.$$

Evidently the constant C_2 must be zero for y and y' to be finite at $x = 0$. But the condition at $x = c$ requires that $C_1 = 0$ also. Thus the only solution of the differential equation that satisfies the boundary conditions is the trivial solution, and we conclude that $\lambda = 0$ is not an eigenvalue of the problem.

When $\lambda < 0$, let $\lambda = -k^2$, where $k > 0$. The differential equation is

$$x^2 y'' + xy' - (k^2 x^2 + \alpha^2) y = 0.$$

The general solution is

$$y = C_1 I_\alpha(kx) + C_2 K_\alpha(kx),$$

where I_α and K_α are modified Bessel functions. The constant C_2 must be zero if y is to be finite at $x = 0$. Then

$$y = C_1 I_\alpha(kx)$$

and the boundary condition at $x = c$ requires that

$$C_1 I_\alpha(kc) = 0.$$

But

$$I_\alpha(\mu) = \sum_{n=0}^{\infty} \frac{(\mu/2)^{2n+\alpha}}{n!\, \Gamma(n + \alpha + 1)}$$

does not vanish for any positive values of μ. Therefore, C_1 must be zero also, and $y \equiv 0$. The original problem, therefore, has no negative eigenvalues.

The eigenfunctions (7.87) have the property that

$$\int_0^c x J_\alpha(k_m x) J_\alpha(k_n x)\, dx = 0, \qquad m \neq n. \tag{7.88}$$

We now derive a formula for the quantities

$$\int_0^c x [J_\alpha(k_n x)]^2\, dx. \tag{7.89}$$

The eigenfunction $y_n(x) = J_\alpha(k_n x)$ satisfies the differential equation

$$x^2 y_n''(x) + x y_n'(x) + (k_n^2 x^2 - \alpha^2) y_n(x) = 0.$$

If we multiply through by the quantity $2 y_n'(x)$, we find that the resulting equation can be written in the form

$$[x^2 [y_n'(x)]^2]' + (k_n^2 x^2 - \alpha^2)[[y_n(x)]^2]' = 0. \tag{7.90}$$

Integrating with respect to x from 0 to c, and using integration by parts on the second term, we find that

$$\int_0^c x[y_n(x)]^2\, dx = \left[\frac{1}{2k_n^2}\, x^2[y_n'(x)]^2 + \frac{1}{2}\left(x^2 - \frac{\alpha^2}{k_n^2}\right)[y_n(x)]^2\right]_0^c. \quad (7.91)$$

Using the fact that

$$y_n(c) = 0,$$

we have

$$\int_0^c x[y_n(x)]^2\, dx = \frac{c^2}{2k_n^2}\, [y_n'(c)]^2. \quad (7.92)$$

The right-hand member of this equation can be further simplified by the use of the relation

$$\frac{d}{dx}\, J_\alpha(x) = -J_{\alpha+1}(x) + \frac{\alpha}{x}\, J_\alpha(x).$$

(This is equation (5.53).) We have

$$y_n'(x) = \frac{d}{dx}\, J_\alpha(k_n x) = k_n J_\alpha'(k_n x) = k_n\left[-J_{\alpha+1}(k_n x) + \frac{\alpha}{k_n x}\, J_\alpha(k_n x)\right]$$

and so

$$y_n'(c) = -k_n J_{\alpha+1}(k_n\, c).$$

From this relation and the relation (7.92), we have

$$\int_0^c x[y_n(x)]^2\, dx = \frac{c^2}{2}\, [J_{\alpha+1}(k_n c)]^2, \qquad n = 1, 2, 3, \dots. \quad (7.93)$$

We shall describe briefly two other important eigenvalue problems that are associated with the differential equation (7.81). The derivations of the various properties listed are left as exercises.

The problem

$$x^2 y'' + xy' + (\lambda x^2 - \alpha^2)y = 0, \qquad 0 < x < c \quad (7.94)$$

$$y, y' \text{ finite as } x \to 0_+$$

$$y'(c) = 0 \quad (7.95)$$

possesses the eigenvalues $\lambda_n = k_n^2$, where k_n is the nth positive root of the equation

$$J_\alpha'(kc) = 0. \quad (7.96)$$

The eigenfunctions are

$$y_n(x) = J_\alpha(k_n x), \qquad n = 1, 2, 3, \dots, \quad (7.97)$$

and

$$\int_0^c x[y_n(x)]^2\, dx = \frac{k_n^2 c^2 - \alpha^2}{2k_n^2}\, [J_\alpha(k_n c)]^2. \quad (7.98)$$

In the special case when $\alpha = 0$, $\lambda_0 = 0$ is also an eigenvalue, with eigen-function

$$y_0(x) = 1. \tag{7.99}$$

We have

$$\int_0^c x[y_0(x)]^2 \, dx = \tfrac{1}{2}c^2. \tag{7.100}$$

The problem

$$x^2 y'' + xy' + (\lambda x^2 - \alpha^2)y = 0, \qquad 0 < x < c \tag{7.101}$$

$$y, y' \text{ finite as } x \to 0+$$

$$hy(c) + y'(c) = 0, \qquad h > 0 \tag{7.102}$$

possesses the eigenvalues $\lambda_n = k_n{}^2$, where k_n is the nth positive root of the equation

$$hJ_\alpha(kc) + kJ_\alpha{}'(kc) = 0. \tag{7.103}$$

The eigenfunctions are

$$y_n(x) = J_\alpha(k_n x), \qquad n = 1, 2 \ 3, \dots, \tag{7.104}$$

and

$$\int_0^c x[y_n(x)]^2 \, dx = \frac{k_n{}^2 c^2 - \alpha^2 + h^2 c^2}{2k_n{}^2} [J_\alpha(k_n c)]^2. \tag{7.105}$$

7.8 EXERCISES

1. Given that the function $J_\alpha(x)$ has infinitely many positive zeros, use Rolle's theorem to show that the function $J_\alpha{}'(x)$ has infinitely many positive zeros.

2. Give a detailed discussion of the problem (7.94), (7.95). Include a derivation of formula (7.98).

3. Show that the function $J_\alpha(x)$ actually changes sign at each point on the interval $(0, +\infty)$ where it vanishes. Use this fact to show that the equation $xJ_\alpha{}'(x) + hJ_\alpha(x) = 0$ has infinitely many positive roots.

4. The restriction $h > 0$ in the boundary conditions (7.102) insures that the problem (7.101), (7.102) has no negative eigenvalues. Give a proof of this fact.

5. Give a detailed discussion of the problem (7.101), (7.102). Include a derivation of formula (7.105).

6. Discuss the eigenvalues and eigenfunctions of the problem

$$xy'' + \lambda y = 0,$$
$$y, y' \text{ finite as } x \to 0+, \qquad y(1) = 0.$$

With respect to what weight function are the eigenfunctions orthogonal on the interval $(0, 1)$?

7. Find the eigenvalues and eigenfunctions of the problem

$$4x^2y'' + (\lambda x^2 - 3)y = 0,$$
$$y, y' \text{ finite as } x \to 0 +, \qquad y'(1) = 0.$$

With respect to what weight function are the eigenfunctions orthogonal on the interval $(0, 1)$?

8. Find the eigenvalues and eigenfunctions of the problem

$$x^2y'' - xy' + (4\lambda x^4 - 3)y = 0,$$
$$y, y' \text{ finite as } x \to 0 +, \qquad y(c) = 0 \qquad (c > 0).$$

With respect to what weight function are the eigenfunctions orthogonal on the interval $(0, c)$?

REFERENCES

1. Coddington, E. A., and Levinson, N., *Theory of Ordinary Differential Equations* McGraw-Hill, New York, 1955.
2. Ince, E. L., *Ordinary Differential Equations*, 4th ed. Dover, New York, 1956.
3. Miller, K. S., *Linear Differential Equations in the Real Domain*. Norton, New York, 1963.

CHAPTER **8**

FOURIER SERIES

8.1 Orthogonal Sets of Functions

On an interval $[a, b]$ let there be assigned a function $w(x)$, called the weight function, that is continuous and positive for $a < x < b$. Let $f(x)$ and $g(x)$ be functions that are defined on $[a, b]$. For brevity, we write

$$(f, g) = \int_a^b w(x)f(x)g(x)\, dx \tag{8.1}$$

and

$$\|f\| = (f, f)^{1/2} = \left(\int_a^b w(x)[f(x)]^2\, dx \right)^{1/2} \tag{8.2}$$

The number (f, g) is called the *inner product* of $f(x)$ and $g(x)$ (with respect to the weight function $w(x)$) and the number $\|f\|$ is called the *norm* of the function $f(x)$ (with respect to the weight function $w(x)$).

A sequence of functions $\{\psi_n(x)\}$ is said to be an *orthogonal set* of functions (or a set of orthogonal functions) with respect to the weight function $w(x)$ if

$$(\psi_m, \psi_n) = \int_a^b w(x)\psi_m(x)\psi_n(x)\, dx = 0, \qquad m \neq n, \tag{8.3}$$

and if $\|\psi_n\| \neq 0$ for all n. (Thus no member of an orthogonal set can be the zero function.) When $w(x) \equiv 1$, we say that the functions ψ_n are *simply* orthogonal. We have already encountered numerous examples of orthogonal sets of functions. The sets of orthogonal polynomials that were investigated in Chapter 6 constitute such sets. The eigenfunctions of a self-adjoint eigenvalue problem also form an orthogonal set, as we saw in Chapter 7.

A set of functions $\{\phi_n(x)\}$ is said to be an *orthonormal set* if it is an orthogonal set and if also $\|\phi_n\| = 1$ for all n. If $\{\psi_n(x)\}$ is an orthogonal set, then the set $\{\phi_n(x)\}$, where

$$\phi_n(x) = \frac{\psi_n(x)}{\|\psi_n\|}, \tag{8.4}$$

is orthonormal. For

$$(\phi_m, \phi_n) = \frac{1}{\|\psi_m\| \, \|\psi_n\|} \int_a^b w(x)\psi_m(x)\psi_n(x) \, dx = \begin{cases} 0, & m \neq n \\ 1, & m = n. \end{cases}$$

We say that the set $\{\psi_n(x)\}$ has been *normalized* by the procedure (8.4). As a first example, let us consider the Legendre polynomials $P_n(x)$, $n = 0, 1, 2, \ldots$. These functions are orthogonal with respect to the weight function $w(x) = 1$ on the interval $-1 < x < 1$, and

$$\|P_n\|^2 = \int_{-1}^1 [P_n(x)]^2 \, dx = \frac{2}{2n + 1}, \quad n \geq 0.$$

Hence the functions

$$\phi_n(x) = \sqrt{\frac{2n + 1}{2}} \, P_n(x), \quad n \geq 0,$$

are orthonormal with weight function $w(x) = 1$ on the interval $-1 < x < 1$. As a second example, let us consider the set of functions $\{\sin(n\pi x/c)\}$, $n = 1, 2, 3, \ldots$. These functions are the eigenfunctions of the eigenvalue problem

$$y'' + \lambda y = 0,$$

$$y(0) = 0, \qquad y(c) = 0,$$

and so are orthogonal with respect to $w(x) = 1$ on the interval $0 < x < c$. Since

$$\int_0^c \left(\sin \frac{n\pi x}{c}\right)^2 dx = \frac{c}{2}, \quad n \geq 1,$$

the functions

$$\phi_n(x) = \sqrt{\frac{2}{c}} \sin \frac{n\pi x}{c}, \quad n \geq 1,$$

are orthonormal on the interval $0 < x < c$.

8.1 EXERCISES

1. Verify that the functions 1, $\cos(n\pi x/c)$, $n = 1, 2, 3, \ldots$, form a simply orthogonal set on the interval $(0, c)$, and find a corresponding orthonormal set.

2. Verify that the functions $\sin[(2n - 1)x/2]$, $n = 1, 2, 3, \ldots$, are simply orthogonal on the interval $(0, \pi)$, and find a corresponding orthonormal set.

3. Find an orthonormal set of functions that corresponds to (a) the set of Hermite polynomials $H_n(x)$, (b) the set of Tchebycheff polynomials $T_n(x)$.

4. Let the functions $f_n(x)$ be orthogonal with respect to a positive weight function $w(x)$ on the interval (a, b). Let $g_n(x) = \sqrt{w(x)} f_n(x)$.

   (a) Show that the functions $g_n(x)$ are simply orthogonal on (a, b).
   (b) If the functions $f_n(x)$ form an orthonormal set, show that the functions $g_n(x)$ also form an orthonormal set.
   (c) Find a simply orthogonal set of functions that corresponds to the set of Laguerre polynomials.

5. Let $w(x)$ be real, continuous, and positive on the interval (a, b). Let $f(x) = f_1(x) + if_2(x)$ and $g(x) = g_1(x) + ig_2(x)$ be complex-valued functions that are defined on (a, b). The inner product of $f(x)$ and $g(x)$ with respect to the weight function $w(x)$ is defined to be

$$(f, g) = \int_a^b w(x) f(x)\overline{g(x)} \, dx.$$

   The functions $f(x)$ and $g(x)$ are said to be orthogonal with respect to $w(x)$ if $(f, g) = 0$.

   (a) Show that $(g, f) = \overline{(f, g)}$.
   (b) Show that $(f, g) = 0$ if, and only if, $(g, f) = 0$.
   (c) Show that (f, f) is real and nonnegative.
   (d) The norm of a complex function $f(x)$ is defined as

$$\|f\| = (f, f)^{1/2}.$$

   Show that $\|f\| = 0$ if, and only if, $f(x) = 0$ at each point on (a, b) where $f(x)$ is continuous.

6. Show that the complex functions $\psi_n(x) = \exp(n\pi ix/c)$, $n = 0, \pm 1, \pm 2, \ldots$, are simply orthogonal on the interval $(-c, c)$. Find a corresponding orthonormal set.

8.2 Fourier Series

Let $\{\psi_n(x)\}$, $n = 0, 1, 2, \ldots$, be an orthogonal set of functions with weight function $w(x)$ on an interval $a < x < b$. Let $f(x)$ be an arbitrary function defined for $a < x < b$. Let us assume that $f(x)$ can be represented by an infinite series of the form

$$f(x) = \sum_{k=0}^{\infty} C_k \psi_k(x), \tag{8.5}$$

where the quantities C_k are constants. Let us multiply both sides of this equation by $w(x)\psi_n(x)$, where n is any nonnegative integer, and then integrate with respect to x from a to b. Assuming that termwise integration of the infinite series is valid, we have

$$\int_a^b w(x)f(x)\psi_n(x)\,dx = \sum_{k=0}^{\infty} C_k \int_a^b w(x)\psi_k(x)\psi_n(x)\,dx.$$

Because of the orthogonality of the functions $\psi_k(x)$, all of the terms in the series on the right vanish except for the term in which $k = n$. Then

$$(f, \psi_n) = C_n(\psi_n, \psi_n)$$

and

$$C_n = \frac{(f, \psi_n)}{\|\psi_n\|^2}, \qquad n \geq 0. \tag{8.6}$$

If the set $\{\psi_n(x)\}$ is orthonormal, so that $\|\psi_n\| = 1$, we have the simpler formula

$$C_n = (f, \psi_n), \qquad n > 0, \tag{8.7}$$

for the coefficients C_n in the series (8.5).

In deriving the formula (8.6) for the coefficients in the series (8.5), we made two large assumptions. We assumed that the function $f(x)$ could be represented by an infinite series of the form

$$\sum_{n=0}^{\infty} C_n\psi_n(x), \tag{8.8}$$

and we also assumed that the termwise integration of an infinite series was permissible. Actually, for an arbitrary function $f(x)$, we have no guarantee that the series (8.8) with coefficients (8.6) will even converge, let alone converge to $f(x)$. Nevertheless, the coefficients (8.6) are called the *Fourier coefficients* of the function $f(x)$ with respect to the orthogonal set $\{\psi_n(x)\}$, and the series (8.8) with coefficients (8.6) is called the *Fourier series* for $f(x)$. One of the main objects of this chapter is to describe conditions under which the Fourier series of a function will actually converge to the function.

There is a certain analogy between Fourier series and vectors that should be mentioned here. Let us consider an ordinary three-dimensional Euclidean space in which $\mathbf{u}$ and $\mathbf{v}$ are vectors. Let us denote the "dot product," or inner product, of $\mathbf{u}$ and $\mathbf{v}$ by the symbol $(\mathbf{u}, \mathbf{v})$, that is,

$$(\mathbf{u}, \mathbf{v}) = \mathbf{u} \cdot \mathbf{v}.$$

If the norm, or length, of a vector $\mathbf{u}$ is denoted by $\|\mathbf{u}\|$, then

$$\|\mathbf{u}\| = (\mathbf{u}, \mathbf{u})^{1/2}.$$

In the three dimensional space, we know that if $\mathbf{u}_1$, $\mathbf{u}_2$, and $\mathbf{u}_3$ are three mutually orthogonal nonzero vectors, then every vector $\mathbf{v}$ can be written in the form

$$\mathbf{v} = C_1\mathbf{u}_1 + C_2\mathbf{u}_2 + C_3\mathbf{u}_3 = \sum_{k=1}^{3} C_k\mathbf{u}_k, \tag{8.9}$$

where C_1, C_2, and C_3 are constants. In order to determine these constants for a particular vector $\mathbf{v}$, we take the inner product of both members of equation (8.9) with u_n, where n is 1, 2, or 3. Then

$$(\mathbf{v}, \mathbf{u}_n) = \sum_{k=1}^{3} C_k(\mathbf{u}_k, \mathbf{u}_n).$$

Because of the orthogonality of the vectors $\mathbf{u}_k$, the only nonvanishing term in the sum on the right is the one with $k = n$. Thus

$$(\mathbf{v}, \mathbf{u}_n) = C_n(\mathbf{u}_n, \mathbf{u}_n),$$

or

$$C_n = \frac{(\mathbf{v}, \mathbf{u}_n)}{\|\mathbf{u}_n\|^2}, \qquad n = 1, 2, 3. \tag{8.10}$$

Equation (8.9) should be compared with equation (8.5) and formula (8.10) should be compared with formula (8.6).

In the case of Fourier series, we deal with functions defined on an interval $a \le x \le b$ rather than with vectors. We speak of a "function space" as opposed to a three-dimensional "vector space." This function space is *infinite dimensional*, in the sense that we need an infinite sequence of mutually orthogonal functions to represent an arbitrary function. In this infinite-dimensional space. life is somewhat more complicated than in the three-dimensional space. In the first place, it turns out that not just any sequence of mutually orthogonal functions is satisfactory. In the second place, some restrictions must be placed on the class of functions that are to be represented by a series of the orthogonal functions—that is, by a Fourier series. We shall discuss these matters further in later sections.

8.2 EXERCISES

1. Let $f(x) = 1$, $0 \le x \le 1$. Find the Fourier series of $f(x)$ with respect to the simply orthogonal set $\{\sin n\pi x\}$, $n = 1, 2, 3, \ldots$.

2. Let $f(x) = 1 - x$, $0 \le x \le 1$. Find the Fourier series of $f(x)$ with respect to the simply orthogonal set $\{\cos n\pi x\}$, $n = 0, 1, 2, \ldots$.

3. Let $f(x)$ be a polynomial. Show that the Fourier series of $f(x)$ with respect to any set of orthogonal polynomials is a *finite* series, and that the series is actually equal to $f(x)$ everywhere.

4. Expand the function $f(x) = x^2$ in a series of (a) Legendre polynomials, (b) Laguerre polynomials.

5. Let $\{\psi_n(x)\}$, $n = 1, 2, 3, \ldots$, be an orthogonal set, and let $\{\phi_n(x)\}$ be a corresponding orthonormal set. Show that corresponding terms in the two Fourier series of a function $f(x)$ are identical.

6. Let $\{\psi_n(x)\}$, $n = 1, 2, 3, \ldots$, be an orthogonal set, with positive weight function $w(x)$, and let $\phi_n(x) = \sqrt{w(x)}\psi_n(x)$. Compare the Fourier series of a function $f(x)$ with respect to the set $\psi_n(x)$ with the Fourier series of the function $f(x)\sqrt{w(x)}$ with respect to the set $\{\phi_n(x)\}$.

7. Let the complex functions $\psi_n(x)$, $n \geq 1$, be orthogonal with respect to the positive real weight function $w(x)$ on the interval (a, b). (See Exercise 5, Section 8.1.) Derive formally the formulas

$$f(x) = \sum_{n=1}^{\infty} C_n \psi_n(x), \qquad C_n = \frac{\int_a^b wf\bar{\psi}_n \, dx}{\int_a^b w|\psi_n|^2 \, dx}$$

for the Fourier series and Fourier coefficients of a complex valued function $f(x)$.

8.3. Examples of Fourier Series

In this section we shall list formulas for the Fourier coefficients of an arbitrary function $f(x)$ corresponding to some specific sets of orthogonal functions. Conditions under which the series actually converge to the function will be discussed in the following sections.

(a) Series of Legendre Polynomials

The Legendre polynomials $P_n(x)$ are orthogonal with respect to the weight function $w(x) = 1$ on the interval $(-1, 1)$ and

$$\|P_n(x)\|^2 = \int_{-1}^{1} [P_n(x)]^2 \, dx = \frac{2}{2n + 1}, \qquad n \geq 0.$$

Therefore, according to the general formula (8.6), the coefficients in the Fourier-Legendre series

$$\sum_{n=0}^{\infty} C_n P_n(x)$$

for an arbitrary function $f(x)$ are given by the formula

$$C_n = \frac{2n + 1}{2} \int_{-1}^{1} f(x)P_n(x) \, dx, \qquad n \geq 0. \tag{8.11}$$

(b) Series of Tchebycheff Polynomials

The Tchebycheff polynomials of the first kind, $T_n(x)$, are orthogonal with respect to the weight function $w(x) = (1 - x^2)^{-1/2}$ on the interval $(-1, 1)$. Since

$$\|T_n(x)\|^2 = \int_{-1}^{1} \frac{[T_n(x)]^2}{\sqrt{1 - x^2}} \, dx = \begin{cases} \pi, & n = 0 \\ \pi/2, & n \geq 1 \end{cases}$$

we can write the Fourier-Tchebycheff series for a function $f(x)$ as

$$\tfrac{1}{2}C_0 T_0(x) + \sum_{n=1}^{\infty} C_n T_n(x),$$

where

$$C_n = \frac{2}{\pi} \int_{-1}^{1} \frac{f(x)T_n(x)}{\sqrt{1-x^2}}\, dx, \qquad n \geq 0. \tag{8.12}$$

(c) Series of Laguerre Polynomials

For the Laguerre polynomials $L_n(x)$, $w(x) = e^{-x}$ and the interval of orthogonality is $(0, +\infty)$. Since

$$\|L_n(x)\|^2 = \int_{0}^{\infty} e^{-x}[L_n(x)]^2\, dx = 1, \qquad n \geq 0,$$

the Fourier-Laguerre series

$$\sum_{n=0}^{\infty} C_n L_n(x)$$

for $f(x)$ has the coefficients

$$C_n = \int_{0}^{\infty} e^{-x} f(x) L_n(x)\, dx, \qquad n \geq 0. \tag{8.13}$$

(d) Series of Hermite Polynomials

For the Hermite polynomials $H_n(x)$, $w(x) = \exp(-x^2)$ and the interval of orthogonality is $(-\infty, +\infty)$. Since

$$\|H_n(x)\|^2 = \int_{-\infty}^{+\infty} \exp(-x^2)[H_n(x)]^2\, dx = 2^n n! \sqrt{\pi}, \qquad n \geq 0,$$

the coefficients in the series

$$\sum_{n=0}^{\infty} C_n H_n(x)$$

for $f(x)$ are

$$C_n = \frac{1}{2^n n! \sqrt{\pi}} \int_{-\infty}^{+\infty} \exp(-x^2) f(x) H_n(x)\, dx, \quad n \geq 0. \tag{8.14}$$

(e) Fourier Sine Series

The functions $\sin(n\pi x/c)$, $n \geq 1$, are simply orthogonal on the interval $(0, c)$ and

$$\int_{0}^{c} \sin^2 \frac{n\pi x}{c}\, dx = \frac{c}{2}, \qquad n \geq 1.$$

The Fourier sine series for a function $f(x)$ has the form

$$\sum_{n=1}^{\infty} C_n \sin \frac{n\pi x}{c},$$

where

$$C_n = \frac{2}{c} \int_0^c f(x) \sin \frac{n\pi x}{c} \, dx, \qquad n \geq 1. \tag{8.15}$$

(f) Fourier Cosine Series

The function $\cos(n\pi x/c)$, $n \geq 0$, are simply orthogonal on the interval $(0, c)$ and

$$\int_0^c \cos^2 \frac{n\pi x}{c} \, dx = \begin{cases} c, & n = 0 \\ \dfrac{c}{2}, & n \geq 1. \end{cases}$$

The Fourier cosine series for a function $f(x)$ can be written in the form

$$\frac{C_0}{2} + \sum_{n=1}^{\infty} C_n \cos \frac{n\pi x}{2}$$

where

$$C_n = \frac{2}{c} \int_0^c f(x) \cos \frac{n\pi x}{c} \, dx, \qquad n \geq 0. \tag{8.16}$$

(g) General Trigonometric Fourier Series

The functions $\{1, \cos(n\pi x/c), \sin(n\pi x/c)\}$, $n \geq 1$, are simply orthogonal on the interval $(-c, c)$, as can be verified by direct integration. For the norms of these functions we have

$$\int_{-c}^c \cos^2 \frac{n\pi x}{c} \, dx = \begin{cases} 2c, & n = 0 \\ c, & n \geq 1 \end{cases}$$

$$\int_{-c}^c \sin^2 \frac{n\pi x}{c} \, dx = c, \qquad n \geq 1.$$

The general trigonometric Fourier series for a function $f(x)$ is defined to be the series

$$\frac{1}{2}a_0 + \sum_{n=1}^{\infty} \left(a_n \cos \frac{n\pi x}{c} + b_n \sin \frac{n\pi x}{c} \right), \tag{8.17}$$

where

$$a_n = \frac{1}{c} \int_{-c}^c f(x) \cos \frac{n\pi x}{c} \, dx, \quad n \geq 0, \qquad b_n = \frac{1}{c} \int_{-c}^c f(x) \sin \frac{n\pi x}{c} \, dx, \qquad n \geq 1. \tag{8.18}$$

In some texts the term "Fourier series" refers only to this type of series, and a series of functions of an arbitrary orthogonal set is called a "generalized Fourier series."

(h) Fourier-Bessel Series

In Chapter 7 we saw that the functions $\{J_\alpha(k_n x)\}$ were orthogonal with weight function $w(x) = x$ on the interval $(0, c)$ if k_n is specified as the nth positive root of one of the equations

(a) $J_\alpha(kc) = 0$,

(b) $J_\alpha'(kc) = 0$,

(c) $hJ_\alpha(kc) + kJ_\alpha'(kc) = 0$, $h > 0$.

The corresponding formulas for the quantities

$$A_n = \int_0^c x[J_\alpha(k_n c)]^2 \, dx$$

are

(a') $$A_n = \frac{c^2}{2}[J_{\alpha+1}(k_n c)]^2$$

(b') $$A_n = \frac{k_n^2 c^2 - \alpha^2}{2k_n^2}[J_\alpha(k_n c)]^2$$

(c') $$A_n = \frac{k_n^2 c^2 - \alpha^2 + h^2 c^2}{2k_n^2}[J_\alpha(k_n c)]^2.$$

The coefficients in the Fourier-Bessel series

$$\sum_{n=1}^\infty C_n J_\alpha(k_n x)$$

for a function $f(x)$ are given by the formula

$$C_n = \frac{1}{A_n}\int_0^c xf(x)J_\alpha(k_n x)\, dx, \qquad n \geq 1. \tag{8.19}$$

In the special case when $\alpha = 0$ and k_n is the nth positive root of equation (b), the series has the form

$$C_0 + \sum_{n=1}^\infty C_n J_0(k_n x),$$

where

$$C_0 = \frac{2}{c^2}\int_0^c xf(x)\, dx \tag{8.20}$$

and the other coefficients are still given by the formula (8.19).

Let us now compute a few Fourier series for specific functions. As a first example, we find the Fourier sine series for the function $f(x) = x$,

$0 \leq x \leq c$. According to part (e) above, the coefficients in the series are

$$C_n = \frac{2}{c} \int_0^c x \sin \frac{n\pi x}{c} \, dx = \frac{2}{c} \left[\frac{c^2}{n^2\pi^2} \sin \frac{n\pi x}{c} - \frac{c}{n\pi} x \cos \frac{n\pi x}{c} \right]_0^c$$

$$= -\frac{2c}{n\pi} \cos n\pi = \frac{2c}{n\pi}(-1)^{n+1}, \qquad n \geq 1.$$

Hence the Fourier sine series is

$$\frac{2c}{\pi} \sum_{n=1}^{\infty} \frac{(-1)^{n+1}}{n} \sin \frac{n\pi x}{c}.$$

We are saying nothing yet about whether the series converges, or whether it converges to $f(x) = x$.

As a second example, let us find the Fourier-Legendre series for the function

$$f(x) = \begin{cases} 0, & -1 \leq x < 0 \\ x, & 0 \leq x \leq 1. \end{cases}$$

According to part (a) above, the coefficients are given by the formula

$$C_n = \frac{2n+1}{2} \int_{-1}^1 f(x)P_n(x) \, dx = \frac{2n+1}{2} \int_0^1 xP_n(x) \, dx, \qquad n \geq 0.$$

Since

$$P_0(x) = 1, \qquad P_1(x) = x, \qquad P_2(x) = \tfrac{1}{2}(3x^2 - 1),$$

the first few coefficients are

$$C_0 = \tfrac{1}{2}\int_0^1 x \, dx = \tfrac{1}{4}, \quad C_1 = \tfrac{3}{2}\int_0^1 x^2 \, dx = \tfrac{1}{2}, \quad C_2 = \tfrac{5}{2}\int_0^1 (\tfrac{3}{2}x^3 - \tfrac{1}{2}x) \, dx = \frac{5}{16}.$$

Thus the series has the form

$$\tfrac{1}{4}P_0(x) + \tfrac{1}{2}P_1(x) + \frac{5}{16}P_2(x) + \cdots.$$

As a final example, let us consider the function

$$f(x) = \begin{cases} 1, & 0 < x < 1 \\ 0, & 1 < x < 2. \end{cases}$$

We shall find the Fourier-Bessel series for $f(x)$, corresponding to the functions $\{J_1(k_n x)\}$, $n \geq 1$, where k_n is the nth positive root of the equation $J_1(2k) = 0$. Using formulas (a') and (8.19) in part (h) above, with $\alpha = 1$ and $c = 2$, we obtain the following formula for the Fourier coefficients of $f(x)$:

$$C_n = \frac{1}{2[J_2(2k_n)]^2} \int_0^1 x^2 J_1(k_n x) \, dx = \frac{1}{2[J_2(2k_n)]^2} \left[\frac{x^2}{k_n} J_2(k_n x) \right]_0^1$$

$$= \frac{J_2(k_n)}{2k_n[J_2(2k_n)]^2}, \qquad n \geq 1.$$

The Fourier-Bessel series is

$$\frac{1}{2}\sum_{n=1}^{\infty}\frac{J_2(k_n)}{k_n[J_2(2k_n)]^2}J_1(k_nx).$$

8.3 EXERCISES

1. Let $f(x) = 0$ for $-1 \le x \le 0$ and $f(x) = x$ for $0 < x \le 1$. Find

   (a) the trigonometric Fourier series for $f(x)$ on the interval $(-1, 1)$;
   (b) the first three terms in the series of Legendre polynomials for $f(x)$.

2. Let $f(x) = e^{-x}$, $0 \le x < +\infty$. Find the first three terms in the series of Laguerre polynomials for $f(x)$.

3. Let $f(x) = x$, $0 \le x \le 2$. Find the Fourier series of $f(x)$ with respect to the orthogonal set $\{\cos n\pi x/2\}$, $n \ge 0$.

4. If $f(x) = x$, $0 < x < 2$, find the Fourier-Bessel series for $f(x)$ with respect to the given orthogonal set:
   (a) $\{J_1(k_nx)\}$, $n \ge 1$, where k_n is the nth positive root of the equation $J_1(2k) = 0$.
   (b) $\{J_1(k_nx)\}$, $n \ge 1$, where k_n is the nth positive root of the equation $J_1'(2k) = 0$.

5. If $f(x) = e^{x^2}$ when $0 \le x \le 1$ and $f(x) = 0$ for all other values of x, find the first three terms in the series of Hermite polynomials for $f(x)$.

6. Derive the formula for the coefficients in the series of Tchebycheff polynomials

$$\frac{1}{2}a_0 + \sum_{n=1}^{\infty}a_nT_n(x)$$

   for a function $f(x)$ by making the change of variable $x = \cos\theta$ and finding the Fourier cosine series for the function $f(\cos\theta)$.

7. (a) Let $\psi_n(x) = P_{2n}(x)$, $n = 0, 1, 2, \ldots$, where the functions $P_{2n}(x)$ are the Legendre polynomials of even degree. Show that the functions $\psi_n(x)$ are simply orthogonal on the interval $(0, 1)$ and derive the formula

$$C_n = (4n + 1)\int_0^1 f(x)\psi_n(x)\,dx$$

   for the Fourier coefficients of a function $f(x)$.
   (b) Let $\phi_n(x) = P_{2n-1}(x)$, $n = 1, 2, 3, \ldots$, where the functions $P_{2n-1}(x)$ are the Legendre polynomials of odd degree. Show that the functions $\phi_n(x)$ are simply orthogonal on the interval $(0, 1)$ and derive the formula

$$C_n = (4n - 1)\int_0^1 f(x)\phi_n(x)\,dx$$

   for the Fourier coefficients of a function $f(x)$.

8. The *Laguerre functions*, $l_n(x)$, are defined by means of the equation $l_n(x) = e^{-x/2}L_n(x)$, $n = 0, 1, 2, \ldots$, where $L_n(x)$ is the Laguerre polynomial of degree n. If $f(x) = 1 - x$ when $0 \leq x \leq 1$ and $f(x) = 0$ when $x > 1$, find the first two terms in the series of Laguerre functions for $f(x)$.

9. Derive the formula

$$C_n = \frac{2}{\pi} \int_0^{\pi} f(x) \sin \frac{2n - 1}{2} x \, dx, \qquad n = 1, 2, 3, \ldots,$$

for the Fourier coefficients of $f(x)$ with respect to the simply orthogonal set $\left\{ \sin \dfrac{2n - 1}{2} x \right\}$, $0 \leq x \leq \pi$.

8.4 Types of Convergence

The "distance" between two numbers p and q may be defined as $|p - q|$. When we say that a sequence of numbers $\{s_n\}$ converges to a number s, we mean that

$$\lim_{n \to \infty} |s_n - s| = 0, \tag{8.21}$$

that is, that the distance between the numbers s_n and s approaches zero as n becomes infinite.

Let us now consider a sequence of *functions* $\{s_n(x)\}$ defined on an interval I. In the usual definition of convergence, we say that the sequence converges to the function $s(x)$ on I if it converges to $s(x)$ at every point of I. This type of convergence is called *pointwise convergence*, for obvious reasons.

Let us consider the space of functions that are defined on a closed interval $[a, b]$. If we restrict ourselves to the class of *continuous* functions, we can define the *distance between two functions* $f(x)$ and $g(x)$ as

$$\max |f(x) - g(x)|, \qquad x \text{ in } [a, b]. \tag{8.22}$$

Let $\{s_n(x)\}$ be a sequence of continuous functions and let $s(x)$ be a continuous function on $[a, b]$. Let

$$\varepsilon_n = \max |s_n(x) - s(x)|, \qquad x \text{ in } [a, b]. \tag{8.23}$$

Thus ε_n is the distance between the functions $s_n(x)$ and $s(x)$. If

$$\lim_{n \to \infty} \varepsilon_n = 0, \tag{8.24}$$

then certainly the sequence $\{s_n(x)\}$ converges† to $s(x)$ pointwise in $[a, b]$. However, it is still possible for the sequence to converge to $s(x)$ at each point of $[a, b]$ even though the situation (8.24) does not occur. We shall presently

---

† In this case, the sequence not only converges at each point of $[a, b]$, but it converges *uniformly* on $[a, b]$.

give an alternative definition for the distance between two functions which turns out to be more natural and more satisfactory for a discussion of the convergence of Fourier series. First, however, we shall describe a certain class of functions that we shall adopt for our "function space."

A function $f(x)$ is said to be *piecewise continuous* on the interval $a \le x \le b$ if it is continuous except at a finite number of points $x_1, x_2, \ldots, x_N$ of $[a, b]$ and if at each point of discontinuity the left and right-hand limits of $f(x)$ exist. (If $x_1 = a$, the right-hand limit must exist at x_1 and if $x_N = b$, the left-hand limit must exist at x_N.) We use the symbols

$$f(x_i-), \qquad f(x_i+) \tag{8.25}$$

to denote the left- and right-hand limits, respectively, of $f(x)$ at $x = x_i$. The function $f(x)$ which is illustrated in Figure 8.1 is piecewise continuous on $[a, b]$. It has only one discontinuity, at $x = x_1$, and

$$f(x_1-) = A, \qquad f(x_1+) = B.$$

The function $g(x)$, which is illustrated in Figure 8.2, is *not* piecewise contin-

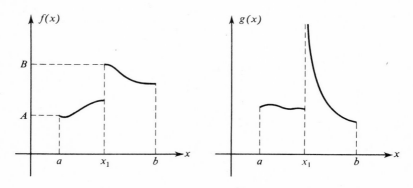

FIGURE 8.1   **FIGURE 8.2**

uous on $[a, b]$. It has only one discontinuity, at $x = x_1$, but the right-hand limit of $g(x)$ does not exist at $x = x_1$.

Let us denote the class, or space, of functions that are piecewise continuous on the interval $[a, b]$ by the symbol $C_p[a, b]$. When it is evident what interval is under consideration, we shall use the simpler symbol C_p. If the functions $f(x)$ and $g(x)$ are both in C_p, then every function of the form

$$\alpha f(x) + \beta g(x),$$

where α and β are constants, is also in C_p. The functions

$$[f(x)]^2, \qquad [g(x)]^2, \qquad f(x)g(x)$$

are also in C_p.

Let $w(x)$ be a function that is continuous and positive for $a < x < b$, and such that the integral

$$\int_a^b w(x)\, dx$$

exists. Note that $w(x)$ need not be continuous at $x = a$ and $x = b$. The above integral may be improper. It can be shown that if $F(x)$ is any function in $C_p[a, b]$, then the integral

$$\int_a^b w(x)F(x)\, dx$$

also exists.

The *inner product* (f, g) of two functions $f(x)$ and $g(x)$ in C_p, with respect to the weight function $w(x)$, is defined to be

$$(f, g) = \int_a^b w(x)f(x)g(x)\, dx. \tag{8.26}$$

The *norm* $\|f\|$ of a function $f(x)$ in C_p is defined to be

$$\|f\| = (f, f)^{1/2} = \left(\int_a^b w(x)[f(x)]^2\, dx \right)^{1/2}. \tag{8.27}$$

The *distance* between two functions $f(x)$ and $g(x)$ in C_p is defined to be

$$\|f - g\|. \tag{8.28}$$

It should be noted that because of the properties of the space C_p and the properties of the weight function $w(x)$, all of the integrals in formulas (8.26), (8.27), and (8.28) exist. We also note that if $\|f\| = 0$, where $f(x)$ is in C_p, then $f(x)$ must be zero on (a, b) except possibly at its points of discontinuity. Thus if $\|f\| = 0$, then $f(x)$ must be zero at all but a finite number of points in $[a, b]$. If $\|f - g\| = 0$, then the functions $f(x)$ and $g(x)$ must be equal at all but a finite number of points in $[a, b]$.

If $f(x)$ and $g(x)$ both belong to C_p, then the *Schwarz inequality*

$$|(f, g)| \le \|f\| \cdot \|g\| \tag{8.29}$$

and the *triangle inequality*

$$\|f + g\| \le \|f\| + \|g\| \tag{8.30}$$

are both valid. The proofs of these inequalities are left as exercises.

Let each of the functions $s_n(x)$, $n \ge 0$, and the function $s(x)$ be of the class $C_p[a, b]$. We say that the sequence $\{s_n(x)\}$ *converges in the mean* to $s(x)$ (with respect to the weight function $w(x)$ on the interval $[a, b]$) if

$$\lim_{n \to \infty} \|s(x) - s_n(x)\| = 0, \tag{8.31}$$

that is, if

$$\lim_{n \to \infty} \int_a^b w(x)[s(x) - s_n(x)]^2\, dx = 0. \tag{8.32}$$

If the sequence $\{s_n(x)\}$ converges to $s(x)$ in the mean on the interval $[a, b]$, it does not necessarily follow that the sequence converges pointwise to $s(x)$ at each point of (a, b) or $[a, b]$. Also, it is possible for a sequence $\{s_n(x)\}$ to converge pointwise to $s(x)$ at each point of $[a, b]$ and yet not converge in the mean to $s(x)$. (Examples are presented in the exercises.) Thus the two types of convergence are different, and one type does not imply the other. For theoretical purposes, convergence in the mean is more satisfactory, especially when the Lebesque integral† is used instead of the Riemann integral of elementary calculus. In applications, however, pointwise convergence is more important. We shall discuss both types of convergence, for Fourier series, in the sections which follow.

8.4 EXERCISES

1. Determine whether or not the given function is piecewise continuous on the indicated interval.

(a) $f(x) = |x|$, $\quad -1 \le x \le 1$

(b) $f(x) = \dfrac{1}{x - 1}$, $\quad 0 \le x \le 2$

(c) $f(x) = \begin{cases} x, & -3 \le x < 0 \\ 1, & 0 < x < 2 \\ x, & 2 \le x \le 3 \end{cases}$ $\quad -3 \le x \le 3$

2. (a) Prove the Schwarz inequality (8.29). Suggestion: if $\|g\| \ne 0$, the function $F(\lambda) = \|f + \lambda g\|^2$ is a second-degree polynomial in λ which is never negative for real λ. Look at the discriminant of the equation $F(\lambda) = 0$.
(b) Prove the triangle inequality (8.30). Suggestion: use the Schwarz inequality.

3. Let $\{\phi_n(x)\}$ be a simply orthogonal set of functions relative to the interval (a, b). Use the Schwarz inequality to show that

$$\left| \int_a^b \phi_n(x)\, dx \right| \le \sqrt{b - a}\, \|\phi_n\|.$$

In particular, show that

$$\left| \int_{-1}^1 P_n(x)\, dx \right| \le \frac{2}{\sqrt{2n + 1}} \le \frac{2}{\sqrt{n}}, \qquad n \ge 1$$

† For a discussion of the Lebesque integral, and convergence in the mean, see Hartman and Mikusiniski, Reference 4 at the end of this Chapter.

4. Let the graph of each of the functions $f_n(x)$, $n = 2$, 3, 4, ..., $0 \le x \le 1$, consist of three line segments, as shown in Figure 8.3.

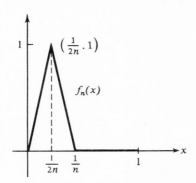

FIGURE 8.3

(a) Describe $f_n(x)$ analytically.

(b) Show that the sequence $\{f_n(x)\}$ converges (pointwise) to zero at each point of the interval $[0, 1]$.

(c) If $\varepsilon_n = \max_{o \le x \le 1} |f_n(x) - 0|$, show that ε_n does not approach zero as n becomes infinite.

(d) Show that the sequence $\{f_n(x)\}$ converges in the mean (with $w(x) = 1$) on the interval $[0, 1]$ to the zero function.

5. Let the graph of the function $f_n(x)$, $n = 2$, 3, 4, ..., $0 \le x \le 1$, consist of three line segments that join, successively, the points

$$(0, 0), \qquad \left(\frac{1}{2n}, n\right), \qquad \left(\frac{1}{n}, 0\right), \qquad \text{and } (1, 0).$$

(a) Draw a graph that shows the configuration of the functions $f_n(x)$, and also describe these functions analytically.

(b) Show that the sequence $\{f_n(x)\}$ converges (pointwise) to zero at each point of the interval $[0, 1]$.

(c) Show that the sequence $\{f_n(x)\}$ does *not* converge in the mean to the zero function on the interval $[0, 1]$.

6. This exercise involves the construction of a sequence of continuous functions $\{f_n(x)\}$ that converges in the mean on the interval $[0, 1]$, but converges pointwise nowhere. To begin with, we divide the interval $[0, 1]$ into three equal subintervals and define functions $f_1(x)$, $f_2(x)$, and $f_3(x)$ as shown in Figure 8.4. Next, we subdivide the interval $[0, 1]$ into $3^2 = 9$ equal parts, and define nine functions f_4, f_5, ..., f_{12} in such a way that each function has the value 1 on one of the subintervals and has the value 0 outside of, at most, three subintervals. A typical case is shown

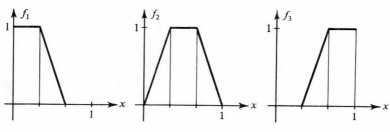

FIGURE 8.4

in Figure 8.5. We next form $3^3 = 27$ more functions of the sequence,

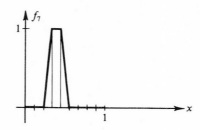

FIGURE 8.5

corresponding to 27 equal subintervals of $[0, 1]$, and so on. It is left to the reader to show that $\{f_n(x)\}$ converges in the mean to the zero function, but converges pointwise nowhere.

8.5 Convergence in the Mean

Let $\{\phi_n(x)\}$, $n \geq 0$, be an orthonormal† set of functions, with weight function $w(x)$ on an interval $[a, b]$. The functions $\phi_n(x)$ are assumed to belong to the space $C_p[a, b]$. If $f(x)$ is an arbitrary function of the space $C_p[a, b]$, its Fourier series is

$$\sum_{k=0}^{\infty} c_k \phi_k(x), \tag{8.33}$$

where

$$c_k = (f, \phi_k) \tag{8.34}$$

is the kth Fourier coefficient of $f(x)$. Let $\{S_n(x)\}$, $n \geq 0$, be the sequence of partial sums of the Fourier series, so that

$$S_n(x) = \sum_{k=0}^{n} c_k \phi_k(x), \qquad n \geq 0. \tag{8.35}$$

† In view of Exercise 5 of Section 8.2, we consider only orthogonal sets that are orthonormal.

The Fourier series (8.33) is said to converge in the mean to $f(x)$ if

$$\lim_{n \to \infty} \| f(x) - S_n(x) \| = 0, \tag{8.36}$$

that is, if

$$\lim_{n \to \infty} \int_a^b w(x) [f(x) - S_n(x)]^2 \, dx = 0. \tag{8.37}$$

If the series does converge in the mean to $f(x)$, we write

$$\text{l.i.m.}_{n \to \infty} S_n = f. \tag{8.38}$$

Before we continue with our discussion of Fourier series, let us consider the possibility of representing $f(x)$ by a general series of the form

$$\sum_{n=0}^{\infty} a_k \phi_k(x), \tag{8.39}$$

where the coefficients a_k are not necessarily the Fourier coefficients. Let

$$T_n(x; a_0, a_1, \dots, a_n) = \sum_{k=0}^{n} a_k \phi_k(x) \tag{8.40}$$

be the nth partial sum of the series (8.39), and let E_n be the quantity

$$E_n = \| f - T_n \|. \tag{8.41}$$

Then

$$E_n^2 = \int_a^b w(x) \left[f(x) - \sum_{k=0}^{n} a_k \phi_k(x) \right]^2 dx. \tag{8.42}$$

If we square the quantity in brackets in equation (8.42), integrate, and remember that the set $\{\phi_n(x)\}$ is orthonormal, we find that

$$E_n^2 = \| f \|^2 + \sum_{k=0}^{n} (a_k^2 - 2 a_k c_k), \tag{8.43}$$

where $c_k = (f, \phi_k)$ is the kth Fourier coefficient of $f(x)$. The equality (8.43) can be written in the form

$$E_n^2 = \| f \|^2 + \sum_{k=0}^{n} (a_k - c_k)^2 - \sum_{k=0}^{n} c_k^2. \tag{8.44}$$

Evidently, for a given nonnegative integer n, the quantity E_n is least when $a_k = c_k$ for $k = 0, 1, 2, \dots, n$. We therefore have the following theorem.

Theorem 1. For any given nonnegative integer n, the best approximation in the mean to a function $f(x)$ by an expression of the form

$$\sum_{k=0}^{n} a_k \phi_k(x)$$

is obtained when the coefficients a_k are the Fourier coefficients of $f(x)$.

If we set $a_k = c_k$, $0 \leq k \leq n$, we see from formula (8.44) that

$$\|f - S_n\|^2 = \|f\|^2 - \sum_{k=0}^{n} c_k{}^2. \tag{8.45}$$

In the general case, we have from formulas (8.44) and (8.45) that

$$\|f - T_n\|^2 = \|f - S_n\|^2 + \sum_{k=0}^{n} (a_k - c_k)^2. \tag{8.46}$$

Hence

$$0 \leq \|f - S_n\| \leq \|f - T_n\|. \tag{8.47}$$

If the series (8.39) converges in the mean to $f(x)$, that is, if

$$\lim_{n \to \infty} \|f - T_n\| = 0,$$

then it must also be true that the Fourier series converges in the mean to $f(x)$, that is, that

$$\lim_{n \to \infty} \|f - S_n\| = 0.$$

From equation (8.46) we see that

$$\lim_{n \to \infty} \sum_{k=0}^{n} (a_k - c_k)^2 = 0$$

also. But this is impossible unless $a_k = c_k$ for $k \geq 0$. We therefore have the following theorem.

Theorem 2.   If a series of the form

$$\sum_{k=0}^{\infty} a_k \phi_k(x)$$

converges in the mean to a function $f(x)$ of the space C_p, then the coefficients a_k must be the Fourier coefficients of $f(x)$.

Let us now consider only the Fourier series, with partial sums $S_n(x)$, for a function $f(x)$ of the space C_p. We have seen that, for each nonnegative integer n, the equality

$$\|f - S_n\|^2 = \|f\|^2 - \sum_{k=0}^{n} c_k{}^2 \tag{8.48}$$

holds. From this equality we see that

$$\|f - S_{n+1}\| \leq \|f - S_n\|$$

for $n \geq 0$. The sequence of numbers whose general term is $\|f - S_n\|$ is therefore nonincreasing, and since it is bounded below by zero, it must converge. If it converges to zero, then the Fourier series for $f(x)$ converges in the mean to $f(x)$. From equation (8.48) we may also deduce the inequality

$$\sum_{k=0}^{n} c_k^2 \leq \|f\|^2, \qquad n \geq 0. \tag{8.49}$$

The sequence of numbers $\{A_n\}$, whose general term is

$$A_n = \sum_{k=0}^{n} c_k^2$$

is nondecreasing and is bounded above by the number $\|f\|^2$. It therefore converges, and we have

$$\sum_{k=0}^{\infty} c_k^2 \leq \|f\|^2. \tag{8.50}$$

This inequality is known as *Bessel's inequality*. It holds regardless of whether the Fourier series for $f(x)$ actually converges in the mean to $f(x)$. The next theorem follows from the above remarks.

Theorem 3.   Let $\{\phi_n(x)\}$, $n \geq 0$, be an orthonormal set of functions, and let $c_k = (f, \phi_k)$ be the kth Fourier coefficient of a function $f(x)$ of the space C_p. Then the series

$$\sum_{k=0}^{\infty} c_k^2$$

converges and

$$\lim_{n \to \infty} c_n = \lim_{n \to \infty} \int_a^b w(x) f(x) \phi_n(x)\, dx = 0. \tag{8.51}$$

As an application of Theorem 3, we shall derive two results that will be useful to us later on. Each of the sets of functions

$$\left\{ \sqrt{\frac{2}{\pi}} \sin nx \right\}, \qquad n \geq 1, \qquad \left\{ \sqrt{\frac{1}{\pi}}, \sqrt{\frac{2}{\pi}} \cos nx \right\}, \qquad n \geq 1, \tag{8.52}$$

is orthonormal on the interval $(0, \pi)$ with weight function $w(x) = 1$. If $f(x)$ is any function of the class $C_p[0, \pi]$, it follows from Theorem 3 that

$$\lim_{n \to \infty} \int_0^{\pi} f(x) \cos nx\, dx = 0, \tag{8.53}$$

$$\lim_{n \to \infty} \int_0^{\pi} f(x) \sin nx\, dx = 0. \tag{8.54}$$

From equation (8.48) we see that the Fourier series for a function $f(x)$ actually converges in the mean to $f(x)$ if, and only if,

$$\|f\|^2 = \sum_{k=0}^{\infty} c_k^2. \tag{8.55}$$

This relation is known as *Parseval's equality*.

8.5 EXERCISES

1. Let $\{\psi_n(x)\}$, $n = 1, 2, 3, \ldots$, be an orthogonal, but not necessarily ortho-normal, set with positive weight function $w(x)$ on the interval (a, b).
   (a) For a given function $f(x)$, let

   $$E_n(a_1, a_2, \ldots, a_n) = \int_a^b w(x)\left[f(x) - \sum_{k=0}^n a_k\psi_k(x)\right]^2 dx.$$

   Show that E_n is a minimum when the constants a_k have the values

   $$a_k = \frac{(f, \psi_k)}{\|\psi_k\|^2}, \qquad k = 1, 2, \ldots, n.$$

   (b) Show that

   $$\sum_{k=0}^\infty \frac{(f, \psi_k)^2}{\|\psi_k\|^2} \leq \int_a^b wf^2 \, dx.$$

2. The function $f(x) = x$, $0 \leq x \leq 1$, is to be approximated in the mean on the interval $[0, 1]$ (with $w(x) = 1$) by an expression of the form

   $$C_1 \sin \pi x + C_2 \sin 2\pi x + C_3 \sin 3\pi x.$$

   Determine the constants C_i so that the best possible mean-square approximation is obtained.

3. Let $f(x) = 0$ when $-1 \leq x < 0$, and $f(x) = 1$ when $0 \leq x \leq 1$. Determine the constants C_0, C_1, C_2 in such a way as to minimize the quantity

   $$\int_{-1}^1 [f(x) - (C_0 + C_1 x + C_2 x^2)]^2 \, dx.$$

4. Let $f(x)$ belong to the class $C_p[-1, 1]$. Show that

   $$\lim_{n \to \infty} \int_{-1}^1 f(x)P_n(x) \, dx = 0,$$

   where $P_n(x)$ is the Legendre polynomial of degree n.

5. What does the Parseval equality become for the orthonormal set

   $$\left\{\sqrt{\frac{2}{c}} \sin \frac{n\pi x}{c}\right\}, \qquad n \geq 1,$$

   and the function $f(x) = 1$, $0 \leq x \leq c$?

6. Let $\{\phi_n(x)\}$, $n \geq 1$, be a complex orthonormal set, with positive weight function $w(x)$ on the interval (a, b). If

   $$C_n = \int_a^b wf\overline{\phi}_n \, dx,$$

where f may be complex, show that

$$\sum_{n=1}^{\infty} |C_n|^2 \leq \int_a^b w|f|^2 \, dx.$$

8.6 Closed Orthogonal Sets

Let $\{\phi_n(x)\}$ be an orthogonal set of functions, with each function belonging to the space $C_p[a, b]$. The set $\{\phi_n(x)\}$ is said to be *closed* in the space $C_p[a, b]$ if every function in the space is represented by its Fourier series, in the sense of convergence in the mean. Evidently, an orthonormal set is closed if, and only if, Parseval's equality holds for every function $f(x)$ in the space. Another important property of a closed orthogonal set is stated in the following theorem.

Theorem 4. If an orthogonal set $\{\phi_n(x)\}$, $n \geq 0$, is closed in the space $C_p[a, b]$, then any function of the space that is orthogonal to every member of the set must be zero except possibly at a finite number of points of $[a, b]$.

Proof. Without loss of generality, we assume that the set $\{\phi_n(x)\}$ is orthonormal. If a function $f(x)$ is orthogonal to every member of the set, then

$$c_k = (f, \phi_k) = 0, \qquad k \geq 0,$$

that is, all the Fourier coefficients of $f(x)$ are zero. According to the Parseval equality, $\|f\| = 0$, so $f(x)$ must be zero at all but a finite number of points of $[a, b]$.

Theorem 4 implies that if we delete one member from an orthogonal set, the remaining functions cannot constitute a closed set, for the deleted function is orthogonal to every member of the new set.

We now wish to indicate some specific orthogonal sets that are closed. There is no single procedure for establishing or disproving that an arbitrary orthogonal set is closed. However, it is well known that orthogonal sets of certain classes are closed. One of these classes is the class of simple sets of orthogonal polynomials. The following theorem is true.

Theorem 5. A simple set of polynomials that is orthogonal on a finite interval (a, b) (with respect to a weight function $w(x)$) is closed in the space $C_p[a, b]$.

Another class of closed orthogonal sets consists of the orthogonal sets of eigenfunctions of self-adjoint eigenvalue problems. Let us consider a self-adjoint problem of the form

$$[p(x)y']' + [\lambda r(x) + q(x)]y = 0, \tag{8.56}$$

$$U_1(y) = 0, \qquad U_2(y) = 0$$

on a finite interval $[a, b]$. It is assumed that $p'(x)$, $q(x)$, $r(x)$ are continuous and that $p(x) > 0$, $r(x) > 0$ for $a \le x \le b$.

Theorem 6.   The set of all eigenfunctions† of the eigenvalue problem (8.56) form a closed set in the space $C_p[a, b]$.

No proof of Theorem 6 is simple enough to present here. A proof of a more general theorem can be found in Coddington and Levinson (see references to Chapter 7.) We can present here a proof of Theorem 5 that is based on two other theorems. The first of these is a famous one known as the Weierstrass approximation theorem.

Theorem 7.   Let the function $g(x)$ be continuous on a finite closed interval $[a, b]$. Then, corresponding to every positive number ε, there is a polynomial $Q(x)$ such that $|g(x) - Q(x)| < \varepsilon$ for $a < x < b$.

This theorem says that a continuous function can be approximated uniformly, as closely as desired, by a polynomial on a closed interval. A proof of the theorem can be found in Courant and Hilbert, listed in the references for this Chapter.

We also need the following theorem.

Theorem 8.   Let $f(x)$ belong to the space $C_p[a, b]$, and let the weight function $w(x)$ be as in Section 8.4. Then, corresponding to every positive number ε, there is a function $g(x)$, continuous on $[a, b]$, such that $\|f(x) - g(x)\| < \varepsilon$.

Proof.   Let $x_1, x_2, \ldots, x_N$ be the points in (a, b) where $f(x)$ is discontinuous. The case $N = 2$ is illustrated in Figure 8.6. Let δ be a small positive number. We define $g(x)$ in the following way: Let $g(a) = f(a+)$, $g(b) = g(b-)$, and in (a, b) let $g(x) = f(x)$ except on the intervals $(x_i - \delta, x_i + \delta)$, $i = 1, 2, \ldots, N$.

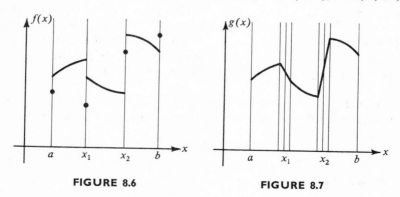

FIGURE 8.6   FIGURE 8.7

† If two linearly independent eigenfunctions correspond to the same eigenvalue, it is assumed that two mutually orthogonal eigenfunctions are chosen.

On each of these intervals let $g(x)$ be such that its graph is a straight-line segment, chosen so that $g(x)$ is continuous on $[a, b]$ (Figure 8.7). Then the function $f(x) - g(x)$ is zero except possibly at the points a and b and on the intervals $(x_i - \delta, x_i + \delta)$ (Figure 8.8). Since $f(x)$ is in $C_p[a, b]$, there is a positive number M_1 such that $|f(x)| \le M_1$ on $[a, b]$. Then $|g(x)| \le M_1$ and $|f(x) - g(x)| \le 2M_1$. Let c and d be numbers such that

$$a < c < x_1 < x_N < d < b.$$

Then there is a positive number M_2 such that $|w(x)| \le M_2$ on $[c, d]$. Choose δ sufficiently small so that $c < x_1 - \delta$ and $x_N + \delta < d$. Then

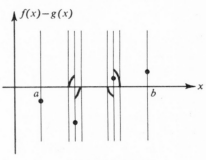

$$\|f - g\| = \left(\int_a^b w[f - g]^2 \, dx \right)^{1/2}$$

$$= \left(\sum_{i=1}^N \int_{x_i - \delta}^{x_i + \delta} w[f - g]^2 \, dx \right)^{1/2}$$

$$\le \sqrt{8M_1{}^2 M_2 N \delta}.$$

FIGURE 8.8

Given ε, choose

$$\delta \le \frac{\varepsilon^2}{32 M_1{}^2 M_2 N}.$$

Then

$$\|f - g\| \le \frac{\varepsilon}{2} < \varepsilon.$$

We now give a proof of Theorem 5, based on Theorems 7 and 8. Let $\{\phi_n(x)\}$, $n \ge 0$, be a simple set of orthogonal polynomials, with weight function $w(x)$. Let

$$\int_a^b w(x) \, dx = K.$$

If $f(x)$ is in $C_p[a, b]$, and if ε is any positive number, there is a continuous function $g(x)$ such that

$$\|f(x) - g(x)\| < \frac{\varepsilon}{2}.$$

Also, there is a polynomial $Q(x)$ such that

$$|g(x) - Q(x)| < \frac{\varepsilon}{2\sqrt{K}}$$

for $a \le x \le b$. Then

$$\|g - Q\| = \left(\int_a^b w(g - Q)^2 \, dx \right)^{1/2} \le \left(\frac{\varepsilon^2}{4K} \int_a^b w \, dx \right)^{1/2} = \frac{\varepsilon}{2}.$$

Then

$$\|f - Q\| \le \|f - g\| + \|g - Q\| < \varepsilon.$$

Let m be the degree of $Q(x)$. Then there exist constants $a_0, a_1, \ldots, a_m$ such that

$$Q(x) = \sum_{i=0}^{m} a_i \phi_i(x).$$

Let $S_n(x)$ be the nth partial sum of the Fourier series of $f(x)$. By Theorem 1,

$$\|f - S_m\| \le \|f - Q\| < \varepsilon,$$

and so

$$\|f - S_n\| < \varepsilon,$$

whenever $n \ge m$. Hence

$$\lim_{n \to \infty} \|f - S_n\| = 0.$$

Let us now consider the Laguerre and Hermite polynomials. For both of these polynomial sets, the interval of orthogonality is infinite. If such a set is to be closed in a space of functions, the space must be such that the improper intervals involved in computing the Fourier coefficients exist.

We define a space V of functions as follows: A function $f(x)$ is said to belong to V if it is piecewise continuous on every finite interval of the form $[0, b]$ and if the integral

$$\int_0^\infty e^{-x}[f(x)]^2 \, dx$$

exists. The Laguerre polynomials $L_n(x)$ belong to V. It can be shown (Exercise 4 below) that if $f(x)$ and $g(x)$ belong to V, then the integrals

$$\int_0^\infty e^{-x}f(x)g(x) \, dx, \qquad \int_0^\infty e^{-x}[\alpha f(x) + \beta g(x)]^2 \, dx,$$

where α and β are any constants, exist. The inner product of two functions $f(x)$ and $g(x)$ in V is defined to be

$$(f, g) = \int_0^\infty e^{-x}f(x)g(x) \, dx.$$

The norm of a function $f(x)$ in V is defined to be

$$\|f\| = (f, f)^{1/2}.$$

The distance between two functions $f(x)$ and $g(x)$ in V is defined to be

$$\|f - g\|.$$

In view of the previous remarks, all the integrals involved in these definitions exist.

We define a space W of functions as follows: A function $f(x)$ is said to belong to W if it is piecewise continuous on every finite interval and if the integral

$$\int_{-\infty}^{+\infty} \exp\,(-x^2)[f(x)]^2\,dx$$

exists. The Hermite polynomials $H_n(x)$ belong to W. It can be shown (Exercise 4) that if $f(x)$ and $g(x)$ belong to W, then the integrals

$$\int_{-\infty}^{+\infty} \exp\,(-x^2)f(x)g(x)\,dx, \qquad \int_{-\infty}^{+\infty} \exp\,(-x^2)[\alpha f(x) + \beta g(x)]^2\,dx$$

exist. The inner product of two functions $f(x)$ and $g(x)$ in W is defined to be

$$(f, g) = \int_{-\infty}^{+\infty} \exp\,(-x^2)f(x)g(x)\,dx.$$

The norm of a function $f(x)$ in W is defined to be $\|f\| = (f, f)^{1/2}$, and the distance between two functions $f(x)$ and $g(x)$ in W is defined to be $\|f - g\|$.

A proof of the following theorem can be based on theorems in Courant and Hilbert (see references at end of Chapter).

Theorem 9.   The Laguerre polynomials are closed in the space V and the Hermite polynomials are closed in the space W.

8.6   EXERCISES

1. Show that the simply orthogonal set $\{\cos n\pi x\}$, $n = 1, 2, 3, \ldots,$ is not closed on the interval $(0, 1)$.

2. (a) If the functions $f(x)$ and $g(x)$, of the class $C_p[a, b]$, have the same Fourier coefficients with respect to a closed orthogonal set, show that $f(x) = g(x)$ at each point of (a, b) where both functions are continuous.

   (b) If the orthogonal set is not closed, is the result necessarily true? Why?

3. Let $w(x)$ be positive and continuous on the closed interval $[a, b]$. If the orthogonal set $\{f_n(x)\}$ [with weight function $w(x)$] is closed on (a, b), prove that the simply orthogonal set $\{g_n(x)\}$, where $g_n(x) = \sqrt{w(x)}\,f_n(x)$, is also closed on (a, b).

4. (a) If $f(x)$ and $g(x)$ belong to the class V, prove that $f(x) + g(x)$ and $f(x)g(x)$ also belong to the class V. Suggestion: in the latter case, integrate from 0 to b, use the Schwarz inequality, and then let b become infinite.

   (b) If $f(x)$ and $g(x)$ belong to the class W, prove that $f(x) + g(x)$ and $f(x)g(x)$ also belong to the class W.

5. Let $f(x)$ belong to the class V. Show that

$$\lim_{n\to\infty} \int_0^\infty e^{-x} f(x) L_n(x)\, dx = 0,$$

where $L_n(x)$ is the Laguerre polynomial of degree n.

6. The Laguerre functions $l_n(x)$ and the Hermite functions $h_n(x)$ are defined by the relations

$$l_n(x) = e^{-x/2} L_n(x), \qquad h_n(x) = e^{-x^2/2} H_n(x), \qquad n \geq 0.$$

State and prove theorems about the closedness of the sets $\{l_n(x)\}$, $\{h_n(x)\}$, using the results stated in the text for the Laguerre and Hermite polynomials.

8.7   Pointwise Convergence of the Trigonometric Series

In this section we shall discuss the convergence of the trigonometric Fourier series at individual points rather than on an interval as a whole. It is known that a Fourier series for an arbitrary function $f(x)$ need not converge at every point. In order to prove theorems about the convergence of Fourier series we must restrict ourselves to the consideration of functions of some suitable class.

One such class of functions is the class of *piecewise smooth* functions. A function $f(x)$ is said to be *piecewise smooth* on a closed interval $[a, b]$ if $f(x)$ and $f'(x)$ are piecewise continuous on $[a, b]$.

An important property of piecewise smooth functions is described in Theorem 10 below. In order to understand the statement of the theorem, however, we need the following definitions. The limit

$$\lim_{x\to x_0+} \frac{f(x) - f(x_0+)}{x - x_0},$$

if it exists, is called the *right-hand derivative* of the function $f(x)$ at $x = x_0$. Similarly, the limit

$$\lim_{x\to x_0-} \frac{f(x) - f(x_0-)}{x - x_0},$$

if it exists, is called the *left-hand derivative* of the function $f(x)$ at $x = x_0$. If the derivative itself of $f(x)$ exists at $x = x_0$, then of course the left- and right-hand derivatives both exist and are equal to $f'(x_0)$.

Theorem 10.   Let $f(x)$ be piecewise smooth on the interval $[a, b]$. Then $f(x)$ possesses a right-hand derivative at $x = a$, a left-hand derivative at $x = b$, and both a left- and right-hand derivative at every point in (a, b).

Proof.   We consider only the right-hand derivative. The existence of the left-hand derivative can be established in a similar fashion. Let x_0 be any point in the interval $[a, b)$. Since $f'(x)$ has only a finite number of discontinuities, there exists an interval (x_0, x_1), where $x_1 > x_0$, on which $f'(x)$ is continuous. For each point x in this interval we have, by the mean value theorem,

$$\frac{f(x) - f(x_0+)}{x - x_0} = f'(\xi),$$

where $x_0 < \xi < x$. The number ξ depends on x. Since $f'(x)$ is piecewise continuous, the limit

$$\lim_{x \to x_0+} f'(x) = \lim_{x \to x_0+} f'(\xi)$$

exists, so $f(x)$ possesses a right-hand derivative at $x = x_0$.

The first type of Fourier series that we shall consider is the general trigonometric series for a function $f(x)$ defined on the interval $[-\pi, \pi]$. The functions $\{1, \cos nx, \sin nx\}$, $n \geq 1$, are simply orthogonal on this interval. The corresponding Fourier series for $f(x)$ is

$$\tfrac{1}{2}a_0 + \sum_{n=1}^{\infty} (a_n \cos nx + b_n \sin nx), \tag{8.57}$$

where

$$a_n = \frac{1}{\pi} \int_{-\pi}^{\pi} f(t) \cos nt \, dt, \qquad n \geq 0, \qquad b_n = \frac{1}{\pi} \int_{-\pi}^{\pi} f(t) \sin nt \, dt, \qquad n \geq 1. \tag{8.58}$$

We note that every term in the series (8.57) is periodic† with period 2π. Hence, if the series converges on the interval $[-\pi, \pi]$, it will converge for all x to a function that is periodic with period 2π. Trigonometric series can be used to represent a periodic function for all x, or to represent a function that is defined only on a finite interval on the interval of definition.

In order to prove the next theorem, about the convergence of the series (8.57), we need the following result:

Lemma. Let

$$D_n(\theta) = \tfrac{1}{2} + \sum_{k=1}^{n} \cos k\theta. \tag{8.59}$$

Then

$$D_n(\theta) = \begin{cases} n + \tfrac{1}{2}, & \text{when } \theta = 2N\pi, \ N = 0, \pm 1, \pm 2, \ldots \\[2mm] \dfrac{\sin(n + \tfrac{1}{2})\theta}{2 \sin \theta/2}, & \text{elsewhere,} \end{cases} \tag{8.60}$$

---

† A function $g(x)$, defined for all x, is said to be periodic with period T if $g(x + T) = g(x)$ for all x.

and

$$\int_0^\pi D_n(\theta)\, d\theta = \int_{-\pi}^0 D_n(\theta)\, d\theta = \frac{\pi}{2}. \tag{8.61}$$

Proof. If we multiply through in equation (8.59) by the quantity $2 \sin \theta/2$, we have

$$2D_n(\theta) \sin \frac{\theta}{2} = \sin \frac{\theta}{2} + \sum_{k=1}^n 2 \cos k\theta \sin \frac{\theta}{2}$$

for all θ. Because of the trigonometric identity

$$2 \cos k\theta \sin \frac{\theta}{2} = \sin\left(k + \frac{1}{2}\right)\theta - \sin\left(k - \frac{1}{2}\right)\theta,$$

we can write

$$2D_n(\theta) \sin \frac{\theta}{2} = \sin \frac{\theta}{2} + \sum_{k=1}^n \left[\sin\left(k + \frac{1}{2}\right)\theta - \sin\left(k - \frac{1}{2}\right)\theta\right].$$

The terms in the sum on the right "telescope" and we have

$$2D_n(\theta) \sin \frac{\theta}{2} = \sin\left(n + \frac{1}{2}\right)\theta.$$

Hence

$$D_n(\theta) = \frac{\sin(n + \frac{1}{2})\theta}{2 \sin \theta/2}$$

when $\sin \theta/2 \neq 0$, that is, when $\theta \neq 2N\pi$, $N = 0,\ \pm 1,\ \pm 2,\ \dots$. For these particular values of θ, we have, from the definition of $D_n(\theta)$,

$$D_n(2N\pi) = \frac{1}{2} + \sum_{k=1}^n 1 = n + \frac{1}{2}.$$

The function $D_n(\theta)$ is a continuous function of θ, so the integrals in equation (8.61) exist. Since the functions $\{1, \cos k\theta\}$, $k \geq 1$, are orthogonal on the interval $[0, \pi]$, we have

$$\int_0^\pi D_n(\theta)\, d\theta = \int_0^\pi 1 \cdot D_n(\theta)\, d\theta = \int_0^\pi 1 \cdot \frac{1}{2}\, d\theta = \frac{\pi}{2}.$$

Since $D_n(-\theta) = D_n(\theta)$, we have

$$\int_{-\pi}^0 D_n(\theta)\, d\theta = \int_0^\pi D_n(\theta)\, d\theta = \frac{\pi}{2}.$$

Theorem 11. Let $f(x)$ be periodic, with period 2π, and let $f(x)$ be piecewise smooth on the interval $[-\pi, \pi]$. Then at every point x_0, the Fourier series (8.57) for $f(x)$ converges to the value $\frac{1}{2}[f(x_0+) + f(x_0-)]$.

Before proving the theorem, we note that the quantity $\frac{1}{2}[f(x_0+) + f(x_0-)]$ is simply the average of the left- and right-hand limits of $f(x)$ at $x + x_0$. If $f(x)$ is *continuous* at $x = x_0$, this quantity is simply $f(x_0)$. The situation at a point of discontinuity is illustrated in Figure 8.9.

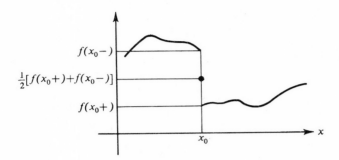

FIGURE 8.9

Proof. Let

$$S_n(x_0) = \tfrac{1}{2}a_0 + \sum_{k=1}^{n} (a_k \cos kx_0 + b_k \sin kx_0) \qquad (8.62)$$

be the nth partial sum of the Fourier series. In order to prove the theorem, we must show that

$$\lim_{n \to \infty} S_n(x_0) = \tfrac{1}{2}[f(x_0+) + f(x_0-)]. \qquad (8.63)$$

We first find a compact expression for $S_n(x_0)$. Using the formulas (8.58) for the coefficients a_k and b_k, we have

$$S_n(x_0) = \frac{1}{2\pi} \int_{-\pi}^{\pi} f(t)\, dt + \frac{1}{\pi} \sum_{k=1}^{n} \int_{-\pi}^{\pi} f(t)[\cos kt \cos kx_0 + \sin kt \sin kx_0]\, dt$$

$$= \frac{1}{\pi} \int_{-\pi}^{\pi} f(t)\left[\frac{1}{2} + \sum_{k=1}^{n} \cos k(t - x_0)\right] dt$$

$$= \frac{1}{\pi} \int_{-\pi}^{\pi} f(t) D_n(t - x_0)\, dt.$$

Making the change of variable $u = t - x_0$, we can write

$$S_n(x_0) = \frac{1}{\pi} \int_{-\pi - x_0}^{\pi - x_0} f(x_0 + u) D_n(u)\, du.$$

Since the integrand is a periodic function of u, with period 2π, we have

$$S_n(x_0) = \frac{1}{\pi} \int_{-\pi}^{\pi} f(x_0 + u) D_n(u)\, du,$$

or

$$S_n(x_0) = \frac{1}{\pi} \int_0^\pi f(x_0 + u)D_n(u)\, du + \frac{1}{\pi} \int_{-\pi}^0 f(x_0 + u)D_n(u)\, du. \quad (8.64)$$

In view of the lemma, we can write

$$\frac{1}{2}[f(x_0+) + f(x_0-)] = \frac{1}{\pi} \int_0^\pi f(x_0+)D_n(u)\, du + \frac{1}{\pi} \int_{-\pi}^0 f(x_0-)D_n(u)\, du, \quad (8.65)$$

since the quantities $f(x_0+)$ and $f(x_0-)$ do not depend on the variable of intergration u. Combining the relations (8.64) and (8.65), we have

$$S_n(x_0) - \frac{1}{2}[f(x_0-) + f(x_0-)] = \frac{1}{\pi}[A_n(x_0) + B_n(x_0)], \quad (8.66)$$

where

$$A_n(x_0) = \int_0^\pi [f(x_0 + u) - f(x_0+)]D_n(u)\, du \quad (8.67)$$

and

$$B_n(x_0) = \int_{-\pi}^0 [f(x_0 + u) - f(x_0-)]D_n(u)\, du. \quad (8.68)$$

If we can prove that

$$\lim_{n\to\infty} A_n(x_0) = \lim_{n\to\infty} B_n(x_0) = 0,$$

then the relation (8.63) will be established. The formula (8.67) for $A_n(x_0)$ can be written as

$$A_n(x_0) = \int_0^\pi \frac{f(x_0 + u) - f(x_0+)}{u} \frac{u/2}{\sin u/2} \sin\left(n + \frac{1}{2}\right) u\, du, \quad (8.69)$$

or

$$A_n(x_0) = \int_0^\pi \phi_1(u) \cos nu\, du + \int_0^\pi \phi_2(u) \sin nu\, du, \quad (8.70)$$

where

$$\phi_1(u) = \frac{f(x_0 + u) - f(x_0+)}{u} \frac{u}{2}, \quad (8.71)$$

$$\phi_2(u) = \frac{f(x_0 + u) - f(x_0+)}{u} \frac{u/2}{\sin u/2} \cos \frac{u}{2}.$$

Since the function $f(x)$ is piecewise smooth on every finite closed interval, it has a right-hand derivative at $x = x_0$. Hence $\phi_1(u)$ and $\phi_2(u)$ possess right-hand limits at $u = 0$. These functions are therefore piecewise continuous on the interval $0 \le u \le \pi$. It now follows from the relations (8.53) and (8.54) of Section 8.5 that

$$\lim_{n\to\infty} A_n(x_0) = 0.$$

Similarly, the existence of a left-hand derivative of $f(x)$ at $x = x_0$ insures that

$$\lim_{n \to \infty} B_n(x_0) = 0.$$

We shall omit the details of the proof of this statement. This concludes the proof of the theorem.

We now consider, instead of periodic functions, functions which are defined only on the interval $[-\pi, \pi]$.

Theorem 12.   Let $f(x)$ be piecewise smooth on the interval $[-\pi, \pi]$. Then the trigonometric Fourier series (8.57) for $f(x)$ converges to $\frac{1}{2}[f(x+) + f(x-)]$ for x in the interval $(-\pi, \pi)$. At $x = \pm\pi$, the series converges to the value $\frac{1}{2}[f(-\pi+) + f(\pi-)]$.

Proof.   Let $F(x)$ be the function that is equal to $f(x)$ for $-\pi \le x \le \pi$ and that is periodic with period 2π. The function $F(x)$ is piecewise smooth on the interval $[-\pi, \pi]$. The Fourier series for $F(x)$ is the same as that for $f(x)$, and by Theorem 11, this series converges to $\frac{1}{2}[F(x+) + F(x-)]$ for all x. It therefore converges to $\frac{1}{2}[f(x+) + f(x-)]$ for $-\pi < x < \pi$. Since $F(-\pi-) = f(\pi-)$ and $F(\pi+) = f(-\pi+)$, the series converges to $\frac{1}{2}[f(-\pi+) + f(\pi-)]$ at $x = \pm\pi$.

As an example, let us consider the function

$$f(x) = \begin{cases} 0, & -\pi < x < 0 \\ 1, & 0 < x < \pi. \end{cases}$$

The function $f(x)$ is piecewise continuous on the interval $[-\pi, \pi]$ and its derivative,

$$f'(x) = 0, \qquad -\pi < x < 0, \qquad 0 < x < \pi,$$

is also piecewise continuous on this interval. Hence $f(x)$ is piecewise smooth on the interval $[-\pi, \pi]$. The graph of $f(x)$ is shown in Figure 8.10.

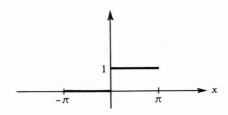

FIGURE 8.10

The Fourier coefficients of $f(x)$ are

$$a_0 = \frac{1}{\pi} \int_{-\pi}^{\pi} f(x)\, dx = \frac{1}{\pi} \int_0^{\pi} \cos nx\, dx = 1,$$

$$a_n = \frac{1}{\pi} \int_{-\pi}^{\pi} f(x) \cos nx\, dx = \frac{1}{\pi} \int_0^{\pi} \cos nx\, dx = 0, \qquad n \geq 1,$$

$$b_n = \frac{1}{\pi} \int_{-\pi}^{\pi} f(x) \sin nx\, dx = \frac{1}{\pi} \int_0^{\pi} \sin nx\, dx$$

$$= \frac{1}{n\pi}(1 - \cos n\pi) = \frac{1}{n\pi}[1 - (-1)^n] = \begin{cases} 0, & \text{if } n \text{ is even} \\ \dfrac{2}{n\pi}, & \text{if } n \text{ is odd.} \end{cases}$$

The Fourier series for $f(x)$ is therefore

$$\frac{1}{2} + \frac{2}{\pi} \sum_{m=1}^{\infty} \frac{\sin(2m - 1)x}{2m - 1}.$$

Although $f(x)$ is not defined outside the interval $(-\pi, \pi)$, the series converges for all x to a function $F(x)$ which is periodic with period 2π. The graph of $F(x)$ is shown in Figure 8.11.

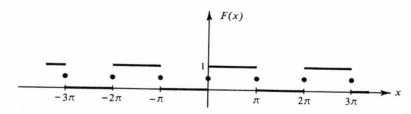

FIGURE 8.11

We now consider the case of a function that is defined on an interval of the form $[-c, c]$, where c is an arbitrary positive number.

Theorem 13. Let $f(x)$ be piecewise smooth on the interval $[-c, c]$. Then the trigonometric Fourier series

$$\frac{1}{2}a_0 + \sum_{n=1}^{\infty} \left(a_n \cos \frac{n\pi x}{c} + b_n \sin \frac{n\pi x}{c} \right) \qquad (8.72)$$

where

$$a_n = \frac{1}{c} \int_{-c}^{c} f(x) \cos \frac{n\pi x}{c}\, dx, \qquad n \geq 0, \qquad (8.73)$$

$$b_n = \frac{1}{c} \int_{-c}^{c} f(x) \sin \frac{n\pi x}{c}\, dx, \qquad n \geq 1,$$

converges to $\frac{1}{2}[f(x+)+f(x-)]$ for $-c < x < c$. At $x = \pm c$, the series converges to the value $\frac{1}{2}[f(-c+)+f(c-)]$.

Proof. If we make the change of variable $t = (\pi/c)x$, the function $F(t) = f[(c/\pi t)]$ is piecewise smooth on the interval $-\pi \le t \le \pi$. The proof of the theorem now follows from Theorem 12. The details are left as an exercise.

We note that the series (8.72) corresponds to the set of functions

$$\left\{ 1, \cos \frac{n\pi x}{c}, \sin \frac{n\pi x}{c} \right\}, \qquad n \ge 1,$$

which is orthogonal on the interval $[-c \cdot c]$.

8.7 EXERCISES

1. Determine whether or not the given function is piecewise smooth on the interval $[-1, 1]$,

(a) $f(x) = |x|$

(c) $f(x) = \sqrt{1 - x^2}$

(b) $f(x) = \begin{cases} 1, & -1 \le x < 0 \\ x, & 0 < x < 1 \end{cases}$

(d) $f(x) = x^{2/3}$

2. Expand the given function in a trigonometric series of the functions $\sin nx$, $\cos nx$, $n \ge 0$. Draw a graph showing the function to which the series converges for $-3\pi \le x \le 3\pi$.

(a) $f(x) = \begin{cases} 1, & -\pi < x < 0 \\ 0, & 0 < x < \pi \end{cases}$

(c) $f(x) = \begin{cases} 1, & -\pi < x \le 0 \\ \cos x, & 0 < x < \pi \end{cases}$

(b) $f(x) = \begin{cases} -x, & -\pi < x < 0 \\ 0, & 0 < x < \pi \end{cases}$

(d) $f(x) = \begin{cases} \pi + x, & -\pi < x < 0 \\ \pi - x, & 0 < x < \pi \end{cases}$

3. Expand the given function in a trigonometric series of the functions $\sin n\pi x/c$, $\cos n\pi x/c$, $n \ge 0$. Draw a graph showing the function to which the series converges for $-3c \le x \le 3c$.

(a) $f(x) = \begin{cases} 0, & -c < x < -\dfrac{c}{2} \\[2mm] 1, & -\dfrac{c}{2} < x < \dfrac{c}{2} \\[2mm] 0, & \dfrac{c}{2} < x < c \end{cases}$

(c) $f(x) = x, \qquad -c < x < c$

(b) $f(x) = \begin{cases} c, & -c < x < 0 \\ x, & 0 < x < c \end{cases}$

(d) $f(x) = |x|, \qquad -c \le x \le c$

4. Complete the proof of Theorem 11 by showing that

$$\lim_{n \to \infty} B_n(x_0) = 0.$$

5. Let $f'(x)$ be continuous and piecewise smooth on the interval $[-c, c]$. If $f(-c) = f(c)$, show that the trigonometric Fourier series for $f'(x)$ can be obtained by termwise differentiation of the series for $f(x)$. Suggestion: write out the series for $f'(x)$ and use integration by parts in the formulas for the coefficients.

6. Let $f(x)$ be piecewise continuous on the interval $[-c, c]$, and denote the Fourier coefficients of $f(x)$ by a_n, $n \geq 0$, and b_n, $n \geq 1$. (Note that the Fourier series of $f(x)$ need not converge to $f(x)$.) Prove that

$$\int_\alpha^\beta f(x)\, dx = \int_\alpha^\beta \frac{1}{2} a_0\, dx + \sum_{n=1}^\infty \int_\alpha^\beta \left(a_n \cos \frac{n\pi x}{c} + b_n \sin \frac{n\pi x}{c} \right) dx$$

for every pair of numbers α, β in the interval $[-c, c]$. Suggestion: the function $F(x) = \int_{-c}^x [f(t) - \frac{1}{2} a_0]\, dt$ is continuous and piecewise smooth on $[-c, c]$ and $F(c) = F(-c) = 0$. Expand $F(x)$ in a Fourier series and use integration by parts to find its Fourier coefficients. Then find $F(\beta) - F(\alpha)$.

7. Let $f(x) = 0$ when $1 < x < 2$ and $f(x) = 1$ when $2 < x < 3$. Expand $f(x)$ in a trigonometric series of period 2. Suggestion: find the Fourier series for the function $F(x)$ that is periodic with period 2 and equal to $f(x)$ on the interval $(1,3)$.

8. Let $f(x)$ be continuous and piecewise smooth on the interval $[-\pi, \pi]$. Show that

$$f(x) = \lim_{n \to \infty} \sum_{k=-n}^n c_k e^{ikx}, \qquad -\pi < x < \pi,$$

where

$$c_k = \frac{1}{2\pi} \int_{-\pi}^\pi f(x) e^{-ikx}\, dx, \qquad k = 0, \pm 1, \pm 2, \ldots .$$

9. Show that the expansion in Problem 8 is valid when $f(x)$ is complex valued—that is, when $f(x) = f_1(x) + if_2(x)$. Assume that $f_1(x)$ and $f_2(x)$ are continuous and piecewise smooth on the interval $[-\pi, \pi]$.

10. Complete the proof of Theorem 13.

11. Let $f(x)$ be periodic with period 2π, and be piecewise *continuous* on the interval $[-\pi, \pi]$. Show, by inspection of the proof of Theorem 11, that the Fourier series for $f(x)$ converges to the value $\frac{1}{2}[f(x+) + f(x-)]$ at each point where the function possesses both a left and right hand derivative. (The assumption that $f(x)$ is piecewise *smooth* guarantees that $f(x)$ possesses a left- and right-hand derivative at *every* point.)

8.8   The Sine and Cosine Series

A function $f(x)$ that is defined on an interval of the form $(-a, a)$, or $[-a, a]$, or $(-\infty, +\infty)$ is said to be *even* if $f(-x) = f(x)$; it is said to be *odd* if $f(-x) = -f(x)$. For example, any function of the form $\cos kx$, where k is a constant, is even, and any function of the form $\sin kx$ is odd. If the functions $f(x)$ and $g(x)$ are both even or both odd, then the product $f(x)g(x)$ is an even function. If $f(x)$ is even and $g(x)$ is odd, then the product $f(x)g(x)$ is odd. These facts are easily verified from the definitions of evenness and oddness. Also, if a function $f(x)$, defined on an interval $[-a, a]$, is odd, then

$$\int_{-a}^{a} f(x)\, dx = 0,$$

and if $f(x)$ is even,

$$\int_{-a}^{a} f(x)\, dx = 2 \int_{-0}^{a} f(x)\, dx.$$

These properties are intuitively evident from the geometrical interpretations of evenness and oddness.

We are now ready to prove the following theorem.

Theorem 14.   Let $f(x)$ be piecewise smooth on the interval $[0, c]$. Then the Fourier sine series for $f(x)$,

$$\sum_{n=1}^{\infty} b_n \sin \frac{n\pi x}{c},$$

$$b_n = \frac{2}{c} \int_{0}^{c} f(x) \sin \frac{n\pi x}{c}\, dx, \qquad n \geq 1,$$

converges to $\frac{1}{2}[f(x+) + f(x-)]$ for $0 < x < c$. At $x = 0$ and $x = c$ it converges to zero. The Fourier cosine series for $f(x)$,

$$\frac{1}{2}a_0 + \sum_{n=1}^{\infty} a_n \cos \frac{n\pi x}{c},$$

$$a_n = \frac{2}{c} \int_{0}^{c} f(x) \cos \frac{n\pi x}{c}\, dx, \qquad n \geq 0,$$

converges to $\frac{1}{2}[f(x+) + f(x-)]$ for $0 < x < c$. At $x = 0$ it converges to $f(0+)$ and at $x = c$ it converges to $f(c-)$.

Proof.   We consider first the sine series for $f(x)$. Let $F(x)$ be an odd function, defined on $[-c, c]$, which is identical to $f(x)$ on $(0, c]$. Then $F(x)$ is piecewise smooth on $[-c, c]$. If we expand $F(x)$ in a full trigonometric Fourier series, the coefficients of the cosine terms,

$$a_n = \frac{1}{c} \int_{-c}^{c} F(x) \cos \frac{n\pi x}{c}\, dx, \qquad n \geq 0,$$

all vanish and the coefficients of the sine terms become

$$b_n = \frac{1}{c} \int_{-c}^{c} F(x) \sin \frac{n\pi x}{c} \, dx = \frac{2}{c} \int_{0}^{c} f(x) \sin \frac{n\pi x}{c} \, dx, \qquad n \geq 1.$$

Thus the full trigonometric series for $F(x)$ is the same as the sine series for $f(x)$. The convergence of the series to the values indicated in the statement of the theorem follows from Theorem 13.

In order to establish the convergence of the cosine series, we form the even function $G(x)$, defined on $[-c, c]$, which is identical to $f(x)$ on $[0, c]$. The full trigonometric series for $G(x)$ turns out to be the same as the cosine series for $f(x)$, and the convergence of the series to the indicated values follows from Theorem 13. This concludes the proof of the theorem.

Although $f(x)$ is defined only on the interval $[0, c]$, its Fourier sine series converges for all x to a function that is odd and periodic with period $2c$. Similarly, the Fourier cosine series for $f(x)$ converges for all x to a function that is even and periodic with period $2c$.

As an example, let us consider the function $f(x) = 1 - x$, where $0 < x < 1$. Here $c = 1$. The coefficients in the sine series for $f(x)$ are

$$b_n = 2 \int_{0}^{1} (1 - x) \sin n\pi x \, dx = \frac{2}{n\pi}, \qquad n \geq 1,$$

and the sine series is

$$\frac{2}{\pi} \sum_{n=1}^{\infty} \frac{\sin n\pi x}{n}.$$

This series converges for all x to the function shown in Figure 8.12.

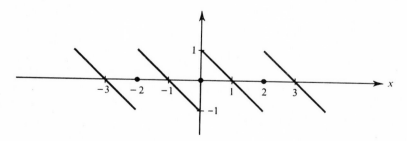

FIGURE 8.12

The coefficients in the cosine series for $f(x)$ are

$$a_0 = 2 \int_{0}^{1} (1 - x) \, dx = 1,$$

$$a_n = 2 \int_{0}^{1} (1 - x) \cos n\pi x \, dx = \begin{cases} 0, & \text{when } n \text{ is even} \\ \dfrac{4}{n^2 \pi^2}, & \text{when } n \text{ is odd} \end{cases}$$

and the cosine series is

$$\frac{1}{2} + \frac{4}{\pi^2} \sum_{m=1}^{\infty} \frac{\cos(2m-1)\pi x}{(2m-1)^2} .$$

This series converges for all x to the function shown in Figure 8.13.

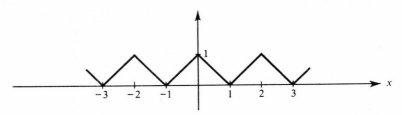

FIGURE 8.13

It should be noted that *both* series converge to $f(x)$ on the interval $(0, 1)$.

8.8   EXERCISES

1. Expand the given function in both a Fourier cosine series and a Fourier sine series on the interval $(0, \pi)$. Draw graphs showing the functions to which the series converge for $-3\pi < x < 3\pi$.

(a) $f(x) = x$, $0 < x < \pi$ (c) $f(x) = \sin x$, $0 < x < \pi$.

(b) $f(x) = \begin{cases} 1, & 0 < x < \dfrac{\pi}{2} \\ 0, & \dfrac{\pi}{2} < x < \pi \end{cases}$ (d) $f(x) = \cos x$, $0 < x < \pi$.

2. Deduce from the series of Problem 1(a) that

$$\sum_{n=1}^{\infty} \frac{1}{(2n-1)^2} = \frac{\pi^2}{8} .$$

3. Expand the function $f(x) = 1$, $0 < x < \pi$, in a Fourier sine series. Deduce from the result that

$$\sum_{n=1}^{\infty} \frac{(-1)^n}{2n-1} = \frac{\pi}{4} .$$

4. Expand the function $f(x) = x^2$, $0 \le x \le \pi$, in a Fourier cosine series. Deduce from the result that

$$\sum_{n=1}^{\infty} \frac{1}{n^2} = \frac{\pi^2}{6} , \qquad \sum_{n=1}^{\infty} \frac{(-1)^{n+1}}{n^2} = \frac{\pi^2}{12} .$$

5. Find both the Fourier sine series and the Fourier cosine series for the

given function on the interval $(0, c)$. Draw graphs showing the functions to which the series converge for $-3c < x < 3c$.

(a) $f(x) = \begin{cases} 0, & 0 < x < \dfrac{c}{2} \\ 1, & \dfrac{c}{2} < x < c \end{cases}$

(c) $f(x) = \begin{cases} x, & 0 < x < \dfrac{c}{2} \\ 0, & \dfrac{c}{2} < x < c \end{cases}$

(b) $f(x) = c - x$, $0 < x < c$

(d) $f(x) = \begin{cases} c - 2x, & 0 < x < \dfrac{c}{2} \\ c, & \dfrac{c}{2} < x < c \end{cases}$

6. Let $f(x)$ be piecewise smooth on the interval $a \le x \le b$. Show that

$$\frac{f(x+) + f(x-)}{2} = \frac{1}{2}a_0 + \sum_{n=1}^{\infty} a_n \cos \frac{n\pi x}{b-a}, \qquad a < x < b,$$

where

$$a_n = \frac{2}{b-a} \int_a^b f(x) \cos \frac{n\pi x}{b-a} \, dx, \qquad n \ge 0.$$

8.9 Other Fourier Series

In our discussion of convergence in the mean, we were able to assert that every simple set of orthogonal polynomials was closed in the space of piecewise continuous function on the interval of orthogonality. In the case of pointwise convergence, there is no corresponding general theorem, and we must consider individual polynomial sets more or less individually. We shall consider here some of the special polynomial sets described in Chapter 6.

Theorem 15. Let $f(x)$ be piecewise smooth on the interval $[-1, 1]$. Then the series of Legendre polynomials for $f(x)$ converges to the value $\frac{1}{2}[f(x+) + f(x-)]$ for $-1 < x < 1$. At $x = -1$, the series converges to $f(-1+)$ and at $x = 1$ it converges to $f(1-)$.

As in the case of the trigonometric Fourier series, it is possible to find a compact expression for the nth partial sum of the series. Proofs of the convergence of the series can be found in the books by Jackson and Sansone listed in the references for this chapter.

Proofs of the convergence of series of Tchebycheff polynomials can be based on the theorem about the convergence of the Fourier sine and cosine series. We shall only state the results here. The proofs are left as exercises.

Theorem 16. Let $f(x)$ be piecewise smooth on the interval $[1-, 1]$. Then the series of Tchebycheff polynomials of the first kind for $f(x)$ converges to $\frac{1}{2}[f(x+) + f(x-)]$ for $-1 < x < 1$. At $x = -1$ it converges to $f(-1+)$

and at $x = 1$ it converges to $f(1-)$. The series of Tchebycheff polynomials of the second kind converges to $\frac{1}{2}[f(x+)] + f(x-)]$ for $-1 < x < 1$.

Conditions for the convergence of the Laguerre and Hermite series are given in the next two theorems.†

Theorem 17.   Let $f(x)$ be piecewise smooth on every finite interval of the form $[0, b]$, $b > 0$, and let the integral

$$\int_0^\infty exp\,(-x)[f(x)]^2\,dx$$

exist. Then the series of Laguerre polynomials for $f(x)$ converges to $\frac{1}{2}[f(x+) + f(x-)]$ for $0 < x < +\infty$.

Theorem 18.   Let $f(x)$ be piecewise smooth on every finite interval and let the integral

$$\int_{-\infty}^{+\infty} exp\,(-x^2)[f(x)]^2\,dx$$

exist. Then the series of Hermite polynomials for $f(x)$ converges to $\frac{1}{2}[f(x+) + f(x-)]$ for all x.

Let us now consider orthogonal sets of functions that are generated by eigenvalue problems. We consider a problem of the form‡

$$[p(x)y']' + [\lambda r(x) + q(x)]y = 0,$$

$$\alpha y(a) + \beta y'(a) = 0, \qquad\qquad (8.74)$$

$$\gamma y(b) + \delta y'(b) = 0,$$

where $p''(x), q(x)$, and $r''(x)$ are continuous and $p(x) > 0, r(x) > 0$ for $a \le x \le b$. It should be noted that the boundary conditions are separated and that the problem is self-adjoint. Let $\{\phi_n(x)\}$, $n \ge 0$, be the set of all eigenfunctions of the problem. A proof of the following general theorem is given by Titchmarsh (see references for this chapter).

Theorem 19.   Let $f(x)$ be piecewise smooth on the interval $[a, b]$. Then the Fourier series for $f(x)$, in terms of the eigenfunctions of the problem (8.74), converges to the value $\frac{1}{2}[f(x+) + f(x-)]$ for $a < x < b$.

The orthogonal sets of Bessel functions that were described in Chapter 7, and in Section 8.3, arise from *singular* eigenvalue problems. Nevertheless, it

---

† From J. V. Uspensky, "On the Development of Arbitrary Functions in Series of Hermite's and Laguerre's Polynomials," *Annals of Mathematics*, (2), vol. 28 (1927), pp. 593–619.

‡ For similar expansion theorems for other types of self-adjoint eigenvalue problems, see the paper by A. C. Zaanen, "On Some Orthogonal Systems of Functions," *Compositio Math.*, vol. 7 (1939), pp. 253–282.

can be shown (see, for example, the books by Tolstov and by Whittaker and Watson) that if $f(x)$ is piecewise smooth on the interval $[0, c]$, each of the series of Bessel functions described in Section 8.3 converges to $\frac{1}{2}[f(x+) + f(x-)]$ for $0 < x < c$.

8.9 EXERCISES

1. Find the first three nonvanishing terms when the given function is expanded in a series of Legendre polynomials on the interval $(-1, 1)$. In part (a), indicate the value of the series at $x = 0$.

   (a) $f(x) = \begin{cases} 0, & -1 < x < 0 \\ 1, & 0 < x < 1 \end{cases}$ (c) $f(x) = |x|, \qquad -1 < x < 1$

   (b) $f(x) = \begin{cases} 0, & -1 < x < 0 \\ x, & 0 < x < 1 \end{cases}$

2. Let $f(x)$ be continuous and piecewise smooth on the interval $[0, 1]$. Show that

   (a) $f(x) = \sum_{n=0}^{\infty} A_n P_{2n}(x), \qquad 0 \le x \le 1,$

   where

   $$A_n = (4n + 1) \int_0^1 f(x) P_{2n}(x) \, dx, \qquad n \ge 0.$$

   (b) $f(x) = \sum_{n=1}^{\infty} B_n P_{2n-1}(x), \qquad 0 < x < 1,$

   where

   $$B_n = (4n - 1) \int_0^1 f(x) P_{2n-1}(x) \, dx, \qquad n \ge 1.$$

   Suggestion: consider the even and odd extensions of $f(x)$.

3. Let $f(x)$ be piecewise smooth on the interval $[-c, c]$. Show that

   $$\frac{f(x+) + f(x-)}{2} = \sum_{n=0}^{\infty} A_n P_n\left(\frac{x}{c}\right), \qquad -c < x < c,$$

   where

   $$A_n = \frac{2n + 1}{2c} \int_{-c}^{c} f(x) P_n\left(\frac{x}{c}\right) dx, \qquad n \ge 0.$$

4. Let $f(\phi)$ be continuous and piecewise smooth on the interval $0 \le \phi \le \pi$. Show that

   $$f(\phi) = \sum_{n=0}^{\infty} A_n P_n(\cos \phi), \qquad 0 \le \phi \le \pi,$$

   where

   $$A_n = \frac{2n + 1}{2} \int_0^\pi f(\phi) P_n(\cos \phi) \sin \phi \, d\phi, \qquad n \ge 0.$$

5. Find the first three terms when the given function is expanded in a series of the functions $P_n(\cos \phi)$ on the interval $(0, \pi)$.

(a) $f(\phi) = \begin{cases} 0, & 0 < \phi < \dfrac{\pi}{2} \\ 1, & \dfrac{\pi}{2} < \phi < \pi \end{cases}$ (b) $f(\phi) = \begin{cases} \sin^2 \phi, & 0 < \phi < \dfrac{\pi}{2} \\ 0, & \dfrac{\pi}{2} < \phi < \pi \end{cases}$

6. Let $f(x)$ be piecewise smooth on the interval $[-1, 1]$. Show that the series of Tchebycheff polynomials $T_n(x)$ for $f(x)$ converges to $[f(x+) + f(x-)]/2$ for $-1 < x < 1$. Also show that the series of the polynomials $S_n(x)$ for $f(x)$ converges to the same values. Suggestion: let $F(\theta) = f(\cos \theta)$, $0 \le \theta \le \pi$, and examine the Fourier cosine and sine series for $F(\theta)$.

7. Find the first three terms when the given function is expanded in a series Laguerre polynomials. To what values does the series converge at a point where $f(x)$ is discontinuous?

(a) $f(x) = \begin{cases} e^x, & 0 < x < 1 \\ 0, & x > 1 \end{cases}$ (b) $f(x) = \begin{cases} 0, & 0 < x < 1 \\ 1, & x > 1 \end{cases}$

8. (a) The Laguerre functions

$$l_n(x) = e^{-x/2} L_n(x), \qquad n \ge 0,$$

are simply orthogonal on the interval $(0, +\infty)$. What conditions on $f(x)$ will guarantee that the series expansion of $f(x)$ in terms of the function $l_n(x)$ will converge to

$$\frac{f(x+) + f(x-)}{2} \qquad \text{for } 0 < x < +\infty?$$

(b) Find the first three terms when the function of Problem 7(b) is expanded in a series of the Laguerre functions $l_n(x)$.

9. Find the first two nonvanishing terms when the given function is expanded in a series of Hermite polynomials.

(a) $f(x) = \begin{cases} e^{x^2}, & |x| < 1 \\ 0, & |x| > 1 \end{cases}$ (b) $f(x) = \begin{cases} 0, & x < 0 \\ 1, & x > 0 \end{cases}$

10. Let k_n be the nth positive root of the equation $J_2(kc) = 0$. Expand the given function $f(x)$ in a series of the functions $J_2(k_n x)$, $n \ge 1$, on the interval $(0, c)$.

(a) $f(x) = x^2, \qquad 0 < x < c$

(c) $f(x) = 1, \qquad 0 < x < c$

(b) $f(x) = \begin{cases} x^2, & 0 < x < \dfrac{c}{2} \\ 0, & \dfrac{c}{2} < x < c \end{cases}$

11. Let k_n be the nth positive root of the equation $J_2{}'(kc) = 0$. Expand the functions of Problem 10 in series of the functions $J_2(k_n x)$ on the interval $(0, c)$.

12. Let $f(x) = 1$ when $0 < x < c/2$ and $f(x) = 0$ when $c/2 < x < c$. Expand $f(x)$ in a series of the functions $J_0(k_n x)$, where k_n is the nth positive root of the equation $J_0{}'(kc) = 0$,

13. Expand the function $f(x) = 1, 0 < x < 1$, in a series of the eigenfunctions of the problem

$$xy'' + y' + \lambda xy = 0,$$

$$y, y' \text{ finite as } x \to 0 +, \qquad hy(0) + y'(0) = 0, \qquad h > 0.$$

14. Expand the function

$$f(x) = \begin{cases} 1, & 0 < x < \tfrac{1}{2} \\ 0, & \tfrac{1}{2} < x < 1 \end{cases}$$

in a series of the eigenfunctions of the problem

$$y'' + \lambda y = 0, \qquad y(0) = 0, \qquad y'(1) = 0.$$

15. Expand the function $f(x) = 1, 0 < x < 1$, in a series of the eigenfunctions of the given problem.

(a) $y'' + 2y' + (\lambda + 1)y = 0, \qquad y(0) = 0, \qquad y(1) = 0.$

(b) $y'' + \lambda y = 0, \qquad y(0) - y'(0) = 0, \qquad y(1) - y'(1) = 0.$

REFERENCES

1. Carslaw, H. S., *Theory of Fourier's Series and Integrals*, 3rd ed. Dover, New York, 1930.
2. Churchill, R. V., *Fourier Series and Boundary Value Problems*, 2nd ed. McGraw-Hill, New York, 1963.
3. Courant, R., and Hilbert, D., *Methods of Mathematical Physics*, vol. 1. Interscience, New York, 1955.
4. Hartman, S., and Mikusiniski, J., *The Theory of Lebesque Measure and Integration*, Pergamon, New York, 1961.
5. Jackson, D., *Fourier Series and Orthogonal Polynomials*, Carus Mathematical Monograph No. 6. The Mathematical Association of America, 1941.
6. Sansone, G., *Orthogonal Functions*. Interscience, New York, 1959.
7. Titchmarsh, E. C., *Eigenfunction Expansions Associated with Second-Order Differential Equations*, part 1, 2nd ed. Oxford, London, 1962.
8. Tolstov, G. P., *Fourier Series*. Prentice-Hall, Englewood Cliffs, New Jersey, 1962.
9. Whittaker, E. T., and Watson, G. N., *Modern Analysis*. Cambridge, London, 1950.

CHAPTER **9**

SYSTEMS OF DIFFERENTIAL EQUATIONS

9.1 First-Order Systems

A first-order system of differential equations is a set of equations of the form

$$\frac{dx_1}{dt} = f_1(t, x_1, x_2, \ldots, x_n)$$

$$\frac{dx_2}{dt} = f_2(t, x_1, x_2, \ldots, x_n)$$

$$\ldots\ldots\ldots\ldots\ldots\ldots\ldots\ldots\ldots \tag{9.1}$$

$$\frac{dx_n}{dt} = f_n(t, x_1, x_2, \ldots, x_n)$$

for n unknown functions x_1, x_2, ..., x_n of the independent variable t. The number of equations, n, is assumed to be equal to the number of unknown functions. By a *solution* of the system is meant an ordered set of n functions $x_1(t)$, $x_2(t)$, ..., $x_n(t)$ which, on some interval I, are differentiable and satisfy the system. The *general solution* of the system is the set of all solutions. An example of a first-order system is

$$\frac{dx_1}{dt} = x_1 + 2x_2 - 4t$$

$$\frac{dx_2}{dt} = 3x_1 + 2x_2 + 5.$$

The pair of functions $x_1(t) = -2t$, $x_2(t) = 3t - 1$ is a solution of this system on the interval $(-\infty, +\infty)$. For we have

$$x_1' - x_1 - 2x_2 + 4t = -2 + 2t - 6t + 2 + 4t = 0,$$

$$x_2' - 3x_1 - 2x_2 - 5 = 3 + 6t - 6t + 2 - 5 = 0$$

for all t.

A *linear* first-order system is a system of the form

$$\frac{dx_i}{dt} = \sum_{j=1}^{n} a_{ij}(t)x_j + b_i(t), \qquad i = 1, 2, \ldots, n. \tag{9.2}$$

For $n = 3$ (three equations and three unknown functions), we have

$$\frac{dx_1}{dt} = a_{11}(t)x_1 + a_{12}(t)x_2 + a_{13}(t)x_3 + b_1(t)$$

$$\frac{dx_2}{dt} = a_{21}(t)x_1 + a_{22}(t)x_2 + a_{23}(t)x_3 + b_2(t)$$

$$\frac{dx_3}{dt} = a_{31}(t)x_1 + a_{32}(t)x_2 + a_{33}(t)x_3 + b_3(t).$$

The functions $a_{ij}(t)$ are called the *coefficients* of the system. When the functions $b_i(t)$ are all identically zero, the system is said to be *homogeneous*; otherwise it is said to be *nonhomogeneous*.

In the *initial value problem* associated with the system (9.2), it is desired to find a solution of the system that satisfies the initial conditions

$$x_1(t_0) = k_1, \qquad x_2(t_0) = k_1, \ldots, \qquad x_n(t_0) = k_n \tag{9.3}$$

at a point $t = t_0$. The quantities k_i are constants. The basic questions about the existence and uniqueness of solutions of such an initial value problem are settled by Theorem 1.

Theorem 1.   Let the functions $a_{ij}(t)$ and $b_i(t)$ be continuous on an interval I that contains the point t_0. Then the system (9.2) possesses one, and only one, solution on the interval I that satisfies the initial conditions (9.3).

The proof that a solution exists is omitted. The proof that there can be at most one solution is outlined in the exercises.

It will be convenient to denote an ordered set of n functions $u_1(t)$, $u_2(t)$, $\ldots$, $u_n(t)$ by the single symbol $\mathbf{u}(t)$. We say that $\mathbf{u}(t)$ is a *vector function* of t, with components $u_i(t)$. The notation

$$\mathbf{u}(t) = \begin{pmatrix} u_1(t) \\ u_2(t) \\ \vdots \\ u_n(t) \end{pmatrix} \tag{9.4}$$

is useful when we wish to display the components of $\mathbf{u}(t)$. The vector function whose components are all identically zero we call the zero vector function; we denote it by the symbol $\mathbf{0}$. If $a(t)$ is an ordinary function, the product $a(t)\mathbf{u}(t)$ is defined to be the vector function with components $a(t)u_i(t)$.

When we wish to talk about several vector functions $\mathbf{u}_1$, $\mathbf{u}_2$, and so on, we shall denote the components of $\mathbf{u}_1$ by u_{11}, u_{22}, ..., u_{1n}, the components of $\mathbf{u}_2$ by u_{21}, u_{22}, ..., u_{2n}, and so on. Thus, in the symbol u_{ij}, the first subscript tells us which vector we are talking about, and the second subscript picks out one component of that vector.

Two vector functions $\mathbf{u}_1$ and $\mathbf{u}_2$, with the same number of components, are said to be equal (written $\mathbf{u}_1 = \mathbf{u}_2$) if their corresponding components are equal that is, if $u_{1j} = u_{2j}$ for $j = 1, 2, \ldots, n$. The sum, $\mathbf{u}_1 + \mathbf{u}_2$, of two vector functions with the same number of components is defined to be the vector with components $u_{1j} + u_{2j}$, $j = 1, 2, \ldots, n$. Thus, if

$$\mathbf{u}_1 = \begin{pmatrix} e^t \\ -t \\ 0 \end{pmatrix}, \qquad \mathbf{u}_2 = \begin{pmatrix} 2e^t \\ 2 \\ t^2 \end{pmatrix},$$

we have

$$\mathbf{u}_1 + \mathbf{u}_2 = \begin{pmatrix} 3e^t \\ 2 - t \\ t^2 \end{pmatrix}.$$

The derivative of a vector function $\mathbf{u}(t)$, which we denote by $d\mathbf{u}/dt$ or $\mathbf{u}'(t)$, is defined as

$$\frac{d\mathbf{u}}{dt} = \begin{pmatrix} u_1' \\ u_2' \\ \vdots \\ u_n' \end{pmatrix}. \tag{9.5}$$

That is, the derivative of $\mathbf{u}(t)$ is the vector function whose components are the derivatives of the corresponding components of $\mathbf{u}(t)$. If c is a constant, then clearly

$$\frac{d}{dt}(c\mathbf{u}) = c\frac{d\mathbf{u}}{dt}.$$

Also, we have

$$\frac{d}{dt}(\mathbf{u}_1 + \mathbf{u}_2) = \frac{d\mathbf{u}_1}{dt} + \frac{d\mathbf{u}_2}{dt}$$

for two differentiable vector functions $\mathbf{u}_1$ and $\mathbf{u}_2$.

Consider now the linear homogeneous system

$$\frac{dx_i}{dt} = \sum_{j=1}^{n} a_{ij}(t)x_j, \qquad i = 1, 2, \ldots, n. \tag{9.6}$$

If we regard a vector as a matrix† with one column, then this system can be written in the more compact form

$$\frac{d\mathbf{x}}{dt} = A(t)\mathbf{x}, \qquad (9.7)$$

where $A(t)$ is the $n \times n$ matrix with elements $a_{ij}(t)$. To see this, we simply observe that the matrix product $A(t)\mathbf{x}$ has the form

$$A(t)\mathbf{x} = \begin{pmatrix} a_{11} & a_{12} \cdots a_{1n} \\ a_{21} & a_{22} \cdots a_{2n} \\ \vdots & \vdots \quad \vdots \\ a_{n1} & a_{n2} \cdots a_{nn} \end{pmatrix} \begin{pmatrix} x_1 \\ x_2 \\ \vdots \\ x_n \end{pmatrix} = \begin{pmatrix} a_{11}x_1 + a_{12}x_2 + \cdots + a_{1n}x_n \\ a_{21}x_1 + a_{22}x_2 + \cdots + a_{2n}x_n \\ \vdots \\ a_{n1}x_1 + a_{n2}x_2 + \cdots + a_{nn}x_n \end{pmatrix}$$

If $\mathbf{x}(t)$ is a solution of the system (9.7), then $c\mathbf{x}(t)$, where c is any constant, is also a solution. For since $\mathbf{x}(t)$ satisfies the system (9.7), we have $c\, d\mathbf{x}/dt = cA(t)\mathbf{x}$, or $d(c\mathbf{x})/dt = A(t)(c\mathbf{x})$. If $\mathbf{x}_1(t)$ and $\mathbf{x}_2(t)$ are both solutions of the system (9.7), then $\mathbf{x}_1(t) + \mathbf{x}_2(t)$ is also a solution. For, using the fact that $A(\mathbf{x}_1 + \mathbf{x}_2) = A\mathbf{x}_1 + A\mathbf{x}_2$, we have

$$\frac{d}{dt}(\mathbf{x}_1 + \mathbf{x}_2) = \frac{d\mathbf{x}_1}{dt} + \frac{d\mathbf{x}_2}{dt} = A\mathbf{x}_1 + A\mathbf{x}_2 = A(\mathbf{x}_1 + \mathbf{x}_2).$$

It follows from these properties that if $\mathbf{x}_1, \mathbf{x}_2, \ldots, \mathbf{x}_m$ are any m solutions of the system (9.7), and if $C_1, C_2, \ldots, C_m$ are any m constants, then $C_1\mathbf{x}_1 + C_2\mathbf{x}_2 + \cdots + C_m\mathbf{x}_m$ is also a solution (Exercise 2 below).

Similarly, the nonhomogeneous linear system

$$\frac{dx_i}{dt} = \sum_{j=1}^{n} a_{ij}(t)x_j + b_i(t), \qquad i = 1, 2, \ldots, n, \qquad (9.8)$$

can be written in the form

$$\frac{d\mathbf{x}}{dt} = A(t)\mathbf{x} + \mathbf{b}(t), \qquad (9.9)$$

where $\mathbf{b}(t)$ is the vector with components $b_i(t)$. If $\mathbf{x}_p(t)$ is any solution of the system (9.9) and if $\mathbf{x}_h(t)$ is any solution of the associated homogeneous system (9.7), then $\mathbf{x}_h(t) + \mathbf{x}_p(t)$ is also a solution of the nonhomogeneous system (9.9). To see this, we observe that since $\mathbf{x}_h' = A\mathbf{x}_h$ and $\mathbf{x}_p' = A\mathbf{x}_p + \mathbf{b}$, we have

$$(\mathbf{x}_h + \mathbf{x}_p)' = \mathbf{x}_h' + \mathbf{x}_p' = A\mathbf{x}_h + A\mathbf{x}_p + \mathbf{b} = A(\mathbf{x}_h + \mathbf{x}_p) + \mathbf{b}.$$

A set of vector functions $\mathbf{u}_1, \mathbf{u}_2, \ldots, \mathbf{u}_m$, (the functions having the same number of components), is said to be *linearly dependent* on an interval I if there exist constants $C_1, C_2, \ldots, C_m$, not all zero, such that

$$C_1\mathbf{u}_1 + C_2\mathbf{u}_2 + \cdots + C_m\mathbf{u}_m = 0$$

† See the appendix for the definition of a matrix and properties of matrices.

on I. If the vector functions are not linearly dependent on I, they are said to be *linearly independent* on I. For vector functions that are solutions of the same linear homogeneous system, we have the following theorem.

Theorem 2. Let the vector functions $x_1(t)$, $x_2(t)$, $\ldots$, $x_n(t)$ be solutions of the homogeneous linear system (9.7) on an interval I. Then the vector functions are linearly dependent on I if, and only if, the determinant

$$\begin{vmatrix} x_{11} & x_{21} \cdots x_{n1} \\ x_{12} & x_{22} \cdots x_{n2} \\ \cdots\cdots\cdots\cdots \\ x_{1n} & x_{2n} \cdots x_{nn} \end{vmatrix} \tag{9.10}$$

is identically zero on I.

Proof. If the solutions x_i are linearly independent on I, there exist constants C_i, not all zero, such that $C_1 x_1 + C_2 x_2 + \cdots + C_n x_n = 0$ for all t in I. In terms of components, we have

$$C_1 x_{1j} + C_2 x_{2j} + \cdots + C_n x_{nj}, \qquad j = 1, 2, \ldots, n.$$

Since the determinant of this system of equations for the constants C_i is the determinant (9.10), the latter must vanish at every point of I.

Conversely, suppose that the determinant (9.10) is identically zero. Let t_0 be any fixed point of I. Then there exist constants C_i, not all zero, such that

$$C_1 x_{1j}(t_0) + C_2 x_{2j}(t_0) + \cdots + C_n x_{nj}(t_0) = 0, \qquad j = 1, 2, \ldots, n.$$

The vector function $x(t) = C_1 x_1 + C_2 x_2 + \cdots + C_n x_n$ is a solution of the system (9.7), and it satisfies $x(t_0) = 0$. By Theorem 1, we must have $x(t) = 0$, so the functions x_i are linearly dependent on I.

A set of n linearly independent vector solutions of the system (9.7) is called a *fundamental set* of solutions for the system. A fundamental set always exists. For let $x_1(t)$, $x_2(t)$, $\ldots$, $x_n(t)$ be the solutions which satisfy the initial conditions

$$x_{ij}(t_0) = \begin{cases} 1, & \text{if } i = j \\ 0, & \text{if } i \neq j. \end{cases}$$

The existence of such solutions is guaranteed by Theorem 1. At $t = t_0$ the determinant (9.10) has the form

$$\begin{vmatrix} 1 & 0 & 0 \cdots 0 \\ 0 & 1 & 0 \cdots 0 \\ 0 & 0 & 1 \cdots 0 \\ \cdots\cdots\cdots\cdots \\ 0 & 0 & 0 \cdots 1 \end{vmatrix}$$

and is equal to 1 there. According to Theorem 2, the solutions are linearly independent.

Our interest in fundamental sets of solutions is because of the following result.

Theorem 3. Let x_1, x_2, ..., x_n constitute a fundamental set for the homogeneous system (9.7), and let C_1, C_2, ..., C_n be arbitrary constants. Then the expression

$$\mathbf{x} = C_1\mathbf{x}_1 + C_2\mathbf{x}_2 + \cdots + C_n\mathbf{x}_n \qquad (9.11)$$

represents the general solution of the system (9.7). If $\mathbf{x}_p$ is any one solution of the nonhomogeneous system (9.9), then the expression

$$\mathbf{x} = C_1\mathbf{x}_1 + C_2\mathbf{x}_2 + \cdots + C_n\mathbf{x}_n + \mathbf{x}_p \qquad (9.12)$$

represents the general solution of that system.

Proof. Let us consider the nonhomogeneous case. We note first of all that for any specific choice of the constants C_i the relation (9.12) defines a solution of the system (9.9). Now let $\mathbf{u}(t)$ be any specific solution of the system (9.9) and let t_0 be any fixed point. Since the determinant (9.10) does not vanish for a fundamental set, there exists a unique set of constants C_1, C_2, ..., C_n such that

$$C_1\mathbf{x}_1(t_0) + \cdots + C_n\mathbf{x}_n(t_0) + \mathbf{x}_p(t_0) = \mathbf{u}(t_0).$$

Let $\mathbf{x}(t) = C_1\mathbf{x}_1(t) + \cdots + C_n\mathbf{x}_n(t) + \mathbf{x}_p(t)$. Then $\mathbf{x}(t)$ is a solution of the system (9.9) and $\mathbf{x}(t_0) = \mathbf{u}(t_0)$. By Theorem 1, $\mathbf{u}(t) = \mathbf{x}(t)$, so $\mathbf{u}(t)$ is of the form (9.12).

In the case of the homogeneous equation, we can repeat the same argument, but with $\mathbf{x}_p = \mathbf{0}$.

As an application of this theory, let us consider the system

$$\frac{dx_1}{dt} = -3x_1 - 2x_2, \qquad \frac{dx_2}{dt} = 3x_1 + 2x_2. \qquad (9.13)$$

This system can be written in matrix form as $d\mathbf{x}/dt = A\mathbf{x}$, where A is the constant matrix

$$A = \begin{pmatrix} -3 & -2 \\ 3 & 2 \end{pmatrix}.$$

It is not hard to verify that each of the vector functions

$$\mathbf{x}_1 = \begin{pmatrix} 2 \\ -3 \end{pmatrix}, \qquad \mathbf{x}_2 = \begin{pmatrix} e^{-t} \\ -e^{-t} \end{pmatrix} \qquad (9.14)$$

is a solution of the system (9.13) on the interval $-\infty < t < +\infty$. Furthermore these functions are linearly independent, since their determinant is

$$\begin{vmatrix} 2 & e^{-t} \\ -3 & -e^{-t} \end{vmatrix} = e_t^{-t},$$

which is not identically zero. Hence the functions (9.14) constitute a fundamental set for the system (9.13), and the general solution of the system is

$$x = C_1 \begin{pmatrix} 2 \\ -3 \end{pmatrix} + C_2 \begin{pmatrix} e^{-t} \\ -e^{-t} \end{pmatrix}.$$

The general solution can be written in scalar form as

$$x_1 = 2C_1 + C_2 e^{-t}, \qquad x_2 = -3C_1 - C_2 e^{-t}.$$

The foregoing discussion serves to introduce some of the basic notions involved in the theory of linear systems of differential equations. We shall now turn our attention to a method of finding solutions of linear systems whose coefficients are constant functions.

9.1   EXERCISES

1. If

$$\mathbf{u} = \begin{pmatrix} -2t \\ e^t \\ t^2 \end{pmatrix}, \qquad \mathbf{v} = \begin{pmatrix} t \\ 3e^t \\ 1 \end{pmatrix},$$

find:

(a) $\mathbf{u} + 2\mathbf{v}$,   (b) $e^{-t}\mathbf{u}$,   (c) $3t^2\mathbf{u} - 4\mathbf{v}$.

2. (a) If $x_1(t)$ and $x_2(t)$ are solutions of the linear homogeneous system (9.7), verify that $C_1 x_1(t) + C_2 x_2(t)$, where C_1 and C_2 are any constants, is also a solution.

(b) If $\mathbf{x}_1, \mathbf{x}_2, \ldots, \mathbf{x}_m$ are solutions of the system (9.7), show that $C_1 \mathbf{x}_1 + C_2 \mathbf{x}_2 + \cdots + C_m \mathbf{x}_m$ is also a solution.

3. Determine whether or not the given set of vector functions is linearly independent on the interval $(-\infty, +\infty)$:

(a) $\mathbf{u} = \begin{pmatrix} -2t \\ e^t \end{pmatrix}, \qquad \mathbf{v} = \begin{pmatrix} 6t \\ -3e^t \end{pmatrix}$

(b) $\mathbf{u} = \begin{pmatrix} t \\ t^2 \end{pmatrix}, \qquad \mathbf{v} = \begin{pmatrix} t^2 \\ t \end{pmatrix}$

(c) $\mathbf{u} = \begin{pmatrix} -2t \\ e^t \\ t^2 \end{pmatrix}, \qquad \mathbf{v} = \begin{pmatrix} 6t \\ -3e^t \\ -t^2 \end{pmatrix}$

4. Let

$$\mathbf{u} = \begin{pmatrix} u_1 \\ u_2 \end{pmatrix}, \qquad \mathbf{v} = \begin{pmatrix} v_1 \\ v_2 \end{pmatrix}.$$

(a) If u_1 and v_1 are linearly independent on an interval I, are $\mathbf{u}$ and $\mathbf{v}$ necessarily linearly independent on I?

(b) Suppose that u_1 and v_1 are linearly dependent on an interval I and that u_2 and v_2 are also linearly dependent on I. Is it necessarily true that $\mathbf{u}$ and $\mathbf{v}$ are linearly dependent on I?

5. Let $\mathbf{x}_1(t)$ and $\mathbf{x}_2(t)$ be solutions of the nonhomogeneous system (9.9). Show that $\mathbf{x}_1(t) - \mathbf{x}_2(t)$ is a solution of the associated homogeneous systems (9.7).

6. (a) Find the matrix A when the system

$$\frac{dx_1}{dt} = x_1 - x_2, \qquad \frac{dx_2}{dt} = -2x_1$$

is written in the form $\mathbf{x}' = A\mathbf{x}$.

(b) Verify that the expression

$$x = C_1 \begin{pmatrix} e^{-t} \\ 2e^{-t} \end{pmatrix} + C_2 \begin{pmatrix} e^{2t} \\ -e^{2t} \end{pmatrix}$$

represents the general solution of the system in part (a).

(c) Write the general solution in scalar form.

(d) Find the solution that satisfies the initial conditions $x_1(0) = 2$, $x_2(0) = 4$.

7. (a) Find the matrix $\mathbf{A}$ and the vector $\mathbf{b}$ when the system

$$\frac{dx_1}{dt} = -x_1 + x_2 - 2, \qquad \frac{dx_2}{dt} = -2x_1 + x_2 + t$$

is written in the form $\mathbf{x}' = A\mathbf{x} + \mathbf{b}$.

(b) Verify that the general solution of the system in part (a) is

$$x_1 = C_1 \cos t + C_2 \sin t + t + 2$$
$$x_2 = C_1(\cos t - \sin t) + C_2(\cos t + \sin t) + t + 5.$$

(c) Write the general solution in vector form.

(d) Find the solution that satisfies the initial conditions $x_1(\pi) = 0$, $x_2(\pi) = 0$.

8. (a) Find the matrix A when the system

$$\frac{dx_1}{dt} = x_2 - 2x_3, \qquad \frac{dx_2}{dt} = -2x_1 + 3x_2 - 4x_3, \qquad \frac{dx_3}{dt} = -x_1 + x_2 - x_3$$

is written in the form $\mathbf{x}' = A\mathbf{x}$.

(b) Verify that the vector functions

$$\mathbf{u} = \begin{pmatrix} 1 \\ 2 \\ 1 \end{pmatrix}, \qquad \mathbf{v} = \begin{pmatrix} -2e^t \\ 0 \\ e^t \end{pmatrix}, \qquad \mathbf{w} = \begin{pmatrix} e^t \\ e^t \\ 0 \end{pmatrix}$$

form a fundamental set for the system of part (a).
(c) Write down the general solution of the system in scalar form.

9. Show that the initial value problem (9.2), (9.3) can have at most one
solution. Suggestion: if $\mathbf{x}_1(t)$ and $\mathbf{x}_2(t)$ are both solutions, then $\mathbf{w} = \mathbf{x}_1$
$- \mathbf{x}_2$ satisfies the associated homogeneous system and $\mathbf{w}(t_0) = \mathbf{0}$. Let
$w_1, w_2, \ldots, w_n$ be the components of $\mathbf{w}$, and let J be a closed bounded
interval containing t_0 and contained in I. There is a positive constant
M such that $|a_{ij}(t)| \le M$, $1 \le i, j \le n$, for t in J. Then, since

$$w_i(t) = \int_{t_0}^{t} \left(\sum_{j=1}^{n} a_{ij}(s) w_j(s) \right) ds, \qquad 1 \le i \le n,$$

we have

$$|w_i(t)| \le M \left| \int_{t_0}^{t} \left(\sum_{j=1}^{n} |w_i(s)| \right) ds \right|, \qquad 1 \le i \le n.$$

If

$$W(t) = |w_1(t)| + |w_2(t)| + \cdots + |w_n(t)|,$$

then

$$|W(t)| \le Mn \left| \int_{t_0}^{t} |W(s)| \, ds \right|.$$

Now use the result of Problem 6, Section 1.2.

10. Let $\mathbf{x}_1(t)$, $\mathbf{x}_2(t)$, $\ldots$, $\mathbf{x}_n(t)$ be linearly independent solutions of the homogeneous system (9.7). Show that the nonhomogeneous system (9.9)
possesses a solution of the form

$$\mathbf{x}_p(t) = C_1(t)\mathbf{x}_1(t) + C_2(t)\mathbf{x}_2(t) + \cdots + C_n(t)\mathbf{x}_n(t),$$

where the functions $C_i(t)$ satisfy the condition

$$C_1'(t)\mathbf{x}_1(t) + C_2'(t)\mathbf{x}_2(t) + \cdots + C_n'(t)\mathbf{x}_n(t) = \mathbf{b}(t).$$

This is the method of variation of parameters, as applied to a *system*.

11. Let $x(t)$ be a solution of the nth order differential equation

$$\frac{d^n x}{dt^n} = f(t, x, x', \ldots, x^{(n-1)}). \tag{1}$$

Show that the vector function $\mathbf{x}(t)$, whose components are

$$x_1 = x, \, x_2 = x', \, x_3 = x'', \ldots, \qquad x_n = x^{(n-1)},$$

is a solution of the first-order system

$$x_1' = x_2, \qquad x_2' = x_3, \ldots, \qquad x_{n-1}' = x_n,$$

$$x_n' = f(t, x_1, x_2, \ldots, x_n). \tag{2}$$

Conversely, if $x(t)$ is a solution of the system (2), show that its first component $x_1(t)$ is a solution of the equation (1).

9.2 Systems With Constant Coefficients

In this section we consider the special, but important, class of linear systems with constant coefficients. For convenience, we use the operator notation

$$D = \frac{d}{dt}, \qquad Df(t) = \frac{df(t)}{dt}.$$

A first-order linear system with constant coefficients is of the form

$$Dx_1 = a_{11}x_1 + a_{12}x_2 + \cdots + a_{1n}x_n + b_1(t)$$

$$Dx_2 = a_{21}x_1 + a_{22}x_2 + \cdots + a_{2n}x_n + b_2(t)$$

$$\cdots\cdots\cdots\cdots\cdots\cdots\cdots\cdots\cdots\cdots\cdots\cdots\cdots\cdots\cdots \tag{9.15}$$

$$Dx_n = a_{n1}x_1 + a_{n2}x_2 + \cdots + a_{nn}x_n + b_n(t),$$

where the quantities a_{ij} are constants. We shall also consider more general linear systems of the form

$$P_{11}(D)x_1 + P_{12}(D)x_2 + \cdots + P_{1n}(D)x_n = b_1(t)$$

$$P_{21}(D)x_1 + P_{22}(D)x_2 + \cdots + P_{2n}(D)x_n = b_2(t)$$

$$\cdots\cdots\cdots\cdots\cdots\cdots\cdots\cdots\cdots\cdots\cdots\cdots\cdots\cdots\cdots \tag{9.16}$$

$$P_{n1}(D)x_1 + P_{n2}(D)x_2 + \cdots + P_{nn}(D)x_n = b_n(t),$$

where the quantities $P_{ij}(D)$ are polynomial operators. Systems of the form (9.16) occur in problems of mechanics and electric circuit theory, as we shall see in Section 9.3.

Every first-order system is of the form (9.16), but not every system of the form (9.16) is a first-order system. In some cases, however, a system of the form (9.16) can be rewritten as a first-order system. This can always be done if it is possible to solve algebraically for the highest derivative of each unknown function that appears. To illustrate, let us consider the system

$$(D^2 + 3)x_1 - (D + 1)x_2 = 0$$

$$-(D + 1)x_1 + Dx_2 = 0. \tag{9.17}$$

The highest derivatives of x_1 and x_2 that appear are D^2x_1 and Dx_2, respectively. Solving algebraically for these quantities, we have

$$D^2x_1 = (D - 2)x_1 + x_2$$
$$Dx_2 = (D + 1)x_1. \tag{9.18}$$

Let us introduce the new variables u_1, u_2, and u_3 according to the relations

$$u_1 = x_1, \qquad u_2 = Dx_1, \qquad u_3 = x_2. \tag{9.19}$$

Observing that $Du_1 = u_2$, and using the system (9.18), we have

$$Du_1 = u_2$$
$$Du_2 = -2u_1 + u_2 + u_3 \tag{9.20}$$
$$Du_3 = u_1 + u_2.$$

Thus if the pair of functions $x_1(t)$, $x_2(t)$ is a solution of the system (9.18) (and hence of the system (9.17)), the corresponding functions $u_i(t)$, as defined by the relations (9.19) form a solution of the first-order system (9.20). Conversely, if $u_1(t)$, $u_2(t)$, $u_3(t)$ are functions that satisfy the system, (9.20), then a solution of the system (9.18) is given by $x_1(t) = u_1(t)$, $x_2(t) = u_3(t)$. Since the first-order system (9.20) possesses a unique solution that satisfies the initial conditions

$$u_1(t_0) = k_1, \qquad u_2(t_0) = k_2, \qquad u_3(t_0) = k_3,$$

we conclude that the system (9.17) possesses a unique solution that satisfies the conditions

$$x_1(t_0) = k_1, \qquad x_1'(t_0) = k_2, \qquad x_2(t_0) = k_3.$$

Two systems of equations are said to be *equivalent* if they have the same general solution. One standard procedure for solving a system of the form (9.16) involves the finding of an equivalent but simpler system. There are three things we can do to a system which will lead to an equivalent system. First, we can simply interchange two equations. In this connection, however, it should be pointed out that although the two systems

$$\begin{cases} x_1' = 1 \\ x_2' = 2 \end{cases}, \qquad \begin{cases} x_2' = 2 \\ x_1' = 1 \end{cases},$$

are equivalent, the two systems

$$\begin{cases} x_1' = 1 \\ x_2' = 2 \end{cases}, \qquad \begin{cases} x_1' = 2 \\ x_2' = 1 \end{cases},$$

are *not* equivalent, because a solution consists of an *ordered* pair of functions.

Second, if we multiply through in one equation, say the first, by a nonzero constant k, the resulting system is equivalent to the old one. For by multiplying through in the first equation of the new system by $1/k$, we regain the original system. In the third place, if we operate on both members of one equation,† say the first, with a polynomial operator $Q(D)$ and add the result to another equation, say the second, the new system (in which only the second equation has changed) is equivalent to the old one. For if we operate on both members of the first equation in the new system with $-Q(D)$ and add the result to the second equation, we regain the original system. To illustrate, let us consider the example

$$(D - 1)x_1 - 4x_2 = 4e^t \tag{9.21}$$
$$-x_1 + (D + 2)x_2 = 6.$$

If we operate on both members of the second equation with $(D - 1)$, it becomes

$$-(D - 1)x_1 + (D^2 + D - 2)x_2 = -6. \tag{9.22}$$

Adding this equation to the first equation of (9.21), we obtain the equivalent system

$$(D^2 + D - 6)x_2 = 4e^t - 6 \tag{9.23}$$
$$-x_1 + (D + 2)x_2 = 6.$$

(Note that the second equation in (9.23) is the same as the second equation in (9.21). The equation (9.22) does not appear in either system.) The system (9.23) has the advantage that one of its equations involves only one unknown. By using the methods of Chapter 1, we find that

$$x_2 = C_1 e^{2t} + C_2 e^{-3t} - e^t + 1.$$

From the second equation of (9.23), we find that

$$x_1 = (D + 2)x_2 - 6 = 4C_1 e^{2t} - C_2 e^{-3t} - 3e^t - 4.$$

The general solution of the system (9.21) can be written in vector form as

$$\mathbf{x} = \begin{pmatrix} x_1 \\ x_2 \end{pmatrix} = C_1 \begin{pmatrix} 4e^{2t} \\ e^{2t} \end{pmatrix} + C_2 \begin{pmatrix} -e^{-3t} \\ e^{-3t} \end{pmatrix} + \begin{pmatrix} -3e^t - 4 \\ -e^t + 1 \end{pmatrix}. \tag{9.24}$$

In the general case (9.16), the idea is to find an equivalent system of the form‡

$$Q_{11}(D)x_1 = f_1(t)$$
$$Q_{21}(D)x_1 + Q_{22}(D)x_2 = f_2(t)$$
$$\cdots\cdots\cdots\cdots\cdots\cdots\cdots\cdots\cdots\cdots\cdots\cdots\cdots \tag{9.25}$$
$$Q_{n1}(D)x_1 + Q_{n2}(D)x_2 + \cdots + Q_{nn}(D)x_n = f_n(t).$$

---

† We assume that the nonhomogeneous terms are sufficiently differentiable to permit this.

‡ The unknowns may have to be renumbered. None of the operators $Q_{ii}(D)$ is the zero operator.

We can solve the first equation for x_1, then find x_2 from the second equation, and so on. The procedure for obtaining the system (9.25) is similar to the elimination process used to solve a system of linear algebraic equations. The reduction of the system (9.16) to the form (9.25) can always be accomplished by operations of the three types previously described. For a proof of this fact, see the books by Ince and by Protter and Morrey listed in the references at the end of this chapter.

As a second example, let us consider the first-order system with three unknowns,

$$(D + 3)x_1 - 4x_2 + 2x_3 = 0$$

$$2x_1 + (D - 3)x_2 + x_3 = 0 \tag{9.26}$$

$$2x_1 - 2x_2 + (D + 2)x_3 = 0.$$

The second equation can be used to eliminate the unknown x_3 from the first and third equations. First, we multiply through in the second equation by 2 and subtract the result from the first equation. Then we operate on both members of the second equation with $(D + 2)$ and subtract the result from the third equation. The equivalent system that results is

$$(D - 1)x_1 + (-2D + 2)x_2 \qquad = 0$$

$$2x_1 + (D - 3)x_2 + x_3 = 0 \tag{9.27}$$

$$(-2D - 2)x_1 + (-D^2 + D + 4)x_2 \qquad = 0.$$

We now eliminate x_1 between the first and third equations. Adding twice the first equation to the third, we have

$$(D - 1)x_1 + (-2D + 2)x_2 \qquad = 0$$

$$2x_1 + (D - 3)x_2 + x_3 = 0 \tag{9.28}$$

$$-4x_1 + (-D^2 - 3D + 8)x_2 \qquad = 0.$$

We can now eliminate x_1 from the first equation. First we multiply through by 4 in the first equation. Then we operate on the third equation with $(D - 1)$ and add the result to the first equation. The result is

$$-D(D - 1)(D + 3)x_2 \qquad = 0$$

$$2x_1 + (D - 3)x_2 + x_3 = 0 \tag{9.29}$$

$$-4x_1 + (-D^2 - 3D + 8)x_2 \qquad = 0.$$

From the first equation of the system (9.29) we have

$$x_2 = C_1 + C_2 e^t + C_3 e^{-3t}.$$

From the third equation,

$$x_1 = \tfrac{1}{4}(-D^2 - 3D + 8)x_2 = 2C_1 + C_2 e^t + 2C_3 e^{-3t}.$$

From the second equation,

$$x_3 = -2x_1 + (3 - D)x_2 = -C_1 + 2C_3 e^{-3t}.$$

The general solution of the system (9.26) can be written in vector form as

$$\mathbf{x} = \begin{pmatrix} x_1 \\ x_2 \\ x_3 \end{pmatrix} = C_1 \begin{pmatrix} 2 \\ 1 \\ -1 \end{pmatrix} + C_2 \begin{pmatrix} e^t \\ e^t \\ 0 \end{pmatrix} + C_3 \begin{pmatrix} 2e^{-3t} \\ e^{-3t} \\ 2e^{-3t} \end{pmatrix}. \tag{9.30}$$

As a final example, we consider the system (9.17), which was

$$\begin{aligned} (D^2 + 3)x_1 - (D + 1)x_2 &= 0 \\ -(D + 1)x_1 + Dx_2 &= 0. \end{aligned} \tag{9.31}$$

To solve this system, we eliminate x_2. If we add the second equation to the first, we obtain the equivalent system

$$\begin{aligned} (D^2 - D + 2)x_1 - x_2 &= 0 \\ -(D + 1)x_1 + Dx_2 &= 0. \end{aligned} \tag{9.32}$$

We now operate on the first equation with D and add the result to the second equation. This yields the system

$$\begin{aligned} (D^2 - D + 2)x_1 - x_2 &= 0 \\ (D^3 - D^2 + D - 1)x_1 &= 0. \end{aligned} \tag{9.33}$$

The second equation here can be written in the factored form

$$(D - 1)(D^2 + 1)x_1 = 0.$$

Then

$$x_1 = C_1 e^t + C_2 \cos t + C_3 \sin t,$$

and from the first equation we have

$$x_2 = (D^2 - D + 2)x_1 = 2C_1 e^t + C_2(\cos t + \sin t) + C_3(-\cos t + \sin t).$$

In vector form, the general solution of the system (9.31) is

$$\mathbf{x} = C_1 \begin{pmatrix} e^t \\ 2e^t \end{pmatrix} + C_2 \begin{pmatrix} \cos t \\ \cos t + \sin t \end{pmatrix} + C_3 \begin{pmatrix} \sin t \\ -\cos t + \sin t \end{pmatrix}. \tag{9.34}$$

We note that three arbitrary constants appear in the expression (9.34) even though the system (9.31) involves only two unknown functions. However, this is in accordance with the fact, already demonstrated, that the system (9.31) is equivalent to a first-order system for three unknown functions.

9.2 EXERCISES

1. Suppose that the functions $b_i(t)$ in the system (9.8) possess derivatives of all orders on an interval I. Prove that the components of every solution possess derivatives of all orders on I.

2. Consider the two systems

(A) $P_{11}(D)x_1 + P_{12}(D)x_2 = b_1(t)$

$\quad P_{21}(D)x_1 + P_{22}(D)x_2 = b_2(t),$

(B) $P_{11}(D)x_1 + P_{12}(D)x_2 = b_1(t)$

$\quad [P_{21}(D) + Q(D)P_{11}(D)]x_1 + [P_{22}(D) + Q(D)P_{12}(D)]x_2$

$$= b_2(t) + Q(D)b_1(t)$$

where the system (B) is obtained from (A) by operating on the first equation of (A) with $Q(D)$ and adding the result to the second equation. Show that every solution of (A) is a solution of (B) and show that every solution of (B) is a solution of (A).

3. Show that the system

(A) $\quad Dx_1 - x_2 = 0$
$\quad\quad -x_1 + Dx_2 = 0$
is equivalent to the system
(B) $\quad Dx_1 - x_2 = 0$
$\quad\quad (D^2 - 1)x_1 = 0,$

but that the system (A) is *not* equivalent to the system

(C) $D^2x_1 - Dx_2 = 0$
$\quad\quad (D^2 - 1)x_1 = 0.$

4. Find the general solution, in both scalar and vector form. When initial conditions are given, find the solution satisfying those conditions.

(a) $(D + 1)x_1 + 5x_2 = 5e^{-t}$
$\quad -x_1 + (D - 1)x_2 = -2e^{-t}, \quad\quad x_1(0) = 0, \quad\quad x_2(0) = 0$

(b) $(D - 3)x_1 - 2x_2 = 2e^t$
$\quad 2x_1 + (D + 1)x_2 = 0, \quad\quad x_1(0) = 3, \quad\quad x_2(0) = -2$

(c) $(D + 3)x_1 - 4x_2 = 2\cos t$
$\quad 2x_1 + (D - 3)x_2 = 1$

(d) $(D + 2)x_1 - 4x_2 = -t$
$\quad 2x_1 + (D - 2)x_2 = 2t$

5. Find the general solution in both scalar and vector form. When initial conditions are given, find the solution that satisfies those conditions.

(a) $Dx_1 = 6x_1 - 7x_2 + 4x_3$
$\quad Dx_2 = 3x_1 - 4x_2 + 2x_3$
$\quad Dx_3 = -5x_1 + 5x_3 - 3x_3, \quad x_1(0) = 5, \quad x_2(0) = 0, \quad x_3(0) = 0$

(b) $Dx_1 = -4x_1 + 4x_2 - x_3$
$Dx_2 = -3x_1 + 3x_2 - x_3$
$Dx_3 = -x_1 + x_2 - x_3,$ $x_1(0) = 2,$ $x_2(0) = 1,$ $x_3(0) = -3$

(c) $Dx_1 = -3x_1 + 4x_2 - 2x_3$
$Dx_2 = -2x_1 + 3x_2 - x_3 + 2 \sin t$
$Dx_3 = 2x_1 - 2x_2 + 2x_3$

(d) $Dx_1 = 4x_1 - 5x_2 + 8x_3 + e^{-t}$
$Dx_2 = -4x_1 + 6x_2 - 8x_3 + e^{-t}$
$Dx_3 = -5x_1 + 7x_2 - 10x_3$

5. Find the general solution. When initial conditions are given, find the solution which satisfies the conditions.

(a) $(D^2 + 2D + 1)x_1 + (D + 1)x_2 = 0$
$-(D + 1)x_1 + (D + 2)x_2 = 0,$
$x_1(0) = 1,$ $x_1'(0) = -1,$ $x_2(0) = 2$

(b) $(D^2 + 3D + 1)x_1 + (D + 1)x_2 = 5 \cos t$
$(D + 1)x_1 - x_2 = \sin t$ $x_1(0) = -1,$ $x_2(0) = -2$

(c) $D^2x_1 - (2D + 1)x_2 = 0$
$(D + 2)x_1 + (D + 2)x_2 = 0$

(d) $D^2x_1 + (D^2 - D + 1)x_2 = 0$
$(D + 1)x_1 + (D^2 + D)x_2 = 0$

7. (a) Rewrite the system of Problem 6(c) as a first-order system. What quantities must be specified at a point t_0 in order that a unique solution be obtained?
(b) Do as in part (a) for the system of Problem 6(d).

8. Find the general solution of the given system for $t > 0$.

(a) $tDx_1 - x_2 = 1$ (b) $tDx_1 - tDx_2 - 2x_2 = -t$
$x_1 - tDx_2 = 0$ $tDx_2 - x_1 = t$

9.3 Applications

Let us first consider the three-dimensional motion of a rigid body. Let the position of the center of mass of the body at time t be given by the relations

$$x = f(t), \qquad y = g(t), \qquad z = h(t), \tag{9.35}$$

where z represents the vertical distance above the surface of the earth. According to Newton's second law of motion,

$$m\mathbf{a} = \mathbf{F}, \tag{9.36}$$

where m is the mass of the body, $\mathbf{F}$ is the force acting on the body, and

$$\mathbf{a} = \frac{d^2x}{dt^2}\mathbf{i} + \frac{d^2y}{dt^2}\mathbf{j} + \frac{d^2z}{dt^2}\mathbf{k} \qquad (9.37)$$

is the acceleration of the center of mass. (The vectors $\mathbf{i}$, $\mathbf{j}$, and $\mathbf{k}$ are the usual unit coordinate vectors.)

Suppose now that $\mathbf{F} = \mathbf{F}_1 + \mathbf{F}_2$, where

$$\mathbf{F}_1 = -mg\mathbf{k} \qquad (9.38)$$

is the force due to gravity, and

$$\mathbf{F}_2 = -c\mathbf{v} = -c\left(\frac{dx}{dt}\mathbf{i} + \frac{dy}{dt}\mathbf{j} + \frac{dz}{dt}\mathbf{k}\right) \qquad (9.39)$$

is a damping force whose magnitude is proportional to the magnitude of the velocity $\mathbf{v}$. By taking components in the vector equation (9.36), we arrive at the system of equations

$$m\frac{d^2x}{dt^2} = -c\frac{dx}{dt}$$

$$m\frac{d^2y}{dt^2} = -c\frac{dy}{dt} \qquad (9.40)$$

$$m\frac{d^2z}{dt^2} = -c\frac{dz}{dt} - mg$$

for the unknown functions $x(t)$, $y(t)$, and $z(t)$ which describe the position of the body. In order to determine the motion of the body exactly, we must know the initial position and velocity of the center of mass. Thus we must have knowledge of the quantities

$$x(0),\ y(0),\ z(0),\ x'(0),\ y'(0),\ z'(0).$$

To illustrate a second type of application, let us consider the electrical network which is shown in Figure 9.1. We denote the currents in the two

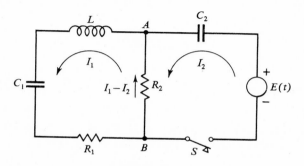

FIGURE 9.1

loops by I_1 and I_2, with positive directions as indicated. The current through the branch from B to A is $I_1 - I_2$. This follows from the law of Kirchhoff that says that the current entering a juncture, or node, (such as A or B) must be equal to the current leaving it. According to Kirchhoff's other law, the sum of the voltage drops around each loop must be equal to the applied voltage in that loop. After the switch S is closed (we assume this to happen at time $t = 0$) we have

$$L\frac{dI_1}{dt} + R_1 I_1 + R_2(I_1 - I_2) + \frac{1}{C_1} Q_1 = 0$$

$$R_2(I_2 - I_1) + \frac{1}{C_2} Q_2 = E(t),$$

(9.41)

where $Q_1(t)$ and $Q_2(t)$ are the charges on the capacitances. Differentiation of the equations (9.41) with respect to t, and a regrouping of terms, yields the system

$$L\frac{d^2 I_1}{dt^2} + (R_1 + R_2)\frac{dI_1}{dt} - R_2\frac{dI_2}{dt} + \frac{1}{C_1} I_1 = 0$$

$$R_2\frac{dI_2}{dt} - R_2\frac{dI_1}{dt} + \frac{1}{C_2} I_2 = E'(t)$$

(9.42)

for the unknowns I_1 and I_2.

We must now determine the initial values of the quantities I_1, I_2, and dI_1/dt. Because of the presence of the inductance in the loop for I_1, we have

$$I_1(0) = 0.$$

(9.43)

Assuming that Q_2 is initially zero, we have from the second of equations (9.41) that

$$I_2(0) = \frac{E(0)}{R_2}.$$

(9.44)

(This condition can also be found by inspection of Figure 9.1. A capacitance acts as a short circuit to a sudden change in the voltage drop across it.) Finally, from the first of equations (9.41), we find that

$$I_1'(0) = \frac{E(0)}{L}.$$

(9.45)

9.3 EXERCISES

1. A projectile of mass m is fired with velocity v_0 from a gun situated on a flat plain. The axis of the gun has angle of inclination α. Assume that the only force acting on the projectile is the force of gravity.

   (a) Find the time it takes for the projectile to return to earth.

(b) Find the horizontal distance traveled. What should be the value of α if this distance is to be a maximum?

(c) Find the maximum height attained.

(d) Show that the path of the projectile is a parabola.

2. A ball is thrown horizontally from the top of a tower 144 feet high with a velocity of 40 ft/sec. Neglecting air resistance, how far from the base of the tower will the ball land? ($g = 32$ ft/sec.^{2})

3. A body of mass m_1 is suspended by means of a spring with spring constant k_1. A second body, of mass m_2, is attached to the first with a spring whose constant is k_2 (Figure 9.2). Let x_1 and x_2 be the directed distances (positive

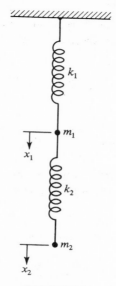

FIGURE 9.2

direction downward) of the bodies from their equilibrium positions.

(a) Show that the motion of the bodies is governed by the system

$$m_1 \frac{d^2 x_1}{dt^2} = -(k_1 + k_2)x_1 + k_2 x_2$$

$$m_2 \frac{d^2 x_2}{dt^2} = k_2 x_1 + k_2 x_2$$

(b) If the motion of each body is damped by a force equal to c times its velocity, find the differential equations of motion.

4. Write down the system of differential equations and initial conditions

for the loop currents in the network of Figure 9.3. The applied voltage

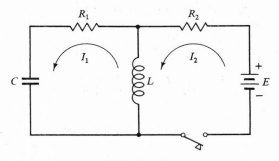

FIGURE 9.3

is a constant, and the switch is closed at $t = 0$.

5. The switch in the network of Figure 9.4 is closed at $t = 0$. Find the loop

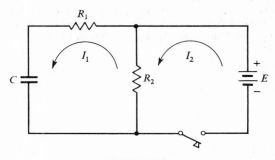

FIGURE 9.4

currents I_1 and I_2 if $R_1 = 50$ ohms, $R_2 = 20$ ohms, $C = 10^{-4}$ farads, and $E = 100$ volts.

6. In the network of Figure 9.5 the switch is closed at time $t = 0$. Show that

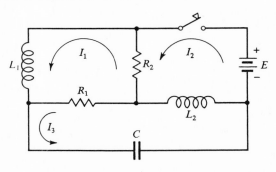

FIGURE 9.5

I_1, I_2, and I_3 form a solution of the initial value problem

$$L_1 \frac{dI_1}{dt} + (R_1 + R_2)I_1 - R_2 I_2 - R_1 I_3 = 0$$

$$L_2 \frac{dI_2}{dt} - L_2 \frac{dI_3}{dt} + R_2 I_2 = E$$

$$R_1 \frac{dI_3}{dt} - R_1 \frac{dI_1}{dt} + R_2 \frac{dI_2}{dt} + \frac{1}{C} I_3 = 0,$$

$$I_1(0) = 0, \ I_2(0) = I_3(0) = \frac{E}{R_1 + R_2}.$$

REFERENCES

1. Coddington, E. A., and Levinson, N., *Theory of Ordinary Differential Equations.* McGraw-Hill, New York, 1955.
2. Ince, E. L., *Ordinary Differential Equations*, 4th ed. Dover, New York, 1953.
3. Kaplan, W., *Ordinary Differential Equations.* Addison-Wesley, Reading, Mass., 1962.
4. Protter, M. H., and Morrey, C. B., *Modern Mathematical Analysis.* Addison-Wesley Reading, Mass., 1964.

CHAPTER **10**

LAPLACE TRANSFORMS

10.1   The Laplace Transform

Let $f(t)$ be a function that is defined on the interval $0 < t < +\infty$. Associated with $f(t)$ is the improper integral

$$\int_0^\infty e^{-st}f(t)\,dt,\tag{10.1}$$

where s is a real† number. It may happen that there is no number s for which this integral exists. If not, there exists a set of real numbers, which we denote by S, such that the integral exists for s in S. In this case, we define the function $F(s)$ as

$$F(s) = \int_0^\infty e^{-st}f(t)\,dt, \qquad s \text{ in } S.\tag{10.2}$$

The function $F(s)$ is called the *Laplace transform* of the function $f(t)$. We write

$$F(s) = \mathscr{L}[f(t)]\tag{10.3}$$

to indicate the relationship between the functions f and F. Actually, we shall be interested only in functions whose transforms exist on an interval of the form $s_0 < s < +\infty$, for some number s_0. Sufficient conditions that the transform of a function exist on such an interval will be discussed in the sequel.

Not every function has a Laplace transform. For instance, if $f(t) = e^{t^2}$, the improper integral (10.1) diverges for all values of s. When s is positive,

† In more advanced treatments of the Laplace transform, s is permitted to be a complex number.

298

however, the function e^{-st} tends to zero fairly rapidly as t becomes infinite. Consequently, many functions do possess Laplace transforms.

Let us now compute the transforms of some specific functions. Starting with the function $f(t) = e^{at}$, where a is a constant, we have

$$\int_0^\infty e^{-st}f(t)\, dt = \int_0^\infty e^{-t(s-a)}\, dt$$

$$= \lim_{T \to \infty} \left[\frac{-1}{s-a} e^{-t(s-a)} \right]_0^T$$

$$= \frac{1}{s-a},$$

if $s > a$. Thus

$$\mathscr{L}[e^{at}] = \frac{1}{s-a}, \qquad s > a. \tag{10.4}$$

As a second example, let $f(t) = \cos at$. Then

$$\int_0^\infty e^{-st}f(t)\, dt = \int_0^\infty e^{-st} \cos at\, dt$$

$$= \lim_{T \to \infty} \left[\frac{e^{-st}}{s^2 + a^2} (a \sin at - s \cos at) \right]_0^T$$

$$= \frac{s}{s^2 + a^2},$$

if $s > 0$. Consequently,

$$\mathscr{L}[\cos at] = \frac{s}{s^2 + a^2}, \qquad s > 0. \tag{10.5}$$

If the functions $f(t)$ and $g(t)$ both possess Laplace transforms for $s > s_0$, then the function $C_1 f(t) + C_2 g(t)$, where C_1 and C_2 are constants, also possesses a transform for $s > s_0$. In fact, from the relation

$$\int_0^\infty e^{-st}[C_1 f(t) + C_2 g(t)]\, dt = C_1 \int_0^\infty e^{-st}f(t)\, dt + C_2 \int_0^\infty e^{-st}g(t)\, dt,$$

we see that

$$\mathscr{L}[C_1 f(t) + C_2 g(t)] = C_1 \mathscr{L}[f(t)] + C_2 \mathscr{L}[g(t)], \qquad s > s_0. \tag{10.6}$$

A particularly important property of Laplace transforms comes to light when we consider the transform of the *derivative* of a function $f(t)$. Let us assume that $f(t)$ and $f'(t)$ are continuous for $0 \le t < +\infty$, and that both functions possess Laplace transforms for $s > s_0$. Using integration by parts, we have

$$\int_0^T e^{-st}f'(t)\, dt = \left[f(t)e^{-st} \right]_0^T + s \int_0^T e^{-st}f(t)\, dt.$$

As $T \to +\infty$, both integrals tend to finite limits for $s > s_0$. Consequently $f(T)e^{-sT}$ must also tend to a finite limit for $s > s_0$. We shall show that this limit is zero. Given any number s_1, where $s_1 > s_0$, let s_2 be a number such that $s_0 < s_2 < s_1$. Since $f(T) \exp(-s_2 T)$ tends to a finite limit, $f(T) \exp(-s_1 T) = f(T) \exp(-s_2 T) \exp[-(s_1 - s_2)T]$ tends to zero. Therefore

$$\lim_{T \to +\infty} \left[f(t)e^{-st} \right]_0^T = -f(0)$$

for $s > s_0$, and we have

$$\mathcal{L}[f'(t)] = sF(s) - f(0), \qquad s > s_0. \tag{10.7}$$

It is because of this property, and its generalization to higher derivatives, that Laplace transforms are useful in the solution of initial value problems for certain types of differential equations. To illustrate, let us consider the simple problem

$$\frac{dx}{dt} + 2x = e^{-t}, \qquad x(0) = 2. \tag{10.8}$$

Let us assume for the moment that the solution function $x(t)$ and its derivative $x'(t)$ both possess Laplace transforms. We denote the transform of $x(t)$ by $X(s)$. From the differential equation we see that

$$\mathcal{L}\left[\frac{dx}{dt} + 2x \right] = \mathcal{L}[e^{-t}] \tag{10.9}$$

or

$$\mathcal{L}\left[\frac{dx}{dt} \right] + 2\mathcal{L}[x] = \frac{1}{s+1}. \tag{10.10}$$

Using the property (10.7), we have

$$sX(s) - 2 + 2X(s) = \frac{1}{s+1}. \tag{10.11}$$

Thus the initial value problem for the function $x(t)$ has been transformed into an algebraic equation for the function $X(s)$. Solving the equation (10.11) for $X(s)$, we have

$$X(s) = \frac{2s + 3}{(s+1)(s+2)},$$

or, upon using partial fractions,

$$X(s) = \frac{1}{s+1} + \frac{1}{s+2}. \tag{10.12}$$

Now, from formula (10.4), we recognize that the function

$$x(t) = e^{-t} + e^{-2t} \tag{10.13}$$

has $X(s)$ as its Laplace transform. It is easy to verify that the function (10.13) is indeed the solution of the initial value problem.

In applying the method of Laplace transforms to the problem (10.8), we went through three main steps. First we transformed a "hard" problem (the initial value problem) into a relatively "easy" problem [the algebraic equation for $X(s)$]. Then we solved the easy problem by finding $X(s)$. Finally we "inverted"; that is, we found the solution $x(t)$ of the original problem from the solution of the transformed problem. This same procedure is followed in the solution of more complicated initial value problems.

Applications of Laplace transforms to differential equations will be considered in the final section of this chapter. Meanwhile, we shall investigate the properties of Laplace transforms in more detail.

10.1 EXERCISES

1. Calculate the Laplace transform of the given function. Determine the values of s for which the transform exists.

(a) $f(t) = 1$

(b) $f(t) = t$

(c) $f(t) = t^n$, n a positive integer.

(d) $f(t) = \sin at$

(e) $f(t) = \sinh at$

(f) $f(t) = \begin{cases} 1, 0 < t < 1 \\ 0, t > 1 \end{cases}$

2. If $f(t) = t^\alpha$, $\alpha > -1$, show that

$$\mathscr{L}[f(t)] = \frac{\Gamma(\alpha + 1)}{s^{\alpha+1}}, \qquad s > 0,$$

where $\Gamma(x)$ is the gamma function.

3. Let $f(t)$ be piecewise continuous for $0 \le t \le T$ and be periodic with period T.

(a) Show that

$$\mathscr{L}[f(t)] = \frac{1}{1 - e^{-sT}} \int_0^T e^{-st}f(t)\, dt, \qquad s > 0.$$

(b) Let $f(t) = 1, 0 < t < T/2$, $f(t) = 0$, $T/2 < t < T$, and $f(t + T) = f(t)$. Find $\mathscr{L}[f(t)]$.
(c) Find the Laplace transform of the function $f(t) = |\sin t|$.

4. By using Laplace transforms, find the solution of the given initial value problem. Verify that your answer is the correct one.

(a) $\dfrac{dx}{dt} - 2x = 2$, $\quad x(0) = -3$

(b) $\dfrac{dx}{dt} + 3x = e^{2t}$, $\quad x(0) = -1$

10.2   Conditions for the Existence of the Laplace Transform

In the examples of the last section, we were able to show that certain functions possessed Laplace transforms by actually carrying out the integration in formula (10.2). In cases where this is difficult, the following theorem from advanced calculus is often useful.

Theorem A.   Let $f(t)$ and $g(t)$ be piecewise continuous on every interval of the form $[c, T]$, where c is fixed and $T > c$. If $|f(t)| \leq g(t)$ for $t \geq c$, and if the integral $\int_c^\infty g(t) \, dt$ converges, then the integral $\int_c^\infty f(t) \, dt$ also converges.

In a moment we shall use Theorem A to establish a set of sufficient conditions for the existence of the Laplace transform of a function. First, however, let us introduce the notation†

$$f(t) = O[g(t)], \tag{10.14}$$

which should be read " $f(t)$ is of the order of $g(t)$." This notation means that there exist positive constants M and N such that

$$|f(t)| \leq Mg(t) \tag{10.15}$$

whenever $t > N$. In particular, if $f(t) = O[e^{at}]$, for some constant a, we say that $f(t)$ is of *exponential order*.

We are now ready to prove the following theorem.

Theorem 1.   Let $f(t)$ be piecewise continuous on every interval of the form $[0, T]$, where $T > 0$, and let $f(t) = O[e^{at}]$, for some constant a. Then the Laplace transform of $f(t)$ exists, at least for $s > a$.

Proof.   According to the hypotheses of the theorem, there exist positive constants M and t_0 such that $|f(t)| \leq Me^{at}$ when $t \geq t_0$. Then $|f(t) \, e^{-st}| \leq Me^{-(s-a)t}$ when $t \geq t_0$. Since the integral $\int_{t_0}^\infty Me^{-(s-a)t} \, dt$ converges when $s > a$, the integral $\int_{t_0}^\infty e^{-st} f(t) \, dt$ also converges when $s > a$, by Theorem A. Since

$$\int_0^\infty e^{-st} f(t) \, dt = \int_0^{t_0} e^{-st} f(t) \, dt + \int_{t_0}^\infty e^{-st} f(t) \, dt, \qquad s > a,$$

the Laplace transform of $f(t)$ exists for $s > a$.

As an important application of Theorem 1, we shall show that if $f(t)$ is a function of the form

$$t^n e^{at} \cos bt, \qquad t^n e^{at} \sin bt, \tag{10.16}$$

---

† The notation $f(t) = o[g(t)]$ also appears in the literature. It means that $f(t)/g(t) \to 0$ as $t \to +\infty$.

where n is a nonnegative integer, then $\mathscr{L}[f(t)]$ exists for $s > a$. We first observe that

$$t^n = O[e^{\varepsilon t}]$$

for every positive number ε. Since $|\cos bt| \leq 1$ and $|\sin bt| \leq 1$ for all t, we have

$$f(t) = O[e^{(a+\varepsilon)t}].$$

By Theorem 1, $\mathscr{L}[f(t)]$ exists for $s > a + \varepsilon$ for every positive number ε. Consequently $\mathscr{L}[f(t)]$ exists for $s > a$.

The above result is important in the study of linear differential equations with constant coefficients. Let us consider the homogeneous equation

$$P(D)x = O, \tag{10.17}$$

where $D = d/dt$ and $P(D)$ is a polynomial operator. Every solution of this equation is a linear combination of functions of the form (10.16). Any derivative of a solution is also a linear combination of functions of this type. We can therefore assert that every solution of the equation (10.17), and every derivative of every solution, is of exponential order and possesses a Laplace transform.

We shall give one more result about functions of exponential order.

Theorem 2.   Let $f(t)$ be piecewise continuous on every interval of the form $[0, T]$, and let $f(t) = O[e^{at}]$ for some constant a. Then the function

$$h(t) = \int_0^t f(u)\,du \tag{10.18}$$

is of exponential order. If $a > 0$, $h(t) = O[e^{at}]$, and if $a \leq 0$, $h(t) = O[1].$†

Proof.   There exist positive constants t_0 and M_1 such that $|f(t)| \leq M_1 e^{at}$ for $t \geq t_0$. Also, there exists a positive constant M_2 such that $|f(t)| \leq M_2$ for $0 \leq t \leq t_0$. Since

$$h(t) = \int_0^{t_0} f(u)\,du + \int_{t_0}^t f(u)\,du$$

for $t > t_0$, we have

$$|h(t)| \leq M_2 \int_0^{t_0} du + M_1 \int_{t_0}^t e^{au}\,du,$$

or

$$|h(t)| \leq M_2 t_0 + \frac{M_1}{a}(e^{at} - e^{at_0}).$$

If $a > 0$, then

$$|h(t)| \leq \left(M_2 t_0 + \frac{M_1}{a}\right)e^{at} \qquad \text{for } t > t_0$$

The notation $h(t) = O[1]$ means the same thing as $h(t) = O[e^{0t}]$.

and then $h(t) = O[e^{at}]$. If $a \le 0$,

$$|h(t)| \le M_2 t_0 + 2\frac{M_1}{a} \qquad \text{for } t > t_0,$$

and $h(t) = O[1]$.

10.2   EXERCISES

1. Suppose that the limit

$$\lim_{t \to +\infty} \frac{f(t)}{g(t)}$$

exists (and is finite). Show that $f(t) = O[|g(t)|]$.

2. Show that, as $t \to +\infty$,

(a) $\sin t = O[1]$

(c) $te^t = O[e^t]$

(b) $\dfrac{e^{-t}}{t+1} = O[e^{-t}]$

(d) $\dfrac{e^{-t}}{t+1} = O\left[\dfrac{1}{t}\right]$

3. Show that the given function possesses a Laplace transform for the indicated values of s:

(a) $f(t) = \dfrac{1}{t+1}, \qquad s > 0$

(c) $f(t) = \dfrac{\sin t}{t}, \qquad s > 0$

(b) $f(t) = \dfrac{e^{at}}{t+1}, \qquad s > a$

(d) $f(t) = t \log t, \qquad s > 0$

4. Let $f(t)$ and $g(t)$ be of exponential order.

(a) Show that the function $C_1 f(t) + C_2 g(t)$, where C_1 and C_2 are constants, is of exponential order.
(b) Show that the function $f(t)g(t)$ is of exponential order.

5. Let the function $b(t)$ be continuous for $t \ge 0$ and be of exponential order. Show that every solution of the equation

$$\frac{dx}{dt} + ax = b(t),$$

where a is a constant, is of exponential order. Show also that the first derivative of every solution is of exponential order.

10.3   Properties of Laplace Transforms

In this section we shall develop some of the more useful properties of Laplace transforms. In the formulas listed below we denote the transforms of $f(t)$ and $g(t)$ by $F(s)$ and $G(s)$, respectively. For properties (A) through (E), we assume that $f(t)$ and $g(t)$ are piecewise continuous on every interval of the form $[0, T]$, and that $f(t) = O[e^{at}]$ and $g(t) = O[e^{bt}]$, for some constants a and b. Then $F(s)$ exists for $s > a$ and $G(s)$ exists for $s > b$.

(A) $\qquad \mathcal{L}[C_1 f(t) + C_2 g(t)] = C_1 F(s) + C_2 G(s), \qquad s > \max(a, b)$.

(B) $\qquad \mathcal{L}[e^{ct} f(t)] = F(s - c), \qquad s > a + c$.

(C) $\qquad \mathcal{L}\left[\int_0^t f(u)\, du \right] = \frac{1}{s} F(s), \qquad s > \max(a, 0)$.

(D) $\qquad \mathcal{L}[t^n f(t)] = (-1)^n \dfrac{d^n}{ds^n} F(s), \qquad s > a$.

(E) If

$$h(t) = \begin{cases} 0, & 0 < t < c \\ f(t - c), & t > c, \end{cases}$$

where c is a positive number, then

$$\mathcal{L}[h(t)] = e^{-cs} F(s), \qquad s > a.$$

(F) Let $f^{(n-1)}(t) = O[e^{at}]$. Let $f(t),\ f'(t),\ \dots,\ f^{(n-1)}(t)$ be continuous for $t \geq 0$, and let $f^{(n)}(t)$ be piecewise continuous on every interval of the form $[0, T]$. Then $\mathcal{L}[f^{(n)}(t)]$ exists for $s > \max(a, 0)$, and

$$\mathcal{L}[f^{(n)}(t)] = s^n F(s) - [s^{n-1} f(0) + s^{n-2} f'(0) + \cdots + f^{(n-1)}(0)].$$

Property (A) follows from Theorem 1 and the definition of the Laplace transform of a function.

To prove property (B), we first note that $e^{ct} f(t) = O[e^{(a+c)t}]$. Then we observe that

$$\mathcal{L}[e^{ct} f(t)] = \int_0^\infty e^{-(s-c)t} f(t)\, dt = F(s - c).$$

To prove property (C), we use the result of Theorem 2, which assures us that the function $h(t) = \int_0^t f(u)\, du$ is of exponential order. Using integration by parts, and observing that $h'(t) = f(t)$, we have

$$\mathcal{L}[h(t)] = \int_0^\infty e^{-st} h(t)\, dt = \left[-\frac{1}{s} e^{-st} h(t) \right]_0^\infty + \frac{1}{s} \int_0^\infty e^{-st} f(t)\, dt.$$

Since $h(0) = 0$, the integrated part vanishes, and we have $\mathcal{L}[h(t)] = F(s)/s$.

Now consider property (D). If we differentiate both members of the equation

$$F(s) = \int_0^\infty e^{-st} f(t)\, dt, \qquad s > a,$$

with respect to s (the assumptions on f insure that $F'(s)$ exists and that

$F'(s)$ can be obtained by differentiation under the integral sign), we find that

$$F'(s) = -\int_0^\infty e^{-st} t f(t)\, dt = -\mathscr{L}[tf(t)].$$

Repeated differentiation with respect to s shows that

$$F^{(n)}(s) = (-1)^n \int_0^\infty e^{-st} t^n f(t)\, dt = (-1)^n \mathscr{L}[t^n f(t)].$$

The verification of property (E) is left as an exercise.

We shall prove property (F) by induction. When $n = 1$, $f(t)$ is assumed to be continuous for $t \geq 0$. Using integration by parts, we have

$$\int_0^T e^{-st} f'(t)\, dt = \left[e^{-st} f(t) \right]_0^T + s \int_0^T e^{-st} f(t)\, dt.$$

Since $f(t) = O[e^{at}]$, it follows that $e^{-sT} f(T) \to 0$ as $T \to +\infty$ for $s > a$. Letting $T \to +\infty$ in the above relation, we have

$$\mathscr{L}[f'(t)] = sF(s) - f(0), \qquad s > a.$$

Suppose that property (F) holds for $n = m$, where m is a positive integer. When $n = m + 1$, the assumption that $f^{(m)}(t) = O[e^{at}]$ implies that the function $f^{(m-1)}(t)$, is of exponential order. Using the same arguments as in the case $n = 1$, we have

$$\mathscr{L}[f^{(m+1)}(t)] = \int_0^\infty e^{-st} f^{(m+1)}(t)\, dt$$

$$= \left[e^{-st} f^{(m)}(t) \right]_0^\infty + s \int_0^\infty e^{-st} f^{(m)}(t)\, dt$$

$$= s\mathscr{L}[f^{(m)}(t)] - f^{(m)}(0).$$

Then

$$\mathscr{L}[f^{(m+1)}(t)] = s[s^m F(s) - s^{m-1} f(0) - \cdots - f^{(m-1)}(0)] - f^{(m)}(0)$$

$$= s^{m+1} F(s) - [s^m f(0) + \cdots + f^{(m)}(0)].$$

Thus if property (F) holds for $n = m$, it also holds for $n = m + 1$. Since it holds for $n = 1$, it holds for every positive integer.

These basic properties of the Laplace transformation operator are frequently useful in finding the transforms of functions. Starting with the formulas

$$\mathscr{L}[t^n] = \frac{n!}{s^{n+1}}, \qquad \mathscr{L}[\cos at] = \frac{s}{s^2 + a^2},$$

$$\mathscr{L}[e^{at}] = \frac{1}{s - a}, \qquad \mathscr{L}[\sin at] = \frac{a}{s^2 + a^2}, \tag{10.19}$$

we can easily find the transforms of many elementary functions by using the properties (A) through (F). For example, by using Property (A), we find that the transform of the function sinh at is

$$\mathscr{L}[\sinh at] = \tfrac{1}{2}\mathscr{L}[e^{at}] - \tfrac{1}{2}\mathscr{L}[e^{-at}]$$

$$= \frac{1}{2}\left(\frac{1}{s-a} - \frac{1}{s+a}\right) = \frac{a}{s^2 - a^2}.$$

As a second example, we find the transform of the function $e^{-2t}\cos 3t$. Since

$$\mathscr{L}[\cos 3t] = \frac{3}{s^2 + 9},$$

it follows from property (B) that

$$\mathscr{L}[e^{-2t}\cos 3t] = \frac{s+2}{(s+2)^2 + 9} = \frac{s+2}{s^2 + 4s + 13}.$$

As an example of the use of property (D), we find the transform of the function $t^2 \sin t$. Since

$$\mathscr{L}[\sin t] = \frac{s}{s^2 + 1},$$

we have

$$\mathscr{L}[t^2 \sin t] = \frac{d^2}{ds^2}\frac{1}{s^2 + 1} = 2\frac{3s^2 - 1}{(s^2 + 1)^3}.$$

As a final example, we consider the function

$$h(t) = \begin{cases} 0, & 0 < t < 1 \\ (t-1)^2, & t > 1, \end{cases}$$

whose graph is shown in Figure 10.1.

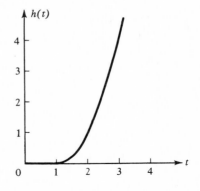

FIGURE 10.1

Since $\mathscr{L}[t^2] = 2/s^3$, it follows from property (E) that

$$\mathscr{L}[h(t)] = e^{-s}\mathscr{L}[t^2] = \frac{2}{s^3}e^{-s}.$$

10.3 EXERCISES

1. Verify property (E).

2. Find the Laplace transform of the given function:

(a) $2e^{-t} - 3\sin 4t$ (d) $t^2 \cos t$
(b) $e^{2t}\sin 3t$ (e) $t \sin 2t$
(c) $e^{-3t}t^4$

3. Find the Laplace transform of the given function:

(a) $e^{2t}\sqrt{t}$

(b) $\int_0^t \sin 2u\, du$

(c) $\int_0^t x^2 e^x\, dx$

(d) $f(t) = \begin{cases} 0, & 0 < t < 2 \\ 1, & t > 2 \end{cases}$

(e) $f(t) = \begin{cases} 0, & 0 < t < \pi \\ \sin(t - \pi), & t > \pi \end{cases}$

4. If the Laplace transform of $f(t)$ is denoted by $F(s)$, find the transform of the given function in terms of $F(s)$:

(a) $f''(t)$, if $f(0) = 1$ and $f'(0) = 2$
(b) $f'''(t)$, if $f(0) = -2$, $f'(0) = 0$, and $f''(0) = 1$

5. Let $F(s) = \mathscr{L}[f(t)]$, and let c be a positive constant. Show that

$$\mathscr{L}[f(ct)] = \frac{1}{c} F\left(\frac{s}{c}\right).$$

6. Let $f(t)$ and $f'(t)$ be piecewise continuous on every interval of the form $[0, b]$ and be of exponential order. Suppose that $f(t)$ has only a finite number of discontinuities for $t > 0$, at the points $t_1, t_2, \ldots, t_k$. Show that

$$\mathscr{L}[f'(t)] = sF(s) - f(0+) - \sum_{i=1}^{k} e^{-st_i}[f(t_i+) - f(t_i-)].$$

10.4   Inverse Transforms

In this section, we shall consider the following problem. Given a function $F(s)$, what functions, if any, have $F(s)$ as their Laplace transforms? To simplify matters, we shall consider only functions of t that are piecewise continuous on every interval of the form $[0, T]$ and are of exponential order. We first prove the following result.

Theorem 3.   Let $f(t)$ be a function of the type described above, and let $F(s) = \mathscr{L}[f(t)]$. Then

$$\lim_{s \to +\infty} F(s) = 0. \tag{10.20}$$

Proof.   There exist positive numbers t_0 and M_1, and a number a, such that $|f(t)| \le M_1 e^{at}$ for $t \ge t_0$. We write

$$F(s) = \int_0^{t_0} e^{-st} f(t)\, dt + \int_{t_0}^{\infty} e^{-st} f(t)\, dt.$$

Since $f(t)$ is piecewise continuous on the finite interval $[0, t_0]$, there exists a positive number M_2 such that $|f(t)| \le M_2$ for $0 \le t \le t_0$. Then

$$|F(s)| \le M_2 \int_0^{t_0} e^{-st}\, dt + M_1 \int_{t_0}^{\infty} e^{-t(s-a)}\, dt,$$

so

$$|F(s)| \leq M_2 \frac{1}{s}(1 - e^{-st_0}) + M_1 \frac{1}{s-a} e^{-t_0(s-a)}, \qquad s > a.$$

Letting $s \to +\infty$, we see that $F(s) \to 0$.

In view of this result, we can state that unless a given function $F(s)$ tends to zero with increasing s, there exists no function of the type considered which has $F(s)$ as its Laplace transform. For instance, if

$$F(s) = \frac{s(s+1)}{s^2 + 2}, \tag{10.21}$$

no function of the type considered has $F(s)$ as its transform, because $F(s) \to 1 \neq 0$ as $s \to +\infty$.

We can also ask if it is possible for two different functions to have the same Laplace transform. A partial answer is given by the following theorem, which we must state without proof.

Theorem 4.   Let $f(t)$ and $g(t)$ be piecewise continuous on every interval of the form $[0, T]$, and let $\mathscr{L}[f(t)] = \mathscr{L}[g(t)]$ for $s > s_0$, for some number s_0. Then at each point t_0 in the interval $[0, +\infty)$ where f and g are both continuous, $f(t_0) = g(t_0)$. In particular, if f and g are both continuous for $t \geq 0$, then $f(t) = g(t)$ for $t \geq 0$.

Let us consider as an example the function

$$F(s) = \frac{1}{s-2}. \tag{10.22}$$

We know that the function e^{2t} has $F(s)$ as its transform. Because of Theorem 4, we can assert that e^{2t} is the only *continuous* function that has $F(s)$ as its transform.

More generally, let $F(s)$ be defined for $s > a$, for some number a, and be such that $F(s) \to 0$ as $s \to +\infty$. We may ask whether there exists a function $f(t)$, continuous for $t \geq 0$ and of exponential order, which has $F(s)$ as its Laplace transform. We know, by Theorem 4, that at most one such function can exist. If such a function $f(t)$ does exist, we call it the *inverse transform* of $F(s)$, and write

$$f(t) = \mathscr{L}^{-1}[F(s)]. \tag{10.23}$$

Sufficient conditions that a function $F(s)$ possess an inverse transform may be found in Reference 1 of this chapter.

It is possible to find the inverse transforms of a number of functions by using the formulas (10.19), and the properties of Laplace transforms that were derived in the last section. For example, let us consider the function

$$F(s) = \frac{3s}{s^2 + 4s + 5}.$$

By completing the square in the denominator, we can write

$$F(s) = \frac{3s}{(s + 2)^2 + 1} = \frac{3(s + 2)}{(s + 2)^2 + 1} - \frac{6}{(s + 2)^2 + 1}.$$

Since

$$\mathscr{L}^{-1}\left[\frac{s}{s^2 + 1}\right] = \cos t, \qquad \mathscr{L}^{-1}\left[\frac{1}{s^2 + 1}\right] = \sin t,$$

we have, from property (B), that

$$\mathscr{L}^{-1}[F(s)] = e^{-2t}(3 \cos t - 6 \sin t).$$

As a second example, we consider the function

$$F(s) = e^{-2s} \frac{1}{s^2}.$$

Now $\mathscr{L}^{-1}[1/s^2] = t$, so by property (E),

$$\mathscr{L}^{-1}\left[e^{-2s}\frac{1}{s^2}\right] = \begin{cases} 0, & 0 \le t < 2, \\ t - 2, & t \ge 2. \end{cases}$$

In cases when $F(s)$ is a rational function, it is often convenient to expand $F(s)$ in a series of partial fractions. For instance, suppose that we wish to find the inverse transform of the function

$$F(s) = \frac{1}{(s - 2)(s^2 + 1)}.$$

Expansion of $F(s)$ in partial fractions yields the formula

$$F(s) = \frac{1}{5}\frac{1}{s - 2} - \frac{1}{5}\frac{s + 2}{s^2 + 1}$$

Then we recognize that

$$\mathscr{L}^{-1}[F(s)] = \tfrac{1}{5}(e^{2t} - \cos t - 2 \sin t).$$

Let us now consider the problem of finding the inverse transform of the product $F(s)G(s)$, where

$$F(s) = \mathscr{L}[f(t)], \qquad G(s) = \mathscr{L}[g(t)].$$

We have

$$F(s)G(s) = \left(\int_0^\infty e^{-sx}f(x)\, dx\right)\left(\int_0^\infty e^{-sy}g(y)\, dy\right) \qquad (10.24)$$

$$= \int_0^\infty \int_0^\infty e^{-s(x+y)}f(x)g(y)\, dx\, dy.$$

The product of the two single integrals can be interpreted as an improper double integral whose region of integration is the first quadrant of a plane in which x and y are rectangular coordinates. Let us now make the change of variables

$$x = t - u, \qquad u = y \tag{10.25}$$
$$y = u, \qquad t = x + y$$

from (x, y) to (t, u). The first quadrant of the xy plane corresponds to the region of the tu plane that is described by means of the inequalities $u \geq 0$ and $t - u \geq 0$. This region is shown in Figure 10.2.

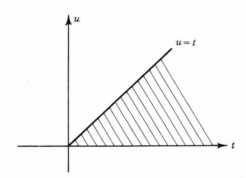

FIGURE 10.2

The iterated integral in formula (10.24) becomes†

$$F(s)G(s) = \int_0^\infty \int_0^t e^{-st} f(t - u) g(u) \, du \, dt$$
$$= \int_0^\infty e^{-st} \left[\int_0^t f(t - u) g(u) \, du \right] dt. \tag{10.26}$$

Consequently

$$\mathscr{L}^{-1}[F(s)G(s)] = \int_0^t f(t - u) g(u) \, du. \tag{10.27}$$

The integral in formula (10.27) is called the *convolution* of the functions f and g. It is sometimes denoted by the symbol $f*g$. It arises in several areas of mathematics other than Laplace transform theory.

As an exercise, we shall use formula (10.27) to find the inverse transform of the function

$$\frac{1}{s^2(s^2 + 1)}.$$

Since

$$\mathscr{L}^{-1}\left[\frac{1}{s^2}\right] = t, \qquad \mathscr{L}^{-1}\left[\frac{1}{s^2 + 1}\right] = \sin t,$$

† The Jacobian of the transformation (10.25) is unity. See reference 4 in this chapter for an alternative treatment.

we have

$$\mathscr{L}^{-1}\left[\frac{1}{s^2(s^2+1)}\right] = \int_0^t (t-u)\sin u \; du$$

$$= \left[-(t-u)\cos u - \sin u\right]_{u=0}^{u=t}$$

$$= t - \sin t.$$

This result could also have been obtained by finding the partial fractions expansion of the given function of s.

The techniques illustrated here can be used only when the given function $F(s)$ can be expressed in a fairly simple way in terms of functions whose inverse transforms are easily recognizeable. For convenience, a short table of functions and their transforms is given at the end of this chapter. A more powerful and direct method for finding inverse transforms exists. This method requires a fairly deep knowledge of complex variables, however, and we cannot discuss it here. We shall be mainly concerned with the solution of initial value problems for differential equations by means of Laplace transforms. The methods at our disposal suffice for the solution of many such problems. In any case, they serve to illustrate the general approach.

10.4 EXERCISES

1. Find the function that is continuous for $t \geq 0$ and has the given function as its Laplace transform.

(a) $\dfrac{1}{(s+1)^2}$

(b) $\dfrac{1}{(s-2)^2+9}$

(c) $\dfrac{s}{(s+1)^2-4}$

(d) $\dfrac{1}{s^2-3s}$

(e) $\dfrac{1}{(s+1)(s+2)}$

(f) $\dfrac{1}{s(s+2)^2}$

2. Find the function that is continuous for $t \geq 0$ and has the given function as its Laplace transform.

(a) $\dfrac{6}{s^2+s-2}$

(b) $\dfrac{3s-8}{s^2-5s+6}$

(c) $\dfrac{s^2+20s+9}{(s-1)^2(s^2+9)}$

(d) $\dfrac{s-4}{s^2+3s+3}$

(e) $\dfrac{1}{s^3-8}$

(f) $\dfrac{3s-2}{s^2-2s+10}$

3. Find the inverse transform of the given function.

(a) $e^{-s} \dfrac{1}{(s-2)^2}$

(d) $\dfrac{1}{s^{5/2}(s^2+1)}$

(b) $e^{-2s} \dfrac{1}{s^2+9\pi^2}$

(e) $\dfrac{1}{s+1} F(s)$

(c) $\dfrac{s}{(s-2)^{3/2}(s^2+1)}$

(f) $\dfrac{1}{s^2+1} F(s)$

4. Let $f(t)$ be continuous for $t \geq 0$. Let $f'(t)$ be piecewise continuous on every interval of the form $[0, T]$ and be of exponential order. Show that

$$\lim_{s \to +\infty} sF(s) = f(0).$$

10.5 Application to Differential Equations

We shall now apply the theory of Laplace transforms to the solution of initial value problems. The method we shall describe applies to those problems where the differential equation, or system of differential equations, is linear and has constant coefficients.

As an illustration let us consider the problem

$$\frac{d^2x}{dt^2} + 4x = e^{-t}, \qquad 0 \leq t < +\infty, \tag{10.28}$$

$$x(0) = 1, \qquad x'(0) = 2. \tag{10.29}$$

We know, from the theory of Chapter 1, that this problem possesses a unique solution $x(t)$. This solution, and its first two derivatives, are continuous for $t \geq 0$. Let us assume, for the moment, that $x(t)$ is of exponential order. Then it possesses a Laplace transform $X(s)$. Let us also assume that $x'(t)$ and $x''(t)$ are of exponential order. Then these functions also possess Laplace transforms, and

$$\mathscr{L}[x'(t)] = sX(s) - x(0) = sX(s) - 1$$

$$\mathscr{L}[x''(t)] = s^2 X(s) - sx(0) - x'(0) = s^2 X(s) - s - 2,$$

by property (F) of section 10.3. Since the function $x(t)$ satisfies the differential equation (10.28), we have

$$s^2 X(s) - s - 2 + 4X(s) = \frac{1}{s+1}, \tag{10.30}$$

or

$$X(s) = \frac{1}{s+4}\left(\frac{3}{s+1} + s + 2\right). \tag{10.31}$$

By using partial fractions, we can write

$$X(s) = \frac{1}{5} \frac{1}{s+1} + \frac{4}{5} \frac{s}{s^2+4} + \frac{11}{10} \frac{2}{s^2+4}. \tag{10.32}$$

Inverting, we arrive at the formula

$$x(t) = \tfrac{1}{5}e^{-t} + \tfrac{4}{5}\cos 2t + \tfrac{11}{10}\sin 2t. \tag{10.33}$$

However, we cannot immediately assert that the function (10.33) is the solution of our initial-value problem. For in the derivation, we made the assumption, not yet justified, that the solution and its first two derivatives were of exponential order.

We shall presently show that our assumptions about the behavior of the solution and its derivatives were correct. But first let us consider the more general problem

$$P(D)x = a_0 x^{(n)} + a_1 x^{(n-1)} + \cdots + a_{n-1}x' + a_n x = b(t), \tag{10.34}$$

$$x(0) = k_0, \; x'(0) = k_1, \ldots, x^{(n-1)}(0) = k_{n-1}. \tag{10.35}$$

Suppose that $b(t)$ possesses a Laplace transform $B(s)$. If we "transform" the equation (10.34) formally, taking into account the initial conditions (10.35), we arrive at the algebraic equation

$$a_0[s^n X(s) - k_0 s^{n-1} - \cdots - k_{n-1}] + a_1[s^{n-1}X(s) - k_0 s^{n-2} - \cdots - k_{n-2}]$$

$$\tag{10.36}$$

$$+ \cdots + a_{n-1}[sX(s) - k_0] + a_n X(s) = B(s)$$

for the function $X(s)$. This equation can be written as

$$P(s)X(s) = B(s) + Q(s), \tag{10.37}$$

where $Q(s)$ is a polynomial whose coefficients depend on the constants k_i. Then

$$X(s) = \frac{B(s) + Q(s)}{P(s)}. \tag{10.38}$$

The justification of this procedure can be based on the following theorem.

Theorem 5. Let $b(t)$ be continuous for $t \geq 0$ and be of exponential order. Then the solution $x(t)$ of the problem (10.34), (10.35) is of exponential order, as are the first n derivatives of the solution.

Proof. We know from the discussion of Section 10.2 that the solutions of the associated homogeneous equation, along with their derivatives, are of exponential order. The solution of the problem (10.34), (10.35) can be expressed in terms of these functions by the use of the method of variation of parameters. From this expression it is easy to see that $x(t)$ has the indicated properties. The details are left to the exercises.

When $b(t)$ is of exponential order, so are the functions $x(t), x'(t), \ldots, x^{(n)}(t)$. Then these functions possess Laplace transforms, and the transforms of the derivatives can be expressed in terms of $\mathscr{L}[x(t)]$ by the use of property (F). In this case, the derivation of the formula (10.38) is valid. In particular, the procedure followed in the example (10.28), (10.29) is valid.

Let us next consider the linear system with constant coefficients

$$\frac{dx_i}{dt} = \sum_{j=1}^{n} a_{ij}x_j + b_i(t), \qquad t \geq 0, \qquad i = 1, 2, \ldots, n, \qquad (10.39)$$

$$x_i(0) = k_i, \qquad i = 1, 2, \ldots, n. \qquad (10.40)$$

Suppose that the components $x_i(t)$ of the solution possess transforms $X_i(s)$, and that the functions $b_i(t)$ possess transforms $B_i(s)$. If we formally transform the equations (10.39), we arrive at the system of algebraic equations

$$sX_i(s) - k_i = \sum_{j=1}^{n} a_{ij}X_j(s) + B_i(s), \qquad i = 1\ 2, \ldots, n \qquad (10.41)$$

for the functions $X_i(s)$. Justification of this procedure can be based on the following theorem, which is the analogue of Theorem 5.

Theorem 6. Let each of the functions $b_i(t)$ be continuous for $t \geq 0$ and be of exponential order. Then the components $x_i(t)$ of the solution of problem (39), (40) are of exponential order, as are their first derivatives.

When the functions $b_i(t)$ are of exponential order, the functions $x_i(t)$ and $x_i'(t)$ therefore possess Laplace transforms, and

$$\mathscr{L}[x_i'(t)] = \mathscr{L}[x_i(t)] - x_i(0).$$

In this case, the derivation of the system (10.41) is valid.

As an example, let us consider the problem

$$(D + 3)x + 5y = 2 \qquad (10.42)$$

$$-x + (D - 1)y = 1,$$

$$x(0) = 1, \qquad y(0) = 0. \qquad (10.43)$$

We note that the hypotheses of Theorem 6 are satisfied. If $X(s)$ and $Y(s)$ denote the transforms of $x(t)$ and $y(t)$, respectively, we have from the system (10.42) that

$$sX(s) - 1 + 3X(s) + 5Y(s) = \frac{2}{s}$$

$$\qquad (10.44)$$

$$-X(s) + sY(s) - Y(s) = \frac{1}{s}.$$

Upon regrouping terms, we have

$$(s + 3)X(s) + 5Y(s) = \frac{2}{s} + 1$$

$$-X(s) + (s - 1)Y(s) = \frac{1}{s}.$$

(10.45)

Solving for $X(s)$ and $Y(s)$, and using partial fractions, we obtain the formulas

$$X(s) = -\frac{7}{2}\frac{1}{s} + \frac{1}{2}\frac{9(s + 1) + 7}{(s + 1)^2 + 1}$$

(10.46)

$$Y(s) = \frac{5}{2}\frac{1}{s} - \frac{1}{2}\frac{5(s + 1) + 1}{(s + 1)^2 + 1}.$$

Taking inverse transforms, we find that

$$x(t) = -\tfrac{7}{2} + \tfrac{9}{2}e^{-t}\cos t + \tfrac{7}{2}e^{-t}\sin t$$

(10.47)

$$y(t) = \tfrac{5}{2} - \tfrac{5}{2}e^{-t}\cos t - \tfrac{1}{2}e^{-t}\sin t.$$

As a check, we note that $x(0) = 1$ and $y(0) = 0$.

As a final example, let us consider the problem

$$D^2x + y = -2$$

(10.48)

$$x + D^2y = 0,$$

$$x(0) = y(0) = x'(0) = y'(0) = 0.$$

(10.49)

The system (10.48) is not a first-order system, so Theorem 6 does not apply. However, the system (10.48) can be rewritten as a first-order system for the quantities x, Dx, y, and Dy. Setting

$$x = u_1, \qquad Dx = u_2, \qquad y = u_3, \qquad Dy = u_4,$$

(10.50)

we obtain the first-order system

$$Du_1 = u_2, \qquad Du_2 = -u_3 - 2, \qquad Du_3 = u_4, \qquad Du_4 = -u_1.$$

(10.51)

The initial conditions (from (10.49)) are

$$u_1(0) = u_2(0) = u_3(0) = u_4(0) = 0.$$

(10.52)

The system (10.51) satisfies the hypotheses of Theorem 6. It possesses a unique solution which satisfies the initial conditions (10.52). The components, $u_i(t)$, of this solution, and their first derivatives, are of exponential order. Consequently, the problem (10.48), (10.49) possesses a unique solution $(x(t), y(t))$, and the quantities $x(t)$, $y(t)$, $Dx(t)$, $Dy(t)$, $D^2x(t)$, $D^2y(t)$ are of exponential order. Therefore we can apply the method of Laplace transforms directly to the problem (10.48), (10.49). Transformation of the equations

(10.48) yields the relations

$$s^2 X(s) + Y(s) = -\frac{2}{s}, \qquad X(s) + s^2 Y(s) = 0. \tag{10.53}$$

From these we find that

$$X(s) = \frac{-2s}{s^4 - 1} = \frac{s}{s^2 + 1} - \frac{s}{s^2 - 1} \tag{10.54}$$

$$Y(s) = \frac{-1}{s^2 + 1} + \frac{1}{s^2 - 1}.$$

Consequently the solution of the problem is

$$x(t) = \cos t - \cosh t, \qquad y(t) = -\sin t + \sinh t. \tag{10.55}$$

10.5 EXERCISES

1. Find the solution of the initial value problem by the use of Laplace transforms.

(a) $x'' + 3x' + 2x = 6 e^t$, $x(0) = 2$, $x'(0) = -1$
(b) $x'' + 2x' + x = 4 \sin t$, $x(0) = -2$, $x'(0) = 1$
(c) $x'' + 4x = 8 \sin t$, $x(0) = 0$, $x'(0) = 2$
(d) $x'' + 4x' + 5x = 8t$, $x(0) = -2$, $x'(0) = 1$
(e) $x''' + 2x'' + x' + 2x = 2$, $x(0) = 3$, $x'(0) = -2$, $x''(0) = 3$

2. Consider the initial value problem

$$x'' + x = f(t), \qquad t \geq 0, \qquad x(0) = x'(0) = 0,$$

where

$$f(t) = \begin{cases} t, & 0 \leq t \leq 1 \\ 1, & t > 1. \end{cases}$$

(a) Find the solution by means of Laplace transform.
(b) Find the solution by using another method.

3. Find, by means of Laplace transforms, the solution of the problem

$$x'' - x = f(t), \qquad t \geq 0, \qquad x(0) = 1, \qquad x'(0) = 0,$$

$$f(t) = \begin{cases} 0, & 0 \leq t \leq 1 \\ (t - 1), & t > 1. \end{cases}$$

4. By using Laplace transforms, express the solution of the problem

$$x'' + x = f(t), \qquad x(0) = 0, \qquad x'(0) = 1$$

as an integral.

5. If $x(t)$ satisfies the given integral equation, determine the Laplace transform of $x(t)$ and then determine $x(t)$.

(a) $x(t) = 2 + \int_0^t e^{t-u} x(u) \, du$ (b) $x(t) = 1 + t + \int_0^t (t - u) \, x(u) \, du.$

6. Find the solution of the initial value problem by the use of Laplace transforms.

(a) $(D + 2)x_1 - 2x_2 = 0$
$\quad -x_1 + (D + 1)x_2 = 2e^t$ $x_1(0) = 0,$ $x_2(0) = 1$

(b) $(D + 1)x_1 + x_2 = 0$
$\quad -5x_1 + (D - 1)x_2 = -4$ $x_1(0) = 1,$ $x_2(0) = 3$

(c) $(D + 2)x_1 + x_2 = e^{-t}$
$\quad -2x_1 + Dx_2 = -e^{-t}$ $x_1(0) = 2,$ $x_2(0) = 0$

(d) $4Dx_1 - (D^2 - D)x_2 = 0$
$\quad -(D + 3)x_1 + x_2 = 0$ $x_1(0) = 0,$ $x_2(0) = 2,$ $x_2(0) = -1$

(e) $-4x_1 + (D^2 + D + 4)x_2 = 2$
$\quad (D + 1)x_1 - x_2 = 2$ $x_1(0) = 2,$ $x_2(0) = 4,$ $x_2'(0) = 2$

7. (a) Consider the differential equation

$$\frac{d^2x}{dt^2} + a\frac{dx}{dt} + bx = h(t),$$

where a and b are constants, $h(t)$ is continuous for $t \geq 0$, and $h(t)$ is of exponential order. Show that every solution of the equation, and the first two derivatives of every solution, are of exponential order. Suggestion: use the method of variation of parameters, and the results of Theorem 2.
(b) Generalize the result of part (a) to the nth-order equation $P(D)x = h(t)$.

8. Consider the system with constant coefficients,

$$(D + a)x + by = h_1(t), \qquad cx + (D + d)y = h_2(t),$$

where $h_1(t)$ and $h_2(t)$ are continuous for $t \geq 0$ and are of exponential order. Show that the components of every solution, along with their first derivatives, are of exponential order. (See Exercise 10, Section 9.1).

A Table of Transforms

	$f(t)$	$F(s)$			$f(t)$	$F(s)$
1.	1	$\dfrac{1}{s}$	8.		$\cosh at$	$\dfrac{s}{s^2 - a^2}$
2.	t^n	$\dfrac{n!}{s^{n+1}}$	9.		$t \sin at$	$\dfrac{2as}{(s^2 + a^2)^2}$
3.	e^{at}	$\dfrac{1}{s - a}$	10.		$t \cos at$	$\dfrac{s^2 - a^2}{(s^2 + a^2)^2}$
4.	$t^n e^{at}$	$\dfrac{n!}{(s - a)^{n+1}}$	11.		$t \sinh at$	$\dfrac{2as}{(s^2 - a^2)^2}$
5	$\sin at$	$\dfrac{a}{s^2 + a^2}$	12.		$t \cosh at$	$\dfrac{s^2 + a^2}{(s^2 - a^2)^2}$
6.	$\cos at$	$\dfrac{s}{s^2 + a^2}$	13.		$\sin at - at \cos at$	$\dfrac{2a^3}{(s^2 + a^2)^2}$
7.	$\sinh at$	$\dfrac{a}{s^2 - a^2}$	14.		$at \cosh at - \sinh at$	$\dfrac{2a^3}{(s^2 - a^2)^2}$

REFERENCES

1. Churchill, R. V., *Operational Mathematics*. 2nd ed. McGraw-Hill, New York, 1958.
2. Holl, D. L., Maple, C. G., and Vinograde, B., *Introduction to the Laplace Transform*. Appleton-Century-Crofts, New York, 1959.
3. Kaplan, W., *Operational Methods for Linear Systems*. Addison-Wesley, Reading, Mass., 1962.
4. Widder, D. V., *Advanced Calculus*, 2nd ed. Prentice-Hall, Englewood Cliffs, N.J., 1960.

CHAPTER **11**

PARTIAL DIFFERENTIAL EQUATIONS AND BOUNDARY-VALUE PROBLEMS

11.1 Introduction

Partial differential equations are classified as to order and linearity in much the same way as ordinary differential equations. The order of an equation is simply the order of the highest-order partial derivatives of the unknown function that appear in the equation. As illustrations, let us consider equations for an unknown function $u(x, y)$ of two independent variables. An equation of the form

$$Au_{xx} + Bu_{xy} + Cu_{yy} + Du_x + Eu_y + Fu = G, \qquad (11.1)$$

where $A, B, \ldots, G$, are given functions of x and y, is a second-order linear equation. (It is assumed that A, B, and C are not all identically zero.) The equation

$$\frac{\partial u}{\partial x} + xy^2 u \frac{\partial u}{\partial y} = \cos y$$

is a first-order nonlinear equation. We shall say that a function $u(x, y)$ is a *solution* of an nth-order partial differential equation if it possesses continuous partial derivatives of order n† and satisfies the equation in some region R of the xy plane.

Throughout this chapter, we shall be concerned mainly with second-order linear partial differential equations of the form (11.1). Such equations are further classified according to the following scheme: An equation of the form (11.1) is said to be of *elliptic type* in a region R if, in that region, $B^2 - 4AC < 0$. It is said to be of *hyperbolic type* if $B^2 - 4AC > 0$, and of *parabolic type* if

---

† It is shown in advanced calculus that such a function is continuous and possesses continuous partial derivatives of orders $1, 2, \ldots, n - 1$.

$B^2 - 4AC = 0$. Important examples of the three types of equations are the following:

(a) Laplace's equation (elliptic),

$$\frac{\partial^2 u}{\partial x^2} + \frac{\partial^2 u}{\partial y^2} = 0.$$

(b) The wave equation (hyperbolic),

$$c^2 \frac{\partial^2 u}{\partial x^2} - \frac{\partial^2 u}{\partial y^2} = 0,$$

where c is a positive constant.

(c) The heat equation (parabolic),

$$k \frac{\partial^2 u}{\partial x^2} - \frac{\partial u}{\partial y} = 0,$$

where k is a positive constant.

In these examples, the coefficients A, B, and C of the general form (11.1) are *constant* functions. The classification of such an equation does not depend on the region R under consideration. However, the equation

$$\frac{\partial^2 u}{\partial x^2} - x \frac{\partial^2 u}{\partial y^2} + u = 0,$$

whose coefficients are not all constant functions, is of hyperbolic type in the half-plane $x > 0$ and of elliptic type in the half-plane $x < 0$. This follows from the fact that $B^2 - 4AC = 4x$.

In the applications to be considered later in this chapter, we shall be concerned with finding a solution of a partial differential equation which also satisfies certain auxiliary conditions, called *boundary conditions*. For instance, we might require that a solution $u(x, y)$ take on prescribed values on a given curve in the xy plane. Or we might require that u and certain of its partial derivatives satisfy a given relation along a curve. A problem that consists of finding a solution of a partial differential equation which also satisfies one or more boundary conditions is called a *boundary-value problem*.

In the study of boundary-value problems, three basic questions are of paramount interest. First is the question of the *existence* of a solution. That is, does a given problem have a solution? The second question concerns the *uniqueness* of a solution. If a solution exists, is it the only possible solution? The third question is a little more difficult to phrase. Briefly, it is the question of whether the solution depends continuously on the prescribed values of the boundary conditions. To put it another way, we would like to know whether a small change in the prescribed values will produce only a small change in the value of the solution function at each point in the region under consideration. This question is important in applications, because the prescribed values are determined by physical measurement, and they are not exact.

A boundary-value problem possessing a unique solution that depends continuously on the prescribed values in the boundary conditions is said to be a *well-posed problem*. A detailed discussion of well-posed boundary-value problems is beyond the scope of this brief introduction. We do wish to point out, however, that in the case of equations of the form (11.1), the kind of boundary conditions that leads to a well-posed problem depends on the type of the equation. For instance, boundary conditions that yield a well-posed problem with a hyperbolic equation do not in general yield a well-posed problem with an equation of elliptic type. Appropriate boundary conditions for the three specific equations mentioned above will be presented in later sections.

For some partial differential equations, it is possible to find expressions that represent all solutions, that is, represent the general solution. Such expressions contain *arbitrary functions* instead of arbitrary constants, as in the case of ordinary differential equations. Let us consider as an example the equation

$$\frac{\partial^2 u}{\partial x \partial y} = 0, \tag{11.2}$$

in the region consisting of the entire xy plane. If $F(x)$ and $G(y)$ are any two functions that possess continuous second derivatives, the function

$$u = F(x) + G(y) \tag{11.3}$$

is a solution of equation (11.2). For we have

$$\frac{\partial u}{\partial y} = G'(y)$$

and

$$\frac{\partial^2 u}{\partial x \partial y} = \frac{\partial}{\partial x} G'(y) = 0.$$

Conversely, every solution of equation (11.2) is of the form (11.3). For if we write the equation as

$$\frac{\partial}{\partial x} \left(\frac{\partial u}{\partial y} \right) = 0,$$

we see that

$$\frac{\partial u}{\partial y} = g(y),$$

and hence that

$$u = G(y) + F(x),$$

where

$$G'(y) = g(y).$$

Even when it is possible to find the general solution of a partial differential equation, it is seldom feasible to select the arbitrary functions involved so that the boundary conditions are satisfied. We shall consider in this chapter only a few specific equations which, although quite special, are very important in mathematical physics. Rather than discuss general solutions of these equations, we shall consider various boundary-value problems for the equations that are motivated by physical considerations. The *method of separation of variables* will be used to obtain solutions of these problems. Although this method is very specialized, many of the problems for which it succeeds are important ones. This method yields a solution in the form of an infinite series. It is useful in establishing the *existence* of a solution. In some cases the solution, originally expressed as an infinite series, can be rewritten in a more compact and useful form. Also, in some cases, the series can be used to compute the values of the solution function.

11.1 EXERCISES

1. Verify that the given partial differential equation has the indicated function as a solution:

(a) $u_{xx} + u_{yy} = 0$, $u(x, y) = \cos ax \cosh ay$
(b) $u_{xx} - u_{yy} = 0$, $u(x, y) = \cos ax \sin ay$
(c) $u_{xx} - u_y = 0$, $u(x, y) = e^{-ay} \sin ax$
(d) $u_{xx} - u_y = 0$, $u(x, y) = y^{-1/2} \exp(-x^2/4y)$, $y > 0$

2. Consider the equation

$$Au_{xx} + Bu_{xy} + Cu_{yy} + Du_x + Eu_y + Fu = 0,$$

where $A, B, \ldots, F$ are constants. If $B^2 - 4AC \neq 0$, show that the equation can be put in the form

$$A'v_{xx} + B'v_{xy} + C'v_{yy} + F'v = 0,$$

where A', B', C', and F' are constants, by means of a change of dependent variable. Suggestion: let

$$u(x, y) = v(x, y) \exp(Mx + Ny),$$

where M and N are constants.

3. Determine the type (elliptic, hyperbolic, or parabolic) of the given equation:

(a) $u_{xy} - 2u_y + 3u = 0$
(b) $u_{xx} - 2u_{xy} + 2u_{yy} - 3u_x + u = 0$
(c) $u_{xx} - 2u_{xy} + u_{yy} - x^2u_y + y^2u_x = 0$
(d) $(y^2 + 1)u_{xx} + (x^2 + 1)u_{yy} - (x^2 + y^2)u = 0$

4. Show that the equation

$$u_{xx} - 2xu_{xy} + yu_{yy} - u = 0$$

is elliptic on one side of the parabola $y = x^2$ and hyperbolic on the other side.

5. Show that every solution of the equation $u_{xx} = 0$, in the entire xy plane, is of the form $u = xF(y) + G(y)$. Conversely, show that any function of this form, where F and G possess continuous second derivatives, is a solution of the equation.

6. Let $u_1(x, y)$ and $u_2(x, y)$ be solutions of the linear equation

$$A(x, y)u_{xx} + B(x, y)u_{xy} + \cdots + F(x, y)u = 0$$

in a region R. Show that the function $C_1 u_1 + C_2 u_2$, where C_1 and C_2 are constants, is also a solution.

7. Consider the equation

$$Au_{xx} + Bu_{xy} + Cu_{yy} = 0,$$

where A, B, and C are constants, with $A \neq 0$. If the equation is of hyperbolic type, show that it possesses solutions of the form

$$u = F(\lambda_1 x + y) + G(\lambda_2 x + y),$$

where F and G are any functions possessing continuous second derivatives, and where λ_1 and λ_2 are roots of the equation

$$A\lambda^2 + B\lambda + C = 0.$$

11.2   The Heat Equation

Consider a very thin slab, with thickness w, of a homogeneous isotropic solid material. Let the sides, S_1 and S_2, of the slab be kept at the temperatures T_1 and T_2, respectively. Consider a cylindrical portion of the slab, with area A (Figure 11.1). It is found by experiment that the rate at which heat is conducted across this portion of the slab is (approximately)

$$-KA \frac{T_2 - T_1}{w} \tag{11.4}$$

where K is a positive constant, called the thermal conductivity. Its value depends on the material of the slab. If $T_1 > T_2$, heat is transferred in the direction from S_1 to S_2, and the quantity (11.4) is positive. If $T_1 < T_2$, heat is conducted in the opposite direction, from S_2 to S_1, and the quantity (11.4) is negative.

Let us now consider a cylindrical bar† of length a and cross-sectional area A. Let x denote the distance along the bar, as measured from one end (Figure 11.2). We assume that the curved surface of the bar is insulated, and that the temperature is uniform over each cross section at any given time. We also assume that the temperatures in the bar are described by a function $u(x, t)$ of x and t, where t denotes time.

---

† Not necessarily with a circular cross section.

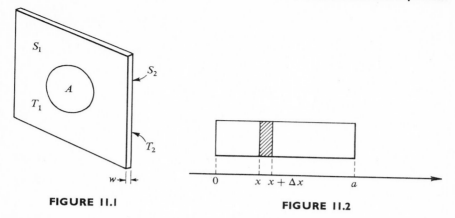

FIGURE 11.1   **FIGURE 11.2**

The rate at which heat is conducted across a thin section of the bar is approximately

$$-KA \frac{u(x + \Delta x, t) - u(x, t)}{\Delta x},$$ (11.5)

according to formula (11.4). On passing to the limit, as $\Delta x \to 0$, we are led to the expression

$$-KAu_x(x, t)$$ (11.6)

for the rate at which heat is conducted across a cross section of the bar. Consequently, the net rate at which heat is absorbed by a section of width Δx is

$$KA[u_x(x + \Delta x,) - u_x(x, t)] = KAu_{xx}(x_1, t) \, \Delta x,$$ (11.7)

where x_1 is between x and $x + \Delta x$. (Here we have applied the mean-value theorem to the function $u_x(x, t)$, considered as a function of x for fixed t.)

But the rate at which heat is absorbed by a thin section is also given by the formula

$$s\rho A u_t(x_2, t) \, \Delta x,$$ (11.8)

where the constant s is the specific heat of the material, ρ is the mass per unit volume, and x_2 is between x and $x + \Delta x$. By equating the quantities (11.7) and (11.8), dividing through by Δx, and then letting Δx approach zero, we obtain the equation

$$u_t(x, t) = ku_{xx}(x, t),$$ (11.9)

where the constant

$$k = \frac{K}{s\rho}$$ (11.10)

is called the *thermal diffusivity* of the material. Thus the temperature function $u(x, t)$ is a solution of the partial differential equation

$$u_t = ku_{xx},$$ (11.11)

which is called the one-dimensional *heat equation*.

In order to determine the temperature in the bar, we must solve the equation (11.11) subject to certain boundary conditions. If the temperatures at the ends of the bar are prescribed, we have boundary conditions of the form

$$u(0, t) = \phi(t), \qquad u(a, t) = \psi(t), \qquad t \geq 0 \qquad (11.12)$$

where ϕ and ψ are given functions. If, instead, the ends of the bar are insulated, then the rate at which heat is conducted across the ends is zero, and we have, by formula (11.6),

$$u_x(0, t) = 0, \qquad u_x(c, t) = 0, \qquad t \geq 0. \qquad (11.13)$$

In either case, we must also know the initial temperature distribution along the bar. This knowledge corresponds to a boundary condition of the form

$$u(x, 0) = f(x), \qquad 0 \leq x \leq a, \qquad (11.14)$$

where f is a given function.

In problems where the temperature depends on two rectangular space coordinates x and y, as well as on the time t, the temperature $u(x, y, t)$ is governed by the two-dimensional heat equation

$$u_t = k(u_{xx} + u_{yy}). \qquad (11.15)$$

In three dimensions, the heat equation has the form

$$u_t = k(u_{xx} + u_{yy} + u_{zz}) \qquad (11.16)$$

In two and three dimensions, the condition that a bounding surface S be insulated corresponds to the requirement that

$$\frac{\partial u}{\partial n} = 0 \qquad (11.17)$$

on S, where $\partial u / \partial n$ is the normal derivative of u, that is, the directional derivative of u in the direction normal to S.

11.2 EXERCISES

1. One end of a bar 2 ft long, whose sides are insulated, is kept at the temperature 0°C, while the other end is kep at 10°C. If the initial temperature distribution is linear along the bar, write down the boundary-value problem that governs the temperature in the bar.

2. (a) If the temperature function for a solid does not depend on the time t (steady state temperature), find the differential equation that the function must satisfy in one, two, and three dimensions.
   (b) Find the steady state temperature in a bar of length a if the ends are kept at temperatures A and B, respectively.

3. Suppose that a cylindrical bar, of length a, is immersed in a medium of constant and uniform temperature T_0, and assume that Newton's law of cooling applies at the ends of the bar. (Newton's law of cooling says that the rate, per unit area, at which heat is transferred across the boundary is proportional to the difference between the temperature of the boundary and that of the surrounding medium). Write down the boundary-value problem for the bar, assuming that the initial temperature distribution is $u(x, 0) = f(x)$.

4. (a) Let each of the functions $u_1(x, t)$, $u_2(x, t)$, ... be a solution of the equation $u_t = ku_{xx}$ in the region $0 < x < a$, $t > 0$, and let each of these N functions satisfy the homogeneous boundary conditions

$$\alpha u(0, t) + \beta u_x(0, t) = 0, \qquad \gamma u(a, t) + \delta u_x(a, t) = 0,$$

where α, β, γ, δ are constants. If C_1, C_2, ..., are constants and N is a fixed positive integer, show that the function

$$u(x, t) = \sum_{n=1}^{N} C_n u_n(x, t)$$

also satisfies the differential equation and boundary conditions.

(b) Let the constants C_n be such that the infinite series

$$\sum_{u=1}^{\infty} C_n u_n(x, t)$$

converges, and can be differentiated term by term once with respect to t and twice with respect to x. Show that the function $u(x, t)$, to which the series converges, satisfies the heat equation and boundary conditions of part (a).

5. (a) By introducing the new independent variables s and τ, where $s = x/a$, $\tau = (k/a^2)t$, show that the heat equation can be put in the form $u_\tau = u_{ss}$.

(b) Suppose that a bar, with initial uniform temperature zero, is immersed in medium of uniform constant temperature T_0, and that the center of the bar attains the temperature $T_0/2$ in time t_0. How long does it take the center of a bar of length $2a$, of the same material and with initial temperature zero, to reach the temperature $T_0/2$? (Assume that the ends of both bars are kept at temperature T_0).

11.3 The Method of Separation of Variables

Let us consider, as a special case of the problems described in the previous section, a bar of length a whose ends are kept at temperature zero, with a prescribed initial temperature distribution. This physical problem then corresponds to the boundary-value problem

$$u_t = ku_{xx}, \tag{11.18}$$

$$u(0, t) = 0, \qquad u(a, t) = 0 \qquad (11.19)$$

$$u(x, 0) = f(x). \qquad (11.20)$$

We must find a function $u(x, t)$ that is a solution of the heat equation (11.18) in the region $0 < x < a$, $t > 0$ (Figure 11.3), and that satisfies the conditions (11.19) and (11.20) on the boundaries of the region.

We begin our attack on the problem by attempting to find solutions of the heat equation that are of the special form

$$u = X(x)T(t), \qquad (11.21)$$

that is, solutions that are the product of a function of x and a function of t.

We impose the requirements

$$X(0) = 0, \qquad X(a) = 0, \qquad (11.22)$$

in order that these "product solutions" will also satisfy the boundary conditions (11.19).

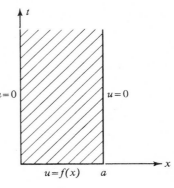

FIGURE 11.3

If the differential equation has a solution of the form (11.21), then we must have

$$XT' = kX''T,$$

or, upon multiplying through by $1/(kXT)$,

$$\frac{X''}{X} = -\frac{T'}{kT}. \qquad (11.23)$$

The left-hand member of this equation is independent of t, while the right is independent of x. Therefore both members must be equal to a constant, which we denote by $-\lambda$. Thus

$$\frac{X''}{X} = -\frac{T'}{kT} = -\lambda,$$

and so the functions $X(x)$ and $T(t)$ must be solutions of the ordinary differential equations

$$X'' + \lambda X = 0 \qquad (11.24)$$

$$T' + \lambda kT = 0. \qquad (11.25)$$

Conversely, if $X(x)$ and $T(t)$ are solutions of equations (11.24) and (11.25), respectively, for the same value of λ, then the product $u = X(x)T(t)$ is a solution of the heat equation. For then

$$u_t - ku_{xx} = XT' - kX''T = -\lambda kXT - k(-\lambda XT) = 0.$$

The differential equation (11.24) and the conditions (11.22) constitute an *eigenvalue problem*. The values of λ for which the problem possesses non-trivial solutions are called *eigenvalues*. These values are

$$\lambda_n = \left(\frac{n\pi}{a}\right)^2, \qquad n = 1, 2, 3, \dots . \tag{11.26}$$

The corresponding nontrivial solutions (eigenfunctions) are

$$X_n(x) = \sin \frac{n\pi x}{a}, \qquad n = 1, 2, 3, \dots , \tag{11.27}$$

and the corresponding functions of t are (from equation (11.25))

$$T_n(t) = \exp\left[-\left(\frac{n\pi}{a}\right)^2 kt\right]. \tag{11.28}$$

Each of the products

$$u_n(x, t) = \exp\left[-\left(\frac{n\pi}{a}\right)^2 kt\right] \sin \frac{n\pi x}{a}, \qquad n = 1, 2, 3, \dots , \tag{11.29}$$

is a solution of the equation (11.18) and satisfies the boundary conditions (11.19). If the constants C_n are such that the series

$$u(x, t) = \sum_{n=1}^{\infty} C_n u_n(x, t) = \sum_{n=1}^{\infty} C_n \exp\left[-\left(\frac{n\pi}{a}\right)^2 kt\right] \sin \frac{n\pi x}{a} \tag{11.30}$$

converges, and can be differentiated termwise a sufficient number of times with respect to x and t, then this series also represents a solution of the differential equation that satisfies the homogeneous boundary conditions (11.19).

However, the constants C_n must be chosen, if possible, in such a way that the series (11.30) satisfies the nonhomogeneous boundary condition (11.20). Thus we require that

$$u(x, 0) = \sum_{n=1}^{\infty} C_n \sin \frac{n\pi x}{a} = f(x), \qquad 0 \le x \le a. \tag{11.31}$$

But then C_n must be the nth coefficient in the Fourier sine series for $f(x)$, that is,

$$C_n = \frac{2}{a} \int_0^a f(x) \sin \frac{n\pi x}{a} \, dx. \tag{11.32}$$

Now let us suppose that $f(x)$ is continuous and piecewise smooth for $0 \le x \le a$, and that $f(0) = f(a) = 0$. Then the series (11.30), with coefficients (11.32), converges to $f(x)$ when $t = 0$, according to the theory of Chapter 8. It can be shown that the series (11.30) converges and represents a continuous function for $0 \le x \le a$, $t \ge 0$. It can also be shown that the series can be differentiated termwise any number of times with respect to x and t for

$0 < x < a$ and $t > 0$. Consequently, the series (11.30) gives a solution of our boundary-value problem. The proof that it is the only possible solution, and that the problem (11.18)–(11.20) is well-posed, is outlined in Exercise 10.

The problem we have discussed was quite special in that the temperatures at the ends of the bar were both kept at the constant value zero. Let us now consider the somewhat more general case where the ends of the bar are kept at constant temperatures A and B. The appropriate boundary-value problem is

$$u_t = k u_{xx}, \qquad 0 < x < a,\, t > 0$$

$$u(0, t) = A,\, u(a, t) = B, \qquad t \geq 0 \tag{11.33}$$

$$u(x, 0) = f(x), \qquad 0 \leq x \leq a.$$

We shall show that by means of a change of the dependent variable this problem can be reduced to one of the type previously considered. To do this, we first determine a linear function of x,

$$g(x) = C_1 x + C_2, \tag{11.34}$$

such that $g(0) = A$, and $g(a) = B$. These latter conditions require that the constants C_1 and C_2 be such that

$$g(0) = C_2 = A, \qquad g(a) = C_1 a + C_2 = B.$$

Consequently, the desired function is

$$g(x) = A + \frac{B - A}{a}. \tag{11.35}$$

Since $g(x)$ is linear,

$$g''(x) \equiv 0. \tag{11.36}$$

Now suppose that $u(x, t)$ is a solution of the boundary-value problem (11.33), and let $v(x, t)$ be defined by the equation

$$v(x, t) = u(x, t) - g(x). \tag{11.37}$$

Then it is easy to verify that the function $v(x, t)$ is a solution of the boundary-value problem

$$v_t = k v_{xx}, \qquad 0 < x < a, \qquad t > 0$$

$$v(0, t) = 0, \qquad v(a, t) = 0, \qquad t \geq 0 \tag{11.38}$$

$$v(x, 0) = f(x) - g(x), \qquad 0 \leq x \leq a.$$

This problem is of the type discussed in the first part of this section. Conversely, if $v(x, t)$ is a solution of the problem (11.38), then the function $u(x, t)$, where

$$u(x, t) = v(x, t) + g(x), \tag{11.39}$$

is a solution of the original problem.

11.3 EXERCISES

1. The ends of a cylindrical bar, at $x = 0$ and $x = a$, are kept at the temperature zero. Find an expression for the temperature $u(x, t)$ if the initial temperature distribution is

(a) $u(x, 0) = 3 \sin \dfrac{\pi x}{a} - 5 \sin \dfrac{4\pi x}{a}$

(b) $u(x, 0) = x^2 - ax$

(c) $u(x, 0) = \begin{cases} x, & 0 \le x \le \dfrac{a}{2} \\[2mm] a - x, & \dfrac{a}{2} < x \le a \end{cases}$

2. (a) Show that the function $v(x, t)$, which is defined by equation (11.37), is a solution of the boundary-value problem (11.38).

(b) If $v(x, t)$ is a solution of the problem (11.38), show that the function $u(x, t)$, which is defined by equation (11.39), is a solution of the problem (11.33).

3. Find the temperature $u(x, t)$ in a bar with ends at $x = 0$ and $x = 1$, if the ends are kept at the indicated constant temperatures and if the initial temperature distribution is as given:

(a) $u(0, t) = 1$, $u(1, t) = 0$, $u(x, 0) = 1 - x$
(b) $u(0, t) = 1$, $u(1, t) = 0$, $u(x, 0) = 1 - x^2$
(c) $u(0, t) = 0$, $u(1, t) = 2$, $u(x, 0) = 2x \cos 2\pi x$.

4. A bar, with ends at $x = 0$ and $x = a$, with insulated ends, has an initial temperature distribution $u(x, 0) = f(x)$.

(a) Write down the boundary-value problem that corresponds to the physical problem.

(b) Show that a solution of the problem is given (at least formally) by

$$u(x, t) = \tfrac{1}{2}C_0 + \sum_{n=1}^{\infty} C_n \exp\left[-\left(n\,\frac{\pi}{a}\right)^2 kt\right]\cos \frac{n\pi x}{a}$$

where

$$C_n = \frac{2}{a} \int_0^a f(x) \cos \frac{n\pi x}{a}\, dx.$$

(c) Find the temperature $u(x, t)$ in the special case when

$$u(x, 0) = 2 \cos \frac{3\pi x}{a}.$$

5. A bar, of length 1, has its end at $x = 0$ insulated and its end at $x = 1$ is

kept at temperature zero. Find an expression for the temperature $u(x, t)$, if

$$u(x, 0) = \begin{cases} 1, & 0 \le x \le \frac{1}{2} \\ 2(1 - x), & \frac{1}{2} < x \le 1. \end{cases}$$

6. A bar of length 1, which has a uniform temperature of 100°C, is immersed in a medium that has the constant uniform temperature of 0°C. Assuming that the sides of the bar are insulated, and that Newton's law of cooling applies at the ends of the bar, find an expression for the temperature $u(x, t)$ in the bar.

7. Consider the boundary-value problem

$$u_t = k u_{xx} + F(x, t), \qquad 0 < x < a, t > 0$$

$$u(0, t) = u(a, t) = 0, \qquad t \ge 0$$

$$u(x, 0) = 0, \qquad 0 \le x \le a,$$

where the nonhomogeneous term $F(x, t)$ can be expanded in a Fourier sine series in x for each fixed t; that is,

$$F(x, t) = \sum_{n=1}^{\infty} f_n(t) \sin \frac{n \pi x}{a}, \qquad 0 < x < a, \qquad t > 0.$$

Show that the problem possesses a formal solution of the form

$$u(x, t) = \sum_{n=1}^{\infty} g_n(t) \sin \frac{n \pi x}{a}$$

and give a formula for the functions $g_n(t)$.

8. By using the result of Problem 7, explain how the solution of the following problem can be found,

$$u_t = k u_{xx} + F(x, t), \qquad 0 < x < a, t > 0$$

$$u(0, t) = u(a, t) = 0, \qquad t \ge 0$$

$$u(x, 0) = f(x), \qquad 0 \le x \le a$$

9. Consider the general problem:

$$u_t = k u_{xx} + F(x, t), \qquad 0 < x < a, \qquad t > 0$$

$$u(0, t) = \phi(t), \qquad u(a, t) = \psi(t), \qquad t \ge 0$$

$$u(x, 0) = f(x), \qquad 0 \le x \le a,$$

where F, f, ϕ, ψ are prescribed. Determine a function $g(x, t)$, of the form

$$g(x, t) = A(t) + x B(t).$$

such that the change of variable

$$u(x, t) = v(x, t) + g(x, t)$$

leads to a boundary-value problem for $v(x, t)$ of the type described in Problem 8.

10. The purpose of this exercise is to show that the boundary-value problem (11.18)–(11.20) is well posed.

(a) Let $u(x, t)$ be continuous on the strip $0 \le x \le a$, $t \ge 0$, and be a solution of the heat equation for $0 < x < a$, $t > 0$. For an arbitrary, but fixed, positive number T, let D_T be the rectangle $0 \le x \le a, 0 \le t \le T$. Let C be the part of the boundary of D_T that falls along the lines $x = 0$, $x = a$, and $t = 0$. (The part of the boundary $t = T, 0 < x < a$, is excluded from C.) The first problem is to show that $u(x, t)$ attains its maximum, and minimum, values for (x, t) in D_T on C. Suppose that this is not the case, and that u attains its maximum value M at a point (x_0, t_0) not on C. If m is the maximum value of u on C, then $m < M$. Define the function $h(x, t)$ as

$$h(x, t) = u(x, t) + \frac{M - m}{2T}(t_0 - t).$$

On C,

$$h(x, t) \le m + \frac{M - m}{2} = \frac{M + m}{2} < M,$$

while

$$h(x_0, t_0) = M.$$

Hence $h(x, t)$ attains its maximum on D_T at a point (x_1, t_1) not on C. Then $h_t(x_1, t_1) \ge 0$ and $h_{xx}(x_1, t_1) \le 0$. Since

$$u_{xx} = h_{xx},$$

we have

$$u_{xx}(x_1, t_1) \le 0,$$

and since

$$u_t = h_t + \frac{M - m}{2T},$$

we have

$$u_t(x_1, t_1) > 0.$$

But this is impossible, since u satisfies the heat equation for $0 < x < a$, $t > 0$. Hence, in D_T, u attains its maximum on C. Since $-u$ also attains its maximum on C, u attains its minimum on C.

(b) Show that there exists at most one solution of the heat equation in the strip $0 < x < a$, $t > 0$, which takes on prescribed values on the boundary of the strip. Suggestion: if u_1 and u_2 are both solutions, then the function $w = u_1 - u_2$ satisfies the heat equation in the strip, and is equal to zero on the boundary. Use the result of part (a).

(c) Let u and v be solutions of the heat equation in the strip $0 < x < a$, $t > 0$, and be continuous for $0 \le x \le a$, $t \ge 0$. If $|u - v| < \varepsilon$ on the boundary of the strip, show that $|u - v| < \varepsilon$ inside the strip. (This result shows that the solution of the problem (11.18)–(11.20) is continuous with respect to the prescribed boundary values.) Suggestion: the function $w = u - v$ is a solution of the heat equation. Consider first a region of the type D_T, and use part (a) to show that $|u - v| < \varepsilon$ in D_T. Then use the fact that T is an arbitrary positive constant.

11.4 Steady State Heat Flow

When the temperature u in a solid is independent of time, it satisfies the equation

$$\Delta u \equiv u_{xx} + u_{yy} + u_{zz} = 0. \tag{11.40}$$

This equation is known as *Laplace's equation* in three dimensions. In case u depends only on two rectangular coordinates x and y, it satisfies Laplace's equation in two dimensions,

$$\Delta u \equiv u_{xx} + u_{yy} = 0. \tag{11.41}$$

As an example, let us attempt to find the steady state temperature $u(x, y)$ in the rectangular slab $0 \le x \le a, 0 \le y \le b, |z| \le h$, whose edge temperatures are prescribed as in Figure 11.4. (We assume that the faces of the slab are

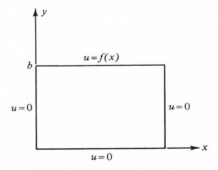

FIGURE 11.4

insulated, so that u depends only on x and y, and not on z). The boundary-value problem we must solve is

$$u_{xx} + u_{yy} = 0, \qquad 0 < x < a, \qquad 0 < y < b,$$
$$u(0, y) = 0, \qquad u(a, y) = 0, \qquad 0 \le y \le b \tag{11.42}$$
$$u(x, 0) = 0, \qquad u(x, b) = f(x), \qquad 0 \le x \le a.$$

If the differential equation has a product solution of the form $u = X(x) Y(y)$, then

$$X'' Y + X Y'' = 0,$$

or

$$\frac{X''}{X} = -\frac{Y''}{Y} = -\lambda, \tag{11.43}$$

where λ is a constant. Thus $X(x)$ and $Y(y)$ must satisfy the ordinary differential equations

$$X'' + \lambda X = 0, \qquad Y'' - \lambda Y = 0. \tag{11.44}$$

The homogeneous boundary conditions of the problem (11.42) require that

$$X(0) = X(a) = 0, \qquad Y(0) = 0. \tag{11.45}$$

If $X(x)$ is not to be identically zero, λ must have one of the values

$$\lambda_n = \left(\frac{n\pi}{a}\right)^2, \qquad n = 1, 2, 3, \dots . \tag{11.46}$$

The corresponding product solutions are found to be

$$u_n(x, y) = \sin\frac{n\pi x}{a} \sinh\frac{n\pi y}{a}, \qquad n = 1, 2, 3, \dots . \tag{11.47}$$

Superimposing, we arrive at the series

$$u(x, y) = \sum_{n=1}^{\infty} C_n \sin\frac{n\pi x}{a} \sinh\frac{n\pi y}{a}, \tag{11.48}$$

where the constants C_n are to be chosen, if possible, so that the nonhomogeneous boundary condition is satisfied. We require that

$$u(x, b) = \sum_{n=1}^{\infty} C_n \sinh\frac{n\pi b}{a} \sin\frac{n\pi x}{a} = f(x). \tag{11.49}$$

Therefore the constants C_n must be chosen according to the formula

$$C_n = \frac{2}{a \sinh(n\pi b/a)} \int_0^a f(x) \sin\frac{n\pi x}{a} \, dx. \tag{11.50}$$

If $f(x)$ is continuous and piecewise smooth for $0 \le x \le a$, with $f(0) = f(a) = 0$, it can be shown that the series (11.48), with coefficients (11.50), represents a solution of the boundary-value problem. The proof that this problem is well posed is outlined in Exercise 4.

11.4 EXERCISES

1. Consider a rectangular slab, as in Figure 11.4, but with prescribed edge temperatures $u(0, y) = 0$, $u(a, y) = 0$, $u(x, 0) = f(x)$, $u(x, b) = g(x)$. Show that the solution of the corresponding boundary-value problem can be obtained by superimposing the solutions of two other problems, each of which has three homogeneous boundary conditions.

2. Find the temperature $u(x, y)$ in a rectangular slab if the edges $x = 0$, $x = a$, $y = 0$ are insulated, and $u(x, b) = f(x)$.

3. Find a function $u(x, y)$ that is a solution of Laplace's equation in the semi-infinite strip $0 < x < a$, $y > 0$, and that satisfies the boundary conditions $u(0, y) = u(a, y) = 0$, $u(x, 0) = f(x)$, $\lim_{y \to \infty} u(x, y) = 0$.

4. The purpose of this exercise is to show that the boundary-value problem (11.42) is well posed.

(a) Let $u(x, y)$ be a solution of Laplace's equation on the rectangle $D : 0 < x < a$, $0 < y < b$, and be continuous on the rectangle $\bar{D} : 0 \le x \le a$, $0 \le y \le b$. Let C denote the boundary of $\bar{D}$. We first wish to show that u attains its maximum, and its minimum, on $\bar{D}$ at a point of C. Suppose that this is not the case. Then u attains its maximum value M at a point (x_0, y_0) in D. If m is the maximum value of u on C, then $m < M$. Define the function $h(x, y)$ as

$$h(x, y) = u(x, y) + \frac{M - m}{2(a^2 + b^2)} [(x - x_0)^2 + (y - y_0)^2].$$

Then $h(x_0, y_0) = M$, and on the boundary C, $h \le m + (M - m)/2 = (M + m)/2 < M$. Hence h attains its maximum on $\bar{D}$ at a point (x_1, y_1) in D. At the point (x_1, y_1) we must have $h_{xx} \le 0$ and $h_{yy} \le 0$. But

$$h_{xx} + h_{yy} = u_{xx} + u_{yy} + \frac{M - m}{a^2 + b^2} = \frac{M - m}{a^2 + b^2} > 0,$$

which is a contradiction. Hence u attains its maximum on $\bar{D}$ at a point of C. Since $-u$ also attains its maximum value on C, u attains its minimum value on C.

(b) Show that the problem (11.42) has at most one solution. Suggestion: Suppose that u_1 and u_2 are both solutions, and let $w = u_1 - u_2$. Then w satisfies Laplace's equation in D and $w = 0$ on C. Use the result of part (a).

(c) We wish to show that the solution of the problem (11.42) depends continuously on the boundary values. Let u and v be solutions of Laplace's equation on D and continuous on $\bar{D}$. If $|u - v| < \varepsilon$ on C, show that $|u - v| < \varepsilon$ on D.

11.5 The Vibrating String

Consider an elastic string that is stretched between the points $x = 0$ and $x = a$ along the x axis (Figure 11.5). In its equilibrium position, the string simply lies along the x axis between the two points. (The effect of gravity will be ignored in this discussion. Its effect is considered in Exercise 1). When set vibrating in a plane, its appearance at a particular time t is as in Figure 11.5.

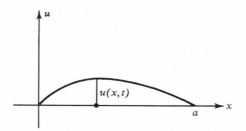

FIGURE 11.5

We shall assume that each point on the string moves along a line perpendicular to the x axis, and we therefore denote by $u(x, t)$ the displacement from the equilibrium position. In order to obtain the differential equation of motion of the string, we consider the forces exerted on a small portion of the string (Figure 11.6). We assume that the string is perfectly flexible, so that the force T, which is exerted at the point P by the part of the string to the left of P, acts in a direction tangential to the string.

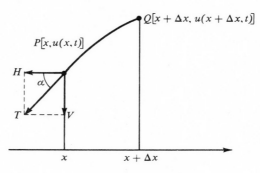

FIGURE 11.6

The horizontal component H and the vertical component V of the tangential force T are

$$H(x, t) = T(x, t) \cos \alpha = \frac{1}{\sqrt{1 + u_x{}^2}} T \qquad (11.51)$$

and

$$V(x, t) = T(x, t) \sin \alpha = \frac{u_x}{\sqrt{1 + u_x{}^2}} T. \qquad (11.52)$$

Let ρ denote the uniform mass per unit length of the string when it is in its equilibrium position. Then $\rho \, \Delta x$ is still the mass of that part of the string between P and Q in Figure 11.6. By considering the horizontal and vertical forces acting on the piece of string, we have

$$H(x + \Delta x, t) - H(x, t) = 0 \tag{11.53}$$

$$\rho \, \Delta x u_{tt}(x_1, t) = V(x + \Delta x, t) - V(x, t), \tag{11.54}$$

where x_1 is between x and $x + \Delta x$. (The second equation here corresponds to the assumption that Newton's second law of motion applies to a continuous medium). Application of the mean-value theorem yields the relations

$$H_x(x_2, t) \, \Delta x = 0 \tag{11.55}$$

$$\rho \, \Delta x u_{tt}(x_1, t) = V_x(x_3, t) \, \Delta x, \tag{11.56}$$

where x_2 and x_3 are between x and $x + \Delta x$. Dividing through by Δx in both equations, and then letting Δx approach zero, we arrive at the equations

$$H_x(x, t) = 0 \tag{11.57}$$

$$u_{tt}(x, t) = V_x(x, t). \tag{11.58}$$

From equations (11.57) and (11.51), we have

$$\frac{T}{\sqrt{1 + u_x{}^2}} = T_0, \tag{11.59}$$

where T_0 depends only on t, and not on x. From equation (11.52), we have

$$V = T_0 u_x. \tag{11.60}$$

Consequently, from equation (11.54), we have

$$u_{tt}(x, t) = \frac{T_0}{\rho} u_{xx}(x, t). \tag{11.61}$$

We shall now make the additional simplifying assumption that T_0 is a constant. (This approximation is justified, in particular, when T is nearly constant and uniform, and when the slope u_x is always small in magnitude, compared with unity). We may choose for T_0 the value of the tension T when the string is at rest in its equilibrium position.

The partial differential equation

$$u_{tt} = c^2 u_{xx}, \tag{11.62}$$

where

$$c^2 = \frac{T_0}{\rho}, \tag{11.63}$$

is called the one-dimensional *wave equation*. In order to describe the motion of the string, we must solve this equation, subject to various boundary conditions. Since the ends of the string are fixed, we have

$$u(0, t) = 0, \qquad u(a, t) = 0, \qquad t \geq 0. \tag{11.64}$$

We must also know the initial position and velocity of the string. This information corresponds to boundary conditions of the form

$$u(x, 0) = f(x), \qquad u_t(x, 0) = g(x), \qquad 0 \leq x \leq a, \qquad (11.65)$$

where f and g are given functions.

In passing, we mention that the equation

$$u_{tt} = c^2(u_{xx} + u_{yy}), \qquad u = u(x, y, t) \qquad (11.66)$$

is known as the two-dimensional wave equation, while in three dimensions, the wave equation has the form

$$u_{tt} = c^2(u_{xx} + u_{yy} + u_{zz}), \qquad u = u(x, y, z, t). \qquad (11.67)$$

11.5 EXERCISES

1. (a) When the effect of gravity on the vibrating string is taken into account, show that the governing differential equation of motion becomes $u_{tt} = c^2 u_{xx} - g$, where g is the gravitational constant.

   (b) Determine a quadratic function $h(x)$ such that $h(0) = h(a) = 0$, and $h''(x) \equiv g$. Then show that the change of variable $v(x, t) = u(x, t) + h(x)$ leads to a boundary-value problem of the type (11.62), (11.64), (11.65), for $v(x, t)$.

2. (a) Show that the wave equation $u_{tt} = c^2 u_{xx}$ can, by means of the change of independent variables $r = x - ct$, $s = x + ct$, be put in the form

$$u_{rs} = 0. \qquad (1)$$

   (b) Show that a solution of the equation (1) in the entire rs plane, is of the form

$$u = f(r) + g(s). \qquad (2)$$

   Conversely, if f and g possess continuous second derivatives (for all r and s, respectively) show that the function (2) is a solution of the equation (1).

3. By using the results of Problem 2, show that a function $u(x, t)$ is a solution of the wave equation in the entire xt plane if, and only if, it is of the form

$$u = f(x - ct) + g(x + ct),$$

   where f and g are functions that possess continuous second derivatives for all values of their arguments.

4. (a) Verify directly that each of the expressions

$$u = f(x - ct), \qquad u = g(x + ct),$$

   where the functions f and g possess continuous second derivatives for all values of their arguments, is a solution of the wave equation.

(b) Show that a solution of the form $u = f(x - ct)$ represents a wave which travels with speed c in the positive x direction. Show that a solution of the form $u = g(x + ct)$ represents a wave which travels with speed c in the negative x direction.

5. Consider the boundary-value problem

$$u_{tt} = c^2 u_{xx}, \qquad \text{all } x \text{ and } t,$$

$$u(x, 0) = f(x), \qquad u_t(x, 0) = g(x), \qquad \text{all } x,$$

where f possesses a continuous second derivative and g a continuous first derivative for all x. Using the result of Problem 3 (or Problem 4), derive the expression

$$u(x, t) = \frac{1}{2} \left[f(x - ct) + f(x + ct) \right] + \frac{1}{2c} \int_{x-ct}^{x+ct} g(s) \, ds$$

for the solution of the problem.

6. Consider a perfectly flexible elastic string that vibrates in a plane, but do not assume that each "particle" of the string moves along a line perpendicular to a coordinate axis. Let $\xi = x$, $\eta = 0$ denote the coordinates of a particle when the string is at rest in its equilibrium position. At time t, the coordinates of this same particle will be $\xi = x + u(x, t)$, $\eta = v(x, t)$, where $u(x, t)$ and $v(x, t)$ are the horizontal and vertical displacements, respectively (Figure 11.7).

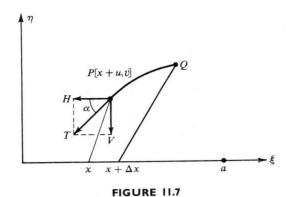

FIGURE 11.7

(a) By considering the forces acting on a small piece of the string, show that

$$\rho u_{tt} = \frac{\partial}{\partial x} \left\{ T \, \frac{1 + u_x}{[(1 + u_x)^2 + v_x^2]^{1/2}} \right\}, \qquad \rho v_{tt} = \frac{\partial}{\partial x} \left\{ T \, \frac{v_x}{[(1 + u_x)^2 + v_x^2]^{1/2}} \right\},$$

where ρ is the density and $T(x, t)$ is the tension in the string.

(b) According to Hooke's law,

$$T - T_0 = E\left(\frac{ds - dx}{dx}\right),$$

where E is a constant, T_0 is the uniform tension in the string when it is at rest, and $(ds - dx)/dx$ is the change in length per unit length. Show that

$$T - T_0 = E(\sqrt{(1 + u_x)^2 + v_x^2} - 1).$$

(c) Show that u and v satisfy the system of nonlinear partial differential equations

$$\rho u_{tt} = E u_{xx} + (T_0 - E)\frac{[u_{xx}v_x - (1 + u_x)v_{xx}]v_x}{[(1 + u_x)^2 + v_x^2]^{3/2}}$$

$$\rho v_{tt} = E v_{xx} + (T_0 - E)\frac{[(1 + u_x)v_{xx} - u_{xx}v_x](1 + u_x)}{[(1 + u_x)^2 + v_x^2]^{3/2}}.$$

11.6 The Solution of the Problem of the Vibrating String

In order to determine the motion of the vibrating string, we must solve the partial differential equation

$$u_{tt} = c^2 u_{xx}, \qquad 0 < x < a, \qquad t > 0, \tag{11.68}$$

subject to the boundary conditions

$$u(0, t) = 0, \qquad u(a, t) = 0, \qquad t \geq 0, \tag{11.69}$$

$$u(x, 0) = f(x), \qquad u_t(x, 0) = g(x), \qquad 0 \leq x \leq a. \tag{11.70}$$

Using the method of separation of variables, we seek solutions of equation (11.68) which are of the form $u = X(x)T(t)$. We find that

$$XT'' = c^2 X''T,$$

or

$$\frac{X''}{X} = \frac{T''}{c^2 T} = -\lambda,$$

where λ is a constant. Then $X(x)$ and $T(t)$ must satisfy the equations

$$X'' + \lambda X = 0 \tag{11.71}$$

and

$$T'' + \lambda c^2 T = 0, \tag{11.72}$$

respectively. We shall also require that

$$X(0) = 0, \qquad X(a) = 0, \tag{11.73}$$

in order that the product solutions satisfy the homogeneous boundary conditions (11.69).

By reasoning that should now be familiar to the reader, we find the values

$$\lambda_n = \left(\frac{n\pi}{a}\right)^2, \qquad n = 1, 2, 3, \ldots, \tag{11.74}$$

for λ, and the corresponding product solutions

$$X_n T_n = \left(A_n \cos \frac{n\pi ct}{a} + B_n \sin \frac{n\pi ct}{a}\right) \sin \frac{n\pi x}{a}, \tag{11.75}$$

where A_n and B_n are constants that as yet are arbitrary. Superimposing, we obtain the formal series solution

$$u(x, t) = \sum_{n=1}^{\infty} \left(A_n \cos \frac{n\pi ct}{a} + B_n \sin \frac{n\pi ct}{a}\right) \sin \frac{n\pi x}{a} \tag{11.76}$$

which satisfies the homogeneous boundary conditions (11.69). We now attempt to choose the constants A_n and B_n in such a way that the non-homogeneous boundary conditions (11.70) are satisfied. These boundary conditions yield the requirements

$$u(x, 0) = \sum_{n=1}^{\infty} A_n \sin \frac{n\pi x}{a} = f(x) \tag{11.77}$$

and

$$u_t(x, 0) = \sum_{n=1}^{\infty} \frac{n\pi c}{a} B_n \sin \frac{n\pi x}{a} = g(x). \tag{11.78}$$

We therefore choose the constants A_n and B_n according to the formulas

$$A_n = \frac{2}{a} \int_0^a f(x) \sin \frac{n\pi x}{a}\, dx, \qquad B_n = \frac{2}{a} \frac{a}{n\pi c} \int_0^a g(x) \sin \frac{n\pi x}{a}\, dx. \tag{11.79}$$

We shall now show that if $f(x)$ and $g(x)$ satisfy certain conditions, the series (11.76) with coefficients (11.79) converges to a function that is a solution of the boundary-value problem. Specifically, we shall require that $f''(x)$ and $g'(x)$ be continuous for $0 \le x \le a$, and that

$$f(0) = f(a) = 0, \qquad f''(0) = f''(a) = 0, \tag{11.80}$$

$$g(0) = g(a) = 0. \tag{11.81}$$

By the use of the trigonometric identities

$$2 \cos \alpha \sin \beta = \sin (\beta - \alpha) + \sin (\beta + \alpha)$$

$$2 \sin \alpha \sin \beta = \cos (\beta - \alpha) - \cos (\beta + \alpha),$$

we can write the series (11.76) in the form

$$u(x, t) = \sum_{n=1}^{\infty} \left\{ \frac{1}{2} A_n \left[\sin \frac{n\pi}{a}(x - ct) + \sin \frac{n\pi}{a}(x + ct) \right] \right. \tag{11.82}$$

$$\left. + \frac{1}{2} B_n \left[\cos \frac{n\pi}{a}(x - ct) - \cos \frac{n\pi}{a}(x + ct) \right] \right\}.$$

We now define the function $F(r)$, for all r, in the following way. We set $F(r) = f(r)$ for $0 \le r \le a$, and require that $F(r)$ be odd and periodic with period $2a$. The restrictions imposed earlier on f insure that F, F', and F'' will be continuous everywhere (Exercise 3). The function $F(r)$ is represented by its Fourier sine series everywhere. The coefficients , b_n, in this series are

$$b_n = \frac{2}{a} \int_0^a F(r) \sin \frac{n\pi r}{a} \, dr = \frac{2}{a} \int_0^a f(r) \sin \frac{n\pi r}{a} \, dr = A_n, \tag{11.83}$$

where A_n is as in formula (11.79). Hence the first group of terms in the series (11.82) converges, for all x and t, to the function

$$\tfrac{1}{2}[F(x - ct) + F(x + ct)]. \tag{11.84}$$

Next, we define the function $G(s)$, for all s, as follows. We set

$$G(s) = \int_0^s g(x) \, dx$$

for $0 \le s \le a$, and we require that $G(s)$ be even and periodic with period $2a$. The restrictions that we placed on $g(x)$ insure that G, G', and G'' will be continuous for all s (Exercise 3). The function $G(s)$ is represented by its Fourier cosine series for all s. The coefficients, a_n, in this series are

$$a_n = \frac{2}{a} \int_0^a G(s) \cos \frac{n\pi s}{a} \, ds = \frac{2}{a} \left[\frac{a}{n\pi} G(s) \sin \frac{n\pi s}{a} \right]_0^a - \frac{2}{a} \frac{a}{n\pi} \int_0^a g(s) \sin \frac{n\pi s}{a} \, ds. \tag{11.85}$$

Here we have used integration by parts, and the fact that $G'(s) = g(s)$. Since $G(0) = 0$, the integrated part vanishes, and we have

$$a_n = -cB_n. \tag{11.86}$$

Hence the second group of terms in the series (11.82) converges to the function

$$\frac{1}{2c} [G(x + ct) - G(x - ct)]. \tag{11.87}$$

(The constant terms in the two cosine series cancel out.)

Combining the results (11.84) and (11.87), we have

$$u(x, t) = \frac{1}{2} [F(x + ct) + F(x - ct)] + \frac{1}{2c} [G(x + ct) - G(x - ct)]. \tag{11.88}$$

This function possesses continuous second order partial derivatives for all x and t, since F'' and G'' are continuous everywhere. This function is also a solution of the wave equation (11.68), as can be verified directly. (See also Exercise 4, Section 5.) That $u(x, t)$ satisfies the boundary conditions (11.69) and (11.70) is contained in the derivation of the formula (11.88). (This can also be verified directly from formula (11.88). See Exercise 4.)

We have shown that a solution of the problems (11.68) to (11.70) exists.

For a discussion of the uniqueness of this solution, and its continuous dependence on the prescribed boundary data, see Exercises 11 and 12.

If f and g do not satisfy the conditions (11.80) and (11.81), then the functions $F''(r)$ and $G''(r)$ will have discontinuities at the points $r = m\pi/a$, $m = 0$, ± 1, ± 2, ... In this case, the second partial derivatives of the function (11.88) will be discontinuous along the lines $x + ct = m\pi/a$, $x - ct = m\pi/a$ in the xt plane. The boundary-value problem (11.68)–(11.70) then has no solution, strictly speaking. However, the function (11.88) is called a *generalized solution* of the problem. For an interpretation of such solutions, see the more advanced treatments in References 4 and 5 of this chapter.

11.6 EXERCISES

1. (a) Show that the derivative of an odd function is even and that the derivative of an even function is odd.
   (b) If $F(x)$ is an odd function that is continuous at $x = 0$, show that $F(0) = 0$.

2. Let $F(x)$ be an odd periodic function, with period $2a$. If $F(x)$ is continuous for all x, show that $F(ma) = 0$, $m = 0$, ± 1, ± 2, ...

3. Let $f(x)$ be defined and continuous for $0 \leq x \leq a$.
   (a) Let $F(x)$ be the odd periodic extension of $f(x)$, with period $2a$. Show that $F(x)$ is continuous for all x if, and only if, $f(0) = f(a) = 0$.
   (b) Let $G(x)$ be the even periodic extension of $f(x)$, with period $2a$. Show that $G(x)$ is continuous for all x.

4. Verify that the function (11.88) satisfies the boundary conditions (11.69) and (11.70).

5. If the initial displacement and velocity of the vibrating string are

$$u(x, 0) = \sin \frac{\pi x}{a}, \qquad u_t(x, 0) = 0, \qquad 0 \leq x \leq a,$$

write down the formula for the displacement $u(x, t)$.

6. Do as in Problem 5 for the case

$$u(x, 0) = \sin \frac{\pi x}{a}, \qquad u_t(x, 0) = \sin \frac{2\pi x}{a}, \qquad 0 \leq x \leq a.$$

7. Show that an elastic string vibrates periodically, and find the period. Describe the effects of changes in the tension and the density on the period of vibration.

8. Let $x = as$ and $t = b\tau$, where b is a constant. Determine b so that the equation $u_{tt} = c^2 u_{xx}$ assumes the form $u_{\tau\tau} = u_{ss}$.

9. Consider the boundary-value problem

$$u_{tt} = c^2 u_{xx} + F(x, t), \qquad 0 < x < a, \qquad t > 0,$$

$$u(0, t) = u(a, t) = 0, \qquad t \geq 0,$$

$$u(x, 0) = u_t(x, 0) = 0, \qquad 0 \leq x \leq a,$$

where

$$F(x, t) = \sum_{n=1}^{\infty} f_n(t) \sin \frac{n\pi x}{a}.$$

Show that this problem possesses a solution of the form

$$u(x, t) = \sum_{n=1}^{\infty} T_n(t) \sin \frac{n\pi x}{a}.$$

10. Give a discussion of the problem

$$u_{tt} = c^2 u_{xx} + F(x, t), \qquad 0 < x < a, \qquad t > 0,$$

$$u(0, t) = \phi(t), \qquad u(a, t) = \psi(t), \qquad t \geq 0,$$

$$u(x, 0) = f(x), \qquad u_t(x, 0) = g(x), \qquad 0 \leq x \leq a,$$

along the lines of Problem 9, Section 11.3.

11. This exercise deals with the uniqueness of the solution of the boundary-value problem (11.69)–(11.70). Suppose that $u_1(x, t)$ and $u_2(x, t)$ are continuous, along with their first- and second-order partial derivatives in the region $\bar{D}: 0 \leq x \leq a, t \geq 0$, and satisfy the wave equation $u_{tt} = c^2 u_{xx}$ in the region $D: 0 < x < a, t > 0$. If $u_1 = u_2$ on the boundary of D, and if $(u_1)_t = (u_2)_t$ on the line segment $0 \leq x \leq a, t = 0$, we wish to show that $u_1 = u_2$ in D. Let $w = u_1 - u_2$. Then $w = 0$ on the boundary of D, $w_t = w_x = w_{xt} = w_{xx} = 0$ on the segment $0 \leq x \leq a, t = 0$, and $w_t = w_{tt} = w_{xt} = 0$ on the rays $x = 0, a, t \geq 0$. Define the function $h(t)$ as

$$h(t) = \int_0^a [(w_t)^2 + c^2(w_x)^2] \, dx, \qquad t \geq 0.$$

Show that $h(0) = 0$ and $h'(t) = 0$, and hence that $h(t) = 0$ for $t \geq 0$. Deduce from this that $w_t = w_x = 0$ in D, and hence that $w = u_1 - u_2 = 0$ in D.

12. Deduce, from the formula (11.88), that the solution of the problem (11.68)–(11.70) depends continuously on the prescribed values $u(x, 0) = f(x), u_t(x, 0) = g(x)$ at $t = 0$.

11.7 The Laplacian in Other Coordinate Systems

Our aim in this section is to obtain expressions for the Laplacian Δu of a function u in some coordinate systems that are not rectangular. Specifically, we shall consider cylindrical and spherical coordinates.

Cylindrical coordinates r, θ, z, may be defined by means of the equations

$$x = r \cos \theta$$
$$y = r \sin \theta \tag{11.89}$$
$$z = z,$$

where $r > 0$, and $-\pi < \theta \leq \pi$. The coordinates r, θ, z have the simple geometrical interpretations shown in Figure 11.8. Let us consider a fixed

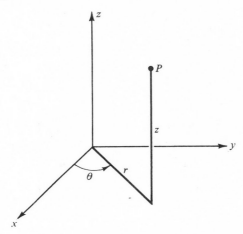

FIGURE 11.8

point P_0, with coordinates r_0, θ_0, z_0. Then each of the equations $r = r_0$, $\theta = \theta_0$, $z = z_0$ describes a surface that passes through the point P_0. These surfaces are, respectively, a cylinder of radius r_0, a half-plane which makes an angle θ_0 with the xz plane, and a horizontal plane which lies a distance $|z_0|$ from the xy plane.

In physical problems that involve a cylindrical surface (for example, the problem of finding the temperature in a cylindrical solid) it is natural to use cylindrical coordinates. For then the equation of the boundary has the simple form $r = $ constant. The relevant partial differential equation, however, becomes more complicated in appearance, as we shall see.

In order to determine the form assumed by Δu in cylindrical coordinates, we must express the partial derivatives of u with respect to x and y in terms of partial derivatives with respect to r and θ. By using the chain rule for partial derivatives we see that

$$u_x = u_r r_x + u_\theta \theta_x , \; u_y = u_r r_y = u_\theta \theta_y \tag{11.90}$$

The partials of r and θ with respect to x and y can be found from the relations (11.89) by the use of implicit differentiation. By differentiating through in these relations, first with respect to x and then with respect to y, we find that

$$1 = r_x \cos \theta - r\theta_x \sin \theta \qquad 0 = r_y \cos \theta - r\theta_y \sin \theta$$
$$0 = r_x \sin \theta + r\theta_x \cos \theta \qquad 1 = r_y \sin \theta + r\theta_y \cos \theta. \tag{11.91}$$

Upon solving the first pair of equations algebraically for r_x and θ_x, and the second pair for r_y and θ_y, we obtain the formulas

$$r_x = \cos \theta \qquad\qquad r_y = \sin \theta$$
$$\theta_x = -\frac{\sin \theta}{r} \qquad\qquad \theta_y = \frac{\cos \theta}{r} \tag{11.92}$$

Substituting these expressions into the formulas (11.86), we find that

$$u_x = u_r \cos \theta - u_\theta \frac{\sin \theta}{r}, \qquad u_y = u_r \sin \theta + u_\theta \frac{\cos \theta}{r} \tag{11.93}$$

For the second-order derivative u_{xx}, we have, by the chain rule again,

$$u_{xx} = \frac{\partial}{\partial r} \left(u_r \cos \theta - u_\theta \frac{\sin \theta}{r} \right) r_x + \frac{\partial}{\partial \theta} \left(u_r \cos \theta - u_\theta \frac{\sin \theta}{r} \right) \theta_x \tag{11.94}$$

$$= u_{rr} \cos^2\theta - 2u_{r\theta} \frac{\sin \theta \cos \theta}{r} + u_{\theta\theta} \frac{\sin^2\theta}{r^2} + u_r \frac{\sin^2\theta}{r^2} + 2u_\theta \frac{\sin \theta \cos \theta}{r^2}.$$

In similar fashion, we find that

$$u_{yy} = u_{rr} \sin^2\theta + 2u_{r\theta} \frac{\sin \theta \cos \theta}{r} + u_{\theta\theta} \frac{\cos^2\theta}{r^2} \tag{11.95}$$

$$+ u_r \frac{\cos^2\theta}{r} - 2u_\theta \frac{\sin \theta \cos \theta}{r^2}$$

From formulas (11.94) and (11.95), we have finally

$$\Delta u = u_{rr} + \frac{1}{r} u_r + \frac{1}{r^2} u_{\theta\theta} + u_{zz} \tag{11.96}$$

$$= \frac{1}{r} (ru_r)_r + \frac{1}{r^2} u_{\theta\theta} + u_{zz}.$$

Spherical coordinates ρ, ϕ, θ may be defined by means of the equations

$$x = \rho \sin \phi \cos \theta$$
$$y = \rho \sin \phi \sin \theta \tag{11.97}$$
$$z = \rho \cos \phi,$$

where $\rho > 0$, $0 \le \phi \le \pi$, and $-\pi < \theta < 2\pi$. The geometrical interpretations of the coordinates ρ, ϕ, θ are shown in Figure 11.9. Through a fixed point P_0, with coordinates ρ_0, ϕ_0, θ_0, there pass the three surfaces $\rho = \rho_0$, $\phi = \phi_0$, $\theta = \theta_0$. These surfaces are, respectively, a sphere of radius ρ_0, a half-cone of angle $2\phi_0$, and a half-plane. It is perhaps needless to say that spherical coordinates are convenient for problems which involve a spherical surface.

The expression for the Laplacian of a function in spherical coordinates can be derived in much the same manner as was done for cylindrical coordinates, although the algebra is a bit more complicated. We shall omit the details here, and shall state only the final result, which is

$$\Delta u = u_{\rho\rho} + \frac{2}{\rho} u_\rho + \frac{1}{\rho^2} u_{\phi\phi} + \frac{\cot \phi}{\rho^2} u_\phi + \frac{1}{\rho^2 \sin^2\phi} u_{\theta\theta} \tag{11.98}$$

$$= \frac{1}{\rho^2}(\rho^2 u_\rho)_\rho + \frac{1}{\rho^2 \sin \phi}(u_\rho \sin \phi) + \frac{1}{\rho^2 \sin^2\phi} u_{\theta\theta}.$$

The formulas (11.96) and (11.98) can be derived more efficiently by vector

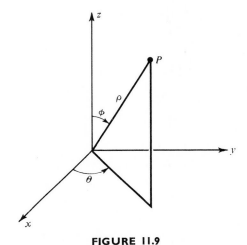

FIGURE 11.9

or tensor methods. Descriptions of such methods are, however, outside the scope of this book.

11.7 EXERCISES

1. Derive the formula (11.95) for u_{yy} in terms of cylindrical coordinates.

2. Derive the relations (11.97) for spherical coordinates from the geometry of Figure 11.9.

3. Derive an expression for u_x in spherical coordinates.

4. Let x' and y' be rectangular coordinates that are obtained from x and y by means of a rotation of axes. Show that

$$u_{x'x'} + u_{y'y'} = u_{xx} + u_{yy}.$$

5. Elliptical cylindrical coordinates u, v, w may be defined by means of the equations

$$x = \cosh u \cos v, \qquad y = \sinh u \sin v, \qquad z = w$$

where $u \geq 0$, $\quad -\pi < v < \pi$, $\quad$ and $-\infty < w < +\infty$.
(a) Show that the surface $u = u_0$, where u_0 is a constant, is an elliptical cylinder.
(b) Express the partial derivatives g_x and g_y of a function $g(x, y, z)$ in terms of the partials g_u and g_v.

11.8   A Problem in Cylindrical Coordinates

Consider a solid circular cylinder of radius c and height h, as in Figure 11.10. Let the top and bottom be insulated, and let the curved surface of the cylinder be kept at temperature zero. Also, let us assume that the temperature distribution within the cylinder at time $t = 0$ depends only on r, where $r = \sqrt{x^2 + y^2}$, and not on θ or z.

If the temperature u depends only on r and t, that is, $u = u(r, t)$, as it seems reasonable to assume, then the three-dimensional heat equation (11.16) has the form

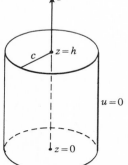

$$u_t = k\left(u_{rr} + \frac{1}{r} u_r\right), \qquad 0 < r < c, t > 0. \quad (11.99)$$

The appropriate boundary conditions for the cylindrical solid are

$$u(c, t) = 0, \qquad t \geq 0 \qquad (11.100)$$

and

$$u(r, 0) = f(r), \qquad 0 \leq r \leq c, \qquad (11.101)$$

where $f(r)$ represents the initial temperature distribution.

FIGURE II.I0

Seeking solutions of the differential equation (11.99) which are of the form

$$u = R(r)T(t),$$

we find easily that

$$RT' = k\left(R''T + \frac{1}{r} R'T\right),$$

or

$$\frac{T'}{kT} = \frac{R'' + (1/r)R'}{R} = -\lambda^2,$$

where λ is a constant. Thus R and T must satisfy the ordinary differential equations

$$rR'' + R' + \lambda^2 rR = 0 \tag{11.102}$$

$$T' + \lambda^2 kT = 0. \tag{11.103}$$

The general solution of equation (11.102) is given in terms of Bessel functions by the expression

$$R(r) = c_1 J_0(\lambda r) + c_2 Y_0(\lambda r). \tag{11.104}$$

We choose $c_2 = 0$ so that $R(r)$, and hence $u(r, t)$, will be finite at $r = 0$ (along the z axis). We also require that

$$R(c) = 0, \tag{11.105}$$

so that out product solutions will satisfy the homogeneous boundary condition (11.100). Then λ must satisfy the equation

$$J_0(\lambda c) = 0. \tag{11.106}$$

Let us denote the nth positive root of this equation by λ_n. For each such value of λ, we obtain a nontrivial product solution,

$$J_0(\lambda_n r)e^{-\lambda_n^2 kt}. \tag{11.107}$$

Superposition yields the formal series

$$u(r, t) = \sum_{n=1}^{\infty} A_n J_0(\lambda_n r)e^{-\lambda_n^2 kt}. \tag{11.108}$$

The nonhomogeneous boundary condition (11.101) requires that

$$u(r, 0) = \sum_{n=1}^{\infty} A_n J_0(\lambda_n r) = f(r). \tag{11.109}$$

The constants A_n should therefore be the coefficients in the Fourier-Bessel series† for $f(r)$, that is,

$$A_n = \frac{2}{c^2 [J_1(\lambda_n c)]^2} \int_0^c rJ_0(\lambda_n r)f(r)\,dr. \tag{11.110}$$

Suppose that $f(r)$ is continuous and piecewise smooth for $0 \leq r \leq c$, and that $f(c) = 0$. Then the series (11.108), with coefficients (11.110), converges to $f(r)$ when $t = 0$. It can be shown that the series (11.108) converges and represents a continuous function of r and t when $0 \leq r \leq c$ and $t \geq 0$. It can also be shown that the series (11.108) can be differentiated term by term any

† See Section 8.2.

number of times with respect to r and t when $0 \le r < c$ and $t > 0$, and that the series represents the (unique) solution of the heat equation in this region.

11.8 EXERCISES

1. Find an expression for the temperature $u(r, t)$ in the cylinder $0 \le r \le c$, $0 \le z \le h$, if all surfaces are insulated, and $u(r, 0) = f(r)$.

2. In the example of this section, suppose that the curved surface of the cylinder had been kept at the constant temperature A, where $A \ne 0$, and that $u(r, 0) = f(r)$, where $f(c) = A$. Find an expression for the temperature $u(r, t)$.

3. A solid cylinder $0 \le r \le c, 0 \le z \le h$ has its ends insulated, and is immersed in a medium of constant uniform temperature zero. Assuming that Newton's law of cooling applies on the curved surface, and that $u(r, 0) = f(r)$, find $u(r, t)$.

4. The top and bottom of the cylinder $0 \le r \le c$, and $0 \le z \le h$ are kept at temperature zero, and the prescribed temperature on the surface $r = c$ is a function of z only. Show that the steady-state temperature $u(r, z)$ in the cylinder is given by the formula

$$u(r, z) = \sum_{n=1}^{\infty} A_n I_0\left(\frac{n\pi r}{h}\right) \sin \frac{n\pi z}{h},$$

where

$$A_n = \frac{2}{h} \int_0^h f(z) \sin \frac{n\pi z}{h} \, dz,$$

I_0 is the modified Bessel function of the first kind, and $u(c, z) = f(z)$.

5. Find the steady-state temperature $u(r, z)$ in the cylinder $0 \le r \le c$, $0 \le z \le h$ if the bottom and curved surface of the cylinder are kept at temperature zero, and along the top $u(r, h) = f(r)$.

6. Consider the steady state temperature $u(r, \theta)$ in a circular plate of radius c, where the prescribed temperature on the rim is $u(c, \theta) = f(\theta)$, $-\pi < \theta \le \pi$. Show that

$$u(r, \theta) = \tfrac{1}{2}A_0 + \sum_{n=1}^{\infty} \left(\frac{r}{c}\right)^{n\pi/c} \left[A_n \cos \frac{n\pi\theta}{c} + B_n \sin \frac{n\pi\theta}{c}\right]$$

where A_n and B_n are the Fourier coefficients of $f(\theta)$. Note that $u(r, \theta)$ must be periodic in θ with period 2π.

7. Consider a thin elastic membrane that is stretched across a frame lying in the xy plane. Assuming that each "particle" of the membrane (or drumhead) vibrates along a line parallel to the z axis, it can be shown that the vertical displacement $u(x, y, t)$ satisfies the two-dimensional wave

equation $u_{tt} = c^2 \Delta u$, at least approximately. Consider a membrane stretched across the circular frame $r = a$, $z = 0$. If initially $y = f(r)$, and if the initial velocity u_t is zero, find a formula for u in terms of r and t.

8. Show, at least formally, that the solution to Problem 6 can be written in the form

$$u(r, \theta) = \frac{1}{2\pi} \int_{-\pi}^{\pi} f(\phi) \frac{c^2 - r^2}{c^2 - 2rc \cos(\theta - \phi) + r^2} \, d\phi.$$

This formula, for a function which satisfies Laplace's equation in the disk $r < c$ and which takes on the prescribed values $f(\theta)$ as $r \to c$, is known as the *Poisson integral formula*.

11.9 A Problem in Spherical Coordinates

Let us consider the problem of finding the steady state temperature in a sphere $0 \le \rho \le c$, if the temperature on the surface is a prescribed function of ϕ. If the temperature u depends only on ρ and ϕ, then the governing differential equation (Laplace's equation) has the form

$$u_{\rho\rho} + \frac{2}{\rho} u_\rho + \frac{1}{\rho^2} u_{\phi\phi} + \frac{\cot \phi}{\rho^2} u_\phi = 0, \tag{11.111}$$

where $u = u(\rho, \phi)$. At the boundary,

$$u(c, \phi) = f(\phi), \qquad 0 \le \phi \le \pi. \tag{11.112}$$

Seeking product solutions of equation (11.111), which are of the form $u = F(\rho) G(\phi)$, we find that

$$\frac{\rho^2 F'' + 2\rho F'}{\rho^2} = -\frac{G'' + \cot \phi G'}{G} = \lambda, \tag{11.113}$$

where λ is a constant. Thus $F(\rho)$ and $G(\phi)$ must satisfy the respective equations

$$\rho^2 F'' + 2\rho F' - \lambda F = 0 \tag{11.114}$$

$$G'' + \cot \phi G + \lambda G = 0. \tag{11.115}$$

The equation for G reduces to Legendre's equation under the change of variable $s = \cos \phi$. It has a solution that is finite at $\phi = 0$ and $\phi = \pi$ if, and only if, λ is one of the values

$$\lambda_n = n(n + 1), \qquad n = 0, 1, 2, \dots. \tag{11.116}$$

The corresponding solutions are

$$G_n(\phi) = P_n(\cos \phi), \tag{11.117}$$

where P_n is the Legendre polynomial of degree n. The equation (11.114) for $F(\rho)$ is of the Cauchy type. Its general solution for $\lambda = \lambda_n$ is

$$F_n(\rho) = C_1 \rho^n + C_2 \rho^{-(n+1)} \tag{11.118}$$

We must choose $c_2 = 0$ if $F_n(\rho)$ is to be finite at $\rho = 0$.

Forming the appropriate products, and superimposing, we arrive at the formal series

$$u(\rho, \phi) = \sum_{n=0}^{\infty} A_n \rho^n P_n(\cos \phi).\qquad(11.119)$$

The constants A_n are to be chosen so as to satisfy the boundary condition (11.112), that is, so that

$$u(c, \phi) = \sum_{n=0}^{\infty} A_n c^n P_n(\cos \phi) = f(\phi),\qquad 0 \le \phi \le \pi.\qquad(11.120)$$

Setting $s = \cos \phi$, this condition becomes

$$\sum_{n=0}^{\infty} A_n c^n P_n(s) = f(\cos^{-1} s),\qquad -1 \le s \le 1.\qquad(11.121)$$

According to the theory of Fourier-Legendre series, we should choose the coefficients A_n to be

$$A_n = \frac{2n+1}{2c^n} \int_{-1}^{1} f(\cos^{-1} s) P_n(s)\, ds\qquad(11.122)$$

$$= \frac{2n+1}{2c^n} \int_{0}^{\pi} f(\phi) P_n(\cos \phi) \sin \phi\, d\phi,\qquad n = 0, 1, 2, \dots.$$

11.9 EXERCISES

1. Find a function $u(\rho, \phi)$ that satisfies Laplace's equation in the infinite region $\rho > c$, takes on the prescribed values $u(c, \phi) = f(\phi)$ on the sphere $\rho = c$, and is finite as $\rho \to \infty$.

2. Find the steady-state temperature $u(\rho, \phi)$ in the spherical shell $a \le \rho \le b$, where $a > 0$, if $u(a, \phi) = f(\phi)$ and $u(b, \phi) = g(\phi)$, $0 \le \phi \le \pi$.

3. Find the steady-state temperature $u(\rho, \phi)$ in the hemisphere $0 \le \rho \le c$, $0 \le \phi \le \pi/2$ if the bottom of the hemisphere is kept at temperature zero and if on the curved surface, $u(c, \phi) = f(\phi)$, $0 \le \phi \le \pi/2$.

4. Suppose that at time $t = 0$, the temperature $u(\rho, t)$ in the solid sphere $0 \le \rho \le c$ is a function of ρ, that is, $u(\rho, 0) = f(\rho)$. If the surface of the sphere is kept at temperature zero, show that

$$u(\rho, t) = \frac{1}{\rho} \sum_{n=1}^{\infty} A_n \sin \frac{n\pi\rho}{c} e^{-(n\pi/c)^2 kt}$$

where

$$A_n = \frac{2}{c} \int_{0}^{c} \rho f(\rho) \sin \frac{n\pi\rho}{c}\, d\rho.$$

11.10   Double Fourier Series

Thus far, we have considered boundary-value problems that involve two independent variables. In applying the method of separation of variables to these problems, we were led to a formal series solution consisting of superimposed product solutions of a linear homogeneous partial differential equation. The coefficients in the series were the Fourier coefficients of a function of a single variable. In problems in which the number of independent variables is greater than two, the method of separation of variables leads, as we shall see, to the notion of a multiple Fourier series.

In order to give an illustration of such a series, let us consider a function of two variables, $f(x, y)$, which is defined on the rectangle $0 \leq x \leq a$, $0 \leq y \leq b$. Suppose that for each fixed y in $[0, b]$, $f(x, y)$ can be expanded in a Fourier sine series. Then

$$f(x, y) = \sum_{m=1}^{\infty} B_m(y) \sin \frac{m\pi x}{a}, \qquad (11.123)$$

where

$$B_m(y) = \frac{2}{a} \int_0^a f(x, y) \sin \frac{m\pi x}{a} \, dx, \qquad 0 \leq y \leq b. \qquad (11.124)$$

If each of the functions $B_m(y)$ can be expanded in a sine series, then

$$B_m(y) = \sum_{n=1}^{\infty} A_{mn} \sin \frac{n\pi y}{b}, \qquad (11.125)$$

where

$$A_{mn} = \frac{2}{b} \int_0^b B_m(y) \sin \frac{n\pi y}{b} \, dy \qquad (11.126)$$

$$= \frac{4}{ab} \int_0^a \int_0^b f(x, y) \sin \frac{m\pi x}{a} \sin \frac{n\pi y}{b} \, dx \, dy.$$

From formulas (11.123) and (11.125), we obtain the expansion

$$f(x, y) = \sum_{m=1}^{\infty} \left(\sum_{n=1}^{\infty} A_{mn} \sin \frac{n\pi y}{b} \right) \sin \frac{m\pi x}{a}. \qquad (11.127)$$

The series (11.127) is called a *doubly iterated series*. In it, the terms

$$A_{mn} \sin \frac{m\pi x}{a} \sin \frac{n\pi y}{b} \qquad (11.128)$$

are first summed, for each fixed m, with respect to n. Then the results are summed with respect to m. Also associated with the doubly infinite collection of terms (11.128) is the *double series*

$$\sum_{m,n=1}^{\infty} A_{mn} \sin \frac{m\pi x}{a} \sin \frac{n\pi y}{b}. \qquad (11.129)$$

To give meaning to such a series, we define the partial sums, $S_{ij}(x, y)$, according to the formula

$$S_{ij}(x, y) = \sum_{m,n=1}^{m=i,n=j} A_{mn} \sin \frac{m\pi x}{a} \sin \frac{n\pi y}{b} . \tag{11.130}$$

The series is said to converge to the sum $f(x, y)$ if to every positive number ε (and to each point (x, y) in the rectangle) there corresponds a pair of integers I and J such that

$$|S_{ij}(x, y) - f(x, y)| < \varepsilon$$

whenever $i > I$ and $j > J$. Under certain conditions, the double series (11.129) and the iterated series (11.127) have the same sum.† We shall not attempt a discussion about questions of convergence and rearrangement of terms for double series. For a rigorous treatment of these matters, see one of the standard works on advanced calculus.

We shall now consider a boundary-value problem that leads to a series of the form (11.129). Let $u(x, y, t)$ represent the time dependent temperature in a rectangular plate $0 \le x \le a$, $0 \le y \le b$, whose edges are kept at temperature zero, and whose initial temperature distribution is $u(x, y, 0) = f(x, y)$. The boundary-value problem for u is

$$\begin{aligned}
u_t &= k(u_{xx} + u_{yy}), & 0 &< x < a, & 0 &< y < b, & t &> 0, \\
u(0, y, t) &= u(a, y, t) = 0, & 0 &\le y \le b, & t &\ge 0, \\
u(x, 0, t) &= u(x, b, t) = 0, & 0 &\le x \le a, & t &\ge 0, \\
u(x, y, 0) &= f(x, y), & 0 &\le x \le a, & 0 &\le y \le b.
\end{aligned} \tag{11.131}$$

We seek product solutions of the differential equation that are of the form

$$u = X(x) Y(y) T(t). \tag{11.132}$$

In view of the homogeneous boundary conditions of the problem, we shall require that

$$X(0) = X(a) = 0, \qquad Y(0) = Y(b) = 0. \tag{11.133}$$

Substituting the expression (11.128) into the differential equation, we find that

$$XYT' = k(X''YT + XY''T),$$

or

$$\frac{X''}{X} = \frac{T'}{kT} - \frac{Y''}{Y} = -\lambda, \tag{11.134}$$

where λ is a constant. Because of the conditions (11.133), λ must have one of the values

$$\lambda_n = \left(\frac{m\pi}{a}\right)^2, \qquad m = 1, 2, 3, \dots . \tag{11.135}$$

---

† If the double series (11.129) converges absolutely, then both the series (11.127) and (11.129) converge, and they have the same sum.

The corresponding functions of x are

$$X_m(x) = \sin \frac{m\pi x}{a}, \qquad m = 1, 2, 3, \ldots . \tag{11.136}$$

From equation (11.134), we have

$$\frac{T'}{kT} + \lambda_m = \frac{Y''}{Y} = -\mu, \tag{11.137}$$

where μ is a constant. This constant must be one of the values

$$\mu_n = \left(\frac{n\pi}{b}\right)^2, \qquad n = 1, 2, 3, \ldots . \tag{11.138}$$

The corresponding functions of y are

$$Y_n(y) = \sin \frac{n\pi y}{b}, \qquad n = 1, 2, 3, \ldots . \tag{11.139}$$

Now from equation (11.137), we obtain the equation

$$T' + (\lambda_m + \mu_n)kT = 0, \tag{11.140}$$

whose solution is

$$T_{mn}(t) = \exp[-(\lambda_m + \mu_n)kt]. \tag{11.141}$$

We now form the product solutions

$$\exp[-(\lambda_m + \mu_n)kt] \sin \frac{m\pi x}{a} \sin \frac{n\pi y}{b}, \qquad m, n = 1, 2, 3, \ldots, \tag{11.142}$$

each of which satisfies the homogeneous boundary conditions of the problem. Superposition gives us the formal double series

$$u(x, y, t) = \sum_{m,n=1}^{\infty} A_{mn} \exp[-(\lambda_m + \mu_n)kt] \sin \frac{m\pi x}{a} \sin \frac{n\pi y}{b}. \tag{11.143}$$

The nonhomogeneous boundary condition of our problem requires that

$$u(x, y, 0) = \sum_{m,n=1}^{\infty} A_{mn} \sin \frac{m\pi x}{a} \sin \frac{n\pi y}{b} = f(x, y). \tag{11.144}$$

In view of our previous discussion of double Fourier series, we choose the constants A_{mn} to be

$$A_{mn} = \frac{4}{ab} \int_0^a \int_0^b f(x, y) \sin \frac{m\pi x}{a} \sin \frac{n\pi y}{b} \, dx \, dy. \tag{11.145}$$

The series (11.143) with coefficients (11.145), is only a formal solution of our problem. In order to establish that the series represents an actual solution, it is necessary to show that it converges to $f(x, y)$ when $t = 0$.

It is also necessary to show, among other things, that the series converges and can be differentiated term by term the appropriate number of times with respect to x, y, and t for $0 < x < a$, $0 < y < b$, and $t > 0$.

11.10 EXERCISES

1. Find the steady-state temperature $u(x, y, z)$ in the cube $0 \le x \le 1$, $0 \le y \le 1$, $0 \le z \le 1$, if $u(x, y, 1) = f(x, y)$ and if the other five faces are kept at temperature zero.

2. Let $u(r, \theta, t)$ represent the temperature in the semicircular plate $0 \le r \le c$, $0 \le \theta \le \pi$. If the edges of the plate are kept at temperature zero, and if $u(r, \theta, 0) = f(r, \theta)$, show that

$$u(r, \theta, t) = \sum_{m,n=1}^{\infty} A_{mn} J_m(\mu_{mn} r) \sin m\theta \exp(-k\mu_{mn}^2 t),$$

where μ_{mn} is the nth positive root of the equation $J_m(\mu c) = 0$, and

$$A_{mn} = \frac{4}{\pi c^2 [J_{m+1}(\mu_{mn} c)]^2} \int_0^c \int_0^{\pi} r f(r, \theta) J_m(\mu_{mn} r) \sin m\theta \, d\theta \, dr.$$

3. Find the temperature $u(r, z, t)$ in the cylinder $0 \le r \le c$, $0 \le z \le h$ if the entire boundary is insulated and if $u(r, z, 0) = f(r, z)$.

4. The ends of the cylinder $0 \le r \le c$, $0 \le z \le h$ are kept at temperature zero, and the temperature on the surface is a prescribed function $f(\theta, z)$ of θ and z. Show that the steady-state temperature $u(r, \theta, z)$ in the cylinder is given by

$$u(r, \theta, z) = \frac{1}{2} \sum_{m=1}^{\infty} A_{m0} \sin \frac{m\pi z}{h} I_0\left(\frac{m\pi r}{h}\right)$$

$$+ \sum_{m,n=1}^{\infty} [A_{mn} \cos n\theta + B_{mn} \sin n\theta] \sin \frac{m\pi z}{h} I_n\left(\frac{m\pi r}{h}\right),$$

where

$$A_{mn} = \frac{2}{h I_n(m\pi c/h)} \int_{-\pi}^{\pi} \int_0^h f(\theta, z) \cos n\theta \sin \frac{m\pi z}{h} \, d\theta \, dz,$$

and B_{mn} is given by a like formula, but with $\cos n\theta$ replaced by $\sin n\theta$.

5. Consider an elastic membrane which, when at rest, covers the rectangle $0 \le x \le a$, $0 \le y \le b$. The edges of the membrane are fastened to a rectangular frame. When set vibrating, the displacements $u(x, y, t)$ of the membrane satisfy, approximately, the two dimensional wave equation $u_{tt} = c^2 \Delta u$. If $u(x, y, 0) = 0$ and $u_t(x, y, 0) = g(x, y)$, express $u(x, y, t)$ as a double Fourier series.

6. Let $u(\rho, \phi, t)$ denote the temperature in the sphere $0 \le \rho \le c$, whose surface is kept at temperature zero, and whose initial temperature is $f(\rho, \phi)$. Show that

$$u(\rho, \phi, t) = \sum_{m=1, n=0}^{\infty} A_{mn} P_n(\cos \phi) \rho^{-1/2} J_{n+1/2}(\mu_{mn}\rho) e^{-\mu_{mn}^2 kt}$$

$$A_{mn} = \frac{2n+1}{c^2[J_{n+3/2}(\mu_{mn}c)]^2} \int_0^\pi \int_0^c \rho^{3/2} f(\rho, \phi) P_n(\cos \phi) J_{n+1/2}(\mu_{mn}\rho) \sin \phi \, d\rho \, d\phi,$$

μ_{mn} being the mth positive root of the equation $J_{n+1/2}(\mu c) = 0$.

7. Show that Laplace's equation in spherical coordinates possesses solutions of the forms

$$\rho^n \cos m\theta \, P_n{}^m(\cos \phi), \qquad \rho^n \sin m\theta \, P_n{}^m(\cos \phi),$$

where the functions $P_n{}^m(x)$ are the associated Legendre functions. (See the exercises of Section 6.7.)

REFERENCES

1. Churchill, R. V., *Fourier Series and Boundary Value Problems*, 2nd ed. McGraw-Hill, New York, 1963.
2. Davis, H. F., *Fourier Series and Orthogonal Functions*. Allyn and Bacon, Boston, 1963.
3. Greenspan, D., *Introduction to Partial Differential Equations*. McGraw-Hill, New York, 1961.
4. Sagan, H., *Boundary and Eigenvalue Problems in Mathematical Physics*. Wiley, New York, 1961.
5. Tolstov, G. P., *Fourier Series*. Prentice-Hall, Englewood Cliffs, New Jersey, 1962.

CHAPTER **12**

NONLINEAR
DIFFERENTIAL EQUATIONS

12.1 First-Order Equations

A first-order differential equation for an unknown function $y(x)$ is an equation of the form

$$F\left(x, y, \frac{dy}{dx}\right) = 0. \tag{12.1}$$

An example of such an equation is

$$x^2 + y - \left(\frac{dy}{dx}\right)^2 = 0. \tag{12.2}$$

A first-order equation of the form

$$\frac{dy}{dx} = f(x, y) \tag{12.3}$$

is said to be of *normal form*. It is with such first-order equations that we shall be concerned mainly. Although the equation (12.2) is not of normal form, we find, upon solving algebraically for dy/dx, the two possibilities

$$\frac{dy}{dx} = \sqrt{x^2 + y}, \quad \frac{dy}{dx} = -\sqrt{x^2 + y}. \tag{12.4}$$

Thus, instead of dealing with equation (12.2) as it stands, we can consider the equations (12.4), which are of normal form.

In the initial-value problem associated with a first-order equation, we seek a solution $y(x)$ which satisfies a condition of the form

$$y(x_0) = y_0, \tag{12.5}$$

where x_0 and y_0 are given numbers. The graph of the solution must pass through the point (x_0, y_0) in the xy plane. The graph of a solution of a differential equation is called an *integral curve*.

The function $f(x, y)$ in equation (12.3) is called the *direction field* associated with the differential equation. At each point where it is defined, the function $f(x, y)$ assigns a slope or direction. An integral curve of the equation (12.3) that passes through the point (x_1, y_1) must have the slope $f(x_1, y_1)$ at that point. A curve with an equation of the form $f(x, y) = c$, where c is a constant, is called an *isocline* of the equation (12.3). At each point on such a curve, the assigned slope has the value c.

As an illustration, let us consider the equation

$$\frac{dy}{dx} = x - y^2. \tag{12.6}$$

The isoclines of this equation are the parabolas $x - y^2 = c$. In Figure 12.1, we have drawn several isoclines of equation (12.6), corresponding to different values of c. The short line segments drawn through points on an isocline have the slope associated with that curve. Where an integral curve crosses an isocline, it must have the slope associated with the latter curve. By using the diagram, it is possible to construct, approximately, integral curves of the differential equation. One such curve is represented by the heavy curve in Figure 12.1.

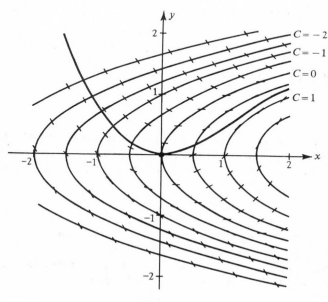

FIGURE 12.1

In some cases, it is possible to solve the differential equation, that is, to find explicit formulas for solutions. We shall now examine a class of first-order equations for which this can sometimes be accomplished.

Let the functions $f(x)$ and $g(y)$ be defined on intervals, and let both functions be continuous on their intervals of definition. Assume that $g(y) \neq 0$. A differential equation of the form

$$\frac{dy}{dx} = \frac{f(x)}{g(y)} \tag{12.7}$$

is said to be *separable*. Suppose that $y(x)$ is a solution on an interval I. Then we have

$$g[y(x)]y'(x) = f(x), \qquad x \text{ in } I.$$

Taking antiderivatives, we have

$$\int g[y(x)]y'(x)\, dx = \int f(x)\, dx$$

or

$$\int g(y)\, dy = \int f(x)\, dx,$$

for some choice of the antiderivatives. Let $F(x)$ and $G(y)$ be functions such that $F'(x) = f(x)$ and $G'(y) = g(y)$. Then the solution $y(x)$ satisfies a relation of the form

$$G(y) = F(x) + C, \tag{12.8}$$

where C is a constant. On the other hand, suppose that on an interval J a function $y(x)$ is differentiable and satisfies a relation of the form (12.8). Differentiating with respect to x, we find that

$$G'[y(x)]y'(x) = F'(x)$$

or

$$g[y(x)]y'(x) = f(x).$$

Hence the function $y(x)$ is a solution of the equation (12.7) on an interval where $y(x) \neq 0$. We have shown that every solution of the equation (12.7) satisfies a relation of the form (12.8), and that every differentiable function that satisfies a relation of the form (12.8) is a solution of the equation (12.7). In practice, it may not be possible to find a formula for y in terms of x from the relation (12.8).

As an example, let us consider the equation

$$\frac{dy}{dx} = y^2 \sin x. \tag{12.9}$$

It is evident that the identically zero function, $y = 0$, is a solution of this equation. In this example, $f(x) = \sin x$ and $g(y) = 1/y^2$. On each of the intervals $(-\infty, 0)$ and $(0, +\infty)$, $g(y)$ is continuous and never zero. Upon "separating the variables," we have

$$\int \frac{dy}{y^2} = \int \sin x \, dx,$$

or

$$-\frac{1}{y} = -\cos x + C.$$

In this case, we can solve for y in terms of x, and we find that

$$y = \frac{1}{\cos x - C}. \tag{12.10}$$

Suppose that we wish to find a solution that satisfies the initial condition $y(0) = \frac{1}{2}$. Setting $x = 0$ and $y = \frac{1}{2}$ in the relation (12.10), we see that we must have

$$\frac{1}{2} = \frac{1}{1 - C}$$

or $C = -1$. Hence a solution that satisfies the given condition is

$$y = \frac{1}{\cos x + 1}, \qquad |x| < \pi. \tag{12.11}$$

It should be noted that the solution exists only on the interval $|x| < \pi$, because at the points $x = \pm \pi$ the denominator, $\cos x + 1$, vanishes.

As a second example, let us consider the equation

$$\frac{dy}{dx} = 2 \frac{x}{y} e^{-y}. \tag{12.12}$$

Here the function $f(x) = x$ is continuous for all x and the function $g(y) = ye^y$ is continuous and different from zero on each of the intervals $(-\infty, 0)$ and $(0, +\infty)$. We have

$$\int ye^y \, dy = 2 \int x \, dx$$

or

$$ye^y - e^y = x^2 + C. \tag{12.13}$$

Here we cannot find y in terms of x explicitly. Nevertheless, any differentiable function $y(x)$ that satisfies the relation (12.13) for any value of C (on an interval where $y(x) \neq 0$) is a solution of equation (12.12). We say that the relation (12.13) defines the solutions of equation (12.12) implicitly.

Certain types of first-order equations that are not separable as they stand become separable under a change of variable. Some of these types are considered in the exercises.

12.1 EXERCISES

1. By using the method of isoclines, construct the graphs of solutions which satisfy the given initial conditions:

   (a) $y' = x^2 + y^2,$ $y(0) = 0,$ $y(0) = \frac{1}{2}$

   (b) $y' = x^2 - y^2,$ $y(0) = 0,$ $y(0) = -1$

   (c) $y' = \dfrac{1}{y - x},$ $y(0) = 1,$ $y(0) = -1$

2. Find all solutions of the given equation, if possible. Otherwise find a general relation that defines all solutions implicitly. When an initial condition is given, find a solution that satisfies that condition.

   (a) $y' = 2xe^{-y},$ $y(0) = 0$ (d) $y' = \dfrac{2x}{1 + y^2}$

   (b) $y' = 2xy^2,$ $y(1) = 0$ (e) $y' = \dfrac{\cos x}{y^2 + 1}$

   (c) $y' = 1 + y^2,$ $y(\pi) = 1$

3. An equation of the form $y' = f(y/x)$ is called *homogeneous*. (The adjective homogeneous has a different meaning here than when applied to a linear differential equation.) Show that the change of dependent variable $v = y/x$ leads to a separable equation for v.

4. Find all solutions of the given equation, if possible. If not, find a relation that defines the solutions implicitly. (See Problem 3.)

   (a) $y' = \dfrac{y}{x + y}$ (c) $y' = \dfrac{x^2 + y^2}{x^2}$

   (b) $y' = \dfrac{xy}{x^2 + y^2}$ (d) $y' = \dfrac{y}{x} - e^{-y/x}.$

5. (a) Show that the change of dependent variable $y = x^n v$ in the equation $y' = x^{n-1}F(y/x^n)$ leads to a separable equation for v.

   (b) Find the solutions of the equation

   $$y' = \frac{2y(x^2 - y)}{x^3}.$$

6. (a) Show that an equation of the form $y' = F(y + ax + b)$ becomes separable under the change of dependent variable $v = y + ax + b$.

   (b) Find all solutions of the equation $y' = (y + x - 2)^2$.

7. (a) Let the function $\psi(x, y)$ be defined and continuous, along with its first partial derivatives, in a region D of the xy plane. Show that through

each point in D there passes exactly one curve of the family of curves $\psi(x, y) = C$, where C is an arbitrary constant.

(b) Let $\psi(x, y)$ and D be as in part (a), and suppose that $\psi_y(x, y) \neq 0$ in D. Let (x_0, y_0) be a point of D and let $y = \phi(x)$ be a differentiable function that satisfies the relation $\psi(x, y) = \psi(x_0, y_0)$. Show that the function $\phi(x)$ is a solution of the differential equation

$$y' = \frac{-\psi_x(x, y)}{\psi_y(x, y)}.$$

8. Find a first-order equation whose solutions are defined, either implicitly or explicitly, by the given relation:

(a) $x^2 + y^2 = C$ (c) $(2 - C)y = Cx$

(b) $y^2 = x + C$ (d) $\sin y = Cx$

12.2 Exact Equations

Let the functions $M(x, y)$ and $N(x, y)$ be continuous in a region D of the xy plane, with $N(x, y)$ never zero in D. The first-order equation

$$M(x, y) + N(x, y) \frac{dy}{dx} = 0 \tag{12.14}$$

is said to be *exact* if the expression $M\,dx + N\,dy$ is an exact differential. By definition, the expression $M\,dx + N\,dy$ is an exact differential if, and only if, there exists a function $\phi(x, y)$, which is continuous along with its first partial derivatives, such that

$$\frac{\partial \phi(x, y)}{\partial x} = M(x, y) \quad \text{and} \quad \frac{\partial \phi(x, y)}{\partial y} = N(x, y). \tag{12.15}$$

If equation (12.14) is exact, it may be written as

$$\frac{\partial \phi}{\partial x} + \frac{\partial \phi}{\partial y} \frac{dy}{dx} = 0. \tag{12.16}$$

If a function $y(x)$ is a solution of this equation on an interval I, then

$$\frac{d}{dx} \phi[x, y(x)] = 0, \quad x \text{ in } I.$$

Thus every solution of the exact equation (12.16) satisfies a relation of the form

$$\phi(x, y) = C, \tag{12.17}$$

where C is a constant. On the other hand, if a differentiable function $y(x)$ satisfies a relation of the form (12.17) on an interval J, then this function is a solution of the equation (12.16), as can be verified by implicit differentiation.

We need, now, a criterion for determining whether or not an equation of the form (12.14) is exact. We also need a method of determining the function $\phi(x, y)$ in case it is exact.

Suppose that, in addition to being continuous, the functions $M(x, y)$ and $N(x, y)$ possess continuous first partial derivatives in a region D. If the expression $M\, dx + N\, dy$ is an exact differential, there exists a function $\phi(x, y)$, with continuous second partial derivatives, such that $M = \partial\phi/\partial x$ and $N = \partial\phi/\partial y$. Then

$$\frac{\partial M}{\partial y} = \frac{\partial^2 \phi}{\partial y \partial x}, \qquad \frac{\partial N}{\partial x} = \frac{\partial^2 \phi}{\partial x \partial y},$$

and because the mixed second partials of ϕ are equal,

$$\frac{\partial M}{\partial y} = \frac{\partial N}{\partial x}. \tag{12.18}$$

On the other hand, if $M(x, y)$ and $N(x, y)$ are continuous along with their first partial derivatives and satisfy the condition (12.18) in a *simply connected region*,† it can be shown that the expression $M\, dx + N\, dy$ is an exact differential. The region consisting of the entire xy plane is a simply connected region. We shall give a proof only for this special case. Let us define a function $\phi(x, y)$ by means of the relation

$$\phi(x, y) = \int_{x_0}^{x} M(\xi, y_0)\, d\xi + \int_{y_0}^{y} N(x, \eta)\, d\eta, \tag{12.19}$$

where x_0 and y_0 are any fixed numbers. Taking the derivative of ϕ with respect to x, we have

$$\frac{\partial \phi}{\partial x} = M(x, y_0) + \int_{y_0}^{y} \frac{\partial N(x, \eta)}{\partial x}\, d\eta.$$

Since the condition (12.18) is satisfied, $\partial N(x, \eta)/\partial x = \partial M(x, \eta)/\partial \eta$, and so we have

$$\frac{\partial \phi}{\partial x} = M(x, y_0) + \int_{y_0}^{y} \frac{\partial M(x, \eta)}{\partial \eta}\, d\eta$$

$$= M(x, y_0) + M(x, y) - M(x, y_0)$$

$$= M(x, y).$$

It is left as an exercise for the reader to show that $\partial\phi/\partial y = N(x, y)$.

Although equation (12.19) gives us a formula for determining the function

---

† A simply connected region is a region such that every simple closed curve in the region contains only points of the region inside it. The interior of a circle or a rectangle is a simply connected region, but the region bounded by two concentric circles is not simply connected.

$\phi(x, y)$ when the equation is exact, this function can often be found by a simpler procedure. To illustrate, let us consider the equation

$$6x + y^2 + (2xy + 1)\frac{dy}{dx} = 0. \tag{12.20}$$

Here

$$M(x, y) = 6x + y^2, \qquad N(x, y) = 2xy + 1,$$

and since

$$\frac{\partial M}{\partial y} = 2y = \frac{\partial N}{\partial x},$$

for all x and y, the differential $M\, dx + N\, dy$ is exact. Hence there exists a function $\phi(x, y)$ such that

$$\frac{\partial \phi}{\partial x} = 6x + y^2, \qquad \frac{\partial \phi}{\partial y} = 2xy + 1. \tag{12.21}$$

From the first of these relations we see, upon integrating with respect to x, that $\phi(x, y)$ must be of the form

$$\phi(x, y) = 3x^2 + xy^2 + f(y).$$

The function $f(y)$ must be chosen so that the second of the conditions (12.21) is satisfied. We must have

$$\frac{\partial \phi}{\partial y} = 2xy + f'(y) = 2xy + 1,$$

so $f(y)$ must be such that $f'(y) = 1$. One possible choice is $f(y) = y$, and for this choice, $\phi(x, y) = 3x^2 + xy^2 + y$.

We now observe that the curve $2xy + 1 = 0$ ($N(x, y) = 0$) separates the xy plane into three regions, as shown in Figure 12.2. In each of these regions, $N(x, y)$ is never zero, and the analysis at the beginning of this section applies. With (x, y) restricted to one of these regions we can assert that a differentiable function $y(x)$ is a solution of equation (12.20) if, and only if, it satisfies a relationship of the form $\phi(x, y) = C$, that is,

$$3x^2 + xy^2 + y = C, \tag{12.22}$$

where C is a constant.

If an equation of the form $M(x, y) + N(x, y)y' = 0$ is not exact, there remains the possibility that it can be made exact by multiplying through by a function $\mu(x, y)$. If such a function exists, it is called an *integrating factor* for the differential equation. If $\mu \neq 0$ at any point, then every solution of the new equation $\mu M + \mu N y' = 0$ is also a solution of the original equation, and vice versa.

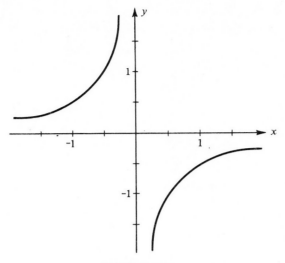

FIGURE 12.2

Let us consider, as an example, the equation

$$3xy^3 + 2y + 2x^2y^2\frac{dy}{dx} = 0, \qquad (12.23)$$

in a region where $xy \neq 0$. This equation is not exact as it stands, since

$$\frac{\partial M}{\partial y} = 9xy^2 + 2, \qquad \frac{\partial N}{\partial x} = 4xy^2.$$

If we multiply through in equation (12.23) by the function $\mu(x, y) = x/y$, however, it becomes

$$3x^2y^2 + 2x + 2x^3y\frac{dy}{dx} = 0,$$

or

$$\frac{d}{dx}(x^3y^2 + x^2) = 0.$$

Hence all solutions of the equation (12.23) are determined by the relation

$$x^3y^2 + x^2 = C.$$

The solutions themselves are given by the formula

$$y = \pm\left(\frac{C - x^2}{x^3}\right)^{1/2}. \qquad (12.24)$$

There is no general procedure for finding an integrating factor for a differential equation. In practice, the finding of one may be quite difficult.

12.2 EXERCISES

1. With $\phi(x, y)$ defined as in equation (12.19), verify that $\partial\phi/\partial y = N(x, y)$.

2. Determine whether or not the given equation is exact. If the equation is exact, find a relationship that defines the solutions implicitly.

   (a) $3y^2 + 2 + (6xy + 2y)y' = 0$
   (b) $e^y + (xe^y - 2)y' = 0$
   (c) $3xy^2 + 1 + (2x^2 - 1)yy' = 0$
   (d) $y \cos xy + 1 + (x \cos xy + 1)y' = 0$
   (e) $4x + y + (x + 2y)y' = 0$

3. Let $A(x)$ be any function such that $A'(x) = a(x)$. Show that an integrating factor for the linear equation $y' + a(x)y = b(x)$ is $e^{A(x)}$.

4. Determine whether or not the given equation has an integrating factor of the form $\mu(x, y) = x^m y^n$. If it does, find a relation that implicitly defines all solutions.

   (a) $3y(y - 1) + x(3y - 2)y' = 0$
   (b) $(y^4 - 6xy) + (2xy^3 + 3x^2)y' = 0$
   (c) $(2x + x^2 y + y^3) + (2y + x^3 + xy^2)y' = 0$

5. Show that the function $\mu(x, y)$ is an integrating factor for the equation $M + Ny' = 0$ if it satisfies the partial differential equation

$$N \frac{\partial\mu}{\partial x} - M \frac{\partial\mu}{\partial y} = \mu\left(\frac{\partial M}{\partial y} - \frac{\partial N}{\partial x}\right).$$

6. Show that $g(y)$ is an integrating factor for the separable equation $y' = f(x)/g(y)$.

7. Show that an integrating factor for the homogeneous equation $y' - f(y/x) = 0$ is

$$\mu(x, y) = \frac{1}{xf(y/x) - y}.$$

12.3 Some Special Types of Second-Order Equations

For certain types of second-order equations, the problem of finding the solutions can be reduced to the problem of finding the solutions of a first-order equation. One such class consists of equations of the form

$$\frac{d^2x}{dt^2} = f\left(t, \frac{dx}{dt}\right),\tag{12.25}$$

in which the dependent variable x is missing. We have denoted the independent variable by t here, since in many applications this variable represents time. If we set $v = dx/dt$, we arrive at the first-order equation

$$\frac{dv}{dt} = f(t, v)\tag{12.26}$$

for v. If $v(t)$ is a solution of this equation, then a solution of equation (12.25) can be found from the relation

$$\frac{dx}{dt} = v(t) \tag{12.27}$$

by integration.

As an illustration, let us consider the equation

$$\frac{d^2x}{dt^2} + 2t\left(\frac{dx}{dt}\right)^2 = 0. \tag{12.28}$$

Setting $v = dx/dt$, we obtain the separable equation

$$\frac{dv}{dt} + 2tv^2 = 0 \tag{12.29}$$

for v. This equation possesses the solution $v = 0$, as well as the family of solutions

$$v = \frac{1}{t^2 - C_1}, \tag{12.30}$$

where C_1 is an arbitrary constant. The solution $v = 0$ ($dx/dt = 0$) corresponds to the constant solutions $x = C$ of equation (12.28). If, in formula (12.30), C_1 is a negative constant, say $C_1 = -k^2$, we have

$$x = \int v \, dt = \frac{1}{k} \tan^{-1} \frac{x}{k} + C_2, \tag{12.31}$$

where C_2 is an arbitrary constant. If, in formula (12.30), C_1 is a positive constant, say $C_1 = k^2$, we have

$$x = \frac{1}{2k} \log \left| \frac{t + k}{t - k} \right| + C_2. \tag{12.32}$$

When $C_1 = 0$ in formula (12.30), we have

$$x = -\frac{1}{t} + C_2.$$

Let us next consider a second-order equation of the form

$$\frac{d^2x}{dt^2} = F\left(x, \frac{dx}{dt}\right), \tag{12.33}$$

in which the independent variable t is missing. Suppose that, on an interval I, a solution $x(t)$ of equation (12.33) is such that $dx/dt \neq 0$. Then either $dx/dt > 0$ or $dx/dt < 0$ on I. Then t can be regarded as a function of x, and the quantities dx/dt and d^2x/dt^2 can also be regarded as functions of x. Setting $dx/dt = v$ and

$$\frac{d^2x}{dt^2} = \frac{dv}{dt} = \frac{dv}{dx}\frac{dx}{dt} = v\frac{dv}{dx}, \tag{12.34}$$

we see that v, regarded as a function of x, satisfies the first-order equation

$$v \frac{dv}{dx} = F(x, v). \tag{12.35}$$

If $v(x)$ is a solution of this equation (on an interval where $v(x) \neq 0$), then $x(t)$ must satisfy the first-order separable equation

$$\frac{dx}{dt} = v(x). \tag{12.36}$$

Conversely, if $x(t)$ is a solution of equation (12.36) (on an interval where $dx/dt \neq 0$), it can be verified by a retracing of steps that $x(t)$ is also a solution of the original equation (12.33).

Let us now consider an application that happens to give rise to an equation of the type (12.33). Suppose that a projectile, of mass m, is fired directly upward from the surface of the earth with velocity v_0. Let us regard the surface of the earth as a sphere of radius R, and let us assume that the center of mass of the earth is located at the center of the sphere. Let $x(t)$ denote the distance of the projectile from the center of the earth at time t. Assuming that Newton's inverse-square law of gravitation holds, we must have

$$m \frac{d^2x}{dt^2} = -mg \frac{R^2}{x^2}, \tag{12.37}$$

where g is the acceleration due to gravity at the surface of the earth. As initial conditions, we have

$$x(0) = R, \qquad x'(0) = v_0. \tag{12.38}$$

Setting $dx/dt = v$ and $d^2x/dt^2 = v\, dv/dx$, we have

$$v \frac{dv}{dx} = -g \frac{R^2}{x^2}. \tag{12.39}$$

From this separable equation we obtain the relation

$$\tfrac{1}{2} v^2 = \frac{gR^2}{x} + C_1.$$

The constant C_1 is determined by the condition that $v = v_0$ when $x = R$. We find that

$$v^2 = \frac{2gR^2}{x} + v_0{}^2 - 2gR. \tag{12.40}$$

Since v is initially positive, we take the positive square root when solving for v in equation (12.40). Thus

$$v = \frac{dx}{dt} = \left(\frac{2gR^2}{x} + v_0{}^2 - 2gR \right)^{1/2}. \tag{12.41}$$

We cannot find a simple formula for x as a function of t. However, we can deduce certain interesting facts from the relation (12.41). The velocity v is initially positive, and x increases with time until the expression in parentheses in the right-hand member of equation (12.41) vanishes. The velocity then becomes negative, and we must take the negative square root when solving for v in equation (12.40). If $v_0^2 - 2gR \geq 0$, however, v can never become negative, no matter how large x becomes. The critical value $v_0 = \sqrt{2gR}$ for v_0 is called the *escape velocity* of the earth. Unless v_0 is greater than, or equal to, this value, the projectile will fall back to the earth. The value of the escape velocity is found to be approximately 7 miles per second. It should be pointed out, however, that in this simple mathematical model we have ignored a number of forces acting on the projectile, such as air resistance and the gravitational forces of other celestial bodies.

12.3   EXERCISES

1. Find all solutions of the given equation:

(a) $\dfrac{d^2x}{dt^2} = e^{-t}\left(\dfrac{dx}{dt}\right)^2$

(c) $\dfrac{d^2x}{dt^2} + \left(\dfrac{dx}{dt}\right)^2 = 1$

(b) $t\,\dfrac{dx}{dt}\dfrac{d^2x}{dt^2} = \left(\dfrac{dx}{dt}\right)^2 + t^4$

(d) $\dfrac{d^2x}{dt^2} - \dfrac{1}{t}\dfrac{dx}{dt} = t\sin t$

2. Find all solutions of the given equation:

(a) $\dfrac{d^2x}{dt^2} = -\dfrac{1}{x^3}$

(c) $x\,\dfrac{d^2x}{dt^2} = \dfrac{dx}{dt}\left(\dfrac{dx}{dt} + 1\right)$

(b) $\dfrac{d^2x}{dt^2} + \left(\dfrac{dx}{dt}\right)^2 - \dfrac{dx}{dt} = 0$

(d) $2x\,\dfrac{d^2x}{dt^2} = \left(\dfrac{dx}{dt}\right)^2 + 1$

3. An object of mass m is dropped from a height h above the earth. Let $x(t)$ denote the distance through which the object has fallen at time t. Assuming that the force due to gravity is a constant, and that the air resistance is equal to a positive constant c times the square of the velocity, find:

(a) The differential equation of motion,
(b) The time it takes for the object to reach the earth,
(c) The velocity with which the object strikes the earth.

4. Consider the motion of a simple pendulum. The mass of the pendulum is assumed to be concentrated at a point which is a distance L from the pivot (Figure 12.3).

(a) Show that the angular deflection θ of the pendulum obeys the equation

$$\frac{d^2\theta}{dt^2} + \frac{g}{L}\sin\theta = 0.$$

(b) To what physical situations do the constant solutions $\theta = n\pi$, $n = 0, \pm 1, \pm 2, \ldots$, correspond?

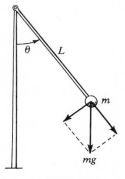

FIGURE 12.3

(c) Suppose that the pendulum is released from rest, at $t = 0$, from the position $\theta = -\alpha$, where $0 < \alpha < \pi$. Show that, on the first half-swing of the pendulum,

$$t = \sqrt{\frac{L}{2g}} \int_{-\alpha}^{\theta} \frac{ds}{\sqrt{\cos s - \cos \alpha}} = \frac{1}{2}\sqrt{\frac{L}{g}} \int_{-\alpha}^{\theta} \frac{ds}{\sqrt{\sin^2 (\alpha/2) - \sin^2 (s/2)}}.$$

(d) By setting $k = \sin (\alpha/2)$ and $\sin (s/2) = k \sin z$, show that

$$t = \sqrt{\frac{L}{g}} \int_{-\pi/2}^{\sin^{-1}[(1/k)\sin(\theta/2)]} (1 - k^2 \sin^2 z)^{-1/2} \, dz.$$

The function

$$F(\phi, k) = \int_{0}^{\phi} (1 - k^2 \sin^2 z)^{-1/2} \, dz$$

is called an elliptic integral of the first kind. It has been tabulated for various values of ϕ and k. (See, for example, B. O. Pierce, *A Short Table of Integrals*, Ginn, New York, 1929.)

(e) Show that the period of the pendulum is equal to

$$4\sqrt{\frac{L}{g}} \, F\left(\frac{\pi}{2}, k\right).$$

5. An object of mass m falls toward the earth from a distance h above the earth. Assuming that the inverse-square law of gravitation holds, and neglecting air resistance and other forces, find

(a) The velocity with which the object strikes the earth,
(b) The time it takes to reach the earth.

12.4 Existence and Uniqueness of Solutions

Let us consider the first-order equation

$$\frac{dy}{dx} = f(x, y), \tag{12.42}$$

where $f(x, y)$ is defined in a region D of the xy plane. Given an arbitrary point (x_0, y_0) in D, we may ask whether there exists an integral curve of the equation that passes through the point. We may also ask whether there can be more than one integral curve that passes through the point. To put these matters in a different way, we want to know whether the initial-value problem associated with the equation (12.42) has a solution, and if it does, whether this solution is unique. In the investigation of these questions, we find that certain restrictions must be placed on the function $f(x, y)$. We therefore begin with the following preliminary considerations.

A function $f(x, y)$ is said to satisfy a *Lipschitz condition* in a region D if there exists a positive constant K such that

$$|f(x, y_1) - f(x, y_2)| \leq K |y_1 - y_2| \qquad (12.43)$$

whenever the points (x, y_1) and (x, y_2) both lie in D. The constant K is called a *Lipschitz constant* for the function $f(x, y)$.

As an example, let us consider the function

$$f(x, y) = a(x)y + b(x) \qquad (12.44)$$

(which is linear in y), where $a(x)$ and $b(x)$ are continuous on a closed interval $\alpha \leq x \leq \beta$. We shall show that the function (12.44) satisfies a Lipschitz condition in the region $\alpha \leq x \leq \beta$, $-\infty < y < +\infty$. Let K be the maximum value of $|a(x)|$ on the interval $[\alpha, \beta]$. Then

$$|f(x, y_1) - f(x, y_2)| = |a(x)(y_1 - y_2)| \leq K |y_1 - y_2|.$$

As a second example, let $f(x, y)$ be continuous, along with its partial derivative $f_y(x, y)$ on a rectangle R of the form

$$|x - x_0| \leq a, \qquad |y - y_0| \leq b. \qquad (12.45)$$

Then $f(x, y)$ satisfies a Lipschitz condition on R, and a Lipschitz constant K is given by the maximum value of $|f_y(x, y)|$ on R. For if (x, y_1) and (x, y_2) lie in R, we have by the mean-value theorem that

$$f(x, y_1) - f(x, y_2) = (y_1 - y_2)f_y(x, y_3),$$

where y_3 is between y_1 and y_2. Since $|f_y(x, y)| \leq K$ for all (x, y) in R, we have

$$|f(x, y_1) - f(x, y_2)| \leq K |y_1 - y_2|.$$

We are now in a position to state and discuss the following basic theorem.

Theorem 1.   Let $f(x, y)$ and $f_y(x, y)$ be continuous on the rectangle R, as defined by the inequalities (12.45). Let M be the maximum value of $|f(x, y)|$ on R, and let $\alpha = \min(a, b/M)$. Then the equation $y' = f(x, y)$ possesses a solution $y(x)$ on the interval $|x - x_0| \leq \alpha$ which satisfies the initial condition $y(x_0) = y_0$. If $y_1(x)$ and $y_2(x)$ are both solutions of the initial value problem on an interval that contains x_0, then $y_1(x) = y_2(x)$; that is, the solution of the initial-value problem is unique.

Although we shall not give a detailed proof of this theorem, we shall describe generally the method employed. To begin with, we reformulate our initial-value problem as an integral equation. If $y(x)$ is a solution of the initial-value problem, we have $y(x_0) = y_0$ and $y'(x) = f[x, y(x)]$ on an interval that contains x_0. Integrating both members of this last equation from x_0 to x, we see that $y(x)$ satisfies the integral equation

$$y(x) - y_0 = \int_{x_0}^{x} f[t, y(t)] \, dt. \qquad (12.46)$$

Conversely, if $y(x)$ is any continuous function that satisfies the integral equation (12.46) on an interval that contains x_0, we see that $y(x_0) = y_0$ and, upon differentiating, that $y'(x) = f[x, y(x)]$. Hence the initial-value problem possesses a solution if, and only if, the integral equation (12.46) possesses a solution.

To prove the existence of a solution of the equation (12.46), we first define a sequence of functions $\{y_n(x)\}$, $n \geq 0$, by setting

$$y_0(x) = y_0 \tag{12.47}$$

and

$$y_{k+1}(x) = y_0 + \int_{x_0}^x f[t, y_k(t)]\, dt, \qquad k \geq 0. \tag{12.48}$$

Let x be restricted to the interval $|x - x_0| \leq \alpha$, where $\alpha = \min(a, b/M)$. Then

$$|y_1(x) - y_0| = \left| \int_{x_0}^x f(t, y_0)\, dt \right| \leq M \left| \int_{x_0}^x dt \right| \leq M\alpha \leq b.$$

Consequently, the points $(x, y_1(x))$, for $|x - x_0| \leq \alpha$, lie in the rectangle R, and this ensures that the function $y_2(x)$ is well defined. It can be shown by induction that each of the functions $y_n(x)$ is well defined. It can also be shown that the sequence $\{y_n(x)\}$ converges to a function $y(x)$ that is a solution of the integral equation (12.46). The fact that $f(x, y)$ satisfies a Lipschitz condition in R is used in establishing the convergence of the sequence (Exercises 6 and 7). The method of proof described above, sometimes called the *method of successive approximations,* is due to Picard.

We now consider the uniqueness part of the theorem. Suppose that $y_1(x)$ and $y_2(x)$ are both solutions of the initial-value problem (and hence of the integral equation (12.46)) on an interval I. Then we have

$$y_1(x) - y_2(x) = \int_{x_0}^x [f(t, y_1(t)) - f(t, y_2(t))]\, dt. \tag{12.49}$$

Since $f(x, y)$ satisfies a Lipschitz condition on the rectangle R, we have

$$|y_1(x) - y_2(x)| \leq K \left| \int_{x_0}^x |y_1(t) - y_2(t)|\, dt \right|. \tag{12.50}$$

It follows (by Exercise 6, Section 1.2) that $y_1(x) - y_2(x) \equiv 0$.

The interval $|x - x_0| \leq \alpha$ may be small even when the rectangle R is large. In the example

$$y' = 2xy^2, \qquad y(0) = 1, \tag{12.51}$$

the functions $f(x, y) = 2xy^2$ and $f_y(x, y) = 4xy$ are continuous everywhere, and hence on any rectangle of the form $|x| \leq a$, $|y - 1| \leq b$. But the solution of the initial-value problem, as found by elementary methods, is

$$y = \frac{1}{1 - x^2}\ ; \tag{12.52}$$

it exists only on the interval $|x| < 1$, and so it is clear that $\alpha < 1$.

In practice, the function $f(x, y)$ and its derivative $f_y(x, y)$ will be continuous in a region D of the xy plane that is not a rectangle. They may even be continuous for all x and y, as in the example above. However, Theorem 1 can be applied by considering a rectangle contained in the region D. Theorem 1 assures the existence of a solution only on an interval $|x - x_0| \le \alpha$, which may be small. However, it may be possible to continue, or extend, the solution to the right of the point $x_0 + \alpha$ (or to the left of the point $x_0 - \alpha$). Suppose that $y(x)$ is a solution on the interval $|x - x_0| \le \alpha$, and that the point $P : (x_0 + \alpha, y(x_0 + \alpha))$ lies in the interior of the region D. Then there exists a rectangle, with center at P and contained in D. According to Theorem 1, a solution $\tilde{y}(x)$, satisfying $\tilde{y}(x_0 + \alpha) = y(x_0 + \alpha)$, exists on some interval $|x - (x_0 + \alpha)| \le \alpha_1$. But by the uniqueness part of Theorem 1, the functions $\tilde{y}(x)$ and $y(x)$ must coincide on the interval on which both are defined. In this way the solution $y(x)$ is continued to the right of the point $x_0 + \alpha$, in fact up to the point $x_0 + \alpha + \alpha_1$. If the point $(x_0 + \alpha + \alpha_1, y(x_0 + \alpha + \alpha_1))$ lies in D, this process can be repeated.

It may happen that the solution can be continued for all x greater than x_0. If not, a deeper analysis shows that the solution can be continued up to a point x_1, and that as $x \to x_1-$, either $y(x)$ becomes infinite or else the integral curve approaches the boundary of the region D.

If, in Theorem 1, we drop the hypothesis that $f_y(x, y)$ exists and is continuous, and assume only that $f(x, y)$ is continuous on the rectangle R, it is still possible to prove that a solution to the initial-value problem exists. However, a different method of proof must be employed. Also, the solution may not be unique. Consider, for example, the problem

$$y' = 3y^{2/3}, \qquad y(0) = 0, \tag{12.53}$$

One solution is found to be $y = x^3$. But it is evident that the zero function, $y = 0$, is also a solution. It should be noted that although $f(x, y) = 3y^{2/3}$ is continuous for all x and y, the function $f_y(x, y) = 2y^{-1/3}$ is not continuous at $(0, 0)$, or at any point on the x axis. Thus Theorem 1 cannot be applied to this initial-value problem.

12.4 EXERCISES

1. Use Theorem 1 to show that the initial-value problem possesses a unique solution. In parts (a) and (b), actually find the solution.

(a) $y' = \dfrac{3\sqrt{x}}{4y}$, $y(1) = -2$

(b) $(x + y) + (x - y)y' = 0$, $y(0) = 1$

(c) $y' = x^2 + y^2$, $y(0) = 0$

2. Find at least two solutions of the given initial-value problem. Show that the hypotheses of Theorem 1 are not satisfied in any rectangle of the form $|x - x_0| \le a$, $|y - y_0| \le b$.

   (a) $y' = \sqrt{1 - y^2}$, $y(0) = 1$ (b) $y' = \frac{3}{2}y^{1/3}$, $y(0) = 0$

3. Find, for the problem $y' = x - y^2$, $y(0) = 1$, the functions $y_0(x)$, $y_1(x)$, and $y_2(x)$ in the sequence of successive approximation defined by the relations (12.47) and (12.48).

4. Do as in Problem 3 for the initial-value problem $y' = x^2 + y^2$, $y(0) = -1$.

5. Prove by induction that each of the functions $y_n(x)$ in the sequence (12.47), (12.48) is well defined and satisfies $|y_n(x) - y_0| \le b$ for $|x - x_0| \le \alpha$.

6. Prove by induction that the functions $y_n(x)$ in the sequence (12.47), (12.48) satisfy the inequalities

$$|y_n(x) - y_{n-1}(x)| \le \frac{MK^{n-1}}{n!}|x - x_0|^n, \qquad n \ge 1,$$

   and hence that

$$|y_n(x) - y_{n-1}(x)| \le \frac{MK^n\alpha^n}{Kn!}, \qquad |x - x_0| \le \alpha, \qquad n \ge 1.$$

   Suggestion: Use the integral equation (12.46), and the fact that $f(x, y)$ satisfies a Lipschitz condition.

7. Observing that

$$y_n(x) = \sum_{k=1}^{n} [y_k(x) - y_{k-1}(x)] + y_0(x),$$

   prove that the sequence $\{y_n(x)\}$ converges for $|x - x_0| \le \alpha$ by proving that the series

$$\sum_{k=1}^{\infty} [y_k(x) - y_{k-1}(x)]$$

   converges. Suggestion: Use the result of Problem 6.

8. Let $f(x, y)$ be continuous and satisfy a Lipschitz condition in a region D. If $y_1(x)$ and $y_2(x)$ are solutions of the equation $y' = f(x, y)$ on an interval I, and if $y_1(x_0) = a_1$ and $y_2(x_0) = a_2$, show that

$$|y_1(x) - y_2(x)| \le |a_1 - a_2| + K\left|\int_{x_0}^{x} |y_1(t) - y_2(t)| \, dt\right|.$$

   From this inequality, show that

$$|y_1(x) - y_2(x)| \le |a_1 - a_2|e^{K|x - x_0|}.$$

12.5   Existence and Uniqueness of Solutions for Systems

Let us now consider a first-order system of equations,

$$\frac{dx}{dt} = f_i(t, x_1, x_2, \ldots, x_n), \qquad i = 1, 2, \ldots, n, \tag{12.54}$$

for n unknown functions $x_1, x_2, \ldots, x_n$ of the independent variable t. If we define the vector quantities $\mathbf{x}$, dx/dt, and $\mathbf{f}$ by means of the relations

$$\mathbf{x} = \begin{pmatrix} x_1 \\ x_2 \\ \vdots \\ x_n \end{pmatrix}, \qquad \frac{d\mathbf{x}}{dt} = \begin{pmatrix} dx_1/dt \\ dx_2/dt \\ \vdots \\ dx_n/dt \end{pmatrix}, \qquad \mathbf{f}(t, \mathbf{x}) = \begin{pmatrix} f_1 \\ f_2 \\ \vdots \\ f_n \end{pmatrix}, \tag{12.55}$$

then the system (12.54) can be written more compactly as

$$\frac{d\mathbf{x}}{dt} = \mathbf{f}(t, \mathbf{x}). \tag{12.56}$$

In the initial-value problem associated with the system (12.56), we seek a vector solution $\mathbf{x}(t)$ that satisfies a condition of the form

$$\mathbf{x}(t_0) = \mathbf{k}, \tag{12.57}$$

where $\mathbf{k}$ is a constant vector whose components may be denoted by $k_1, k_2, \ldots, k_n$.

The following theorem, whose proof we omit, is basic in the study of first-order systems.

Theorem 2.   Let the functions $f_i(t, \mathbf{x})$, $1 \leq i \leq n$, be continuous, along with their first partial derivatives with respect to $x_1, x_2, \ldots, x_n$ in the $n + 1$ dimensional "rectangle" $|t - t_0| \leq a$, $|x_i - k_i| \leq b_i$, $1 \leq i \leq n$. Then there exists a positive number α, where $0 < \alpha \leq a$, such that the initial-value problem (12.56), (12.57) possesses a solution $\mathbf{x}(t)$ on the interval $|t - t_0| \leq \alpha$. If $\mathbf{x}_1(t)$ and $\mathbf{x}_2(t)$ are both solutions of the initial-value problem on an interval, then $\mathbf{x}_1(t) \equiv \mathbf{x}_2(t)$.

The initial-value problem can be shown (Exercise 1) to be equivalent to the system of integral equations

$$\mathbf{x}(t) = \mathbf{k} + \int_{t_0}^{t} \mathbf{f}[s, \mathbf{x}(s)] \, ds, \tag{12.58}$$

where $\int_{t_0}^{t} \mathbf{f} \, ds$ is defined to be the vector whose components are $\int_{t_0}^{t} f_i \, ds$. The existence of a solution can be established by the method of successive approximations. The procedure is to define

$$\mathbf{x}_0(t) = \mathbf{k} \tag{12.59}$$

and

$$\mathbf{x}_{i+1}(t) = \mathbf{k} + \int_{t_0}^{t} \mathbf{f}[s, \mathbf{x}_i(s)] \, ds, \qquad i \geq 0, \tag{12.60}$$

and then to show that the sequence $\{\mathbf{x}_i(t)\}$ converges† to a vector function $\mathbf{x}(t)$ that is a solution of the integral equation (12.58).

Usually, in a given problem, the functions $f_i(t, \mathbf{x})$ and their partial derivatives $\partial f_i / \partial x_j$ will be continuous in a region D of $n + 1$ dimensional space that is not a rectangle. Here again, we can apply the theorem by considering a rectangle contained in D. Here, also, it may be possible to continue the solution $\mathbf{x}(t)$ to the right of the point $t_0 + \alpha$ (and to the left of the point $t_0 - \alpha$). It may be possible to continue the solution to the right for all $t \geq t_0$. If not, it can be shown that the solution exists up to a point t_1, and that as $t \to t_1 -$, either one or more of the components of $\mathbf{x}(t)$ becomes infinite, or else the solution curve approaches the boundary of the region D.

Let us consider the specific initial-value problem

$$\frac{dx_1}{dt} = \sin(x_1 x_2) + 2t, \qquad \frac{dx_2}{dt} = x_1^2 - x_2^2,$$

$$x_1(0) = 1, \qquad x_2(0) = 0. \tag{12.61}$$

Here

$$f_1(t, x_1, x_2) = \sin(x_1 x_2) + 2t, \qquad f_2(t, x_1, x_2) = x_1^2 - x_2^2,$$

and

$$\partial f_1 / \partial x_1 = x_2 \cos(x_1 x_2),$$

$$\partial f_1 / \partial x_2 = x_1 \cos(x_1 x_2),$$

$$\partial f_2 / \partial x_1 = 2x_1,$$

$$\partial f_2 / \partial x_2 = -2x_2.$$

Each of these functions is continuous for all values of t, x_1, and x_2. Theorem 2 assures us that the problem (12.61) possesses a solution, but only on some interval $|t| \leq \alpha$. The number α may be small.

A single differential equation, of the form

$$x^{(n)} = f(t, x, x', \ldots, x^{(n-1)}), \tag{12.62}$$

is equivalent to a first-order system for the quantities

$$x_1 = x, \quad x_2 = x', \quad x_2 = x'', \ldots, x_n = x^{(n-1)}. \tag{12.63}$$

---

† Let the jth component of $\mathbf{x}_i(t)$ be denoted by $x_{ij}(t)$, and the jth component of $\mathbf{x}(t)$ by $x_j(t)$. The sequence of vector functions $\{\mathbf{x}_i(t)\}$ is said to converge to the vector function $\mathbf{x}(t)$ if the ordinary sequence $\{x_{ij}(t)\}$ converges to $x_j(t)$, for $j = 1, 2, \ldots, n$.

For if $x(t)$ is a solution of equation (12.62), then the corresponding functions $x_i(t)$, $1 \leq i \leq n$, satisfy the relations

$$x_1' = x_2$$
$$x_2' = x_3$$
$$\cdots\cdots\cdots \qquad\qquad (12.64)$$
$$x_{n-1}' = x_n$$
$$x_n' = f(t, x_1, x_2, \ldots, x_n).$$

Conversely, if a set of functions $x_1(t)$, $x_2(t)$, $\ldots$, $x_n(t)$ constitutes a solution of the system (12.64), then the component $x_1(t)$ is a solution of the equation (12.62). For from the first $n - 1$ equations of the system (12.64) we have

$$x_i = x_{i-1}' = x_{i-2}'' = \cdots = x_1^{(i-1)}, \qquad i = 1, 2, \ldots, n,$$

and from the last equation we have

$$x_n' = x_1^{(n)} = f(t, x_1, x_1', \ldots, x_1^{(n-1)}).$$

The next theorem follows immediately from Theorem 2.

Theorem 3. Let the function $f(t, x_1, x_2, \ldots, x_n)$ be continuous, along with the first partial derivatives $\partial f/\partial x_j$ in the $n + 1$ dimensional rectangle $|t - t_0| \leq a$, $|x_i - k_i| \leq b_i$, $1 \leq i \leq n$. Then there exists a positive number α, where $0 < \alpha \leq a$, such that on the interval $|t - t_0| \leq \alpha$ the equation (12.62) possesses a solution which satisfies the initial conditions $x^{(i)}(t_0) = k_i$, $1 \leq i \leq n$. This solution is unique.

12.5 EXERCISES

1. Show that the initial-value problem (12.56), (12.57) is equivalent to the system of integral equations (12.58).

2. Use Theorem 1 to show that the initial-value problem

$$\frac{dx_1}{dt} = \sin(tx_1) + \cos x_2, \qquad \frac{dx_2}{dt} = x_1{}^2 - x_2 + t^2, \qquad x_1(0) = x_2(0) = 0,$$

possesses a unique solution.

3. (a) Use Theorem 1 to show that the initial-value problem

$$\frac{dx_1}{dt} = x_1{}^2 x_2, \qquad \frac{dx_2}{dt} = -x_2{}^2, \qquad x_1(0) = x_2(0) = 1$$

possesses a unique solution.
(b) Find the solution of the problem in part (a). On what interval of the t axis does this solution exist?

4. (a) Use Theorem 3 to show that the initial-value problem

$$\frac{d^2x}{dt^2} + 2t\left(\frac{dx}{dt}\right)^2 = 0, \qquad x(0) = 1, \qquad x'(0) = -1$$

possesses a unique solution.

(b) Find the solution of the problem in part (a). On what interval of the t axis does this solution exist?

5. Show that Theorem 3 follows from Theorem 2.

12.6   The Phase Plane

Let us consider a first-order system for two unknown functions,

$$\frac{dx}{dt} = F(t, x, y), \qquad \frac{dy}{dt} = G(t, x, y). \tag{12.65}$$

An ordered pair of numbers (x, y) can be regarded as the rectangular Cartesian coordinates of a point in a plane. If the functions $x(t)$, $y(t)$ constitute a solution of the system (12.65), the relations $x = x(t)$, $y = y(t)$ can be interpreted as the parametric equations of a curve in the xy plane. This xy plane is called the *phase plane* for the system (12.65). A curve in this plane that is described parametrically by a solution of the system is called a *trajectory* of the system. A point (x_0, y_0) such that $F(t, x_0, y_0) = G(t, x_0, y_0) = 0$ for all t is called a *critical point* of the system (12.65). If such a point exists, the system possesses the constant solution $x = x_0$, $y = y_0$. The trajectory of such a solution consists of the single point (x_0, y_0).

It is necessary to make a distinction between a *solution* of the system (12.65) and a *trajectory* of that system. For different solutions may represent the same trajectory parametrically, as we shall see in the examples which follow.

The system

$$\frac{dx}{dt} = x, \qquad \frac{dy}{dt} = 3x + 2y \tag{12.66}$$

has for its general solution

$$x = C_1 e^t, \qquad y = C_1 e^t + C_2 e^{2t}.$$

When $C_1 = 0$, we have $x = 0$ and $y = C_2 e^{2t}$. In this case, the trajectory consists of the positive y axis when $C_2 > 0$ and the negative y axis when $C_2 < 0$. If $C_2 = 0$, we have $x = C_1 e^t$ and $y = C_1 e^t$. The trajectory consists of the ray $y = x$, $x > 0$, when $C_1 > 0$, and the ray $y = x$, $x < 0$, when $C_1 < 0$. In the general case, when $C_1 C_2 \neq 0$, the trajectories lie on the parabolas $y = x + (C_2/C_1^2)x^2$. Actually, each trajectory consists of only part of a parabola, the part with $x > 0$ if $C_1 > 0$ and the part with $x < 0$ if $C_1 < 0$. Some typical trajectories are shown in Figure 12.4. The arrows indicate the

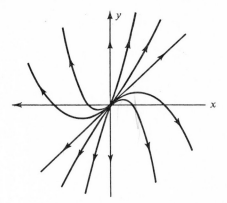

FIGURE 12.4

direction of increasing t. The trivial solution $x = 0$, $y = 0$, corresponds to
the single point $(0, 0)$. We note that the solution for which $x(0) = y(0) = 1$
is $x = e^t$, $y = e^t$, while the solution for which $x(0) = y(0) = 2$ is $x = 2e^t$,
$y = 2e^t$. The two solutions are different, but each represents the trajectory
that consists of the ray $y = x$, $x > 0$.

A single second-order differential equation, of the form

$$\frac{d^2x}{dt^2} = f\left(t, x, \frac{dx}{dt}\right), \tag{12.67}$$

is equivalent to the system

$$\frac{dx}{dt} = y, \qquad \frac{dy}{dt} = f(t, x, y). \tag{12.68}$$

We can therefore speak of trajectories and phase planes for equations such
as (12.67).

The equation

$$\frac{d^2x}{dt^2} + x = 0 \tag{12.69}$$

is equivalent to the system

$$\frac{dx}{dt} = y, \qquad \frac{dy}{dt} = -x. \tag{12.70}$$

The general solution of this system can be written as

$$x = A \cos (t - \alpha), \qquad y = -A \sin (t - \alpha),$$

where A and α are arbitrary constants, with $A \geq 0$. In the phase plane, the
equations of the trajectories are $x^2 + y^2 = A^2$. The circles are traversed in

the clockwise direction as t increases. Some sample trajectories are shown in Figure 12.5. Clearly many solutions represent the same trajectory.

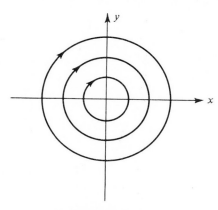

FIGURE 12.5

In the last example, the trajectories were closed curves. Closed trajectories of a system (12.65) arise from *periodic solutions*. A solution $x(t)$, $y(t)$ is said to be periodic with period T if it exists for all t and if

$$x(t + T) = x(t), \qquad y(t + T) = y(t)$$

for all t. The trajectory which is described by a periodic solution of period T is traversed once as t traverses an interval of length T. In the example (12.69), the solutions are periodic with period 2π.

We shall be particularly interested in systems of the form

$$\frac{dx}{dt} = P(x, y), \qquad \frac{dy}{dt} = Q(x, y), \tag{12.71}$$

in which the independent variable t does not appear explicitly. Such a system is said to be *autonomous*. We shall consider such systems in a region D of the xy plane in which the functions $P(x, y)$ and $Q(x, y)$, and their first partial derivatives, are continuous. If (x_0, y_0) is any point of D and if t_0 is any real number, there exists a unique solution of the system (12.71) that satisfies $x(t_0) = x_0$, $y(t_0) = y_0$. This fact follows from Theorem 2. Each trajectory of the autonomous system (12.71) is represented by a one-parameter family of solutions. For if $x(t)$, $y(t)$ is a solution of the system, it is easily verified (Exercise 3) that $x(t + c)$, $y(t + c)$, for any constant c, is also a solution. Each of the solutions represents the same trajectory.

Suppose that $P(x, y) \neq 0$ in the region D. If $x(t)$, $y(t)$ is a solution of the system, then $dx/dt \neq 0$. Hence t can be regarded as a function of x, and since

$$\frac{dy/dt}{dx/dt} = \frac{Q(x, y)}{P(x, y)},$$

we see that y, regarded as a function of x, satisfies the first-order equation

$$\frac{dy}{dx} = \frac{Q(x, y)}{P(x, y)}. \tag{12.72}$$

Consequently, the trajectories of the system (12.71) coincide with the integral curves of the equation (12.72). Such an interpretation is not possible, in general, for a nonautonomous system of the form (12.65).

Let us consider the system

$$\frac{dx}{dt} = (x^2 + 1)y, \qquad \frac{dy}{dt} = 2xy^2. \tag{12.73}$$

For $y \neq 0$ we have

$$\frac{dy}{dx} = \frac{2xy}{x^2 + 1}$$

and

$$y = C(x^2 + 1)$$

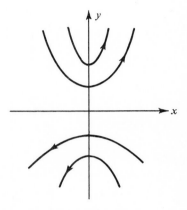

FIGURE 12.6

Some of these parabolic trajectories are shown in Figure 12.6. The direction of increasing t can be found from the first of the equations (12.73), by noting that dx/dt has the same sign as y. We also note that $x = C'$, $y = 0$ is a solution for every value of C'. These solutions are represented by points on the x axis of the phase plane.

12.6 EXERCISES

1. Find all solutions of the given system and sketch some of its trajectories. Indicate the direction of increasing t.

(a) $\dfrac{dx}{dt} = y$, $\qquad \dfrac{dy}{dt} = -4x$ $\qquad$ (c) $\dfrac{dx}{dt} = -x$, $\qquad \dfrac{dy}{dt} = x^2 y^2$

(b) $\dfrac{dx}{dt} = -x$, $\qquad \dfrac{dy}{dt} = x - 2y$ $\qquad$ (d) $\dfrac{dx}{dt} = x$, $\qquad \dfrac{dy}{dt} = x + 2e^{2t}$

2. Suppose that $P(x, y)$ and $Q(x, y)$ both vanish at the point $(x_0 y_0)$. Show that the autonomous system (12.71) possesses the constant solution $x = x_0$, $y = y_0$.

3. If $x(t)$, $y(t)$ is a solution of the autonomous system (12.71), show that $x(t + c)$, $y(t + c)$, where c is any constant, is also a solution. Show that each solution of this family represents the same trajectory.

4. Let $x_1(t)$, $y_1(t)$ and $x_2(t)$, $y_2(t)$ be solutions of the system (12.71) such that their trajectories have a common point. Show that there exists a constant c such that $x_2(t) = x_1(t + c)$ and $y_2(t) = y_1(t + c)$. Hence show that the two trajectories coincide.

5. Sketch some of the trajectories of the system

$$\frac{dx}{dt} = -y(x^2 + y^2), \qquad \frac{dy}{dt} = x(x^2 + y^2),$$

indicating the direction of increasing t.

6. Sketch some of the trajectories of the system

$$\frac{dx}{dt} = e^y, \qquad \frac{dy}{dt} = 2xe^y,$$

indicating the direction of increasing t.

7. Sketch some of the trajectories of the system

$$\frac{dx}{dt} = xy, \qquad \frac{dy}{dt} = y(y - 3x^2),$$

indicating the direction of increasing t.

8. (a) Show that a second order equation of the form

$$\frac{d^2x}{dt^2} = f\left(x, \frac{dx}{dt}\right),$$

is equivalent to an autonomous system.

(b) Find the autonomous system which corresponds to the equation with constant coefficients,

$$\frac{d^2x}{dt^2} + a\frac{dx}{dt} + bx = 0.$$

12.7 Critical Points

Let the functions $P(x, y)$ and $Q(x, y)$ and their first partial derivatives be continuous in a region D of the xy plane. A point (x_0, y_0) in D where

$$P(x_0, y_0) = Q(x_0, y_0) = 0$$

is called a *critical point* for the autonomous system

$$\frac{dx}{dt} = P(x, y), \qquad \frac{dy}{dt} = Q(x, y). \tag{12.74}$$

If (x_0, y_0) is a critical point, then the constant functions $x(t) = x_0$, $y(t) = y_0$

constitute a solution of the system. The trajectory of the solution consists of the single point (x_0, y_0) in the phase plane.

In order to obtain a physical interpretation of a critical point, let us consider the straight-line motion of a particle whose position and velocity are denoted by x and $y = dx/dt$, respectively. If the equation of motion of the particle has the form

$$\frac{d^2x}{dt^2} = f\left(x, \frac{dx}{dt}\right),$$

then the corresponding first-order system,

$$\frac{dx}{dt} = y, \qquad \frac{dy}{dt} = f(x, y),$$

is autonomous. A critical point $(x_0, 0)$ corresponds to a state of rest, or equilibrium, for the particle, in which $x(t) \equiv x_0$ and $x'(t) \equiv 0$.

We shall be concerned with the behavior of solutions of a system (12.74) near a critical point. For the ensuing discussion, we shall need a number of definitions.

A critical point (x_0, y_0) of the system (12.74) is said to be *isolated* if there exists a circle,

$$(x - x_0)^2 + (y - y_0)^2 = h^2, \qquad h > 0,$$

inside which the system has no other critical point.

A trajectory of the system (12.74), which is represented by the family of solutions $x(t + c)$, $y(t + c)$, is said to *approach* the critical point† (x_0, y_0) as t becomes positively infinite if

$$\lim_{t \to +\infty} x(t) = x_0, \qquad \lim_{t \to +\infty} y(t) = y_0. \tag{12.75}$$

Similarly, we say that a trajectory approaches the critical point (x_0, y_0) as t becomes negatively infinite if $x(t) \to x_0$ and $y(t) \to y_0$ as $t \to -\infty$.

A critical point (x_0, y_0) is said to be *stable* if to every positive number ε there corresponds a positive number δ such that, whenever a solution $x(t)$, $y(t)$ satisfies

$$(|x(0) - x_0|^2 + |y(0) - y_0|^2)^{1/2} < \delta, \tag{12.76}$$

it exists for $t \geq 0$ and satisfies

$$(|x(t) - x_0|^2 + |y(t) - y_0|^2)^{1/2} < \varepsilon. \tag{12.77}$$

for $t \geq 0$. The critical point is said to be *asymptotically stable* if it is stable and if there exists a positive number δ_0 such that

$$\lim_{t \to +\infty} x(t) = x_0, \qquad \lim_{t \to +\infty} y(t) = y_0$$

---

† If for any solution $x(t)$, $y(t)$, we have $x(t) \to x_0$ and $y(t) \to y_0$ as $t \to +\infty$, and if the point (x_0, y_0) lies in D, it can be shown that (x_0, y_0) must be a critical point.

whenever $(|x(0) - x_0|^2 + |y(0) - y_0|^2)^{1/2} < \delta_0$. A critical point that is not stable is said to be *unstable*.

Geometrically speaking, when a critical point is stable, solutions that start (at $t = 0$) sufficiently close to the point stay close to the point (Figure 12.7).

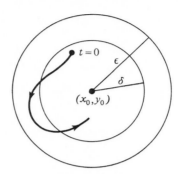

FIGURE 12.7

Let us illustrate the above concepts by means of some simple examples.

EXAMPLE 1.   The solution of the system

$$\frac{dx}{dt} = -x, \qquad \frac{dy}{dt} = -2y$$

for which $x(0) = x_0$, $y(0) = y_0$ is $x(t) = x_0 e^{-t}$, $y(t) = y_0 e^{-2t}$. Given ε, let $\delta = \varepsilon$. Then if $(x_0^2 + y_0^2)^{1/2} < \delta$, we have $|[x(t)]^2 + [y(t)]^2|^{1/2} \leq (x_0^2 + y_0^2)^{1/2} < \varepsilon$ for $t \geq 0$. Hence the critical point $(0, 0)$ is stable. Since $x(t) \to 0$ and $y(t) \to 0$ as $t \to +\infty$ for every solution, the critical point is asymptotically stable.

EXAMPLE 2.   The system

$$\frac{dx}{dt} = y, \qquad \frac{dy}{dt} = -x$$

was considered in Section 12.6 (equation (12.70)). Since the trajectories are circles with centers at the origin, a solution satisfying

$$|[x(0)]^2 + [y(0)]^2|^{1/2} < \varepsilon$$

satisfies

$$|[x(t)]^2 + [y(t)]^2|^{1/2} < \varepsilon \qquad \text{for } t \geq 0.$$

The critical point $(0, 0)$ is therefore stable. It is not asymptotically stable, because no trajectory approaches the origin.

EXAMPLE 3. Consider the system

$$\frac{dx}{dt} = x, \qquad \frac{dy}{dt} = y.$$

The solution for which $x(0) = x_0$, $y(0) = 0$ is $x(t) = x_0 e^t$, $y(t) = 0$. No matter how small the value of $|x_0|$, $x(t) \to \infty$ if $x_0 \neq 0$. Hence the critical point $(0, 0)$ is unstable.

We begin our study of stability by considering critical points of *linear* autonomous systems. More specifically, we consider systems of the form

$$\frac{dx}{dt} = ax + by, \qquad \frac{dy}{dt} = cx + dy, \qquad (12.78)$$

where a, b, c, and d are constants. We shall assume that $ad - bc \neq 0$. Then the system (12.78) has exactly one critical point which is located at the origin of the phase plane.

Solutions of the system (12.78) can be found by the methods of Chapter 9. We consider three cases. If $b \neq 0$, we can eliminate y between the two equations. In this case, the system (12.78) is seen to be equivalent to the system

$$[(D - a)(D - d) - bc]x = 0, \qquad (D - a)x - by = 0, \qquad (12.79a)$$

where $D = d/dt$. Here x can be found from the first equation, and then y can be found from the second equation without integration. If $c \neq 0$, the system (12.78) is equivalent to the system

$$[(D - a)(D - d) - bc]y = 0, \qquad -cx + (D - d)y = 0. \qquad (12.79b)$$

If $b = c = 0$, the system (12.78) has the form

$$(D - a)x = 0 \qquad (D - d)y = 0. \qquad (12.79c)$$

From the equations (12.79a, b, c) we see that the system (12.78) possesses a nontrivial solution of the form $x = A e^{\lambda t}$, $y = B e^{\lambda t}$ if, and only if, λ is a root of the equation

$$(\lambda - a)(\lambda - d) - bc \equiv \lambda^2 - (a + d)\lambda + (ad - bc) = 0. \qquad (12.80)$$

We note that $\lambda = 0$ cannot be a root of this equation, in view of the hypothesis that $ad - bc \neq 0$.

If λ_1 and λ_2 are distinct roots of the equation (12.80), then all solutions of the system (12.78) are of the form

$$x = A_1 \exp(\lambda_1 t) + A_2 \exp(\lambda_2 t), \qquad y = B_1 \exp(\lambda_1 t) + B_2 \exp(\lambda_2 t),$$

where A_i, B_i are constants. If λ_1 and λ_2 are complex, say $\lambda_1 = \alpha + i\beta$ and $\lambda_2 = \alpha - i\beta$, the solutions may be written in real form as

$$x = e^{\alpha t}(A_1 \cos \beta t + A_2 \sin \beta t), \qquad y = e^{\alpha t}(B_1 \cos \beta t + B_2 \sin \beta t).$$

If $\lambda_1 = \lambda_2$ (in which case λ_1 and λ_2 are real), the solutions are of the form

$$x = (A_1 + A_2 t) \exp(\lambda_1 t), \qquad y = (B_1 + B_2 t) \exp(\lambda_1 t).$$

If either, or both, of the roots λ_1 and λ_2 has a positive real part, is it clear that the critical point $(0, 0)$ of the system (12.78) cannot be stable. If both λ_1 and λ_2 have negative real parts, then the trajectory described by every nontrivial solution approaches the critical point at $t \to +\infty$.

We shall now show that if λ_1 and λ_2 both have real parts which are less than, or equal to, zero, then the origin is a stable critical point. Let $x_1(t)$, $y_1(t)$ and $x_2(t)$, $y_2(t)$ be the solutions of the system (12.78) for which $x_1(0) = 1$, $y_1(0) = 0$, $x_2(0) = 0$, $y_2(0) = 1$. Then there exists a positive constant M such that $|x_i(t)| \leq M$, $|y_i(t)| \leq M$, $i = 1, 2$, for $t \geq 0$. Let (p, q) be an arbitrary point in the xy plane. The solution $x(t)$, $y(t)$ of the system (12.78) for which $x(0) = p$, $y(0) = q$ is

$$x(t) = p x_1(t) + q x_2(t), \qquad y(t) = p y_1(t) + q y_2(t). \qquad (12.81)$$

Then

$$|x(t)| \leq M(|p| + |q|), \qquad |y(t)| \leq M(|p| + |q|) \qquad (12.82)$$

for $t \geq 0$. Given ε, let us choose $\delta = \varepsilon/4M$. Then if $(p^2 + q^2)^{1/2} < \delta$, certainly $|p| < \delta$, $|q| < \delta$. From the inequalities (12.82) we see that

$$|x(t)| < 2M\delta = \frac{\varepsilon}{2} \qquad \text{and} \qquad |y(t)| < 2M\delta = \frac{\varepsilon}{2} \qquad \text{for } t \geq 0.$$

Then

$$[x(t)]^2 + [y(t)]^2 < \frac{2\varepsilon^2}{4},$$

or

$$\{[x(t)]^2 + [y(t)]^2\}^{1/2} < \frac{\varepsilon}{\sqrt{2}} < \varepsilon.$$

Hence the origin is a stable critical point. We summarize these results in the following theorem.

Theorem 4.   The critical point $(0, 0)$ of the linear system (12.78) is stable if, and only if, both roots of the auxiliary equation (12.80) have nonpositive real parts. The critical point is asymptotically stable if, and only if, both roots have negative real parts.

The proof of the following corollary is left as an exercise.

Corollary.   The critical point $(0, 0)$ of the linear system (12.78) is asymptotically stable if, and only if, $a + d < 0$ and $ad > bc$.

12.7 EXERCISES

1. Locate the critical points of the given equation, or system of equations. Determine whether or not each critical point is isolated.

(a) $\dfrac{d^2x}{dt^2} + \dfrac{dx}{dt} + (x^2 - 1) = 0$

(b) $\dfrac{d^2x}{dt^2} + \sin x = 0$

(c) $\dfrac{dx}{dt} = x - y, \qquad \dfrac{dy}{dt} = x^2 - 3y + 2$

(d) $\dfrac{dx}{dt} = y^2 - 3x + 2, \qquad \dfrac{dy}{dt} = x^2 - y^2$

(e) $\dfrac{dx}{dt} = \cos y, \qquad \dfrac{dy}{dt} = \sin x$

2. If $ad - bc = 0$, show that the system (12.78) possesses infinitely many critical points, none of which is isolated.

3. (a) If $AD - BC \neq 0$, show that the system

$$\frac{dx}{dt} = Ax + By + E, \qquad \frac{dy}{dt} = Cx + Dy + F$$

possesses a single critical point (x_0, y_0).
(b) Show that the system of part (a) can be put in the form (12.78) by means of the change of variables $u = x - x_0$, $v = y - y_0$.

4. Show that a critical point of a system (12.74) which is not isolated cannot be asymptotically stable.

5. Prove the corollary to Theorem 4.

6. Determine whether the origin is a stable or unstable critical point for the given system. If it is stable, determine whether it is asymptotically stable.

(a) $\dfrac{dx}{dt} = y, \qquad \dfrac{dy}{dt} = -4x$

(b) $\dfrac{dx}{dt} = -x + y, \qquad \dfrac{dy}{dt} = x - 2y$

(c) $\dfrac{dx}{dt} = 2x + y, \qquad \dfrac{dy}{dt} = 3x - 2y$

(d) $\dfrac{dx}{dt} = -x + 2y, \qquad \dfrac{dy}{dt} = -2x - y$

7. Consider the equation

$$\frac{d^2x}{dt^2} + a\frac{dx}{dt} + bx = 0,$$

where a and b are constants.

(a) Show that the equation has an isolated critical point at $(0, 0)$ if, and only if, $b \neq 0$.

(b) Show that the critical point $(0, 0)$ is asymptotically stable if, and only if, $a > 0$ and $b > 0$.

8. Show that the equation $d^2x/dt^2 = 2x^3$ has an isolated critical point at $(0, 0)$ which is unstable. Suggestion: Sketch some of the trajectories.

12.8 Stability for Nonlinear Systems

We begin with some geometrical considerations. Associated with the autonomous system

$$\frac{dx}{dt} = P(x, y), \qquad \frac{dy}{dt} = Q(x, y) \tag{12.83}$$

is the vector function

$$\mathbf{V}(x, y) = P(x, y)\mathbf{i} + Q(x, y)\mathbf{j}. \tag{12.84}$$

At a point that is not a critical point of the system (12.83), $\mathbf{V}$ has a definite direction. We call the function $\mathbf{V}(x, y)$ the *direction field* of the system (12.83). Consider a trajectory described by the solution $x(t)$, $y(t)$. Suppose that

$$x(t_1) = x_1, \; y(t_1) = x_1,$$

and that the point (x_1, y_1) is not a critical point. Then the vector

$$x'(t_1)\mathbf{i} + y'(t_1)\mathbf{j} = \mathbf{V}(x_1, y_1)$$

is tangent to the trajectory at (x_1, y_1) and points in the direction of increasing t. If $E(x, y)$ is a function that is continuous along with its first partial derivatives in a region containing the trajectory, the rate of change of E along the trajectory is

$$\frac{d}{dt}E[x(t), y(t)] = \frac{\partial E}{\partial x}\frac{dx}{dt} + \frac{\partial E}{\partial y}\frac{dy}{dt} = \frac{\partial E}{\partial x}P + \frac{\partial E}{\partial y}Q. \tag{12.85}$$

In vector notation,

$$\frac{dE}{dt} = \mathbf{V} \cdot \text{grad } E, \tag{12.86}$$

where $\mathbf{V}$ is the direction field (12.84).

In what follows, it will sometimes be convenient to use polar coordinates (r, θ), as defined by the relations $x = r \cos \theta$, $y = r \sin \theta$. In talking about a solution $x(t)$, $y(t)$ of the system (12.83), we shall write,

$$r(t) = \sqrt{[x(t)]^2 + [y(t)]^2}.$$

We shall also need the following definitions.

A function $E(x, y)$ with the properties that $E(0, 0) = 0$ and $E(x, y) > 0$ for $0 < r < h$, for some positive number h, is said to be *positive-definite*. Similarly, if $E(0, 0) = 0$ and $E(x, y) < 0$ for $0 < r < h$, we say that $E(x, y)$ is *negative-definite*. If $E(0, 0) = 0$ and $E(x, y) \geq 0$ for $0 < r < h$, we say that $E(x, y)$ is *positive-semidefinite*; if $E(0, 0) = 0$ and $E(x, y) \leq 0$ for $0 < r < h$, we say that $E(x, y)$ is *negative-semidefinite*. Functions of the form $Ax^{2m} + By^{2n}$, where A and B are positive constants and m and n are positive integers, are clearly positive-definite. Since a function $E(x, y)$ is negative-definite if, and only if, the function $-E(x, y)$ is positive-definite, functions of the form $-(Ax^{2m} + By^{2n})$, with $A > 0$, $B > 0$, are negative-definite. The functions x^{2m}, y^{2m}, and $(x - y)^{2m}$ are positive-semidefinite, but they are not positive-definite.

We now turn to the questions of stability and asymptotic stability of an isolated critical point (x_0, y_0) of the system (12.83). Without loss of generality, we can take the critical point to be $(0, 0)$. For if this is not the case, the translation of coordinates $u = x - x_0$, $v = y - y_0$ puts the critical point at the origin of the uv plane. The results that we now prove are due to Liapunov.

Theorem 5. In a region of the form $0 \leq r < h$, where $h > 0$, let the function $E(x, y)$ be continuous along with its first partial derivatives and be positive-definite. Then
(a) If the function

$$\frac{\partial E}{\partial x} P + \frac{\partial E}{\partial y} Q$$

is negative-semidefinite, the critical point $(0, 0)$ of the system (12.83) is stable;
(b) If the function

$$\frac{\partial E}{\partial x} P + \frac{\partial E}{\partial y} Q$$

is negative-definite, the critical point is asymptotically stable.

We remark that a function $E(x, y)$ of one of the types described above is called a *Liapunov function* for the system (12.83). Also, sufficient conditions that the critical point be unstable are given in Exercise 7.

Proof. The proof is based on these ideas. The function $E(x, y)$ has a proper minimum at $(0, 0)$. The surface $z = E(x, y)$ resembles a paraboloid which is tangent to the xy plane at the origin. Along the trajectory of a solution $x(t)$, $y(t)$, E is nonincreasing. We shall show that this implies that $r(t)$ cannot increase very much, at least if $r(0)$ is small. In case (b), E is actually decreasing along the trajectory. We shall show that $E(t) \to 0$, which implies that $r(t) \to 0$ since E is positive-definite.

Given ε, let α be a positive number such that $\alpha < \min(\varepsilon, h)$. Since the function $E(x, y)$ is positive-definite, it has a positive minimum m on the circle $r = \alpha$. Since $E(x, y) \to 0$ as $(x, y) \to (0, 0)$, there is a positive number δ such that $E(x, y) < m$ whenever $r < \delta$. Let $x(t)$, $y(t)$ be any solution of the system (12.83) for which $0 < r(0) < \delta$. Since $dE/dt \le 0$, $E[x(t), y(t)] < m$ for $t \ge 0$, and hence $r(t) < \alpha < \varepsilon$ for $t \ge 0$. Hence the critical point $(0, 0)$ is stable.

In case (b), $dE/dt < 0$, so E is a decreasing function of t that is bounded below by zero. Hence E must tend to a finite limit L as $t \to +\infty$. The problem now is to show that $L = 0$. If this is the case, $r(t)$ must approach zero, since E is positive-definite. We can then conclude that the critical point is asymptotically stable.

Clearly $L \ge 0$. Suppose that $L > 0$. Then $E[x(t), y(t)] \ge L$ for $t \ge 0$. Since $E(x, y) \to 0$ as $(x, y) \to (0, 0)$, there exists a positive number β such that $E(x, y) < L$ when $r < \beta$. In the region $\beta \le r \le \alpha$ the function $P\partial E/\partial x + Q\partial E/\partial y$ has a negative maximum which we denote by $-k$. Then $dE/dt \le -k$ for $t \ge 0$. Since

$$E[x(t), y(t)] = E[x(0), y(0)] + \int_0^t \frac{dE}{dt}\, dt,$$

we have

$$E[x(t), y(t)] \le E[x(0), y(0)] - kt$$

for $t \ge 0$. But the right member of this inequality becomes negatively infinite as $t \to +\infty$, which contradicts the hypothesis that $E \ge 0$. Hence $L = 0$. This concludes the proof of the theorem.

The difficulty in applying Theorem 5 lies in the problem of the construction of a suitable Liapunov function. In a given case, a certain amount of ingenuity may be required. We shall consider here one example. In the next section, a general class of problems will be considered. For fuller discussions of the method, see References 2, 5, and 8 at the end of this chapter. The system

$$\frac{dx}{dt} = -2y^3, \qquad \frac{dy}{dt} = 2x - y^3 \tag{12.87}$$

has a single critical point at $(0, 0)$. We attempt to construct a Liapunov function of the form $E(x, y) = Ax^{2m} + By^{2n}$. For such a function,

$$\frac{dE}{dt} = 2mAx^{2m-1}(-2y^3) + 2nBy^{2n-1}(2x - y^3)$$

$$= 4(-mAx^{2m-1}y^3 + nBxy^{2n-1}) - 2nBy^{2n+2}.$$

If we choose $m = 1$, $n = 2$, $A = 2$, and $B = 1$, then $dE/dt = -4y^6$ (which is negative-semidefinite) and $E = 2x^2 + y^4$ (which is positive-definite). Hence the critical point $(0, 0)$ of the system (12.87) is stable. Notice that we have not proved that the critical point is not asymptotically stable.

In the construction of Liapunov functions, the following result is sometimes useful.

Theorem 6. The function

$$E(x, y) = Ax^2 + Bxy + Cy^2, \tag{12.88}$$

where A, B, and C are constants, is positive-definite if, and only if,

$$A > 0, \qquad 4AC - B^2 > 0, \tag{12.89}$$

and it is negative-definite if, and only if,

$$A < 0, \qquad 4AC - B^2 > 0. \tag{12.90}$$

Proof. Setting $y = 0$ in the expression (12.88), we have $E(x, 0) = Ax^2$. Hence $E(x, 0) > 0$ for $x \neq 0$ if, and only if, $A > 0$. For $y \neq 0$, we may write

$$E(x, y) = y^2 \left[A\left(\frac{x}{y}\right)^2 + B\left(\frac{x}{y}\right) + C \right].$$

But the polynomial $A\lambda^2 + B\lambda + C$, which is positive for large λ when $A > 0$, does not vanish or change sign if, and only if, its discriminant $B^2 - 4AC$ is negative. Hence the conditions (12.89) are necessary and sufficient that $E(x, y)$ be positive-definite. The second part of the theorem can be proved by considering the function $-E(x, y)$.

12.8 EXERCISES

1. Determine if the given function is positive-definite, or negative-definite, or neither.
   (a) $x^2 - xy + y^2$ (b) $2x^2 - 3xy + y^2$ (c) $-x^2 + 3xy - 3y^2$

2. Show that a function of the form $Ax^3 + Bx^2y + Cxy^2 + Dy^3$ can be neither positive-definite nor negative-definite.

3. What is the geometrical significance of the condition

$$xP(x, y) + yQ(x\ y) = \mathbf{V}(x, y) \cdot (x\mathbf{i} + y\mathbf{j}) < 0, \qquad 0 < r < h?$$

   Show that if this condition is satisfied, the critical point $(0, 0)$ of the system (12.83) is asymptotically stable.

4. Show that the origin is an asymptotically stable critical point for the system

$$\frac{dx}{dt} = -x^3 + y^3, \qquad \frac{dy}{dt} = -x^3 - y^3.$$

5. Show that the origin is an asymptotically stable critical point for the system

$$\frac{dx}{dt} = x^3 - 2xy, \qquad \frac{dy}{dt} = 3y^3 + x^2.$$

6. Show that the critical point $(0, 0)$ of the system

$$\frac{dx}{dt} = -x^3 + y^2, \qquad \frac{dy}{dt} = -2xy$$

is stable.

7. Let every neighborhood of $(0, 0)$ contain at least one point where $E(x,y)$ is positive. If $P\,\partial E/\partial x + Q\,\partial E/\partial y$ is positive-definite, show that the critical point $(0, 0)$ of the system (12.83) is unstable.

8. Show that the system

$$\frac{dx}{dt} = x + y^2, \qquad \frac{dy}{dt} = -x^3 y + y^3$$

has an unstable critical point at $(0, 0)$.

9. Suppose that $f(0) = 0$ and that $xf(x) > 0$ for $x \neq 0$ (that is, $f(x) > 0$ for $x > 0$ and $f(x) < 0$ for $x < 0$).

(a) Show that the function

$$E(x, y) = \tfrac{1}{2}y^2 + \int_0^x f(s)\,ds$$

is positive-definite.

(b) Show that the critical point $x = 0$, $dx/dt = 0$ is stable for the equation

$$\frac{d^2x}{dt^2} + f(x) = 0.$$

10. Consider the equation

$$\frac{d^2x}{dt^2} + g(x)\frac{dx}{dt} + f(x) = 0,$$

where $f(0) = 0$ and $xf(x) > 0$ for $x \neq 0$. If $g(x) \geq 0$ in some interval $|x| < h$, show that the critical point $x = 0$, $dx/dt = 0$ is stable.

11. Theorem 5 can be generalized to systems of higher dimensions. Consider the n-dimensional autonomous system

$$\frac{d\mathbf{x}}{dt} = \mathbf{f(x)}, \tag{1}$$

where $\mathbf{x}$ has components $x_1, x_2, \ldots, x_n$. Suppose that $\mathbf{f(0) = 0}$, so that the system has a critical point at $\mathbf{x = 0}$. If we define the length of the

vector $\mathbf{x}$, written $|\mathbf{x}|$, as $|\mathbf{x}| = (x_1{}^2 + x_2{}^2 + \cdots + x_n{}^2)^{1/2}$, then the defini-
tions of stability, asymptotic stability, positive-definite function $E(\mathbf{x})$,
etc., carry over to n dimensions. State and prove the generalization of
Theorem 5 for the system (1). (See, for example, Reference 2 at the end
of this chapter.)

12.9 Perturbed Linear Systems

Suppose that the system

$$\frac{dx}{dt} = P(x, y), \qquad \frac{dy}{dt} = Q(x, y) \tag{12.91}$$

has a critical point at $(0, 0)$. If the functions $P(x, y)$ and $Q(x, y)$ can be
expanded in Taylor series of two variables about the point $(0, 0)$, then we
have

$$\frac{dx}{dt} = P_x(0, 0)x + P_y(0, 0)y + \cdots,$$

$$\frac{dy}{dt} = Q_x(0, 0)x + Q_y(0, 0)y + \cdots, \tag{12.92}$$

where the dots indicate terms of second degree and higher in x and y. When
$|x|$ and $|y|$ are small, these higher-degree terms, and their sums, will be very
small. If we simply omit these terms, the resulting system is linear. It is
interesting to consider what properties of solutions of the system (12.91) are
preserved in this "linearization" process.

More generally, we shall consider systems of the form

$$\frac{dx}{dt} = ax + by + p(x, y), \qquad \frac{dy}{dt} = cx + dy + q(x, y), \tag{12.93}$$

where a, b, c, d are constants, $p(x, y)$, $q(x, y)$ are continuous along with their
first partial derivatives (in a region D that contains the origin), and

$$\lim_{(x,y)\to(0,0)} \frac{(px, y)}{\sqrt{x^2 + y^2}} = \lim_{(x,y)\to(0,0)} \frac{q(x, y)}{\sqrt{x^2 + y^2}} = 0. \tag{12.94}$$

Note that these last conditions imply that $p(0, 0) = q(0, 0) = 0$, so the system
(12.93) has a critical point at the origin. Associated with the system (12.93) is
the linear system

$$\frac{dx}{dt} = ax + by, \qquad \frac{dy}{dt} = cx + dy. \tag{12.95}$$

A system of the form (12.93), when the conditions (12.94) are satisfied, is
sometimes referred to as a *perturbed linear system*. An example of such a
system is

$$\frac{dx}{dt} = -y + x^2, \qquad \frac{dy}{dt} = x - y + 2xy, \tag{12.96}$$

with $p(x, y) = x^2$, and $q(x, y) = 2xy$. Using polar coordinates r and θ, we see that

$$\frac{|p(x, y)|}{\sqrt{x^2 + y^2}} = \left|\frac{r^2 \cos^2 \theta}{r}\right| \leq r, \qquad \frac{|q(x, y)|}{\sqrt{x^2 + y^2}} = \left|\frac{2r^2 \cos \theta \sin \theta}{r}\right| \leq 2r,$$

so $p(x, y)/r$ and $q(x, y)/r$ approach zero as $(x, y) \to (0, 0)$. Hence the conditions (12.94) are satisfied.

We now prove a theorem about the asymptotic stability of a critical point of a perturbed linear system.

Theorem 7. If the critical point $(0, 0)$ of the linear system (12.95) is asymptotically stable, then the critical point $(0, 0)$ of the nonlinear system (12.93) is also asymptotically stable.

Proof. To prove the theorem, we shall exhibit a Liapunov function for the system (12.93). We define

$$E(x, y) = \tfrac{1}{2}(Ax^2 + 2Bxy + Cy^2), \tag{12.97}$$

where

$$A = \frac{c^2 + d^2 + (ad - bc)}{\Delta}, \qquad B = -\frac{ac + bd}{\Delta}$$

$$C = \frac{a^2 + b^2 + (ad - bc)}{\Delta}, \qquad \Delta = -(a + d)(ad - bc). \tag{12.98}$$

In view of the corollary to Theorem 4, $a + d < 0$ and $ad - bc > 0$, so $\Delta > 0$ and $A > 0$. Also,

$$\Delta^2(AC - B^2) = [(a^2 + b^2 + c^2 + d^2)(ad - bc) + (a^2 + b^2)(c^2 + d^2)]$$

$$- (a^2c^2 + 2abcd + b^2d^2)$$

$$= (a^2 + b^2 + c^2 + d^2)(ad - bc) + 2(ad - bc)^2,$$

so $AC - B^2 > 0$. According to Theorem 6, the function $E(x, y)$ is positive-definite.

A fairly lengthy, but routine, calculation shows that†

$$(ax + by)\frac{\partial E}{\partial x} + (cx + dy)\frac{\partial E}{\partial y} = -(x^2 + y^2) \tag{12.99}$$

and this function is clearly negative-definite. Hence the function $E(x, y)$ is a Liapunov function for the linear system (12.95). We shall show that it is also a Liapunov function for the nonlinear system (12.93).

---

† The function $E(x, y)$ was actually constructed by attempting to find constants A, B, C, such that the relation (12.99) held.

Setting

$$P(x, y) = ax + by + p(x, y)$$

and

$$Q(x, y) = cx + dy + q(x, y),$$

we have

$$P\frac{\partial E}{\partial x} + Q\frac{\partial E}{\partial y} = -(x^2 + y^2) + (Ax + By)p(x, y) + (Bx + Cy)q(x, y).$$

In terms of polar coordinates, this expression can be written as

$$-r^2 + r[(A\cos\theta + B\sin\theta)p(x, y) + (B\cos\theta + C\sin\theta)q(x, y)].$$

Let $M = \max(|A|, |B|, |C|)$. In view of our hypothesis (12.94), there exists a positive constant h such that

$$|p(x, y)| < \frac{r}{6M}, \qquad |q(x, y)| < \frac{r}{6M}$$

whenever $0 \leq r < h$. Then, for $0 < r < h$, we have

$$P\frac{\partial E}{\partial x} + Q\frac{\partial E}{\partial y} < -r^2 + 4Mr\frac{r}{6M} = -\frac{1}{3}r^2 < 0.$$

Hence the function $E(x, y)$ is a Liapunov function for the system (12.93). We conclude that the critical point $(0, 0)$ of this system is asymptotically stable.

As a first example, let us consider the system (12.96), which was

$$\frac{dx}{dt} = -y + x^2, \qquad \frac{dy}{dt} = x - y + 2xy. \tag{12.100}$$

The associated linear system is

$$\frac{dx}{dt} = -y, \qquad \frac{dy}{dt} = x - y. \tag{12.101}$$

In this system, $a = 0$, $b = -1$, $c = 1$, and $d = -1$. Then $a + d = -1 < 0$ and $ad - bc = 1 > 0$, so the critical point $(0, 0)$ is asymptotically stable, both for the linear system (12.101) and for the nonlinear system (12.100).

As a second example, let us consider the damped motion of a simple pendulum. If the pendulum has mass m and length L, and if the damping force is equal to c times the velocity, we have (Figure 12.3)

$$mL^2\frac{d^2\theta}{dt^2} + cL^2\frac{d\theta}{dt} + mgL\sin\theta = 0,$$

or

$$\frac{d^2\theta}{dt^2} + \frac{c}{m}\frac{d\theta}{dt} + \frac{g}{L}\sin\theta = 0. \tag{12.102}$$

Setting $\theta = x$ and $d\theta/dt = y$, we obtain the system formulation

$$\frac{dx}{dt} = y, \qquad \frac{dy}{dt} = -\frac{c}{m}y - \frac{g}{L}\sin x. \qquad (12.103)$$

Since

$$\sin x = x - \frac{x^3}{3!} + \cdots,$$

we may write

$$\frac{dx}{dt} = y, \qquad \frac{dy}{dt} = -\frac{g}{L}x - \frac{c}{m}y + \frac{g}{L}(x - \sin x), \qquad (12.104)$$

where

$$\lim_{(x,y)\to(0,0)} \frac{g}{L}\frac{x - \sin x}{\sqrt{x^2 + y^2}} = 0.$$

It is easy to verify that the critical point $(0, 0)$ of the associated linear system

$$\frac{dx}{dt} = y, \qquad \frac{dy}{dt} = -\frac{g}{L}x - \frac{c}{m}y$$

is asymptotically stable. Consequently the origin is also an asymptotically stable critical point for the system (12.103). Thus, for small initial disturbances, the oscillations of the pendulum die out with time.

12.9   EXERCISES

1. Show that the roots of the equation $\lambda^2 - (a + d)\lambda + (ad - bc) = 0$ both have positive real parts if, and only if, $a + d > 0$ and $ad - bc > 0$. Suggestion: let $\lambda = -\mu$.

2. If both roots of the equation

$$\lambda^2 - (a + d)\lambda + (ad - bc) = 0$$

have positive real parts, show that $(0, 0)$ is an unstable critical point for the system (12.93). (Actually, if even one root has a positive real part, it can be shown that the critical point is unstable.) Suggestion: show that there exists a positive-definite function of the form $E(x, y) = \frac{1}{2}(Ax^2 + Bxy + Cy^2)$ such that $(ax + by)E_x + (cx + dy)E_y = x^2 + y^2$. Use the result of Exercise 7, Section 12.8.

3. Verify that $(0, 0)$ is a critical point for the given system, and investigate its stability.

(a) $dx/dt = -x + y - 2xy, \qquad dy/dt = -y + xy - y^3$

(b) $dx/dt = -3y + x \cos y, \qquad dy/dt = x - 2y + x^2$

(c) $dx/dt = 2x + y + x(e^y - 1), \qquad dy/dt = x + y + 3xy^4$

(d) $dx/dt = x + (x^2 + y^2)^{3/2}, \qquad dy/dt = x + 2y$

4. If the critical point $(0, 0)$ of the linear system (12.95) is stable, but not asymptotically stable, the origin may or may not be stable for the non-linear system (12.93). Show this by proving that $(0, 0)$ is asymptotically stable for the system

$$\frac{dx}{dt} = y - x^3, \qquad \frac{dy}{dt} = -x - y^3$$

but unstable for the system

$$\frac{dx}{dt} = y + x^3, \qquad \frac{dy}{dt} = -x + y^3$$

12.10   Periodic Solutions

It will be recalled that a solution $x(t)$, $y(t)$ of the system

$$\frac{dx}{dt} = P(x, y), \qquad \frac{dy}{dt} = Q(x, y) \tag{12.105}$$

is said to be periodic with period T if the solution exists for all t and if $x(t + T) = x(t)$, $y(t + T) = y(t)$ for all t. The trajectory of a periodic solution is a closed curve in the phase plane. If $P(x, y)$ and $Q(x, y)$ possess continuous first partial derivatives (in a region D), then only one trajectory can pass through a given point. Consequently, if a solution $x(t)$, $y(t)$ exists for $t_0 \le t \le t_0 + T$ for some number t_0, and if

$$x(t_0 + T) = x(t_0), \qquad y(t_0 + T) = y(t_0),$$

then the solution must exist for all t and be periodic with period T. Of course, a constant solution $x = x_0$, $y = y_0$, which corresponds to a critical point of the system (12.105), is periodic. Every positive number T is a period of such a solution, according to our definition. From now on, when we speak of a periodic solution, we shall mean a nonconstant periodic solution.

In the case of a linear system,

$$\frac{dx}{dt} = ax + by, \qquad \frac{dy}{dt} = cx + dy, \tag{12.106}$$

a periodic solution occurs when, and only when, the roots of the auxiliary equation

$$\lambda^2 - (a + d)\lambda + (ad - bc) = 0$$

are pure imaginary. In this case, *every* nonconstant solution is periodic. The trajectories are ellipses (Exercise 1). Thus, for a linear system, either every nonconstant solution is periodic or else no solution (other than $x(t) = y(t) = 0$) is periodic.

For a nonlinear system, this is not the case. Let us consider, for example, the system

$$\frac{dx}{dt} = -y + x(1 - x^2 - y^2), \qquad \frac{dy}{dt} = x + y(1 - x^2 - y^2). \quad (12.107)$$

Solutions of this system can be found by introducing polar coordinates r, θ, where

$$x = r \cos \theta, \qquad y = r \sin \theta. \qquad (12.108)$$

Implicit differentiation yields the relations

$$x \frac{dx}{dt} + y \frac{dy}{dt} = r \frac{dr}{dt}, \qquad x \frac{dy}{dt} - y \frac{dx}{dt} = r^2 \frac{d\theta}{dt} \qquad (12.109)$$

between the derivatives with respect to t of x and y and the derivatives of r and θ. If we multiply through in the first equation of the system (12.107) by x and in the second by y, and add, we find that

$$r \frac{dr}{dt} = r^2(1 - r^2). \qquad (12.110)$$

Similarly, if we multiply through in the first equation by y and in the second by x, and subtract, we find that

$$r^2 \frac{d\theta}{dt} = r^2. \qquad (12.111)$$

Now $r = 0$ corresponds to the solution $x = 0$, $y = 0$ of the system (12.107). For $r \neq 0$ we consider the system

$$\frac{dr}{dt} = r(1 - r^2), \qquad \frac{d\theta}{dt} = 1. \qquad (12.112)$$

The equations are uncoupled and separable, and the solutions are found to be

$$r = \frac{1}{\sqrt{1 + c_1 e^{-2t}}}, \qquad \theta = t + c_2, \qquad (12.113)$$

where c_1 and c_2 are constants. The corresponding solutions of the original system (12.107) are

$$x = \frac{\cos(t + c_2)}{\sqrt{1 + c_1 e^{-2t}}}, \qquad y = \frac{\sin(t + c_2)}{\sqrt{1 + c_1 e^{-2t}}}. \qquad (12.114)$$

Let us now study the relations (12.113). For $c_1 = 0$, we have the solutions

$$r = 1, \qquad \theta = t + c_2, \qquad (12.115)$$

which describe the circular trajectory $x^2 + y^2 = 1$. When $c_1 < 0$, we see that $r > 1$ and that $r \to 1$ as $t \to \infty$. When $c_1 > 0$, we have $r < 1$, and again $r \to 1$

as $t \to +\infty$. Thus the other trajectories spiral toward the circle $x^2 + y^2 = 1$ as $t \to +\infty$, either from the inside or from the outside. This situation is illustrated in Figure 12.8. The nonlinear system (12.107) possesses only one closed trajectory.

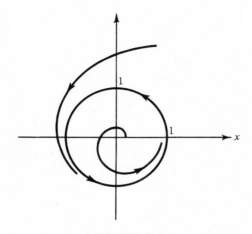

FIGURE 12.8

We were able to show the existence of a periodic solution of the system (12.107) by actually finding the solutions of the system. In most cases, however, we cannot expect to be able to do this. Sufficient conditions for the existence of a periodic solution are given by the Poincare-Bendixon theorem, which we now state without proof.

Theorem 8.   Let $P(x, y)$ and $Q(x, y)$ possess continuous first partial derivatives in a region G. Let D be a *bounded* region such that D and its boundary are contained in G. Let R denote the region that consists of D and its boundary and assume that R contains no critical point of the system (12.105). If $x(t)$, $y(t)$ is a solution of the system that exists and stays in R for $t \ge t_0$, for some number t_0, then either

(a) the solution is periodic, or (b) the solution spirals toward a periodic solution of the system (12.105) as $t \to +\infty$. In either case, the system possesses a periodic solution.

The difficulty in applying the Poincare-Bendixon theorem is in showing that a solution stays inside a region R. One way to do this is to show that on the boundary of R, the vector $\mathbf{V} = P\mathbf{i} + Q\mathbf{j}$ points into R. Then a solution that once enters R can never leave it. We consider as an illustration the system

$$\frac{dx}{dt} = 2x + y - x(x^2 + y^2)^2, \qquad \frac{dy}{dt} = -x + 2y - y(x^2 + y^2)^2. \qquad (12.116)$$

This system possesses the single critical point $(0,0)$. The component of $\mathbf{V}$ in the direction away from the origin (the radial component) is

$$\mathbf{V} \cdot \frac{x\mathbf{i} + y\mathbf{j}}{r} = \frac{1}{r}[2x^2 + xy - x^2(x^2 + y^2)^2 - xy + 2y^2 - y^2(x^2 + y^2)^2]$$

$$= \frac{1}{r}(2r^2 - r^5) = 2r - r^4.$$

On the circle $r = 1$, this component is positive, while on the circle $r = 2$, it is negative. If we take for our region R the annular region $1 \le r \le 2$, we see that the vector $\mathbf{V}$ points into R on the boundary of R. Also, R contains no critical points of the system (12.116). According to the Poincare-Bendixon theorem, the system must possess at least one periodic solution.

Although it is quite general, the Poincare-Bendixon theorem is usually not easy to apply. Other, less general, but more practical, criteria for the existence of periodic solutions have been developed. Liénard established the existence of periodic solutions for certain classes of equations of the general form

$$\frac{d^2x}{dt^2} + f(x)\frac{dx}{dt} + g(x) = 0. \tag{12.117}$$

(An equation of the form (12.117) is called a *Liénard equation.*) Levinson and Smith later gave more general results. We shall present one theorem without proof. In order to state the theorem, we define the functions $F(x)$ and $G(x)$ as

$$F(x) = \int_0^x f(s)\, ds, \qquad G(x) = \int_0^x g(s)\, ds, \tag{12.118}$$

where $f(x)$ and $g(x)$ are the same functions that appear in the equation (12.117).

Theorem 9.   Let the functions $f(x)$ and $g'(x)$ be continuous for all x and satisfy the following conditions:

(a) $f(x)$ is even and $g(x)$ is odd, with $g(x) > 0$ for $x > 0$;
(b) There exists a positive number a such that $F(x) < 0$ for $0 < x < a$, $F(x) > 0$ for $x > a$, and $F(x)$ is monotonically increasing† for $x > a$;
(c) $\displaystyle\lim_{x \to +\infty} F(x) = +\infty, \qquad \lim_{x \to +\infty} G(x) = +\infty.$

Then the equation (12.117) possesses a periodic solution whose closed trajectory encloses the origin of the phase plane. This periodic solution is unique in the sense that the equation has no other closed trajectory. Furthermore, every other trajectory except the point $(0, 0)$ spirals toward the closed trajectory as $t \to +\infty$.

---

† A function $F(x)$ is said to be monotonically increasing if $F(x_2) \ge F(x_1)$ whenever $x_2 > x_1$. A sufficient condition for $F(x)$ to be monotonically increasing is that $F'(x) \ge 0$.

As an application for this theorem, we consider the *van der Pol equation*

$$\frac{d^2x}{dt^2} + \mu(x^2 - 1)\frac{dx}{dt} + x = 0, \qquad (12.119)$$

where μ is a positive constant. This equation arises in the study of vacuum tube circuits. Here $f(x) = \mu(x^2 - 1)$ and $g(x) = x$. Clearly $f(x)$ is even and $g(x)$ is odd, and $g(x) > 0$ for $x > 0$. Since $F(x) = \mu(\frac{1}{3}x^3 - x)$ and $G(x) = \frac{1}{2}x^2$, we have $F(x) \to +\infty$ and $G(x) \to +\infty$ as $x \to +\infty$. Also, writing $F(x) = \frac{1}{3}\mu x(x^2 - 3)$, we see that $F(x) < 0$ for $0 < x < \sqrt{3}$ and $F(x) > 0$ for $x > \sqrt{3}$. Since $F'(x) = f(x) = \mu(x^2 - 1)$ is positive for $x > 1$, certainly $F(x)$ is increasing for $x > \sqrt{3}$. Thus the hypotheses of Theorem 9 are satisfied and we conclude that the equation (12.119) has a periodic solution.

12.10 EXERCISES

1. Show that when the roots of its auxiliary equation are pure imaginary, the trajectories of the linear system (12.106) are ellipses.

2. Find the solutions of the system

$$\frac{dx}{dt} = y + 8(x^2 + y^2 - 4), \qquad \frac{dy}{dt} = -x + 8y(x^2 + y^2 - 4).$$

Show on a graph the pattern of the trajectories.

3. Show that the system

$$\frac{dx}{dt} = 3x + y - x\exp(x^2 + y^2), \qquad \frac{dy}{dt} = -x + 3y - y\exp(x^2 + y^2)$$

possesses at least one periodic solution.

4. Show that the given equation possesses a periodic solution.

(a) $\dfrac{d^2x}{dt^2} + (x^4 - x^2)\dfrac{dx}{dt} + x = 0$

(b) $\dfrac{d^2x}{dt^2} + c(x^{2m} - k^2)\dfrac{dx}{dt} + x^{2n-1} = 0$

where c and k are positive constants, and m and n are positive integers.

5. Consider the equation $d^2x/dt^2 + f(x) = 0$, where $f(0) = 0$ and $xf(x) > 0$ for $x \neq 0$. Show that the trajectories are closed curves that enclose the origin. Suggestion: show that the trajectories are given by $\frac{1}{2}y^2 + F(x) = C$, where

$$F(x) = \int_0^x f(s)\,ds.$$

6. (a) Assume that the system (12.105) has an isolated critical point at (0, 0). Also assume that there exists a positive-definite Liapunov function $E(x, y)$ such that $P\partial E/\partial x + Q\partial E/\partial y$ is identically zero in a region of the form $0 \le r \le h$. Show that the equation possesses a periodic solution. Suggestion: use the Poincare-Bendixon theorem.

(b) Show that the equation of Problem 5 is a special case, with

$$E(x, y) = \tfrac{1}{2}y^2 + F(x)$$

(c) Show that the system

$$\frac{dx}{dt} = -x^3 y + y^2, \qquad \frac{dy}{dt} = -xy + x^4$$

possess a periodic solution.

REFERENCES

1. Birkhoff, G., and Rota, G., *Ordinary Differential Equations.* Ginn, New York, 1962.
2. Cesari, L., *Asymptotic Behavior and Stability Problems in Ordinary Differential Equations.* Springer, Berlin, 1959.
3. Coddington, E. A., and Levinson, N., *Theory of Ordinary Differential Equations.* McGraw-Hill, New York, 1955.
4. Hurewicz, W., *Lectures on Ordinary Differential Equations.* The M. I. T. Press, Cambridge, Mass., 1958.
5. LaSalle, J. P., and Lefschetz, S., *Stability by Liapunov's Direct Method with Applications.* Academic Press, New York, 1961.
6. Lefschetz, S., *Differential Equations: Geometric Theory*, 2nd ed. Wiley, New York, 1963.
7. Pontryagin, L. S., *Ordinary Differential Equations.* Addison-Wesley, Reading, Mass., 1962.
8. Saaty, T. L., and Bram. J., *Nonlinear Mathematics.* McGraw-Hill, New York, 1964.

APPENDIX

This appendix presents, in summary form, some material from linear algebra that is used in the text. It includes definitions and properties of matrices and determinants, as well as results for systems of linear algebraic equations. For proofs of the stated facts, see the references listed at the end of the appendix. A set of exercises has also been included.

Let m and n be positive integers. A *matrix*, of size $m \times n$, is an ordered set of numbers a_{ij}, where $1 \leq i \leq m$, $1 \leq j \leq n$. The numbers a_{ij} are called the *elements* of the matrix. In describing a matrix, it is convenient to place the elements in a rectangular array with m rows and n columns, as shown below.

$$
\begin{pmatrix}
a_{11} & a_{12} \cdots a_{1n} \\
a_{21} & a_{22} \cdots a_{2n} \\
\cdots\cdots\cdots\cdots\cdots\cdot \\
a_{n1} & a_{n2} \cdots a_{nn}
\end{pmatrix}
\tag{A1}
$$

We shall denote matrices by capital letters A, B, C, and so on, and shall denote the elements of a matrix by the corresponding lower-case symbol. Thus a_{ij} denotes the element in the ith row and jth column of the matrix A.

Two matrices A and B are said to be equal, written $A = B$, if they are of the same size and if their corresponding elements are equal. Thus if A and B are of size $m \times n$, they are equal if, and only if, $a_{ij} = b_{ij}$ for $1 \leq i \leq m$, $1 \leq j \leq n$.

If A is any matrix and c is any real number, the product cA is defined to be the matrix whose size is that of A and whose elements are the numbers ca_{ij}.

407

For example, if

$$A = \begin{pmatrix} 2 & 0 & -1 \\ 1 & -3 & 4 \end{pmatrix},$$

then

$$2A = \begin{pmatrix} 4 & 0 & -2 \\ 2 & -6 & 8 \end{pmatrix}.$$

If A and B are matrices of the same size, the sum $A + B$ is defined to be the matrix of the same size as A and B whose elements are $a_{ij} + b_{ij}$. Thus, if

$$A = \begin{pmatrix} 2 & 0 & -1 \\ 1 & -3 & 4 \end{pmatrix}, \qquad B = \begin{pmatrix} 1 & 2 & 3 \\ 4 & 5 & 6 \end{pmatrix},$$

then

$$A + B = \begin{pmatrix} 2+1 & 0+2 & -1+3 \\ 1+4 & -3+5 & 4+6 \end{pmatrix} = \begin{pmatrix} 3 & 2 & 2 \\ 5 & 2 & 10 \end{pmatrix}.$$

The sum of two matrices that are not of the same size is not defined.

Let A be a matrix of size $p \times n$ and let B be a matrix of size $n \times q$. Then the number of columns of A is the same as the number of rows of B. The product, AB, is defined to be the matrix C, of size $p \times q$, whose elements c_{ij} are given by the formula

$$c_{ij} = \sum_{k=1}^{n} a_{ik} b_{kj}, \qquad 1 \le i \le p, \qquad 1 \le j \le q. \tag{A2}$$

Thus the element c_{ij} in the ith row and jth column of C is formed by multiplying each element in the ith row of A by the corresponding element in the jth column of B, and then adding the n products so formed. As an example, let

$$A = \begin{pmatrix} 1 & -2 \\ 2 & 0 \\ -3 & 1 \end{pmatrix}, \qquad B = \begin{pmatrix} -1 & 4 \\ 2 & 1 \end{pmatrix}.$$

Then

$$AB = \begin{pmatrix} 1(-1) + (-2)2 & 1 \cdot 4 + (-2)1 \\ 2(-1) + 0 \cdot 2 & 2 \cdot 4 + 0 \cdot 1 \\ (-3)(-1) + 1 \cdot 2 & (-3)4 + 1 \cdot 1 \end{pmatrix} = \begin{pmatrix} -5 & 2 \\ -2 & 8 \\ 3 & -11 \end{pmatrix}.$$

We note that the product BA is not defined, since B is of size 2×2 and A is of size 3×2. In general, $BA \ne AB$, even when both products are defined.

A matrix is said to be *square* if it has the same number of rows as it does columns. A square matrix, of size $n \times n$, is said to be of *order n*. Associated with a square matrix A, with elements a_{ij}, is a number, called the *determinant* of A. We denote this number by det A, and write

$$\det A = \begin{vmatrix} a_{11} & a_{12} \cdots a_{1n} \\ a_{21} & a_{22} \cdots a_{2n} \\ \cdots\cdots\cdots\cdots\cdots \\ a_{n1} & a_{n2} \cdots a_{nn} \end{vmatrix}. \tag{A3}$$

For a matrix A of order one, with a single element a_{11}, we define

$$\det A = a_{11}. \tag{A4}$$

We shall presently define determinants of matrices of higher order by induction.

If, in a matrix A of order n, we delete the ith row and jth column, we form a matrix of order $n - 1$. The determinant of this matrix is called the *minor* of the element a_{ij}. We denote the minor by M_{ij}. The number $A_{ij} = (-1)^{i+j}M_{ij}$ is called the *cofactor* of the element a_{ij}. We now define, inductively, the determinant of a matrix of order n by means of the formula

$$\det A = a_{11}A_{11} + a_{12}A_{12} + \cdots + a_{1n}A_{1n}. \tag{A5}$$

According to this formula, to obtain the determinant of A, we multiply each element in the first row of A by its cofactor, and then add the n products so formed.

The determinant of a matrix of order one was defined by formula (A4). The minors of a matrix of order two are determinants of first-order matrices. We therefore have the formula

$$\begin{vmatrix} a_{11} & a_{12} \\ a_{21} & a_{22} \end{vmatrix} = a_{11}a_{22} + a_{12}(-a_{21}) = a_{11}a_{22} - a_{12}a_{21}. \tag{A6}$$

If A is a matrix of order three, its minors are determinants of second-order matrices, and they can be found using formula (A6). Actually, it can be shown that if the elements of *any* row, or column, of a square matrix A are multiplied by their cofactors and the products added, the sum is equal to the determinant of A. This result is valid for matrices of arbitrary order. In the worked example below, which concerns the determinant of a matrix of order three, we have used the third column.

$$\begin{vmatrix} 1 & 0 & 2 \\ 2 & -1 & 1 \\ 3 & 2 & 3 \end{vmatrix} = 2\begin{vmatrix} 2 & -1 \\ 3 & 2 \end{vmatrix} - \begin{vmatrix} 1 & 0 \\ 3 & 2 \end{vmatrix} + 3\begin{vmatrix} 1 & 0 \\ 2 & -1 \end{vmatrix}$$

$$= 2(7) - 2 + 3(-1) = 9.$$

If A and B are square matrices of the same size, then the product AB is defined. It can be shown that $\det(AB) = \det A \cdot \det B$. Other properties of determinants are stated below. It is assumed that A is a square matrix.

(a) If all the elements in any one row (or column) of A are zero, then $\det A = 0$.

(b) If two rows (or columns) of A are identical, or proportional, then $\det A = 0$.

(c) If B is obtained from A by interchanging any two rows (or columns) of A, then $\det B = -\det A$.

(d) If B is obtained from A by multiplying each element of one row (or column) of A by the same constant k, then $\det B = k \det A$.

(e) If B is formed from A by adding to each element of one row (or column) of A, k times the corresponding element of some other row (or column), then $\det B = \det A$.

(f) If B is the matrix whose rows are the same as the columns of A, that is, if $b_{ij} = a_{ji}$, then $\det B = \det A$.

Associated with the linear system of n equations for n unknowns,

$$a_{11}x_1 + a_{12}x_2 + \cdots + a_{1n}x_n = b_1$$
$$a_{21}x_1 + a_{22}x_2 + \cdots + a_{2n}x_n = b_2 \tag{A7}$$
$$\cdots\cdots\cdots\cdots\cdots\cdots\cdots\cdots\cdots\cdots\cdots\cdots\cdots$$
$$a_{n1}x_1 + a_{n2}x_2 + \cdots + a_{nn}x_n = b_n$$

is the square $n \times n$ matrix A with element a_{ij}. If $\det A \neq 0$, this system possesses a unique solution given by the formula

$$x_j = \frac{\det B_j}{\det A}, \qquad j = 1, 2, \ldots, n, \tag{A8}$$

where B_j is the same as A, except that the elements in the jth column have been replaced by $b_1, b_2, \ldots, b_n$. This formula is known as *Cramer's rule*. If $\det A = 0$, the system (A7) either has no solution, or else it has infinitely many solutions.

The *homogeneous* linear system

$$a_{11}x_1 + a_{12}x_2 + \cdots + a_{1n}x_n = 0$$
$$a_{21}x_1 + a_{22}x_2 + \cdots + a_{2n}x_n = 0 \tag{A9}$$
$$\cdots\cdots\cdots\cdots\cdots\cdots\cdots\cdots\cdots\cdots\cdots\cdots\cdots$$
$$a_{n1}x_1 + a_{n2}x_2 + \cdots + a_nx_{nn} = 0$$

is a special case of the general linear system (A7), in which all the terms b_j are zero. The system (A9) always possesses the trivial solution $x_j = 0$, $1 \leq j \leq n$. If $\det A \neq 0$, this is the only possible solution. However, if $\det A = 0$, the system (A9) possesses infinitely many nontrivial solutions.

EXERCISES

1. If a and b are constants, and A is a matrix, show that

   (a) $aA + bA = (a + b)A$ (b) $(ab)A = a(bA)$

2. If c is a constant, and A and B are matrices, show that

   (a) $c(A + B) = cA + cB$ (b) $c(AB) = (cA)B = A(cB)$

In part (a), it is assumed that the sum $A + B$ is defined, and in part (b) it is assumed that the product AB is defined.

3. If

$$A = \begin{pmatrix} 2 & -1 \\ 0 & 3 \end{pmatrix}, \qquad B = \begin{pmatrix} 1 & 1 \\ 2 & 4 \end{pmatrix},$$

find

   (a) $-3A$ (b) $A + B$ (c) $A - 2B$

4. If

$$A = \begin{pmatrix} 4 & 1 & -1 \\ 2 & 0 & 3 \end{pmatrix}, \qquad B = \begin{pmatrix} -2 & 0 & 1 \\ 2 & -1 & 1 \end{pmatrix},$$

find (a) $-2A$,   (b) $3A - B$.

5. Compute the products AB and BA, if A and B are as in Problem 3.

6. Compute whichever, if any, of the products AB and BA are defined.

   (a) $A = \begin{pmatrix} 4 & -2 \\ 2 & 1 \\ 0 & 1 \end{pmatrix}$ $B = \begin{pmatrix} 2 & 1 \\ -1 & 3 \end{pmatrix}$

   (b) $A = \begin{pmatrix} 1 & -1 & 2 \\ 2 & 1 & 1 \\ 0 & 3 & -1 \end{pmatrix}$, $B = \begin{pmatrix} -1 & 1 \\ 2 & 0 \\ 1 & 3 \end{pmatrix}$

   (c) $A = \begin{pmatrix} 2 & 1 & 1 \\ 1 & 0 & 3 \end{pmatrix}$, $B = \begin{pmatrix} 1 & -2 \\ 1 & 1 \\ -2 & 1 \end{pmatrix}$

7. (a) If A, B, and C are matrices of the same size, show that $(A + B) + C = A + (B + C)$.

(b) If A, B, and C are matrices such that the products AB and BC are both defined, show that the products $(AB)C$ and $A(BC)$ are defined and are equal.

8. If A and B are both matrices of size 2×2, show that

$$\det(AB) = \det A \cdot \det B.$$

9. Evaluate the given determinant:

(a) $\begin{vmatrix} 2 & -1 \\ 3 & 5 \end{vmatrix}$

(b) $\begin{vmatrix} 0 & -2 \\ 1 & 3 \end{vmatrix}$

(c) $\begin{vmatrix} 2 & -1 & 0 \\ 1 & 2 & -1 \\ 3 & 3 & 6 \end{vmatrix}$

(d) $\begin{vmatrix} -2 & -1 & 2 \\ 0 & 2 & 3 \\ 1 & -1 & 1 \end{vmatrix}$

(e) $\begin{vmatrix} 1 & -1 & 0 & 1 \\ 2 & 1 & 1 & -1 \\ 1 & 3 & -2 & 0 \\ 1 & 0 & 3 & 2 \end{vmatrix}$

(f) $\begin{vmatrix} 2 & -1 & 4 & 0 \\ 1 & 3 & -2 & 1 \\ 0 & 3 & 1 & -1 \\ 1 & 0 & 2 & -2 \end{vmatrix}$

10. Show that the given system has a unique solution, and find this solution by the use of determinants.

(a) $\begin{aligned} 2x - y &= 3 \\ x + y &= -1 \end{aligned}$

(c) $\begin{aligned} 2x - y + z &= 1 \\ x + y &= -2 \\ y - 3z &= 0 \end{aligned}$

(b) $\begin{aligned} 2x + 3y &= 0 \\ 3x - 2y &= 4 \end{aligned}$

(d) $\begin{aligned} 3x - y &= 0 \\ x + 2y + z &= 1 \\ 3y - 2z &= -4 \end{aligned}$

11. Determine whether or not the given homogeneous system has a non-trivial solution.

(a) $\begin{aligned} x - 2y &= 0 \\ -2x + 4y &= 0 \end{aligned}$

(c) $\begin{aligned} x - 3y + 2z &= 0 \\ y - z &= 0 \\ 2x - 5y + 3z &= 0 \end{aligned}$

(b) $\begin{aligned} 2x - 3y &= 0 \\ x + y &= 0 \end{aligned}$

(d) $\begin{aligned} 2y - z &= 0 \\ x + y + z &= 0 \\ 2x - y &= 0 \end{aligned}$

REFERENCES

1. Hohn, F. E., *Elementary Matrix Algebra*, 2nd ed. Macmillan, New York, 1964.
2. Thomas, G. B., *Calculus and Analytic Geometry*, 2nd ed. Addison-Wesley, Reading, Mass., 1962.
3. Vance, E. P., *Modern College Algebra*. Addison-Wesley, Reading, Mass., 1962.

ANSWERS TO
MISCELLANEOUS EXERCISES

Chapter 1

Section 1.1

1. (a) $Lu_1 = 4(3x^3 - 7x^2 + 2)$, $Lu_2 = (x - 2)e^x$
(c) $Lw = 3(x^4 - 3x^3 + 2x) + i(3x^3 - 7x^2 + 2)$
10. (a) $y = \frac{1}{3}x^3 + C$ (c) $y = Cx$

Section 1.2

1. (b) $y = \cos 3x - \frac{3}{2}\sin 3x$. It is the only solution.
3. (b) $y = -4x + x^{-2}$. It is the only solution.

Section 1.3

1. (a) $y = 2x^{-2}e^{1-x}$ (c) $y = 3/(x + 1)$
3. (a) $y = (Cx^{-2} + \frac{1}{4}x^2)e^{-x}$ (c) $y = Ce^{-1/x} - 1$ (e) $y = 2x + \frac{1}{2}x\log^2 x$
7. $50\sqrt[3]{2} = 62.00$ grams
9. $25e^{-6/5} = 13.03$ pounds

Section 1.6

1. (a) $W = 2$ (c) $W = -a$ (e) $W = 6e^{2x}$
3. $W = 1/(x^2 - 1)$
8. (a) $(x - 1)y'' - xy' + y = 0$ (c) $x^2(1 + x^2)y'' + (1 + 2x - x^4)y' - (x + 1)^2 y = 0$

Section 1.7

1. (a) $y = C_1 e^{2x} + C_2 e^{-2x}$ (c) $y = C_1 + C_2 e^x + C_3 e^{-x}$

Section 1.8

1. (a) $(D - 2)(D + 3)y = 0$ (c) $(D + 1)(D - 2)^2 y = 0$
2. (a) $(D^2 - 4D + 5)y = 0$ (c) $(D^3 - 5D^2 - D - 15)y = 0$
3. (a) $y'' - y' - 6y = 0$ (c) $y'' - 2y' + 2y = 0$ (e) $y''' - 5y'' + 7y' + 13y = 0$

Section 1.9

1. (a) $y = C_1 e^{2x} + C_2 e^{3x}$ (c) $y = (C_1 + C_2 x)e^{-2x}$
(e) $y = C_1 \cos 2x + C_2 \sin 2x$
2. (a) $y = (C_1 + C_2 x + C_3 x^2)e^x$ (c) $y = (C_1 + C_2 x)e^{2x} + C_3 e^{-x}$
(e) $y = (C_1 + C_2 x)\cos 2x + (C_3 + C_4 x)\sin 2x$

3. (a) $y = (15/2)e^x - (3/2)e^{3x}$ (c) $y = -\cos x + \sqrt{3} \sin x$
7. (a) $D^2 - 4D + 4$ (c) $D^2 - 3D + 2$

Section 1.10

1. (a) $y = C_1 x^{-2} + C_2 x^6$ (c) $y = C_1 x^2 + C_2 x^2 \log x$
   (e) $y = C_1 \cos(3 \log x) + C_2 \sin(3 \log x)$

   (g) $y = x^{-1/2} \left[C_1 \cos \left(\frac{\sqrt{7}}{2} \log x \right) + C_2 \sin \left(\frac{\sqrt{7}}{2} \log x \right) \right]$

   (i) $y = C_1 x^{-1} + C_2 \cos(2 \log x) + C_3 \sin(2 \log x)$
2. (a) $y = 2x - \frac{1}{4}x^2$ (c) $y = 2x^2 [\cos(\log x) - 2 \sin(\log x)]$
4. (a) $y = C_1 x^{-2} + C_2 x^6$ (c) $y = |x|^{1/2}(C^1 + C_2 \log|x|)$
6. (a) $y = C_1(x + 2) + C_2(x + 2)^{-3}$

Section 1.12

2. (a) $y = C_1 \cos x + C_2 \sin x - 2 + \sin x \log|\sec x + \tan x|$
   (c) $y = C_1 e^x + C_2 x e^x - \frac{1}{2}e^x \log(x^2 + 1) + xe^x \tan^{-1} x$
3. (a) $y = (x + 1) \sin x + \cos x \log \cos x$
4. (a) $y = C_1 x + C_2 x e^x - x^2$ (c) $y = C_1(x + 1) + C_2 e^x + x^2 e^x$
5. $y = \begin{cases} 0, & x \le 0 \\ \cosh x - 1, & x > 0 \end{cases}$

Section 1.13

1. (a) $y = (C_1 + C_2 x)e^x + \frac{1}{4}e^{-3x}$ (c) $y = -3 + 2e^{3x} + 2xe^{3x}$
   (e) $y = C_1 e^{-x} + C_2 e^{2x} - e^x + \frac{1}{3}xe^{-x}$
   (g) $y = C_1 + C_2 e^{-2x} + \frac{3}{4}(x - x^2)$
   (i) $y = C_1 \cos x + C_2 \sin x - 2 \cos 2x$
   (k) $y = e^x(C_1 \cos x + C_2 \sin x) + 3e^x + (1/5) \cos x - (2/5) \sin x$
   (m) $y = C_1 \cos x + C_2 \sin x + (x^2 - 2x + 1)e^x$
   (o) $y = (C_1 + C_2 x + C_3 x^2)e^x + (2/3)x^3 e^x$
2. (a) $y = C_1 x^2 + C_2 x^{-5}e - \frac{1}{3}x$ (c) $y = C_1 + C_2 x^3 - \frac{1}{2}x^2$

Section 1.14

1. (a) $x = 5 \cos 2\sqrt{2}\,t$, $A = 5$, $P = \pi/\sqrt{2}$
7. (a) $t = (m/c) \log[(cv_0 + mg)/mg]$ (b) $x = (mv_0/c) - (m^2g/c^2) \log[(cv_0 + mg)/mg]$
9. $I = -(Q_0/LC\alpha)e^{-Rt/(2L)} \sin \alpha t$, $\alpha = (1/2L)[(4L/C) - R^2]^{1/2}$
11. $I = (1/40)(1 - e^{-2t})$

Chapter 2

Section 2.1

1. (a) $y = C_1 x + C_2 x e^{1/x}$ (c) $y = C_1 e^x + C_2 e^x \log|x|$
   (e) $y = C_1 x^2 + C_2 x^2 e^{-x} + x^2 e^x$
2. (a) $y = C_1 x + C_2(1/x) + C_3(1/x)e^x$

Section 2.2

2. (a) $y = (1/x)(C_1 e^{-2x} + C_2)$ (c) $y = C_1 x^{-2} + C_2 x^{-2} e^{-x} - x^{-1}e^{-x}$
3. (a) $y = (C_1 + C_2 x) \exp(-\frac{1}{2}x^2 - x)$
   (c) $y = e^{-x}[C_1 + C_2 \log|x| + \int e^x/x \, dx]$

Section 2.3

1. (a) $u'' + 2u = 0$ (c) $x^3 u''' - 18 xu' + (2x^3 - 12)u = 0$

3. (a) $t^7(d^2y/dt^2) + (t^3 + 1)y = 0$ $(t = 1/x)$ (c) $2t^{1/2}(d^2y/dt^2) - y = 0$ $(t = x^2)$

5. (a) $y = C_1 \exp(-x^2) + C_2 \exp(-x^2/2)$ (c) $x^4 v' + x^6 v^2 + 3x^3 v - 1 = 0$

7. (a) $y'' + x^2 y = 0$ (c) $x^4 y'' - y = 0$

Section 2.4

7. For any real number α, let $[\alpha]$ be the largest integer which is not greater than α. If N is the number of zeros, then $[(b - a)\sqrt{A}/\pi] \leq N \leq [(b - a)\sqrt{B}/\pi] + 1$

Chapter 3

Section 3.2

1. (a) (i) $\sqrt{2}$ (iii) $\sqrt{13}$

3. (a) $2i$ (c) $2 - i$ (e) $4z^2 + 6iz - 9$

4. (a) $u = x^3 - 3xy^2$, $v = 3x^2 y - y^3$

    (c) $u = (x^2 - y^2)/(x^2 + y^2)^2$, $v = -2xy/(x^2 + y^2)^2$

5. (a) The circle with center at $z = 2i$ and radius 3

    (c) The region between the two concentric circles with center at $z = 2 - i$ and radii 1 and 2

Section 3.3

1. (a) Converges to zero   (c) Diverges

3. (a) Diverges   (c) Converges

Section 3.4

1. (a) $R = 1$ (c) $R = 1$ (e) $R = 0$

2. (a) $f(z) + g(z) = \sum_{n=0}^{\infty} (3 - n)(z + 1)^n$, $f(z)g(z) = \sum_{n=0}^{\infty} \frac{(n + 1)(4 - n)}{2}(z + 1)^n$

    (c) $f(z) + g(z) = \sum_{n=1}^{\infty} \frac{n^2 + 1}{n} z^n$, $f(z)g(z) = \sum_{n=0}^{\infty} \left(\sum_{k=0}^{n} \frac{n - k + 1}{k + 1} \right) z^{n+2}$

Section 3.5

1. (a) $f(z) = -4i - 10(z - 2i) + 6i(z - 2i)^2 + (z - 2i)^3$,   all z

    (c) $f(z) = \sum_{n=0}^{\infty} \frac{2^n}{n!} z^2$,   all z

3. (a) $f(z) = \sum_{n=0}^{\infty} (-2)^n z^n$, $|z| < 1/2$ (c) $f(z) = \sum_{n=0}^{\infty} z^{3n+1}$, $|z| < 1$

4. (a) $f(x) = \sum_{n=0}^{\infty} \frac{(-1)^n x^{2n}}{4^{n+1}}$, $|x| < 2$ (c) $f(x) = \sum_{n=0}^{\infty} \left(\sum_{k=0}^{n} \frac{1}{k!} \right)(-1)^n x^n$, $|x| < 1$

Chapter 4

Section 4.3

1. (a) Every point is an ordinary point.

    (c) Singular points $x = -1$ and $x = \frac{1}{2}$. Every other point is an ordinary point.

2. (a) $y = A_0 \left[1 + \sum_{m=1}^{\infty} \frac{(-1)^m x^{3m}}{3^m m! \, 2 \cdot 5 \cdot 8 \cdots (3m - 1)} \right]$

$$+ A_1 \left[x + \sum_{m=1}^{\infty} \frac{(-1)^m x^{3m+1}}{3^m m! \, 4 \cdot 7 \cdot 10 \cdots (3m + 1)} \right], \text{ all } x$$

(c) $y = A_0 \sum_{m=0}^{\infty} \frac{(2m)!}{2^{2m}(m!)^2} x^{2m} + A_1 \sum_{m=1}^{\infty} \frac{2^{2m-2}[(m-1)!]^2}{(2m-1)!} x^{2m-1}, \qquad |x| < 1$

(e) $y = A_0(1 + \frac{1}{2}x^2 + \frac{1}{6}x^3 + \frac{1}{12}x^4 + \frac{1}{24}x^5 + \cdots)$

$\qquad + A_1(x + \frac{1}{6}x^3 + \frac{1}{12}x^4 + \frac{1}{30}x^5 + \cdots), \qquad$ all x

4. (a) $y = A_0\left[1 + \frac{1}{2}(x-1)^2 + \sum_{m=2}^{\infty}(-1)^m \frac{3 \cdot 7 \cdot 11 \cdots (4m-5)}{(2m)!}(x-1)^{2m}\right]$

$\qquad + A_1\left[(x-1) + \sum_{m=2}^{\infty}(-1)^{m+1}\frac{1 \cdot 5 \cdot 9 \cdots (4m-7)}{(2m-1)!}(x-1)^{2m-1}\right], \qquad$ all x

(c) $y = A_0\left[1 + \sum_{m=1}^{\infty}(-1)^m\frac{1 \cdot 5 \cdot 17 \cdots (4m^2-8m+5)}{(2m)!}(x-2)^{2m}\right] + A_1\left[(x-2)\right.$

$\qquad - \frac{1}{3}(x-2)^3 + 2\sum_{m=3}^{\infty}(-1)^{m+1}\frac{1 \cdot 10 \cdot 26 \cdots (4m^2-12m+10)}{(2m-1)!}(x-2)^{2m-1}\right],$

$\qquad |x-2| < 1$

7. (a) $y = A_0 \sum_{m=0}^{\infty} x^{2m}/(2^m m!) + A_1 \sum_{m=1}^{\infty} (2^m m! x^{2m-1}/(2m)!$

$\qquad + \frac{1}{2}x^2 + \frac{1}{6}x^3 + \frac{1}{8}x^4 + \frac{1}{24}x^5 + \cdots, \qquad$ all x

Section 4.4

1. (a) Regular singular point $x = -2$, irregular singular point $x = 0$.
(c) Regular singular point $x = -1/2$, irregular singular point $x = 0$.
3. $y = Cx$

Section 4.6

1. (a) $y = 3C_1 x^{1/2} \sum_{n=0}^{\infty} \frac{2^{n+1}(n+1)}{(2n+3)!}x^n + C_2 x^{-1}\left[1 - \sum_{n=1}^{\infty}\frac{2^{n-1}(n-1)!}{(2n-2)!}x^n\right]$

(c) $y = C_1 x^{1/3}\left[1 + \frac{2}{9}x - 2\sum_{n=2}^{\infty}\frac{(-1)^n 1 \cdot 4 \cdot 7 \cdots (3n-5)}{9^n n!}x^n\right] + C_2 x$

3. (a) $y = C_1\left[1 - 2(x+1) + \frac{2}{3}(x+1)^2\right]$

$\qquad + C_2(x+1)^{1/2}\left[1 - \frac{3}{4}(x+1) + 3\sum_{n=2}^{\infty}\frac{(2n-4)!}{2^{3n-2}n!(n-2)!}(x+1)^n\right]$

4. (a) $y = 2C_1 x \sum_{n=0}^{\infty}\frac{(-1)^n x^n}{(n+2)!} + C_2 x^{-1}(1-x)$

(c) $y = C_1 \frac{x^3}{1+x} + C_2(1 - x + x^2)$ $\qquad$ (e) $y = C_1 \sum_{n=0}^{\infty}\frac{x^n}{n!(n+1)!}$

Section 4.7

2. (a) $y = C_1 y_1(x) + C_2 \left[y_1(x) \log x - 2 \sum_{n=1}^{\infty} \frac{(-1)^n \phi(n)}{(n!)^2} x^n \right], \qquad y_1(x) = \sum_{n=0}^{\infty} \frac{(-1)^n x^n}{(n!)^2}$

(c) $y = C_1 y_1(x) + C_2 \left[y_1(x) \log x - 2x^2 - \sum_{n=2}^{\infty} \frac{(-1)^n x^{n+1}}{n(n-1)} \right], \qquad y_1(x) = x + x^2$

Section 4.8

2. (a) $y = C_1 y_1(x) + C_2 \left[y_1(x) \log x - 1 - x - \sum_{n=2}^{\infty} \frac{\phi(n) + \phi(n-1)}{(n-1)! \, n!} x^n \right],$

$y_1(x) = \sum_{n=0}^{\infty} \frac{x^{n+1}}{n! \, (n+1)!}$

(c) $y = C_1 y_1(x) + C_2 \left[y_1(x) \log x + 1 - \sum_{n=2}^{\infty} \frac{(\phi(n))}{(n-1)!} x^n \right], \; y_1(x) = x \sum_{n=0}^{\infty} \frac{x^n}{n!} = x e^x$

Section 4.9

1. (a) $y = C_1 x [p(x) \cos \log x - q(x) \sin \log x] + C_2 x [q(x) \cos \log x + p(x) \sin \log x],$

$p(x) = 1 - \tfrac{3}{5} x + \tfrac{1}{5} x^2 + \cdots, \, q(x) = \tfrac{1}{5} x - \tfrac{3}{20} x^2 + \cdots$

(c) $y = C_1 x^{-1} [p(x) \cos (2 \log x) - q(x) \sin (2 \log x)]$

$\qquad\qquad\qquad\qquad + C_2 x^{-1} [q(x) \cos (2 \log x) + p(x) \sin (2 \log x)],$

$p(x) = 1 + \tfrac{4}{5} x + \tfrac{3}{13} x^2 + \cdots, \qquad q(x) = \tfrac{2}{5} x + \tfrac{2}{13} x^2 + \cdots$

Section 4.10

1. (a) Irregular singular points at $x = 0$ and $x = \infty$.

(c) Regular singular point at $x = 2$, irregular singular point at ∞.

3. (a) $y = C_1 \sum_{m=0}^{\infty} \frac{(-1)^m}{2^m \, m!} x^{-2m} + C_2 \sum_{m=1}^{\infty} \frac{(-1)^m 2^m \, m!}{(2m+1)!} x^{-(2m+1)}$

(c) $y = 3 C_1 x^{-1} \sum_{m=0}^{\infty} \frac{2^{m+1} \, (m+1)!}{(2m+2)!} x^{-m} + C_2 x^{1/2} \left[1 - \sum_{m=1}^{\infty} \frac{2^{2m-1} \, (m-1)!}{(m+1)! \, (2m-2)!} x^{-m} \right]$

Chapter 5

Section 5.1

1. (a) $\sqrt{\pi}/2$ \qquad (c) $-2\sqrt{\pi}$

Section 5.2

3. (a) 0.990 \qquad (c) -0.196

Section 5.3

1. (a) $\dfrac{1}{2^\alpha \Gamma(\alpha + 1)}$

Section 5.4

3. $Y_3(x) = \dfrac{8 - x^2}{x^2} Y_1(x) - \dfrac{4}{x} Y_0(x)$

Section 5.6

1. $y = x^{1/2}[C_1 J_{1/4}(\tfrac{1}{2} x^2)] + C_2 J_{-1/4}(\tfrac{1}{2} x^2)]$
3. $y = x^{-2}[C_1 J_1(2x) + C_2 Y_1(2x)]$
5. $y = x^{1/2}[C_1 I_{1/3}(\tfrac{2}{3} x^{3/2}) + C_2 I_{-1/3}(\tfrac{2}{3} x^{3/2})]$
7. $y = x^{-1}[C_1 I_2(2x^{1/2}) + C_2 K_2(2x^{1/2})]$

9. (a) $\left(\dfrac{2}{\pi x}\right)^{1/2} \left[\dfrac{3 - x^2}{x^2} \sin x - \dfrac{3}{x} \cos x\right]$ (c) $-\left(\dfrac{2}{\pi x}\right)^{1/2} \cos x$

    (e) $-\left(\dfrac{2}{\pi x}\right)^{1/2} \left(\sinh x + \dfrac{\cosh x}{x}\right)$

Chapter 6

Section 6.1

1. (a) $\|\sin (n\pi x/c)\| = \sqrt{c/2}$

3. $x = \dfrac{2}{b - a} z - \dfrac{a + b}{b - a}$

Section 6.2

1. (a) $\phi_0 = 1,$ $\phi_1 = x - \tfrac{1}{2},$ $\phi_2 = x^2 - x + \tfrac{1}{6}$
    (c) $\phi_0 = 1,$ $\phi_1 = x - 1,$ $\phi_2 = x^2 - 4x + 2$

Section 6.6

1. $P_1 : x = 0,$ $P_2 : x = \pm 1/\sqrt{3},$ $P_3 : x = 0, \pm\sqrt{3/5}$

Section 6.8

1. $Q(x) = \tfrac{8}{3} P_0(x) + \tfrac{3}{5} P_1(x) + \tfrac{4}{3} P_2(x) + \tfrac{2}{5} P_3(x)$

Chapter 7

Section 7.1

1. (a) $\lambda_n = [(2n + 1)/2]^2,$ $y_n(x) = \sin [(2n + 1)/2]x,$ $n \geq 0$
    (c) $\lambda_n = k_n^2,$ where k_n is the nth positive root of the equation $\tan k = 1/k,$
       $y_n(x) = \cos k_n x,$ $n \geq 1$
    (e) $\lambda_n = n^2,$ $y_n(x) = e^{-x} \sin nx,$ $n \geq 1$
    (g) $\lambda_n = (n\pi)^4,$ $y_n(x) = \cos n\pi x,$ $n \geq 0$

Section 7.2

3. (a) $(xy')' + [x - (1/x)]y = 0$ (c) $(xe^{-x}y')' + e^{-x}y = 0$

Section 7.3

1. (a) 7   (c) 25
4. (a) Independent   (c) Dependent

Section 7.4

1. (a) Self-adjoint
    (c) Not self-adjoint as it stands. This problem becomes self-adjoint if the differential
       equation is multiplied through by e^x.

Section 7.5

1. (a) $\lambda_n = (n\pi/c)^2$, $\quad y_n(x) = \sin(n\pi x/c)$. $\quad n \geq 1$
(c) $\lambda_n = n^2$, $\quad y_n(x) = e^{-x} \sin n\pi x$, $\quad n \geq 1$

Section 7.8

7. $\lambda_n = k_n{}^2$, where k_n is the nth positive root of the equation $J_1(k/2) + kJ_1{}'(k/2) = 0$;
$y_n(x) = x^{1/2} J_1(k_n x/2)$; $\quad w(x) = 1$

Chapter 8

Section 8.1

1. $\{1/c, \; 2/c \cos n\pi x/c\}$, $\quad n \geq 1$

3. (a) $(2^n n! \sqrt{\pi})^{-1/2} H_n(x)$, $\quad n \geq 0$

Section 8.2

1. $\dfrac{4}{\pi} \displaystyle\sum_{m=1}^{\infty} \dfrac{\sin(2m-1)\pi x}{2m-1}$

4. (a) $x^2 = \tfrac{1}{3} P_0(x) + \tfrac{2}{3} P_2(x)$

Section 8.3

1. (a) $\left(\dfrac{1}{4}\right) + \displaystyle\sum_{n=1}^{\infty} \left[\dfrac{(-1)^n - 1}{n^2 \pi^2} \cos n\pi x + \dfrac{(-1)^{n+1}}{n\pi} \sin n\pi x \right]$

3. $1 - \dfrac{8}{\pi^2} \displaystyle\sum_{m=1}^{\infty} \dfrac{1}{(2m-1)^2} \cos \dfrac{2m-1}{2} \pi x$

4. (a) $2 \displaystyle\sum_{n=1}^{\infty} \dfrac{J_1(k_n x)}{k_n J_2(2k_n)}$

5. $\dfrac{1}{\sqrt{\pi}} \left[H_0(x) + \dfrac{1}{2} H_1(x) - \dfrac{1}{12} H_2(x) + \cdots \right]$

Section 8 4

1. (a) Continuous $\qquad$ (c) Piecewise continuous

Section 8.5

3. $C_0 = \tfrac{1}{2}$, $\quad C_1 = \tfrac{3}{4}$, $\quad C_2 = 0$

5. $\dfrac{8c}{\pi^2} \displaystyle\sum_{m=1}^{\infty} \dfrac{1}{(2m-1)^2} = c$

Section 8.7

1. (a) Piecewise smooth $\qquad$ (c) Not piecewise smooth

2. (a) $\dfrac{1}{2} - \dfrac{2}{\pi} \displaystyle\sum_{m=1}^{\infty} \dfrac{\sin(2m-1)x}{(2m-1)}$

(c) $\dfrac{1}{2} + \dfrac{1}{2} \cos x + \dfrac{1}{\pi} \displaystyle\sum_{n=1}^{\infty} \dfrac{1}{n} \left[(-1)^n \dfrac{2n^2-1}{n^2-1} - 1 \right] \sin nx$

3. (a) $\dfrac{1}{2} + \dfrac{2}{\pi} \displaystyle\sum_{m=1}^{\infty} \dfrac{(-1)^{m+1}}{2m-1} \cos \dfrac{2m-1}{c} \pi x$ $\qquad$ (c) $\dfrac{2c}{\pi} \displaystyle\sum_{n=1}^{\infty} \dfrac{(-1)^{n+1}}{n} \sin \dfrac{n\pi x}{c}$

7. $\dfrac{1}{2} + \dfrac{2}{\pi} \displaystyle\sum_{m=1}^{\infty} \sin \dfrac{(2m-1)\pi x}{(2m-1)}$

Section 8.8

1. (a) $\dfrac{\pi}{2} - \dfrac{4}{\pi} \displaystyle\sum_{m=1}^{\infty} \cos \dfrac{(2m-1)x}{(2m-1)^2}, \qquad 2 \displaystyle\sum_{n=1}^{\infty} \dfrac{(-1)^{n+1} \sin nx}{n}$

(c) $\dfrac{2}{\pi} - \dfrac{4}{\pi} \displaystyle\sum_{m=1}^{\infty} \dfrac{\cos 2mx}{(4m^2 - 1)}, \qquad \sin x$

5. (a) $\dfrac{2}{\pi} \displaystyle\sum_{n=1}^{\infty} \dfrac{\cos(n\pi/2) - (-1)^n}{n} \sin \dfrac{n\pi x}{c}, \qquad \dfrac{1}{2} + \dfrac{2}{\pi} \displaystyle\sum_{m=1}^{\infty} \dfrac{(-1)^m}{2m-1} \cos \dfrac{(2m-1)\pi x}{c}$

(c) $\dfrac{c}{\pi} \displaystyle\sum_{n=1}^{\infty} \left[\dfrac{2\sin(n\pi/2)}{n^2\pi} - \dfrac{\cos(n\pi/2)}{n} \right] \sin \dfrac{n\pi x}{c},$

$\dfrac{c}{8} + \dfrac{c}{\pi} \displaystyle\sum_{n=1}^{\infty} \left[\dfrac{2(\cos(n\pi/2) - 1)}{n^2\pi} + \dfrac{\sin(n\pi/2)}{n} \right] \cos \dfrac{n\pi x}{c}$

Section 8.9

1. (a) $\frac{1}{2}P_0(x) + \frac{3}{4}P_1(x) - \frac{7}{16}P_3(x) + \cdots$ **(c)** $\frac{1}{2}P_0(x) + \frac{5}{8}P_2(x) - \frac{3}{16}P_4(x) + \cdots$

5. (a) $\frac{1}{2}P_0(\cos\phi) - \frac{3}{4}P_1(\cos\phi) + \frac{7}{16}P_3(\cos\phi) + \cdots$

7. (a) $L_0(x) + \frac{1}{2}L_1(x) + \frac{1}{6}L_2(x) + \cdots$

9. (a) $\dfrac{1}{\sqrt{\pi}}[2H_0(x) - \dfrac{1}{6}H_2(x) + \cdots]$

10. (a) $2c \displaystyle\sum_{n=1}^{\infty} \dfrac{J_2(k_n x)}{k_n J_3(k_n c)}$ **(c)** $\dfrac{2}{c^3} \displaystyle\sum_{n=1}^{\infty} \dfrac{2k_n c + (4 + c^2 k_n{}^2)J_3(k_n c)}{k_n{}^3 [J_3(k_n c)]^2} J_2(k_n x)$

11. (a) $4c^2 \displaystyle\sum_{n=1}^{\infty} \dfrac{J_2(k_n x)}{(c^2 k_n{}^2 - 4)J_2(k_n c)}$ **(c)** $\dfrac{4}{c^2} \displaystyle\sum_{n=1}^{\infty} \dfrac{c_2 k_n{}^2 - 4J_2(k_n c)}{k_n{}^2(c^2 k_n{}^2 - 4)[J_2(k_n c)]^2} J_2(k_n x)$

13. $2 \displaystyle\sum_{n=1}^{\infty} \dfrac{k_n J_1(k_n)}{(k_n{}^2 + h^2)[J_0(k_n)]^2} J_0(k_n x), \qquad$ where $hJ_0(k_n) + k_n J'_0(k_n) = 0$

15. (a) $2\pi e^{-x} \displaystyle\sum_{n=1}^{\infty} \dfrac{n[1 - e(-1)^n]}{\pi^2 n^2 + 1} \sin n\pi x$

Chapter 9

Section 9.1

1. (a) $\begin{pmatrix} 0 \\ 7e^t \\ t^2 + 2 \end{pmatrix}$ **(c)** $\begin{pmatrix} -6t^2 - 4t \\ (3t^2 - 12)e^t \\ 3t^4 - 4 \end{pmatrix}$

3. (a) Linearly dependent   **(c)** Linearly independent

6. (c) $x_1 = C_1 e^{-t} + 2C_2 e^{2t}, \qquad x_2 = C_1 e^{-t} - C_2 e^{2t}$

     (d) $x_1 = (10/3)e^{-t} - (4/3)e^{2t}, \; x_2 = (10/3)e^{-t} + (2/3)e^{2t}$

8. (c) $x_1 = C_1 - 2C_2 e^t + C_3 e^t, \qquad x_2 = 2C_1 + C_3 e^t, \qquad x_3 = C_1 + C_2 e^t$

Section 9.2

3. $x_1 = 0$, $x_2 = 1$ is a solution of (C) but not of (A).

4. (a) $x_1 = (5/2) \sin 2t$, $\qquad x_2 = -\cos 2t - (1/2) \sin 2t + e^{-t}$
   (c) $x_1 = C_1 e^t + 2C_2 e^{-t} - 4 + 3 \cos t + \sin t$
   $\qquad x_2 = C_1 e^t + C_2 e^{-t} - 3 + 2 \cos t$

5. (a) $x_1 = 15 \cos t + 20 \sin t - 10e^{-t}$
   $\qquad x_2 = 10 \cos t + 5 \sin t - 10e^{-t}$
   $\qquad x_3 = -25 \sin t$
   (c) $x_1 = 2C_1 + C_3 e^t + 4(\cos t - \sin t)$
   $\qquad x_2 = C_1 + C_2 e^t + \cos t - 3 \sin t$
   $\qquad x_3 = -C_1 + 2C_2 e^t - 2C_3 e^t + 2(\sin t - \cos t)$

6. (a) $x_1 = (1/2)e^{-t} + te^{-t} + (1/2)e^{-3t}$, $\qquad x_2 = e^{-t} + e^{-3t}$
   (c) $x_1 = C_1 e^{-t} + C_2 te^{-t} + 3C_3 e^{-2t}$ $\qquad x_2 = -C_1 e^{-t} - C_2 te^{-t} - 4C_3 e^{-2t}$

7. (a) $Du_1 = u_2$, $\quad Du_2 = -4u_1 - 2u_2 - 3u_3$, $\quad Du_3 = -2u_1 - u_2 - 2u_3$, where $u_1 = x_1$, $u_2 = Dx_1$, and $u_3 = x_2$. The quantities $x_1(t_0)$, $x'_1(t_0)$, and $x_2(t_0)$ must be specified.

8. (a) $x_1 = C_1 t + C_2 t^{-1}$, $\qquad x_2 = C_1 t - C_2 t^{-1} - 1$

Section 9.3

1. (a) $(2/g)v_0 \sin \alpha$ $\qquad$ (b) $(1/g)v_0^2 \sin 2\alpha$, $\qquad \alpha = \pi/4$ $\qquad$ (c) $v_0^2(2g)^{-1} \sin^2 \alpha$

5. $I_1(t) = 2e^{-200t}$, $\qquad I_2(t) = 2e^{-200t} + 5$ (amperes)

Chapter 10

Section 10.1

1. (a) $\mathscr{L}[1] = 1/s$, $\quad s > 0$ $\qquad$ (c) $\mathscr{L}[t^n] = n!/s^{n+1}$, $\quad s > 0$
   (e) $\mathscr{L}[\sinh at] = a/(s^2 - a^2)$, $\quad s > a$

3. (c) $\mathscr{L}[|\sin t|] = (s^2 + 1)^{-1} \coth (\pi s/2)$

4. (a) $x = -2e^{2t} - 1$

Section 10.3

2. (a) $2/(s + 1) - 12/(s^2 + 16)$ $\qquad$ (c) $24/(s + 3)^5$ $\qquad$ (e) $4s/(s^2 + 4)^2$

3. (a) $\dfrac{\sqrt{\pi}}{2(s - 2)^{3/2}}$ $\qquad$ (c) $\dfrac{2}{s(s - 1)^3}$ $\qquad$ (e) $e^{-\pi s}/(s^2 + 1)$

4. (a) $s^2 F(s) - s - 2$

Section 10.4

1. (a) te^{-t} $\qquad$ (c) $e^{-t} \cosh 2t$ $\qquad$ (e) $e^{-t} - e^{-2t}$

2. (a) $2e^t - 2e^{-2t}$ $\qquad$ (c) $\frac{8}{5} e^t + 3te^t - \frac{8}{5} \cos 3t - \frac{6}{5} \sin 3t$

   (e) $\dfrac{1}{12} e^{2t} - \dfrac{1}{12} e^{-t} \cos \sqrt{3}t - \dfrac{\sqrt{3}}{9} e^{-t} \sin \sqrt{3}t$

3. (a) $f(t) = \begin{cases} 0, & 0 \le t \le 1 \\ (t - 1)e^{2(t-1)}, & t > 1 \end{cases}$ $\qquad$ (c) $\left(1/\sqrt{\pi} \right) \displaystyle\int_0^t \sqrt{u} e^{2u} \cos (t - u)\, du$

   (e) (e) $\displaystyle\int_0^t f(t - u)e^{-u}\, du$

Section 10.5

1. (a) $x = e^{-2t} + e^t$ (c) $x = -\frac{1}{3}\sin 2t + \frac{8}{3}\sin t$ (e) $x = e^{-2t} + \cos t + 1$

3. $x = \begin{cases} \cosh t, 0 \le t \le 1 \\ \cosh t + (1 - t) + \sinh(t - 1), t > 1 \end{cases}$

5. (a) $x = 1 + e^{2t}$

6. (a) $x_1 = e^t - \frac{1}{3}e^{-3t} - \frac{2}{3}$, $x_2 = \frac{3}{2}e^t + \frac{1}{6}e^{-3t} - \frac{2}{3}$

     (c) $x_1 = e^{-t}(2\cos t - \sin t)$, $x_2 = e^{-t}(1 - \cos t + 3\sin t)$

     (e) $x_1 = -\frac{2}{5}e^{-t}\cos 2t + \frac{4}{5}e^{-t}\sin 2t + 2t + \frac{12}{5}$

     $x_2 = \frac{8}{5}e^{-t}\cos 2t + \frac{4}{5}e^{-t}\sin 2t + 2t + \frac{12}{5}$

Chapter 11

Section 11.1

3. (a) Hyperbolic   (c) Parabolic

Section 11.2

1. $u_t(x, t) = k u_{xx}(x, t)$, $0 < x < 2$, $t > 0$

     $u(0, t) = 0$, $u(2, t) = 10$, $t \ge 0$

     $u(x, 0) = 5x$, $0 \le x \le 2$

3. $u_t(x, t) = k u_{xx}(x, t)$, $0 < x < a$, $t > 0$

     $u(x, 0) = f(x)$, $0 \le x \le a$

     $-KA u_x(0, t) = c[T_0 - u(0, t)]$, $-KA u_x(a, t) = c[u(a, t) - T_0]$, $t \ge 0$, where c is the positive constant of proportionality.

5. (b) $4t_0$

Section 11.3

1. (a) $u(x, t) = 3\sin(\pi x/a)e^{-(\pi/a)^2 kt} - 5\sin(4\pi x/a)e^{-(4\pi/a)^2 kt}$

     (c) $u(x, t) = \dfrac{4a}{\pi^2}\displaystyle\sum_{m=1}^{\infty}\dfrac{(-1)^{m+1}}{(2m-1)^2}\sin\dfrac{(2m-1)\pi x}{a}\exp\left[-\dfrac{(2m-1)^2\pi^2}{a^2}kt\right]$

3. (a) $u(x, t) = 1 - x$

     (c) $u(x, t) = 2x - \dfrac{16}{3\pi}\sin \pi x\, e^{-\pi^2 kt}$

$$+ \frac{3}{2\pi}\sin 2\pi x\, e^{-4\pi^2 kt} + \frac{16}{\pi}\sum_{n=3}^{\infty}\frac{(-1)^{n+1}}{n(n^2-4)}\sin n\pi x\, e^{-\pi^2 kt}$$

5. $u(x, t) = \dfrac{16}{\pi^2}\displaystyle\sum_{n=1}^{\infty}\dfrac{\cos[(2n-1)\pi x/2]}{(2n-1)^2}e^{-(2n-1)^2\pi^2 kt/4}$

7. $g_n(t) = e^{-(n\pi/a)^2 kt}\displaystyle\int_0^t f_n(s)e^{(n\pi/a)^2 ks}\, ds$

Section 11.4

3. $u(x, y) = \displaystyle\sum_{n=1}^{\infty} a_n \sin(n\pi x/a)e^{-n\pi y/a}$, $a_n = \dfrac{2}{a}\displaystyle\int_0^a f(x)\sin n\pi x/a\, dx$

Section 11.6

5. $u(x, t) = \sin(\pi x/a)\cos(\pi ct/a)$

7. The period is $2a/c = 2a\sqrt{\rho/T_0}$. It decreases with the tension and increases with the density.

Section 11.7

3. $u_x = \sin\phi\cos\theta\, u_\rho + (\cos\phi\cos\theta/\rho)u_\phi - u_\theta\sin\theta/(\rho\sin\phi)$

5. $g_x = [1/(\sinh^2 u + \sin^2 v)]\,[\sinh u\cos v\, g_u - \cosh u\sin v\, g_v]$

$g_y = [1/(\sinh^2 u + \sin^2 v)]\,[\cosh u\sin v\, g_u + \sinh u\cos v\, g_v]$

Section 11.8

1. $u(r,t) = A_0 + \sum\limits_{n=1}^{\infty} A_n J_0(\lambda_n r)e^{-\lambda_n^2 kt}$,   where $J'_0(\lambda_n c) = 0$ and

$$A_n = \frac{2}{c^2[J_0(\lambda_n c)]^2}\int_0^c rf(r)J_0(\lambda_n r)dr$$

3. $u(r,t) = \sum\limits_{n=1}^{\infty} A_n J_0(\lambda_n r)e^{-\lambda_n^2 kt}$,   where $\lambda_n J'_0(\lambda_n c) + HJ_0(\lambda_n c) = 0$

and

$$A_n = \frac{2}{c^2}\frac{\lambda_n^2}{(\lambda_n^2 + H^2)[J_0(\lambda_n c)]^2}\int_0^c rf(r)J_0(\lambda_n r)\ dr.$$

(At the boundary, $u_v(c,t) + Hu(c,t) = 0$, where H is a positive constant.)

5. $u(r,z) = \sum\limits_{n=1}^{\infty} A_n \sinh\lambda_n z\, J_0(\lambda_n r)$, where $J_0(\lambda_n c) = 0$ and

$$A_n = \frac{2}{c^2 \sinh\lambda_n h\, [J_1(\lambda_n c)]^2}\int_0^c rf(r)J_0(\lambda_n r)\ dr$$

Section 11.9

1. $u(\rho,\phi) = \sum\limits_{n=0}^{\infty} A_n(c/\rho)^{n+1}P_n(\cos\phi)$, $A_n = \dfrac{2n+1}{2}\int_0^\pi f(\phi)P_n(\cos\phi)\sin\phi\, d\phi$

3. $u(\rho,\phi) = \sum\limits_{m=1}^{\infty} A_m(\rho/c)^{2m-1}\, P_{2m-1}(\cos\phi)$,

$$A_m = (4m-1)\int_0^{\pi/2} f(\phi)\, P_{2m-1}(\cos\phi)\sin\phi\, d\phi$$

Section 11.10

1. $u(x,y,z) = \sum\limits_{m,n=1}^{\infty} A_{mn}\sin m\pi x\,\sin n\pi y\,\sinh(\sqrt{m^2+n^2}\,\pi z)$,

$$A_{mn} = \frac{4}{\sinh(\sqrt{m^2+n^2}\,\pi)}\int_0^1\int_0^1 f(x,y)\sin m\pi x\,\sin n\pi y\, dy\, dx$$

3. $u(r,z,t) = \tfrac{1}{2}\sum\limits_{m=0}^{\infty} A_{m0}\, J_0(\mu_m r)\exp(-\mu_m^2 kt)$

$$+ \sum\limits_{m=0,n=1}^{\infty} A_{mn} J_0(\mu_m r)\cos\frac{n\pi z}{h}\exp\left\{\left[-\mu_m^2 - \left(\frac{n\pi}{h}\right)^2\right]kt\right\},$$

$$A_{mn} = \frac{4}{c^2 h\,[J_0(\mu_m c)]^2}\int_0^h\int_0^c rf(r,z)J_0(\mu_m r)\sin\frac{n\pi z}{h}\ dr\, dz, \text{ where } J'_0(\mu_m c) = 0.$$

Chapter 12

Section 12.1

2. (a) $y = \log(x^2 + 1)$ (c) $y = \tan(x + \pi/4)$, $\pi/4 < x < 5\pi/4$
(e) $y^3 + 3y - 3\sin x = C$

4. (a) $y = Ce^{x/y}$ (c) $y = x - \dfrac{2x}{\log|x| + C}$ and $y = x$

5. (b) $y = \dfrac{x^2}{2\log|x| + C}$ and $y = 0$

8. (a) $y' = -x/y$ (c) $y' = y/x$

Section 12.2

2. (a) $3xy^2 + 2x + y^2 = C$ (c) Not exact   (e) $2x^2 + xy + y^2 = C$
4. (a) $x^3y^2(y - 1) = C$ (c) No integrating factor of the indicated form exists.

Section 12.3

1. (a) $x = C_1 \log|e^t + C_1| + C_2$ and $x = e^t + C$

(c) $x = \log|e^t + C_1 e^{-t}| + C_2$ and $x = \pm t + C$

2. (a) $x = \pm \left[\dfrac{C_1^2(t + C_2)^2 - 1}{C_1} \right]^{1/2}$ and $x = \pm[\pm 2t + C]^{1/2}$

(c) $x = C_2 e^{C_1 t} + 1/C_1$ and $x = -t + C$ and $x = 0$

3. (a) $m(d^2x/dt^2) + c(dx/dt)^2 = mg$ (b) $t = (m/cg)^{1/2} \cosh^{-1} e^{ch/m}$
(c) $v = (mg/c)^{1/2}[1 - e^{-2ch/m}]^{1/2}$
5. (a) $v = [(2ghR)/(R + h)]^{1/2}$
(b) $t = [(R + h)h/2gR)]^{1/2} + [(R + h)/R][(R + h)/(2g)]^{1/2} \sin^{-1}[h/(R + h)]^{1/2}$

Section 12.4

1. (a) $y = -(x^{3/2} + 3)^{1/2}$, $x > 0$

2. (a) $y = 1$ and $y = \begin{cases} \cos x, & -\pi \le x < 0 \\ 1, & x \ge 0 \end{cases}$

3. $y_0 = 1, y_1 = 1 - x + \frac{1}{2}x^2, y_2 = 1 - x + \frac{3}{2}x^2 - \frac{2}{3}x^3 + \frac{1}{4}x^4 - \frac{1}{20}x^5$

Section 12.5

3. $x_1 = \dfrac{1}{1 - \log(t + 1)}$, $x_2 = \dfrac{1}{t + 1}$, $-1 < t < e - 1$

Section 12.6

1. (a) The solutions are $x = A\cos(2t - \alpha)$, $y = -2A\sin(2t - \alpha)$. The trajectories are the ellipses $x^2/A^2 + y^2/(4A^2) = 1$.
(c) The solutions are $x = C_1 e^{-t}$, $y = 2/(C_1^2 e^{-2t} + C_2)$ and $x = 0$, $y = C$. The trajectories are the curves $y = 2/(x^2 + C_2)$ and the points $(0, C)$.

5. $x^2 + y^2 = C$
7. $y = Cx - 3x^2$

Section 12.7

1. (a) Isolated critical points $(\pm 1, 0)$
   (c) Isolated critical points $(1, 1)$ and $(2, 2)$
   (e) Isolated critical points $(m\pi, \pi/2 + n\pi)$, where m and n are integers
6. (a) Stable, but not asymptotically stable   (c) Unstable

Section 12.8

1. (a) Positive-definite   (c) Negative-definite

Section 12.9

3. (a) Asymptotically stable   (c) Unstable

Appendix

3. (a) $-3A = \begin{pmatrix} -6 & 3 \\ 0 & -9 \end{pmatrix}$ (c) $A - 2B = \begin{pmatrix} 0 & -3 \\ -4 & -5 \end{pmatrix}$

6. (a) $AB = \begin{pmatrix} 10 & -2 \\ 3 & 5 \\ -1 & 3 \end{pmatrix}$ (c) $AB = \begin{pmatrix} 1 & -2 \\ -5 & 1 \end{pmatrix}$, $BA = \begin{pmatrix} 0 & 1 & -5 \\ 3 & 1 & 4 \\ -3 & -2 & 1 \end{pmatrix}$

9. (a) 13   (c) 39   (e) -44
10. (a) $x = 2/3$, $y = -5/3$ (c) $x = -1/8$, $y = -15/8$, $z = -5/8$
11. The systems of both parts (a) and (c) possess nontrivial solutions.

INDEX

Numbers in parentheses indicate exercises